CARE OF BOOKS

Teachers, pupils and borrowers of books should carefully observe the following suggestions:

(1) Never touch a book unless your hands are clean and dry.
(2) Never turn down the corner of a leaf.
(3) Never turn an open book on its face.
(4) Never leave one in the sunlight or on a dusty shelf or desk.
(5) Do not mark books.
(6) Keep them away from heat and dampness.
(7) Do not wet your fingers to turn a leaf.

NAME OF PUPIL	SCHOOL YEAR
1. Rodger House	
2. Emily Ellis	
3.	
4. Kim Hendrickel	
5.	
6. Tom Fahing	
7. Frank Myhee	

Form 127—Model Publishing Co., St. Louis, Mo.

LIVESTOCK and POULTRY PRODUCTION

SECOND EDITION

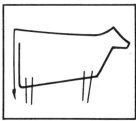

LIVESTOCK and
POULTRY PRODUCTION

SECOND EDITION

Clarence E. Bundy
Professor of Agricultural Education
Iowa State University

Ronald V. Diggins
Vocational Agriculture Instructor
Eagle Grove, Iowa

PRENTICE-HALL, INC. Englewood Cliffs, N. J.

PRENTICE-HALL VOCATIONAL AGRICULTURE SERIES

BEEF PRODUCTION. *Diggins and Bundy*

CROP PRODUCTION. *Delorit and Ahlgren*

DAIRY PRODUCTION. *Diggins and Bundy*

EXPLORING AGRICULTURE. *Evans and Donahue*

FRUIT GROWING. *Schneider and Scarborough*

JUDGING LIVESTOCK, DAIRY CATTLE, POULTRY, AND CROPS. *Youtz and Carlson*

LEADERSHIP TRAINING AND PARLIAMENTARY PROCEDURE FOR FFA. *Gray and Jackson*

LIVESTOCK AND POULTRY PRODUCTION. *Bundy and Diggins*

MODERN FARM BUILDINGS. *Ashby, Dodge, and Shedd*

MODERN FARM POWER. *Promersberger and Bishop*

POULTRY PRODUCTION. *Bundy and Diggins*

PROFITABLE FARM MANAGEMENT. *Hamilton and Bryant*

PROFITABLE FARM MARKETING. *Snowden and Donahoo*

PROFITABLE SOIL MANAGEMENT. *Knuti, Korpi, and Hide*

PROFITABLE SOUTHERN CROPS. *Walton and Holt*

THE RANGE AND PASTURE BOOK. *Donahue, Evans, and Jones*

RECORDS FOR FARM MANAGEMENT. *Hopkins and Turner*

SHEEP PRODUCTION. *Diggins and Bundy*

SOIL — USE AND IMPROVEMENT. *Stallings*

SOILS — AN INTRODUCTION TO SOILS AND PLANT GROWTH. *Donahue*

SWINE PRODUCTION. *Bundy and Diggins*

USING ELECTRICITY ON THE FARM. *Hamilton*

YOUR FUTURE IN POULTRY FARMING. *Goodman and Tudor*

© 1954, 1961 by Prentice-Hall, Inc.
Englewood Cliffs, New Jersey

Library of Congress Catalog No.: 61-5029

PRINTED IN THE UNITED STATES OF AMERICA
53855 - E

Features of the SECOND EDITION ■ ■ ■ ■

This second edition of LIVESTOCK AND POULTRY PRO-DUCTION is enlarged and even more informative than the first, the wide acceptance of which has been most gratifying. We present in one book the most complete and up-to-date information available on this broad subject. The basic principles and practices needed in solving production, management, and marketing problems are made clear without the necessity of reading through a maze of technical and semitechnical material. The suggestions of a number of evaluators, well-known in the field, have been incorporated.

It is the intent of the authors that this book be utilized as a source of information in vocational-agricultural classes where problem-solving methods are used in teaching animal production.

Results of research conducted by a large number of agricultural experiment stations and by the U. S. Department of Agriculture have been reviewed. Livestock and poultry marketing information has been obtained from meat packing and other processing industries. We have been assisted by the purebred livestock breed associations in bringing together the latest data concerning type and production of animals. Recent publications of many state agricultural colleges have also been used in assembling the information included in the text.

Methods and practices in swine, beef and dairy cattle, sheep, and poultry production alter rapidly, and during the past five years great changes have come about. It is our goal to inform the reader of these changes and to assist him in improving the livestock and poultry pro-duction on his farm.

Each type of livestock and fowl has been treated separately. The subject matter has been organized and indexed systematically so that the reader can quickly find the information desired. The descriptive material in the book has been supplemented by nearly four hundred illustrations and sixty-eight tables.

In the preparation of the manuscript, we have drawn heavily upon our experiences during the past thirty years in farming, vocational agriculture, and agricultural education work. We have worked closely with hundreds of livestock producers and educators in the agricultural field. Considerable information and many of the recommended prac-tices have been obtained directly from such authoritative sources.

ACKNOWLEDGMENTS

We are indebted to many individuals and organizations for illustrative and other materials included in the text. We are especially indebted to the Bureau Animal Industry of the U. S. Department of Agriculture, Cornell University, Iowa State University, Kansas State University, Michigan State University, Oklahoma State University, University of California, University of Illinois, University of Minnesota, University of Nebraska, University of Wisconsin, and University of Wyoming.

Illustrative material was also obtained from *Wallaces' Farmer and Iowa Homestead, The National Hog Farmer, Successful Farming, Farm Journal and Country Gentleman, Poultry Tribune, Turkey World,* and *Broiler Growing.*

The secretaries of the various livestock breed associations were very helpful. Valuable materials were obtained from The United Duroc Record Association, American Yorkshire Club, Inc., American Berkshire Association, Chester White Swine Record Association, OIC Swine Breeders Association, Inc., Poland China Record Association, *National Spotted Poland China Record and Bulletin,* Tamworth Swine Association, American Landrace Association, Inc., American Hampshire Herdsmen, American Hereford Association, American Aberdeen-Angus Breeders' Association, *Polled Hereford World,* American Shorthorn Breeders' Association, Brahman Breeders' Association, American Santa Gertrudis Breeders' International, Holstein-Friesian Association of America, Ayrshire Breeders' Association, The American Guernsey Cattle Club, Brown Swiss Cattle Breeders' Association, American Milking Shorthorn Society, Red Poll Cattle Club of America, Devon Cattle Club, American Rambouillet Sheep Breeders' Association, American Cheviot Sheep Society, Inc., Continental Dorset Club, American Hampshire Sheep Association, American Shropshire Breeders' Association, Registry Association, American Sheep Breeders' Association, American Oxford Down Sheep Record Association, American Suffolk Sheep Society, Columbia Sheep Breeders' Association of America, and American Corriedale Association, Inc.

vi

We are very appreciative of illustrative materials received from the Eastern Iowa Breeders' Association, Eli Lilly and Company, The Farm Clinic, The Rath Packing Company, Kent Feeds, Inc., Farmers' Hybrid Hogs, Wilson and Company, Duncan Electric Manufacturing Company, Doane Agricultural Service, Inc., Dodgen and Company, M & M Products Company, Oscar Mayer and Company, Swift and Company, George A. Hormel and Company, Livestock Conservation Incorporated, Union Pacific Railroad, John Deere and Company, Sunbeam Corporation, Great Lakes Steel Corporation, DeLaval Separator Company, The Creamery Package Manufacturing Company, United States Steel Corporation, *Australian Queensland Country Life*, Arbor Acres Farm, Inc., The Schenck Hatchery, DeKalb Agricultural Association, Inc., Automatic Poultry Feeder Company, Linn's Hatchery, Beacon Milling Company, Northco Ventilating Company, Nichols Incorporated, James Manufacturing Company, Aluminum Corporation of America, Dr. Salsbury's Laboratories, American Scientific Laboratories, Inc., Buckeye Incubator Company, and the Morrell Packing Company, Strathglass Farm (cover transparency).

Members of the animal husbandry, dairy husbandry, poultry husbandry, and dairy and food industries staffs at Iowa State University also provided valuable assistance in the preparation of the manuscript.

We are also grateful to a large number of vocational agricultural instructors and many reviewers who made helpful suggestions.

Clarence E. Bundy
Ronald V. Diggins

TABLE OF CONTENTS

Features of the Second Edition v

Livestock Feeding and Nutrition

1. Food Nutrients 1
2. Composition and Classification of Feeds 13
3. Digestion in Ruminants and Simple-Stomach Animals . . 31
4. Measuring the Value of Feeds 36

Pork Production

5. The Pork Production Industry 44
6. Selection of Breeding and Feeding Stock 51
7. Feeding and Management of the Breeding Herd . . . 84
8. Feeding and Management of Market Hogs 98
9. Disease and Parasite Control 147
10. Marketing Hogs 164

Beef Production

11. The Beef Production Industry 181
12. Selection of Breeding and Feeding Stock 187
13. Feeding and Management of the Breeding Herd . . . 214
14. Feeding and Management of Stockers and
    Fattening Cattle 246
15. Buying and Selling Beef Cattle 273

Dairy Production

16. The Dairy Production Industry 287
17. Selection of Breeding Stock 299
18. Feeding and Management of the Producing Herd . . 322
19. Feeding and Management of Young Dairy Stock . . . 356
20. Marketing Dairy Products 373

Dual-Purpose Cattle

21. Breeding and Management of Dual-Purpose Cattle . . 390

Cattle Diseases and Parasites

22. Keeping Cattle Healthy 396

Sheep Production

23. The Sheep Production Industry 416
24. Selection of Breeding and Feeding Stock 421

25. Feeding and Management of the Breeding Flock . . . 448
26. Feeding Lambs 491
27. Control of Diseases and Parasites 508
28. Marketing Sheep and Wool 529

Poultry Production

29. The Poultry Production Industry 547
30. Selecting Chicks and Birds for Production 559
31. Feeding and Management of the Laying Flock . . . 579
32. Feeding and Management of Young Chickens 598
33. Turkey Production and Management 614
34. Control of Diseases and Parasites 627
35. Marketing Poultry Products 643

Inheritance and Reproduction

36. Reproduction, Inheritance, and Pedigrees in
    Animal Breeding 664

Index 675

1

Food Nutrients

Livestock on the farm means more meat, eggs, and milk on the tables of American homes. It means a healthier population and, consequently, a stronger America. To the farmer it means a more fertile land. Livestock converts grains and hays into valuable food products, and the residues are incorporated into the land to make it richer and more productive. The farmer's returns for his time and effort depend largely upon his knowledge of the science of animal husbandry and the application of science to the livestock enterprise.

To become a good livestock producer, one must first know what foods animals require in order to grow, reproduce, and furnish man with the meat, eggs, milk, and wool he desires. To understand the requirements of livestock, the individual must first become familiar with certain terms.

Nutrients

The term *nutrient* means a single class of foods or group of like foods that aids in the support of life and makes it possible for animals to produce efficiently the things we expect of them.

Classes of Nutrients. Nutrients are divided into five classes: carbohydrates, fats, proteins, minerals, and vitamins. Water may be classified as a sixth nutrient, but because of the various functions of water in the animal body it will be discussed separately. Each of these nutrient classes has an important part to play in the animal body, and unless they are supplied in the feed, best results with our livestock cannot be expected.

Carbohydrates. Carbohydrates are divided into two groups: *Nitrogen-free extract* (*N. F. E.*) and *fiber*. Nitrogen-free extract is that portion of the carbohydrates that is largely made up of the more easily digested and more completely digestible sugars and starches. The cereal grains, such as corn, sorghum, wheat, barley, oats, and rye, are rich in starch, containing 60 per cent or more. The more fibrous parts of the plants are made up largely of cellulose and lignin. These substances are far less digestible than the sugars and starches and are found primarily in the hays and fodders. The more mature the plants are when made into hay or fodder, the more fiber they contain. As will be pointed out later, ruminant animals, such as cattle, sheep, and goats, can digest much larger quantities of fiber than can poultry or simple-stomach animals, such as swine.

The carbohydrates, N. F. E. and fiber combined, are very important in livestock feeding, as they make up about 75 per cent of the total nutrients found in plants. Both N. F. E. and fiber are made up of the same chemical elements (carbon, hydrogen, and oxygen), but are in a different combination in the N. F. E. than in fiber.

Fats. Fats and oils are much alike except that fats are solid at ordinary temperature and oils are liquid. For the purpose of livestock feeding both are referred to as fats. Fats are made up of the same chemical elements as carbohydrates but in a different combination. Fats are quite easily digested by animals, and while the fat content of most seeds and plants is considerably less than that of carbohydrates, the fats are an important nutrient in livestock rations.

Proteins. Proteins are made up of a group of acids known as *amino acids*. Twenty-five or more amino acids have been identified. Amino acids are made up of hydrogen, carbon, and oxygen but differ from fats and carbohydrates, as they also contain about 16 per cent nitrogen. They combine to form the large number of proteins that exist. During the process of digestion the proteins are broken down into the amino acids, which are carried by the blood stream to the various parts of the body and deposited as needed. It is not definitely known how many of the amino acids are needed by the animal body. All animals are apparently able to manufacture some amino acids from others if supplied in large enough quantities. It has been pretty well established that at least ten amino acids are required in the ration of simple-stomach animals, such as swine, and eleven in the rations of poultry, especially baby chicks.

The ruminant animals, such as cattle, sheep, and goats, possess considerable ability to manufacture all the required amino acids from any one or more, if supplied in large enough quantity in the ration. Therefore, it appears that the quantity, rather than the number, of amino acids is important in the ration for ruminants. Ruminants can utilize urea, a high nitrogen compound, combining the nitrogen with the carbohydrates they have been fed to form amino acids necessary for their nutrition.

While ten amino acids are known to be essential in the rations of simple-stomach animals and eleven for poultry, the amount of each varies with the class of animals and the stage of maturity. Some are needed in larger quantities during the growing period, while others are required in larger quantities for reproduction. No single source of protein will supply all the amino acids in their proper balance for any animal in this class at all stages of growth and production. Therefore, the kinds and amounts of protein-rich feed must be varied throughout these stages for best results. The following table lists the amino acids considered essential in poultry rations at some time during the growth and reproduction periods.

Amino Acids Essential for Poultry

Arginine	Phenylalanine
Isoleucine	Lysine
Histidine	Tryptophan
Leucine	Valine
Methionine	Glycine
Threonine	

Note—Two amino acids that are not essential in poultry rations may be used to replace a part of methionine and phenylalanine. Cystine may replace up to one half the methionine requirements and tyrosine may replace seven-sixteenths of the phenylalanine.

Figure 1-1. This animal developed rickets early in life when maintained on a vitamin D-deficient ration and not allowed exposure to direct sunlight. Note the bowed front legs and enlarged joints. (Courtesy L. L. Madsen, U.S.D.A. Bureau of Animal Industry)

While a great many feeds contain proteins and several are noted for their high protein content, one must select a combination of protein-rich feeds which will meet the requirements for each class of livestock according to the stage of growth and production. Some high-protein feeds have little value as swine and poultry feeds when fed alone, because of their imbalance or lack of essential amino acids. Recommended rations, containing a proper combination of protein feeds, will be listed in the chapters dealing with each class of farm livestock.

Minerals. Minerals are generally divided into two groups, major minerals and trace minerals. The major minerals are salt, calcium, and phosphorus. They are needed in the largest quantity and are most likely to be lacking in the feed supplied. The trace minerals are those needed in very small amounts, though essential to the health of the animal. They include iron, copper, manganese, iodine, cobalt, sulphur, magnesium, zinc, potassium, and boron.

Vitamins. There are several vitamins necessary for proper nutrition of animals, but, as with the amino acids, the requirements in the ration vary with the class of animals. Simple-stomach animals and poultry require vitamin A and most of the B-complex group, which includes thiamine, riboflavin, niacin, pyrodoxin, pantothenic acid, choline, pyracin, tara-amino benzoic acid, inosital, folic acid, and biotin. Other vitamins utilized by livestock include B_{12}, C, D, K, and some unidentified vitamins. Vitamin C is apparently produced in the digestive system of all classes of farm animals and no consideration need be given it in the ration. Vitamin K is produced in sufficient quantity in the digestive system of all farm animals except for poultry. Poultry rations need to include this vitamin. Vitamin K has been used as a treatment in some livestock ailments, particularly calf scours.

Figure 1-2. These lambs were born dead because the ewe was fed a vitamin A-deficient ration during gestation. (Courtesy University of California)

Figure 1-3. This animal shows roughness of hair coat, anemia, and lack of appetite due to cobalt deficiency. (Courtesy C. F. Huffman, Michigan Agricultural Experiment Station)

Vitamin B_{12} is produced by ruminant animals but must be included in the ration of swine and poultry. Vitamin D, known as *the sunshine vitamin*, is supplied by sunlight to animals when sufficiently exposed. However, because of long winters in much of the country, when sunlight may be at a minimum, or when animals are kept in houses for long periods of time, this vitamin may be deficient and an ample supply should be included in the ration for all classes of farm livestock.

Vitamin E seems to be required in the ration by all classes of livestock. However, the effects of a deficiency are more pronounced in some classes of livestock than in others. Calves, small lambs, and poultry seem to be affected more than older cattle, sheep, and swine.

Water. The animal body is made up of from about 56 to 70 per cent water, and nutrients must be in liquid form before they can be absorbed by the body. Water is important in controlling body temperature. In ruminants water is important in the fermentation that takes place in the animal's digestive system as part of the digestive process. Livestock must have an abundance of fresh, clean water if the best results are to be expected.

Feed Additives. Within the last few years a number of drugs or drug-like substances have been introduced into the field of livestock nutrition. These products include a number of antibiotics, hormones or hormone-like substances, arsenic compounds, detergents, tranquilizers, rumen organisms, and a product known by the trade name of Dynafac. While beneficial results, as measured by increased growth, fattening ability, and feed savings, have resulted when many of these feed additives have been properly used, they cannot be considered food nutrients. A food nutrient becomes a part of the body cells and is necessary for the proper function of these cells. The feed additives do not become a part of the animal body.

Antibiotics. The antibiotics that have been used as feed additives include aureomycin (chlortetracycline), terramycin (oxytetracycline), penicillin, bacitracin, hygromycin B, and streptomycin. The class and age of livestock and the conditions under which they are produced determine the effectiveness of the antibiotics and the kinds of antibiotic that will give the best results. These conditions and recommendations are given in the sections dealing with each kind of livestock.

Figure 1-4. The cow on the left received a phosphorus supplement while grazing on a phosphorus-deficient range for two and a half years. The cow on the right received none. Note the thriftier appearance of the cow and calf that received the phosphorus supplement. (Courtesy U.S.D.A. Bureau of Animal Industry)

Hormones. Certain glands in the body secrete substances called hormones. These hormones have much to do with regulating or stimulating growth, fattening, reproduction, and other body functions. It has been learned through experiments that some man-made products, when fed to animals, have the same effect as the natural hormone. Among these hormone-like substances is a product commonly known as stilbestrol. Stilbestrol closely resembles the natural female hormone known as estrogen. This hormone, when fed to beef cattle and sheep or when implanted in pellet form under the skin, has induced a faster rate of growth and fattening.

Iodinated Casein. Iodinated casein is a product similar to the natural hormone thyroxine; it has induced greater milk production, especially in brood sows, and to some extent in other livestock. Recommendations as to the use of hormones will be given in the chapters dealing with each class of livestock.

Arsenicals. Arsenic, a poison when improperly fed, has been found to have growth-stimulating ability on some classes of livestock, especially little pigs, chicks, and poults. (See chapters on the livestock classes.) The arsenic compounds used as feed additives include arsenilic acid, sodium arsanilate, and 3-nitro-4 hydroxyphenyl arsonic acid. The latter is usually referred to as 3 nitro.

Dynafac. "Dynafac" is a trade name given to a product which consists of bone meal and a chemical compound known as tetra alkylammonium stearate. The manufacturers of the product claim it has gain-stimulating properties, especially when fed to beef cattle. However, more research will need to be completed before we can safely draw any conclusions.

Detergents or Surfactants. Detergents or surfactants, such as the common household detergents, have been fed experimentally to several classes of farm livestock. Some have shown beneficial results while others failed to show any value in their use. Experiments with poultry indicate possible advantages in including detergents in the ration.

Tranquilizers. Tranquilizers are drugs that have a calming effect upon livestock and may have a growth-stimulating effect through their action on hormone-secreting glands in the body. The experimental evidence as to their value is too limited to draw any definite conclusions, but there are indications that tranquilizers may have value for certain classes of livestock when properly fed.

Rumen Organisms. It is pointed out in Chapter 3 that digestion in ruminant animals is largely dependent upon bacteria and other organisms found in the rumen. Some evidence exists that when these organisms are supplied, especially to young dairy calves that are removed from their mothers within a few days, beneficial results occur. Commercial products containing rumen organisms have been produced as a feed additive for cattle and sheep. As with many of the other feed additives, more research will need to be completed before their value, if any, can be determined.

Functions of Nutrients and Feed Additives

The various nutrients and feed additives have functions in the animal body that are many and complicated. It is not the purpose of this book to discuss in detail the numerous and varied functions of each of the nutrients, but rather to discuss the primary functions of each nutrient so that the reader will gain a knowledge of the importance of each in the animal body.

Carbohydrates (function). Carbohydrates furnish heat and energy for animals and provide materials necessary for fattening. The animal requires more total carbohydrates than all of the other nutrients combined. Since most feeds are much higher in this than in other nutrients it is not difficult to provide adequate carbohydrates in the ration.

Fats (function). Fats are concentrated forms of energy. They provide 2.25 times as much heat and energy as do carbohydrates. One pound of fat will equal two and one-fourth pounds of carbohydrates in heat, energy, and fattening value. An excess amount of fat may produce harmful effects. Liquid fats, such as peanut oil or soybean oil, may produce soft lard when fed to swine. The feeding of an excess amount of seeds high in oil such as peanuts or soybeans, will have the same effect on swine. Some fats may produce liquid butter fat when fed to dairy cattle. Cod liver oil will actually decrease milk production when included in the dairy cow ration. However, relatively large quantities of animal fats have been included in the rations of beef cattle with successful results. Most animals require less than 3 per cent fat. Since animals on a high fat ration will satisfy their energy requirements more quickly they are inclined to consume less total feed. Therefore, the protein and vitamin level will need to be increased or deficiencies in these important nutrients may occur.

Proteins (function). Proteins, or rather the amino acids of which they are made, are essential in livestock feeding because they help to form the greater part of the muscles, internal organs, skin, hair, wool, feathers, hoofs, and horns. Eggs and milk both contain protein; therefore, animals producing these two products or those suckling young must have enough protein for their own body needs and extra amounts for the products they produce.

Minerals (function). Minerals are needed in nearly all parts of the body but are used primarily in the bones and in the teeth. Minerals make up an important part of the blood. Even the heart depends upon mineral balance to maintain its regular beating. Many disease conditions in livestock, such as anemia, digestive trouble, and some types of paralysis, can be traced to lack of one or more of the needed minerals.

Vitamins (function). The purpose or function of many of these vitamins is not clear, but we do know that serious results occur when feeds are given which do not provide the necessary vitamins. If vitamin A is lacking, animals fail to reproduce, eyesight is impaired, and growth slows down. If we do not provide the B-complex group for swine and poultry, appetite fails, skin disorders appear, and disease may become a problem. B_{12} improves the protein in grains and other feeds. A lack of vitamin E may cause a failure of the reproductive system and muscular disorders. Vitamin D is essential for proper utilization of minerals, calcium, and phosphorus, while vitamin K gives the blood its ability to clot, preventing excessive bleeding from injuries.

Feed Additives (function). The function of the feed additives is not completely understood by nutrition experts at this time. The growth-stimulating effects of the antibiotics and the arsenic compounds are thought to be due to their ability to control undesirable bacteria in the digestive tract. The fact that these additives have given the best results under poor sanitation gives evidence of the truth of this theory. These products are effective in the prevention and treatment of internal parasites and diseases. Animals that are kept in a healthy condition do not need to utilize their energy to ward off infectious diseases and parasites. Such animals are bound to do well when supplied with adequate nutrients.

Growth, fattening, and milk production are regulated by hormones secreted by body glands. An increase of these hormones over the amount normally provided by the glands apparently gives increased growth and milk production to some classes of animals when properly fed. Rumen organisms, defined in Chapter 3, may help to increase the number of beneficial organisms necessary for digestion in ruminants, especially young animals. The value of tranquilizers would be in their calming effect and possibly in their ability to stimulate the secretions of certain body glands.

Some livestock nutrition experts believe that detergents improve digestion and assimilation of fats by breaking up the fat particles. They may also have functions similar to those of the arsenicals and antibiotics.

Digestible Nutrients

The term *digestible nutrients* refers to that portion of any feed that is digestible. All feeds contain a certain percentage of material that is not digestible in the animal body. The protein of various feeds differs widely in digestibility, as do the carbohydrates. The extent to which they are digestible depends largely upon the class of livestock. Ruminants digest a larger portion of the fiber than simple-stomach animals and poultry. However, cattle do not digest whole grains as thoroughly as sheep, goats, and other classes of farm animals. Whole grains are less thoroughly masticated by cattle and large quantities pass through the digestive system unbroken. The amount of digestible nutrients in various feeds is given in tables in Chapter 2. However, these are based on averages for cattle and sheep. For practical purposes it may be assumed that the concentrates and very low-fiber feeds would have nearly equal digestibility for swine and poultry. However, high-fiber feeds would be much less digestible to swine and poultry than shown in the tables. Therefore, only the highest-quality legume roughages should be fed to these animals.

Balanced Rations

A ration is the amount of feed which is given to an animal during a twenty-four-hour period. A balanced ration is one which supplies in their correct proportion all the food nutrients necessary to nourish the animal properly during a twenty-four-hour period. The amount of the various nutrients required to balance a ration is determined by the kind of animal and the purpose for which the animal is kept. Thus, the needs of the dairy cow differ from those of the beef cow, much as the needs of the brood sow and the growing pig differ.

Summary

In summarizing the various food nutrients and their functions in the animal body, let us compare the animal with the modern farm tractor. The tractor has a chassis or framework, which might be termed the skeleton. Just as the chassis of the tractor is made from certain kinds of iron and steel, so the skeleton of an animal is made up largely of a certain material, namely, mineral. The moving parts of the tractor and the engine proper are comparable to the muscles and the internal organs of the animal. Here again, a certain material is needed in the manufacture of these parts just as proteins are needed in the animal body.

Before the engine can move, it must be fed energy. Gasoline or fuel oil furnishes energy, as do the carbohydrates and fats fed to livestock.

The tractor needs oil and grease to lessen wear, prevent breakdown, and make the parts run smoothly. The amount is small, but without it the machine becomes a stationary mass. The vitamins and feed additives have a similar purpose in the animal body. Last of all water is used, as in an engine, to regulate the temperature.

In order for the machine to continue to run, a mechanic must be on the job replacing worn parts. In the animal, the blood can be thought of as a mechanic carrying materials to various parts so that they may continue to function.

If any parts become worn and are not replaced or if the wrong kind of fuel is fed to the motor, the machine slows down, fails to run smoothly, or stops. If livestock is not fed the kind of material necessary for proper body function, it, too, slows down or stops production.

• *Questions*

1. What is meant by the term *nutrient?*
2. List the classes of nutrients.
3. What is the main function of each nutrient class?
4. How do fats and carbohydrates differ in their ability to produce energy and fatty tissue?
5. What are the major minerals?
6. Why are trace minerals so called?
7. Why is an abundance of clean, fresh water important to livestock production?
8. Why have feed additives become important in certain livestock feeds?
9. What is meant by *digestible nutrient?*
10. Why does the amount of fiber reduce the digestibility of a feed?
11. To what part of a feed does the term nitrogen-free extract refer?
12. What is the difference between a ration and a balanced ration?

• *References*

Anderson, Arthur L., *Introductory Animal Husbandry,* The Macmillan Company, New York, 1948.

Morrison, Frank B., *Feeds and Feeding,* The Morrison Publishing Company, Ithaca, New York, 1956.

U. S. Department of Agriculture, *Better Feeding of Livestock,* Farmers' Bulletin No. 2052, 1952.

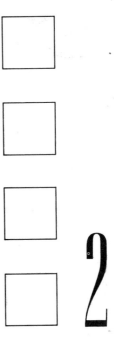

2

Composition and Classification of Feeds

Livestock feeds are generally classified according to the amount of total digestible nutrients they provide, or according to the amount of a specific nutrient they furnish in the ration. They are usually divided into two general classes—roughages and concentrates.

Roughages

Feeds containing relatively large amounts of fiber or nondigestible material are called *roughages*. This group of feeds includes hays, silage, fodder, and other similar feeds.

Legume Roughages. Legumes are plants that have the ability to use nitrogen which they take from the air. Legumes are higher in nitrogen than are other plants, and since nitrogen is essential in the manufacture of proteins, legumes are higher in protein than are other roughages. The common legumes are alfalfa, all the clovers, trefoil, soybeans, lespedeza, various kinds of peas, beans, and a large number of other less widely grown plants.

Nonlegume Roughages. Nonlegume roughages as a class are lower in protein. When they are fed as the only roughage, they seldom provide enough protein to meet the needs even of ruminants. The use of nonlegume roughages generally calls for an increased amount in the protein concentrates fed to balance the ration. The common nonlegume roughages are brome grass, timothy, bluegrass, prairie grass, corn fodder, corn silage, and fodder or silage made from the various sorghums.

Concentrates

Concentrates are feeds which have a comparatively high digestibility. They are relatively low in fiber and include all grains and many by-products of grains and animals, such as wheat middlings, tankage, and soybean oil meal.

Protein Concentrates. Protein concentrates may be classed as a subdivision of concentrates; they make up the group of concentrates which furnish a relatively high percentage of protein. The exact percentage of protein which a feed must contain before it may be considered a protein concentrate has not been definitely defined; but since most grains and roughages contain less than 20 per cent protein, we can consider any feed which contains 20 per cent or more a protein concentrate. Such feeds are mixed with farm-produced grains and roughages to increase the protein content of the ration. Protein concentrates are generally classified as animal or vegetable proteins.

Animal Proteins. Proteins that are derived from animals or animal by-products, such as tankage, meat scraps, fish meal, dried skim milk, or dried buttermilk, are called animal proteins.

In addition to probably containing amino acids not found in other proteins, animal proteins also contain growth factors, not fully understood at this time, which make them especially valuable in the feeding of swine and poultry. Cattle and sheep, because of the type of their digestive systems, are able to manufacture some amino acids that simple-stomach animals must get from animal proteins. For this reason, and because of their expense, animal proteins are not generally considered important in the rations of cattle and sheep.

Vegetable Proteins. Vegetable proteins are those found in plants or in the by-products of plants. The chief vegetable protein concentrates are soybean oil meal, linseed oil meal, cottonseed meal, and peanut oil meal.

The plant or vegetable proteins, as a class, are not nearly as complete nor as high in quality as are the animal proteins, but in the feeding of ruminants they provide the essential amino acids. In swine or poultry rations, one or more animal proteins are generally considered necessary in order to give the amino acid balance essential for best results.

Sources of Carbohydrates

Grains. Of the common feeds which are fed to livestock, the grains provide the best source of energy and have the highest fattening value. Among the grains used extensively for feed are corn, oats, sorghum, and barley. Rye and wheat are used to some extent in certain areas of the United States.

Corn. Yellow corn is one of the best feed grains for all classes of livestock. It ranks high in total digestible nutrients (about 80 per cent for No. 2 grade), low in fiber, and higher in fat than any cereal grain except oats. Corn is very palatable to all classes of livestock.

Although corn ranks high among livestock feeds, it has deficiencies which must be corrected by the use of other feeds. Protein and mineral deficiencies are the most pronounced.

Oats. As a livestock feed, oats rank second in popularity to corn. They have about the same general nutritional value as corn but contain more fiber and are less digestible. (Oats average about 70 per cent digestible as compared to 80 per cent for corn.) Their protein content is a little higher than that of corn but, like that of corn, is lacking in quality. In general, oats have about the same deficiencies as corn.

The fiber content is largely in the hulls, and for this reason the number of hulls determines the food value of the oats. Oats grown under certain weather conditions, and certain varieties of oats may contain a very large proportion of hulls; oats which are grown without hulls or those which have had the hulls removed by mechanical means have a food value that is equal to, or higher than, that of corn.

Barley. Barley is a very good substitute for corn and can be fed successfully to all classes of livestock. Like corn and oats, it is high in nitrogen-free extract or carbohydrates. It is less digestible than corn and has more fiber, but has the advantage of containing more protein.

Barley is higher in food value per hundred pounds than oats, and in general is considered better than oats as a fattening feed. In parts of the United States a disease known as *scab of barley* has been serious. Barley infected with scab cannot be fed to swine but can be utilized by cattle. Swine will not eat barley infected with scab unless there is no other feed available. When swine are forced to consume scabby barley, digestive troubles often develop.

Wheat. Wheat resembles the other cereal grains in nutritional value, having a higher carbohydrate content and a higher protein content than does corn. There is considerable variation in the food value of wheat, depending upon the variety and the locality in which it is grown.

Wheat is a very good substitute for corn, and if the price is in line, it can be used to replace a large part of the corn fed to all classes of livestock.

Rye. Because rye has about the same general food value as other grains, it would seem a good substitute for them. However, rye is not palatable to livestock and, when fed in large quantities, may cause digestive trouble and a reduction in feed intake. It should be mixed with other grains and fed only as a part of the ration.

Grain Sorghums. Grain sorghums resemble corn in all respects except that they are lower in fat. The sorghums make very good livestock feed and are well liked by all classes of stock. Sorghum grain is rather hard, and grinding is necessary if it is to be fully digested.

Molasses. Molasses has a fairly high nitrogen-free extract content and furnishes a readily digestible supply of carbohydrates. As a livestock feed it is valued for its palatability. Molasses is generally used as a supplement to other feeds in order to increase consumption. Livestock, particularly beef cattle which are being fattened, can be induced to consume more feed if molasses is mixed with the ration, and the fattening process may be speeded up.

Poor or unpalatable roughages, such as corncobs, can be made more appetizing by the use of molasses.

Roughages as a Source of Carbohydrates. Roughages provide a relatively cheap source of carbohydrates, and good-quality roughages, such as those produced by legumes or corn silage, will often provide enough carbohydrates for stock cattle or matured sheep without any other carbohydrate feeds being supplied. However, in fattening livestock the digestibility of roughages is too low to produce finished animals unless the ration is supplemented with grains.

The kind of roughage, the method of harvesting, and the stage of maturity at the time of cutting are very important factors influencing food value. Legumes and grasses cut at a late stage of maturity may not have more than half the value per ton of those cut at the proper time. As an example, alfalfa cut when only a few flowers are showing will contain from 15 to 20 per cent more digestible nutrients and from 25 to 30 per cent more proteins than will alfalfa cut after it reaches full bloom.

In the case of grain crops cut for silage, the grain should be reasonably mature for highest food value. Corn silage should be cut just as the lower leaves begin to dry out.

Sources of Fats

Grains and Oil Seed Crops. Almost all livestock feeds contain some fats. Such feeds as soybeans and peanuts are especially high in fat, containing from 18 to 47 per cent while the common feed grains such as corn, oats, sorghum, and barley range from 1.9 to 5.5 per cent.

Animal Fats and Oils. Animal fats such as lard and tallow and the vegetable oils have been used both experimentally and practically to increase the energy value of livestock rations. When a considerable increase in the fat content of livestock rations seems desirable, the animal fats and soybean and peanut oil are most commonly used.

Protein Concentrates. Both animal and vegetable protein concentrates contain fats. The amount depends upon the methods of processing but ranges from 1.5 to 15 per cent. The animal protein concentrates are generally considerably higher in fat content than the vegetable protein feeds. This is especially true when the solvent process of removing the oil from the seeds is used.

Animal protein feeds come from animal by-products, dairy products, and dairy by-products.

Animal By-products. *Tankage and Meat Scraps.* Tankage and meat scraps are very much alike in composition. Both are by-products of packing houses or products of rendering plants. The digestible protein content will vary considerably, depending upon the contents of the feed. If the product contains a large percentage of hair or gristle, the total protein content may be high, but the digestible protein content may be relatively low.

Since it is impossible for the user to determine what amount of nondigestible protein a feed contains, it is wise to buy only from a company known to be reliable.

Meat and Bone Scraps. The combination of meat and bone scraps contains a higher percentage of bone. Since bone is lower in protein than are meat scraps, the total protein content of the feed is generally lower.

In the manufacture of all animal products that go into livestock feed, the material is heated to prevent the carrying of disease.

Blood Meal. Blood meal is made from the blood collected at the packing houses. In the manufacturing process, the material is heated and dried. Blood meal is high in total protein, but its quality and digestiblity are lower than that of good-grade tankage or meat scraps.

Fish Meal. Fish meal is manufactured either from the waste material of the fish industry or from fish not considered good for human consumption.

Fish meal is one of the best feeds for swine and poultry because of its high percentage of good-quality protein.

Dairy Products and By-products. *Skim Milk and Buttermilk.* Both of these products contain over 90 per cent water, but the dry matter is about one-third protein. Nearly all the protein is digestible, and when these products are available, they furnish one of the best sources of protein for swine, poultry, and very young ruminants.

Dried Skim Milk and Buttermilk. A heating process drives off most of the water in skim milk and buttermilk, leaving the milk solids in a dry condition. These dried milk solids furnish a high-protein food of good quality.

Sources of Vegetable Protein

All seeds, roughages, and grain by-products furnish various amounts of proteins, but the chief sources of vegetable proteins are the seed by-products and legume roughages.

Seed By-products. *Soybean Oil Meal.* Soybean oil meal is the residue left from soybeans after the oil has been removed. The residue is ground or formed into pellets and marketed as livestock feed.

Soybean oil meal varies in protein content from 41 to 46 per cent, depending upon the method of manufacture. The protein is of very high quality, and may be used to furnish a major part of the protein concentrate in rations for most livestock.

Soybeans. Soybeans have the highest protein content of any seeds commonly used for feed. Soybeans will average about 37 per cent total protein, but the quality is low. The protein in soybeans is improved by the heating process used in the manufacture of soybean oil meal. This explains the high-quality protein found in the meal as compared to that in the raw soybeans.

If their price is low in comparison with the price of other forms of vegetable proteins, ground soybeans may be used to furnish a part of the protein in rations for cattle and older swine.

Cottonseed Meal and Cake. When cotton is processed, the seed is removed from the lint and the oil is extracted from the seed. The seed residue is manufactured into meal or cake and sold as a protein concentrate.

The protein content of cottonseed meal varies from 38 to 47 per cent, depending upon the variety of cotton from which the seed is taken and upon the method of processing. Cottonseed meal is a good source of protein for ruminants, but it should be used in limited amounts only as a protein concentrate for nonruminants.

Linseed Meal. When flax seed is processed, the oil is removed from the seed and the residue is made into livestock feed. The oil is known as *linseed oil*, and the meal as *linseed oil meal*. Linseed oil meal is one of the most widely used protein feeds. Its protein content ranges from 31 to 36 per cent, and it may be successfully used as the only protein feed for cattle and sheep. For swine and poultry, linseed meal should be used as only a part of the protein concentrate in the ration.

Peanut Oil Meal. Peanut oil meal is the residue of the peanut from which the oil has been removed. Peanut oil meal can be used as a protein feed for all classes of livestock but it is generally preferred as a swine or dairy cattle feed. When fed as the only protein, it may be too laxative. Best results are obtained when peanut oil meal is used in combination with other proteins.

Corn Gluten Meal. Corn gluten meal is a by-product of corn used in the manufacture of corn oil and corn starch. The protein content ranges from 40 to 44 per cent. Corn gluten meal may be used as a part of the protein in livestock rations. The quality of protein is not high, and best results are obtained when this meal is fed in combination with other proteins.

Legume Roughages. Legumes, when fed as dry roughages, silage, or pasture, furnish an excellent source of high-quality protein. Under some conditions legumes will furnish all the needed protein. Stock cattle may be successfully wintered on legume forage without any other protein feeds being provided. Legumes furnish a cheap source of protein, and when legume forage is used in the ration, the amount of protein concentrates may be reduced without affecting the growth or production of the livestock.

Urea. Urea cannot be classed as either an animal or vegetable protein. In fact it is not a protein at all, but rather a compound containing about 40 per cent nitrogen. It has been pointed out that the amino acids contain nitrogen as well as carbon, hydrogen, and oxygen. The bacteria in the digestive system of ruminants can combine the nitrogen from urea with the carbon, hydrogen, and oxygen found in the carbohydrates and form amino acids. Therefore a limited amount of urea may be used as a protein substitute in the feeding of ruminants.

Sources of Vitamins

Livestock, when fed a well-balanced ration consisting of grains, protein concentrates, and good forage, generally gets enough of the needed vitamins. However, under certain conditions which will be discussed in later chapters, it may be necessary to select feeds high in essential vitamins. Vitamins most likely to be deficient in the feed are A or carotene, the B-complex group, D, and E.

Vitamin A. *Vitamin A in Forage.* Vitamin A is found in plants and in plant products as carotene, which is converted into vitamin

A in the digestive system of animals. Green plants have an abundance of carotene, and there is seldom any need to give any special attention to the vitamin A content of a ration for livestock on pasture.

When forage crops are harvested, a large part of the carotene may be lost unless special care is taken to preserve it. Roughages that retain their green color and most of the leaves when cured will still be high in carotene content. Very little carotene is lost when roughages are converted into silage. Legume and grass crops harvested during the natural growing period and in good weather have a much higher carotene content than do mature or badly weathered forages. Forages lose much of their carotene content when kept in storage for long periods of time.

Vitamin A in Grains. Carotene is found in yellow corn and is an important source of vitamin A. Legume forages, however, contain a much higher percentage of this vitamin than does corn.

Commercial Sources of Vitamin A. The fish liver oils are one of the best sources of concentrated amounts of vitamin A. Cod liver oil is often used as a vitamin A supplement for small pigs and chickens not on pasture. For feed-mixing purposes vitamin A may also be purchased in a supplement containing a mixture of several other vitamins.

Vitamin B-Complex Group. *Vitamin B-Complex Group in Forages.* With the exception of vitamin B_{12}, which will be discussed separately, forages provide an excellent source of the B-complex group of vitamins.

Vitamin B-Complex Group in Animal Products. The animal products, especially milk or milk products, furnish substantial amounts of vitamin B-complex.

Vitamin B-Complex Group in Grains. Grain crops provide, to some extent, most of the B vitamins, but they are not rich enough in these essential vitamins to be relied upon entirely. Unless a good forage is fed, some other source of the B group should be included in the ration.

Vitamin B Group in Brewers' Yeast and Distillers' Solubles. When there is a need for more of the B vitamins than those supplied by the ration being fed, small amounts of yeast or distillers' solubles are often used to boost the B content of the ration.

B_{12} *in Animal Products.* Although vitamin B_{12} is included in the B-complex group, it is found in a limited number of feeds; for this reason it is discussed separately. With the exception of commercial sources, B_{12} is found only in animal products, such as milk, tankage, meat scraps, fish meal, and similar feeds.

Ruminants manufacture B_{12} during the process of digestion, and, with the exception of very young ruminants, it does not have to be supplied in their feed. Swine following cattle are supplied B_{12} to some extent through the feces of the cattle.

B_{12} is one of the important ingredients in animal proteins necessary for growth in poultry and swine. When B_{12} is supplied in other forms, the amount of animal protein fed swine and poultry can be considerably reduced without affecting the growth rate of the animal.

Commercial Sources of Vitamin B_{12}. Many laboratories and feed companies manufacture concentrated forms of vitamin B_{12}, which may be purchased for feed-mixing purposes.

Vitamin D. *Vitamin D in Sunlight.* Vitamin D is often called the *sunshine vitamin*, and animals exposed to direct sunlight seldom suffer from a vitamin D deficiency. However, animals that are kept inside, especially young pigs and chickens, must have special attention given to the D content of their ration.

Vitamin D in Forage Crops. Forage crops, especially sun-cured legume hays, are very good sources of vitamin D. The D vitamin is absorbed by the legume during curing.

Commercial Sources of Vitamin D. Concentrated amounts of vitamin D may be secured in fish liver oils and irradiated yeast. These two materials are the best supplements to a ration low in vitamin D.

Cod liver oil, when fed to ruminants over a long period of time, has shown injurious results. This may be due to a destruction of vitamin E caused by the fish liver oil. When it becomes necessary to add a vitamin D supplement to the ration of ruminants such as dairy calves housed inside, a vitamin concentrate such as irradiated yeast is recommended.

Vitamin E. *Vitamin E in Farm Feeds.* Vitamin E is found in nearly all forages, feed grains, and protein concentrates. Animals fed a reasonably well-balanced ration seldom need additional amounts of this vitamin.

Vitamin E is essential for fertility. Bulls and other male animals used heavily in breeding programs may show some benefit from additional amounts of vitamin E.

Wheat Germ Oil as a Source of Vitamin E. When amounts of vitamin E greater than those supplied by the ordinary ration are desired, wheat germ oil is usually considered a good source. Wheat germ oil is manufactured commercially and can be purchased through most feed dealers.

Other more concentrated commercial sources of vitamin E are available when large quantities are needed, as in the treatment of stiff lamb disease. (See Chapter 27.)

Vitamin K. Alfalfa leaf meal is high in vitamin K. Also a product produced commercially called Menadione replaces the K vitamin needs of poultry, which, in the treatment of certain disorders, seems to be the only class of farm animals for which special consideration need be given this vitamin in the ration.

Commercial Vitamin Premixes. Vitamin premixes are available for all classes of livestock. They are often combined with antibiotics in what is termed an antibiotic vitamin premix. One desiring a vitamin supplement for any class of livestock can purchase one or more that provide all the vitamins likely to be deficient in the feed. When this supplement is properly mixed with the rest of the feed, the vitamins will be present in the necessary amounts.

Sources of Minerals

Several minerals are needed in well-balanced livestock rations. Most of the essential minerals are present in common livestock feeds, but the amounts are generally not great enough to provide for the mineral needs of farm livestock. Therefore, mineral supplements are generally recommended.

Minerals in Farm-produced Feeds. All farm-grown feeds contain minerals, but the legume forages are the best sources. Legumes are high in both phosphorus and calcium. The mineral content of all farm-grown feeds depends upon the soil on which they are grown. Legumes grown on well-limed and phosphated soils have a higher content of these important minerals than do those grown on acid and low-phosphorus soils.

The trace mineral content of grains and roughages depends largely upon the types of soil on which they were grown. The presence or absence of trace minerals in the soil may not necessarily affect the yield of the crop, but it does affect the value of the feed from a mineral standpoint.

Minerals in Protein Concentrates. Animal protein feeds, especially meat and bone scraps, tankage, and fish meal, are excellent sources of minerals. The mineral content in these feeds varies from 15 to 25 per cent, and the necessity for other mineral supplements is reduced when such feeds are used in the ration. Since all protein feeds are relatively high in price, they are fed primarily for their protein content. The amount fed is seldom enough to meet the mineral needs of the animal.

Vegetable protein meals are much lower in mineral content than are the animal proteins, but higher than are the farm grains.

Chief Sources of Mineral Supplements. High-quality ground limestone is one of the best sources of calcium for mixing mineral supplements. Limestone is cheap and available in most areas.

Steamed bone meal, which is manufactured by cooking clean bones under steam pressure, is the most common phosphorus supplement. It is also a very good source of calcium.

Salt is needed by all livestock and is easily obtainable either in loose or block form. Mineralized salt, which contains a mixture of trace minerals, is also available.

Trace minerals can best be secured by purchasing what is commonly known as *trace mineral mixture*. This mixture contains the trace minerals in proper proportion, and can be mixed with limestone, salt, and bone meal to make up a complete mineral mixture.

Sources of Feed Additives

Recent experiments have shown that many feed additives are very important for promoting growth in certain types of livestock. No farm-produced feeds contain these additives; therefore, we must rely upon commercial sources for supplementing rations with these important substances.

When we mix our own feeds, an antibiotic-vitamin supplement may be purchased and mixed in the ration according to the manufacturer's directions. There is evidence that a mixture of the known beneficial antibiotics may be better than any single antibiotic.

Stilbestrol must be purchased commercially mixed with a protein supplement or as pellets for implanting. The product has not

TABLE 1

AVERAGE COMPOSITION OF COMMON CONCENTRATES
HIGH IN ENERGY AND FAT-PRODUCING VALUE

(*Expressed in per cent*)

Feed	Total Dry Matter	Total Digestible Nutrients	Total Protein	Digestible Protein	N-free Extracts or Carbohydrates	Fat	Mineral Matter	Fiber
Barley	89.4	77.7	12.7	10.0	66.6	1.9	2.8	5.4
Beet pulp (dried)	91.2	69.7	8.8	4.1	58.7	0.6	3.5	19.6
Corn (No. 2)	85.0	80.1	8.7	6.7	69.2	3.9	1.2	2.0
Ground ear corn	86.1	73.2	7.4	5.3	66.2	3.2	1.3	8.0
Feterita (grain)	89.4	79.8	12.2	9.5	70.1	3.2	1.7	2.2
Kafir (grain)	89.8	81.6	10.9	8.8	72.7	2.9	1.6	1.7
Milo (grain)	89.0	79.4	10.9	8.5	70.7	3.0	2.1	2.3
Blackstrap cane molasses	73.4	53.7	3.0	0	61.7	0	8.6	0
Beet molasses	80.5	60.8	8.4	4.4	62.0	0	10.1	0
Oats (hulled)	90.4	91.9	16.2	14.6	63.7	6.1	2.2	2.2
Oats	90.2	70.1	12.0	9.4	58.6	4.6	4.0	11.0
Rye	89.5	76.5	12.6	10.0	70.9	1.7	1.9	2.4
Wheat	89.5	80.0	13.2	11.1	69.9	1.9	1.9	2.6
Wheat bran	90.1	66.9	16.9	13.3	53.1	4.5	6.1	10.0
Wheat middlings	90.1	79.2	17.5	15.4	60.0	4.5	3.8	4.3

TABLE 2

AVERAGE COMPOSITION OF COMMON PROTEIN CONCENTRATES

(*Expressed in per cent*)

Feed	Total Dry Matter	Total Digestible Nutrients	Total Protein	Digestible Protein	N-free Extracts or Carbohydrates	Fat	Mineral Matter	Fiber
Blood meal	91.6	60.4	82.2	60.4	0.9	1.9	5.7	0.9
Buttermilk (dried)	92.0	83.1	31.8	28.6	43.6	6.1	10.0	0.5
Corn gluten meal	91.6	79.7	43.2	36.7	38.9	2.2	3.5	3.8
Cottonseed meal	92.7	72.6	43.3	35.9	27.4	5.1	6.0	11.0
Fish meal	92.0	70.8	60.9	53.6	5.4	6.9	18.3	0.9
Linseed meal, solvent process	91.0	70.3	36.6	30.7	38.3	1.0	5.8	9.3
Meat scraps	94.2	66.7	54.9	45.0	2.5	9.4	24.9	2.5
Meat & bone scraps	93.7	65.3	49.7	40.8	3.1	10.6	28.1	2.2
Milk (dried-skim)	94.0	80.7	34.7	31.2	50.3	1.2	7.8	0.2
Peanut oil meal, solvent process	93.0	77.3	52.3	47.6	26.3	1.6	5.9	6.9
Soybean seed	90.0	87.6	37.9	33.7	24.5	18.0	4.6	5.0
Soybean oil meal, solvent process	90.4	78.1	45.7	42.0	31.4	1.3	6.1	5.9
Tankage (high-grade)	92.8	65.8	59.4	50.5	2.6	7.5	21.4	1.9

TABLE 3

AVERAGE COMPOSITION OF COMMON DRY ROUGHAGES

(Expressed in per cent)

Feed	Total Dry Matter	Total Digestible Nutrients	Total Protein	Digestible Protein	N-free Extracts or Carbohydrates	Fat	Mineral Matter	Fiber
Alfalfa hay (average)	90.5	50.7	15.3	10.9	36.7	1.9	8.0	28.6
Alfalfa hay (high-grade)	90.5	52.7	17.5	12.8	39.5	2.4	8.4	22.7
Alfalfa meal (dehydrated)	92.7	54.4	17.7	12.4	38.4	2.5	10.1	24.0
Birdsfoot trefoil	91.2	55.0	14.2	9.8	41.9	2.1	6.0	27.0
Bluegrass hay	89.4	54.8	8.2	4.8	42.1	2.8	6.5	29.8
Brome grass hay	88.8	49.3	10.4	5.3	39.9	2.1	8.2	28.2
Clover hay—red (good)	88.3	51.8	12.0	7.2	40.3	2.5	6.4	27.1
Clover hay—red (second cutting)	88.1	54.1	13.4	8.4	40.4	2.9	6.9	24.5
Corncobs (ground)	90.4	45.7	2.3	0	54.0	0.4	1.6	32.1
Corn fodder (medium water, well-eared)	82.6	53.9	6.8	3.3	46.7	2.1	5.2	21.8
Corn stover (ears removed)	90.6	51.9	5.9	2.1	46.5	1.6	5.8	30.8
Fescue hay	89.2	52.7	7.0	3.7	43.2	1.9	6.8	30.3
Hegari (fodder)	86.3	52.4	6.1	3.2	52.8	1.7	7.5	18.2
Kafir (fodder)	90.0	53.6	8.7	4.5	44.2	2.6	9.0	25.5
Lespedeza hay (annual)	90.0	45.1	13.1	5.6	42.2	2.5	5.3	26.9
Lespedeza hay (perennial)	89.0	41.4	13.2	4.4	42.7	1.7	4.9	26.5
Oat hay	88.1	47.3	8.2	4.9	42.2	2.7	6.9	28.1
Oat straw	89.7	44.7	4.1	0.7	41.0	2.2	6.3	36.1
Orchard grass hay	88.7	47.4	7.5	3.5	42.7	2.4	6.8	30.4
Prairie hay, Western (good)	91.3	45.1	6.0	2.0	44.0	3.0	8.6	29.7
Reed canary grass hay	91.1	45.1	7.7	4.8	44.3	2.3	7.6	29.2
Sorghum (fodder sweet)	88.8	52.4	6.2	3.3	48.1	2.4	7.1	25.0
Soybean hay (seed well developed)	88.0	52.5	15.2	10.8	35.2	4.7	6.2	26.7
Sudan grass hay	89.6	50.0	11.2	6.3	41.3	1.5	9.5	26.1
Timothy hay (good)	89.0	50.8	7.5	4.1	44.4	2.4	4.7	30.0

TABLE 4

AVERAGE COMPOSITION OF PASTURE LEGUMES AND GRASSES

(Expressed in per cent)

Feed	Total Dry Matter	Total Digestible Nutrients	Total Protein	Digestible Protein	N-free Extracts or Carbohydrates	Fat	Mineral Matter	Fiber
Alfalfa	24.4	14.8	4.6	3.5	10.0	0.9	2.2	6.7
Bluegrass	30.2	20.7	5.5	4.1	13.4	1.2	2.5	7.6
Brome grass	25.0	18.3	5.1	3.9	10.7	1.0	2.4	5.8
Clover (Ladino)	16.6	12.4	4.1	3.3	7.5	0.8	1.7	2.5
Clover (red)	25.0	16.8	4.0	2.8	11.2	0.9	2.1	6.8
Clover (alsike)	22.0	15.7	4.1	3.2	10.4	0.9	1.9	4.7
Clover (sweet)	20.8	12.8	4.1	3.2	9.2	0.7	1.9	4.9
Fescue	30.5	18.8	3.0	1.6	14.0	1.0	2.4	10.1
Lespedeza (annual)	25.0	12.7	4.1	2.0	9.2	0.5	3.2	8.0
Rape	16.3	12.8	2.9	2.4	8.0	0.6	2.2	2.6
Timothy	23.9	15.4	4.7	3.5	11.1	0.9	2.6	4.6
Trefoil	22.7	13.3	3.4	4.5	9.5	0.8	2.3	5.6

TABLE 5

AVERAGE COMPOSITION OF COMMON KINDS OF SILAGE

(Expressed in per cent)

Feed	Total Dry Matter	Total Digestible Nutrients	Total Protein	Digestible Protein	N-free Extracts or Carbohydrates	Fat	Mineral Matter	Fiber
Alfalfa	36.0	21.3	6.0	4.1	13.7	1.4	3.2	11.7
Corn	27.6	18.3	2.3	1.2	16.2	0.8	1.6	6.7
Corn stalk silage	23.7	14.0	1.6	0.6	12.0	0.7	1.6	7.8
Grass-legume mixture	33.3	19.1	5.2	2.9	14.2	1.3	3.8	8.8
Grain sorghum	30.0	17.1	2.6	1.4	18.6	0.7	2.1	6.0

Tables 1 through 5 adapted by special permission of the Morrison Publishing Company, Ithaca, New York, from *Feeds and Feedings,* 22nd edition, by F. B. Morrison.

been made available in premix forms to farmers and feed mixers such as the elevators.

Iodinated casein and arsenic compounds may be purchased by feed mixers as a premix and incorporated with the ration. Detergents are available in nearly every household. Rumen organisms, Dynafac, and tranquilizers are available in commercial feeds.

Nutrient Values of Livestock Feeds

Grains and roughages vary considerably in nutrient value, depending upon their variety, the locality and type of soil in which they are grown, their stages of maturity, the methods of harvesting, and the length of time in storage. The manufacturing process determines to some extent the value of feeds. For these reasons average compositions of various feeds generally have to be used when planning livestock rations. Tables 1 through 5 give the average composition of commonly used livestock feeds.

It has been pointed out in Chapter 1 that the digestibility of the feeds as given in Tables 1 to 5 are averages for cattle and sheep. For practical livestock feeding the grains, grain products, and protein concentrates may be assumed to have about the same digestibility for swine and poultry when fed in a well-balanced ration and not more than the amount recommended. High-quality legume pasture, silage, or hay would have nearly equal value for swine and poultry as compared to cattle and sheep. However, such low-quality roughages as straw, corncobs, and corn stover should be avoided as poultry feeds. Such feeds are sometimes used in swine rations to furnish bulk and limit the feed intake when self-feeding is practiced. A good example would be in the case of brood sows. The operator may wish to self-feed but find that it is necessary to add ground cobs to the grain and supplement mixture to prevent overeating, which may result in too much fattening for best results.

Summary

Feeds are divided into two groups: roughages and concentrates. Roughages are those feeds relatively high in fiber, such as legume and grass hays, fodders, and silages. Concentrates are the low-fiber feeds and include the grains, dairy products, and feeds manufactured from seed, dairy, and animal by-products.

Protein concentrates are feeds high in protein; they are classified as vegetable or animal proteins depending upon the material from which they are made.

The grains are higher in fattening and energy value than are other common feeds; however, roughages, although lower in nitrogen-free extract and higher in fiber, are generally a source of low-cost carbohydrates.

Tankage, meat scraps, meat and bone scraps, fish meal, milk, and milk products are all good sources of animal protein.

The vegetable proteins are supplied in soybean oil meal, linseed meal, cottonseed meal, and other feeds derived from plants. Legumes when used as feed will replace much of the protein available from other sources.

Older animals receiving rations consisting of legumes, proteins, and grains seldom need added vitamins, except possibly B_{12}. However, vitamin concentrates are often essential for best results in feeding young animals. The vitamin concentrates are found in such feeds as fish liver oil (vitamins A and D) and wheat germ oil (vitamin E). The B-complex group may be purchased in a vitamin premix available in most localities.

Feed additives have an important place in livestock feeding, and are usually provided in a premix or in commercially ready mixed feeds.

• *Questions*

1. What are the two main classes of feeds?
2. How do roughages and concentrates differ?
3. List several common roughages.
4. Why are legumes higher in protein than are other roughages?
5. Name some common legumes.
6. Name some common nonlegume roughages.
7. What are some of the common feeds known as concentrates?
8. What are protein concentrates?
9. What is the chief difference between animal and vegetable proteins?
10. List the feeds commonly fed for their carbohydrate content.
11. List some of the common animal protein feeds.
12. What are some popular vegetable protein feeds?
13. What vitamins are most likely to be lacking in livestock rations?

14. Explain how vitamins may be added to a ration when the ordinary foods fail to provide essential amounts.
15. What materials may be used in mixing a mineral supplement for livestock?
16. Give two common methods of supplying feed additives in the ration.

• *References*

Anderson, Arthur L., *Introductory Animal Husbandry*, The Macmillan Company, New York, 1948.

Bohstedt, G., *Antibiotics and Vitamin B_{12} in Livestock Feeding*, Circular 392, University of Wisconsin, Madison, Wisconsin, 1951.

Morrison, Frank B., *Feeds and Feeding*, 22nd edition, The Morrison Publishing Company, Ithaca, New York, 1956.

U. S. Department of Agriculture, *Better Feeding of Livestock*, Farmers' Bulletin No. 2052, 1952.

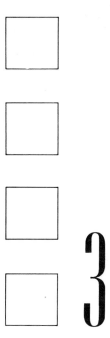

3

Digestion in Ruminants and in Simple-Stomach Animals

Some knowledge of the differences in digestive systems is necessary to understand livestock feeding and the reasons why some feeds are more valuable for one class of animals than for another.

Digestion in Ruminants

To understand the food requirements of ruminants, we should know how they digest and utilize feed. Ruminants are animals that have four compartments to their stomachs, as contrasted to the simple-stomached animals that have a single-compartment stomach. Examples of ruminants among common farm animals are cattle, sheep, and goats. Hogs are the most common example of simple-stomached animals; poultry, although not classed as simple-stomached animals, have a similar digestive system.

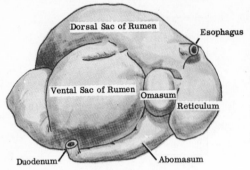

Figure 3-1. The stomach of a mature ruminant animal. Note the size of the rumen compared to the other three stomach compartments. (Drawing by David Wright)

Figure 3-2. Here we see a comparison of the mature (left) and young (right) ruminant stomach. (Drawing by David Wright)

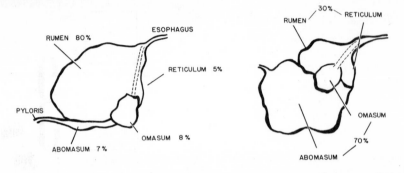

Because of their type of digestive system, ruminants do not present so many feeding problems as do animals with a simple stomach. As will be shown later, ruminants can actually manufacture many of the vitamins and some protein amino acids that have to be fed to simple-stomached animals. They are also able to digest large quantities of roughage.

The compartments of the ruminant stomach are known as the *rumen, reticulum, omasum,* and *abomasum.*

Function of the Four Compartments. *Rumen.* The rumen is the first and by far the largest compartment of the stomach. It serves as a storage area for large quantities of feed, especially roughages, and has a capacity, depending upon the size of the animals, of from 40 to 60 gallons in mature cattle.

During the process of eating, ruminants chew their food just enough to make swallowing possible. While the food is in the rumen, it is worked upon by millions of bacteria and other microorganisms. These microorganisms are able to transform low-quality proteins and even some nitrogen compounds into essential protein amino acids. They also manufacture many needed vitamins, including the vitamin B-complex group. The proteins and vitamins are used by the bacteria. As the bacteria die, they are in turn digested by the animal, furnishing both vitamins and protein.

After the ruminants have consumed their feed, regurgitation or chewing the cud takes place. The food is brought up from the rumen and the chewing is completed. It is then swallowed again, returning to the rumen for further bacterial action.

The presence of the rumen, and the bacterial action that takes place in it, explains why these animals can digest large quantities of roughage and convert it into human food; for this reason, too, the B-complex vitamins and highly complex protein feeds are seldom necessary in their ration. As will later be shown, proteins are an essential part of the ruminant ration, but they need not be nearly so varied and complete as for swine and poultry. In very young ruminants the rumen is not developed, and during the first few weeks they must receive a diet containing most of the food nutrients.

Reticulum. The reticulum is closely associated with the rumen, and it is here that many foreign bodies, such as wire and nails, are retained. If these objects are not pointed or too sharp, they may be held in the reticulum for long periods without any serious damage. The main functions of the reticulum are to furnish additional storage space and to sort out and hold foreign materials that may cause serious damage to the other body organs.

Omasum. The omasum, or third compartment of the stomach, consists of strong muscular walls. Its function is not too well

Figure 3-3. (A) The stomach of a pig. Note the single compartment. (B) Principal digestive organs of poultry. (Drawings by Harlan Clark)

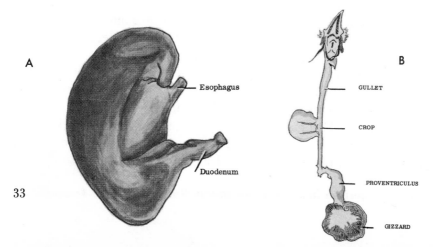

A

Esophagus

Duodenum

B

GULLET

CROP

PROVENTRICULUS

GIZZARD

33

understood, but seem to be that of squeezing out the water from the feed before it enters the abomasum or true stomach.

Abomasum. The abomasum is the fourth compartment or true stomach; its functions are similar to those of the simple-stomach in swine or similar animals. Gastric juice, which is necessary in protein digestion, is secreted in the abomasum. When the food leaves the abomasum, it goes into the small intestine, where the digestible portion is absorbed into the bloodstream; the remainder is passed into the large intestine and eliminated as waste.

Digestion in Simple-Stomach Animals

In simple-stomach animals food is swallowed directly into the single-compartment stomach, where it is mixed with the digestive juices. Very little bacterial action takes place, and there is no conversion from low-quality to high-quality proteins. Simple-stomach animals have less ability to manufacture the vitamins than do ruminants and are unable to digest large quantities of fiber. The digestive process in simple-stomach animals is very similar to that of ruminants after the food enters the abomasum.

We must give much more consideration to the protein, vitamin, and mineral content of rations fed to swine and poultry than to the content of those fed to cattle and sheep. It must also be remembered that high-fiber feeds have little value for swine or poultry.

Digestion in Poultry

Poultry cannot be classed as a simple-stomach animal, though its digestive system is somewhat similar. Very little digestion through bacterial action takes place, and poultry digests smaller amounts of fiber than does any other class of farm livestock.

Functions of the Digestive Organs. *Crop.* Food taken in through the mouth moves down the esophagus into the crop. The crop acts as a reserve to hold and moisten feed. Very little digestion takes place in this organ.

Proventriculus. The proventriculus is a small organ that receives food from the crop. Here digestive juices are secreted and mixed with the food. Food goes from here to the gizzard.

Gizzard. The chief function of the gizzard is to grind and crush the coarse food before it enters the small intestine, where the digestible portion is absorbed into the bloodstream.

Unlike ruminant feeding, a ration for poultry should include all the essential protein amino acids. All of the vitamins except C known to be required by animals must be included in the ration of poultry for best results.

Summary

The stomachs of ruminants, such as cattle, sheep, and goats, have four compartments. The rumen is, by far, the largest compartment and serves as a storage place for bulky feeds and as a place for bacterial action.

Because of bacterial action, which is part of the digestive process, ruminants can digest large quantities of fiber and convert low-quality proteins into essential amino acids. The microorganisms also manufacture most of the B-vitamins, which are later absorbed by the animal.

Swine and poultry have a simple digestive system and must rely directly upon the feed they consume to obtain all classes of nutrients. They have much less ability to digest fiber than do ruminants.

• Questions

1. Name the four compartments in the ruminant stomach.
2. What is the principal digestive process that takes place in the rumen?
3. Explain why ruminants can convert comparatively low-quality protein feeds and a certain amount of nitrogen compounds into usable amino acids.
4. Why do we have less difficulty in supplying older ruminants with the B-vitamins?
5. How do ruminants, swine, and poultry rank in their ability to digest fiber?

• References

Dykstra, R. R., *Animal Sanitation and Disease Control*, The Interstate Printers and Publishers, Danville, Illinois, 1949.

Stamm, G. W., *Veterinary Guide for Farmers*, Windsor Press, New York, 1950.

Winter, A. R., and Funk, E. M., *Poultry Science and Practice*, J. B. Lippincott Company, Philadelphia, 1951.

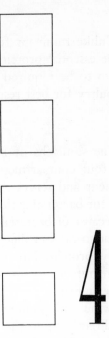

Measuring the Value of Feeds

No single method of determining the value of feeds is accurate enough for all purposes. Many factors must be considered if a reasonably correct appraisal of any feed or group of feeds is to be made.

Classes of Animals Affect Feed Value

The kind of livestock fed is important in determining the value of a feed. Cattle and other ruminants can digest large quantities of fiber; therefore, roughages, particularly fodders, grass hays, and various poor-quality roughages, may have considerable value as cattle feed but none or very little as feed for swine. Cattle, for instance, can make efficient use of a certain amount of corncobs or cornstalks, whereas such feeds would be of little value in swine or poultry feeding.

Cottonseed meal can be given in relatively large amounts to cattle or sheep, often being the only protein-concentrate fed. However, when fed in large quantities to swine or poultry, it has a toxic effect, and does not provide the amino acid or protein balance necessary for these animals.

The value of different feeds for the various classes of livestock will be discussed in the chapters which deal with the specific animals.

Determining Feed Values in Terms of Digestible Nutrients

One of the most widely accepted methods of determining feed values is based on the total digestible nutrient content of the feed. Modern feeding standards list the total digestible nutrients and the digestible proteins of the more widely used livestock feeds. A study of these tables (see pages 25-27) will tell us the average amount of digestible nutrients in a given amount of any one feed for ruminants. For example, in Table 1, No. 2 corn is shown as having a total digestibility of 80.1 per cent. This means that one bushel of shelled corn, which weighs 56 pounds, will provide 44.856 pounds of digestible nutrients. If corn costs $1.50 per bushel, then $1.50 divided by 44.856 will give us the cost of one pound of digestible nutrients supplied by corn.

To determine the cheapest source of digestible nutrients for any class of animals, the price per bushel, ton, or hundred pounds, whichever is the more common unit of measure, should be divided by the pounds of total digestible nutrients. This will give a comparative cost of various feeds based on feeding value. One must remember the kind of livestock involved before using this method of evaluating feed. As pointed out in Chapter 1, swine and poultry will digest approximately the same percentage of grains and of grain and animal by-products as cattle and sheep; however, extremely high-fiber feeds, such as cornstalks, straw, or corncobs, would have very little digestibility for these animals and would be considered as having little or no value in swine and poultry rations. Although the cost per pound of total digestible nutrients is a very good guide to the value of a feed, it is not the whole answer.

Carbohydrates and Fats as Measures of Feed Value. Feeds are generally fed to do a specific job in the animal body. Corn is a fattening feed because of its high carbohydrate content, whereas soybean oil meal is fed for its high-protein content.

If we wish to fatten a bunch of lambs or steers, it will be necessary to use one or more of the grains, such as corn, barley, wheat, or oats, along with enough protein to balance the ration. We will probably be interested in which feed will produce a hundred pounds of gain the most cheaply. In our comparison of fattening feeds, we are interested in the nitrogen-free extract or carbohydrates as well as in the total digestible nutrients.

Proteins as Measures of Feed Value. Many feeds are purchased primarily for their protein content. They are used to increase the protein percentage in the ration, and the cost should be determined on a digestible protein basis.

In selecting protein feeds, we should consider whether the product will give the amino acid balance needed for the class of livestock to be fed. Such proteins as cottonseed meal, soybean meal, or linseed meal will produce nearly equal results when fed to ruminants. The cost per pound of digestible protein may be used to determine which one to feed. However, in swine and poultry rations, none of these feeds, nor any combination of them, will give the protein balance necessary for best results.

Generally, grains and roughages are not fed primarily for their protein content. Yet, if they are high in this important nutrient, the cost of feeding is generally lower because less protein concentrates are necessary. For example, cattle fed legume hay will require less protein concentrates for the production of beef or milk than will those receiving a low-protein roughage. The protein content of roughages and grains becomes important in determining their feeding value.

Mineral Content as a Measure of Feed Value. Livestock feeds are seldom given primarily for their mineral content. Minerals are provided by feeding salt, limestone, phosphorus compounds, and trace mineral mixtures. However, the calcium and phosphorus content of good legume forage and the mineral content of animal protein supplements are important considerations when determining their food value.

There are many different grades of limestone. Calcium is the important mineral supplied by limestone; therefore, calcium content is the chief measure of limestone value.

Bone meal, when added to the ration in the proper proportion, will generally give the needed amount of calcium and phosphorus.

Vitamins as Measures of Feed Value. Most farm feeds provide vitamins to some extent, but legume forage is especially valuable for its vitamin content. The high vitamin A content of yellow corn explains the chief difference between yellow and white corn as a livestock feed.

Fish liver oils and other vitamin preparations must be measured in terms of their vitamin content, because otherwise they have very little value.

Quality of Feeds

The amount of nutrients varies considerably in the same kind of feed, depending upon its quality.

Many factors, such as variety, type of soil, weather conditions, and age, affect the value of a feed and explain the wide range in digestible nutrients which may occur in the same kind of feed.

Corn may vary from 6 per cent to over 9 per cent protein, and alfalfa will range from 8 to 19 per cent protein. It is important that we consider carefully the quality of the product in judging the value of a feed.

Factors Affecting Quality of Feeds. Varieties of the same crop will differ in food value. The amount of protein in wheat varieties grown under the same conditions will vary from 10 to 16 per cent. Oats that produce a plump berry with thin hulls are much higher in digestible nutrients than are those with a large proportion of hulls. State agricultural experiment stations can be relied upon to furnish information regarding varieties of crops for their particular state, together with comparative feeding values.

Soils. Recent experiments and analyses have shown that feeds produced on soils well supplied with plant foods have a higher feeding value than do those produced on poor land.

The mineral content of alfalfa and the protein in corn may vary, depending upon the soil. Land well supplied with nitrogen, from which plants make protein, will produce higher protein feeds than will soils deficient in this plant food. Alfalfa grown on soils that are well supplied with lime and phosphorus will be richer in these elements than will alfalfa grown on deficient soils.

The appearance of a forage or grain may not be the best guide as to its food value. A knowledge of the area, or even the farm, where it was grown is important.

Weather. Weather conditions influence feed values. Corn that is high in moisture as a result of cold, wet seasons will have much fewer digestible nutrients per pound than will dry corn. Small grains may have a high percentage of hull to berry; therefore the proportion of fiber is increased as a result of hot, dry weather conditions, particularly when the kernels are forming.

The same kind of crop will vary in feeding value from year to year. The temperature, length of growing season, and amount and distribution of rainfall all affect the nutrient value of crops.

Balancing a Ration Improves Its Digestibility. Milk, eggs, and meat are manufactured by animals according to a set formula. The percentage of each nutrient in these products remains about the same regardless of the kind of ration fed. If animals are given a low-protein feed, they must eat greater quantities of the feed, and the excess carbohydrates will be eliminated as waste. For example, experiments have shown that hogs fed a ration made up entirely of corn will consume about 13 bushels for every 100 pounds of gain. However, if the corn is balanced with a good protein supplement plus adequate minerals and vitamins, there will be a saving of approximately six bushels of corn per 100 pounds of gain. Balancing a ration will increase the value of all feeds used in the ration.

Commercial Mixed Feeds

There are many companies engaged in the business of producing livestock feeds. Commercially mixed feeds for all classes of livestock are available in every community. When questions arise as to the value of one company's product as compared to that of another, we must consider the reliability of the manufacturer and the success that feeders have had with his products. A study of the analysis given on the container may be helpful. Most states permit feed companies to sell under what is known as the *closed formula* or *open formula*.

Closed Formula. Under the closed formula, feed companies are generally required to give the minimum crude protein, minimum crude fat, minimum nitrogen-free extract, and maximum amount of fiber contained in the feed. They must also list the ingredients that were used in making the product, but, except for mineral or ash, they are not required to tell how much of each ingredient has been used. Some states require that the percentage of mineral be listed. For example, a feed may be listed as containing soybean oil meal, tankage, meat scraps, and bone meal. Although this is a true statement of the ingredients used, it fails to give the amount of each product in the feed. Many feed companies prefer the closed formula because it prevents duplication of their products by other companies or livestock feeders.

The following is a typical closed-formula label that might appear on the feed bag:

Weight 100 Lbs. Net

FAST GROW PIG MEAL

Guaranteed Analysis

Crude protein not less than	26.00%
Crude fat not less than	4.50%
Nitrogen-free extract not less than	43.00%
Crude fiber not more than	8.50%

Ingredients: Alfalfa meal, wheat bran, tankage, soybean oil meal, fish meal, rolled oats, yellow corn, molasses, antibiotic and vitamin supplement, calcium 6.0%, phosphorus 1.3%, salt 5.0%, iodine .0002%.

Open Formula. Feed companies selling open-formula feeds must list the minimum percentage of protein, fat, and nitrogen-free extract, the maximum amount of fiber, and the weight of each ingredient contained in the feed. Following is an example of an open-formula feed label:

FAST GROW CHICK FEED

Guaranteed Analysis

Protein not less than	21.00%
Fat not less than	3.40%
Fiber not more than	7.40%
Nitrogen-free extract not less than	45.00%

Formula
(Pounds per ton)

470	yellow corn	150	dehydrated alfalfa meal
350	ground oats	320	soybean oil meal
150	wheat bran	100	meat and bone scraps
20	dried brewers' yeasts	15	salt
350	wheat shorts	5	trace mineral concentrate
40	ground limestone	5	vitamin antibiotic supplement
25	steamed bone meal		

Summary

Many factors must be considered in evaluating feed. The more important are the kind of animal to be fed and the purpose for which the particular feed is being used.

Feeds that are intended as fattening feeds must be judged primarily for their carbohydrate content and total digestibility. However, their protein, mineral, and vitamin contents are also important because the percentage of these nutrients in the feed determines the amount of other concentrates needed to balance the ration. The quality and percentage of digestible protein in a feed fed largely for its protein content is the chief measure of its value.

Mineral and vitamin concentrates are measured in terms of the essential minerals and vitamins present.

Quality of feeds is affected by weather, soils, harvesting, and varieties of crops.

The value of any feed is determined largely by how well the ration is balanced. Feeding more of any nutrient than the animal requires is wasteful. Commercial feeds are sold under open-formula or closed-formula analysis. More information is given on the label when the open-formula is used. The value of commercial feeds can be judged largely by the reliability of the company and the success feeders have had with its product.

• Questions

1. How does the class of livestock to be fed affect the value of the feed?

2. Show by example how you would determine the value of a feed, using total digestible nutrients as a measure.

3. Show how you would determine the value of a protein feed, using digestible protein as a measure.

4. Generally, roughages are not fed primarily for their protein content. Why, then, is the protein content of a roughage important in determining the value?

5. If concentrated amounts of vitamins A, D, E, B_{12}, and other B-vitamins are needed, what sources will furnish them?

6. How do soils and weather affect feed values?

7. Explain why poorly balanced rations waste feed.

8. Explain the chief difference in the two types of labels used for commercial feed mixtures.

References

Anderson, Arthur L., *Introductory Animal Husbandry*, The Macmillan Company, New York, 1948.

Colorado State College, *Livestock Feeds and Feeding*, Bulletin 384-8, Fort Collins, Colorado, 1952.

Morrison, Frank B., *Feeds and Feeding*, 22nd edition, The Morrison Publishing Company, Ithaca, New York, 1956.

U. S. Department of Agriculture, *Better Feeding of Livestock*, Farmers' Bulletin No. 2052, 1952.

PORK PRODUCTION

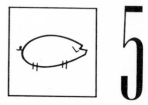

5

The Pork Production Industry

Hogs are produced on more than 60 per cent of the farms and ranches in this country. They may be found on nearly 85 per cent of the farms in Iowa, and on 70 per cent or more of the farms in Illinois, Indiana, Missouri, Tennessee, Alabama, Mississippi, Louisiana, Georgia, and South Carolina. Hogs are produced on less than 20 per cent of the farms and ranches in only six states.

About one-third of the farm income of some of the Corn Belt states is derived from the sale of hogs. In Iowa, where 86 cents of every farm dollar comes from livestock, nearly 40 cents comes from the sale of hogs.

Leading States in Hog Production. Corn and hog production go hand in hand, so the leading hog-producing states are in the Corn Belt. Iowa, Illinois, Indiana, Missouri, Minnesota, and Ohio were the six high states in number of pigs produced in 1957. These

Figure 5-1. Hog profits begin with good litters. This Hampshire litter is off to a good start. (Courtesy Eli Lilly and Company)

six states accounted for 66 per cent of the nation's 1957 pig crop. Iowa alone produced in 1957 more pigs than the 39 low-producing states, and nearly twice as many pigs as Illinois, the second largest-producing state.

Hog producers in the Corn Belt have been concerned with increased interest in hog production in the South. On January 1, 1958, there were 38 million hogs on farms in the 12 North Central States. Only six million hogs were on farms in the eight South Central states. Hog numbers on January 1, 1958, were lower in the South Central states as compared to the 1947-1956 average than were hog numbers in the North Central states.

Consumer Demand for Pork and Lard

The future of pork production in this country will be determined to a large extent by the desire of American people for pork and lard, and by their willingness to pay a reasonable price for these products. Pork and lard must compete with other animal and vegetable products in palatability, in nutritive value, in availability, in ease of merchandising and storage, and in price.

The average person in this nation consumed in 1953 a total of 182 pounds of meat and 13.1 pounds of lard. This was the highest per capita meat consumption on record up to that time. The average American in 1957 consumed approximately 62 pounds of pork, 84 pounds of beef, 9 pounds of veal, nearly 4 pounds of lamb and mutton, 25 pounds of chicken, 6 pounds of turkey and 12 pounds of lard.

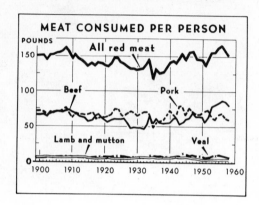

Figure 5-2. Meat consumed per person in the United States. (Courtesy U. S. Department of Agriculture)

The Lard Problem

The substitution of vegetable oils and fats in cooking and the decrease in use of animal fats in soap-making have lowered the demand for lard. Today consumers are eating pork, but they are eating the lean cuts, the hams, loins, picnics, and Boston butts. They buy less fat cuts and lard. As a result, we are producing more lard than we can sell profitably, even though we export lard to other countries. Almost 25 per cent of our total lard production was exported in 1957.

Lard represents about 15 per cent of the weight of the live hog, but only about ten cents of each dollar spent for pork products is spent for lard.

The amount of lard consumed per person per year in this country has not changed materially during the past 20 years. A major problem of hog breeders and feeders is to find a way to produce a pork carcass with a higher percentage of lean meat and a lower yield of fat cuts and lard.

Hog-Corn Price Ratios

Since corn is the basic feed in producing hogs, and feed costs represent about 80 per cent of the production costs, it is usually possible to determine the extent that hog production will be profitable by comparing the price of hogs with the price of corn. The term *hog-corn ratio* represents the relationship between the two, based upon the number of bushels of corn that can be bought for the price of 100 pounds of pork.

Figure 5-3. Duroc pigs on pasture in Illinois. (United Duroc Record Assn.)

A break-even hog-corn price ratio is about 13.5 to one. That is, 100 pounds of live hog should bring the price of 13.5 bushels of corn.

Advantages of Hog Production

Hog production is well adapted to specialized and diversified types of farming, and the returns come much more quickly than do those from many other enterprises. The investment in swine breeding stock and in equipment is relatively small, and it is possible to get in and out of the business in a comparatively short time. The feeding of corn and other grains to hogs is a profitable method of marketing these grains. It also is an efficient way of producing meat. A pound of pork can be produced on as little as 2½ to 3½ pounds of feed. The young chicken is the only other animal which can produce a pound of meat on this amount of feed.

Hogs can be raised on small or large farms, and in small or large numbers. They make excellent use of pasture, but can be produced profitably on dry lot. They do not require expensive housing and equipment. The labor requirements in producing hogs are lower than those in dairy and poultry production.

Disadvantages of Hog Production

During recent years a number of diseases have caused heavy losses on some farms and in some areas. Rhinitis, brucellosis,

Figure 5-4. Crossbred pigs on alfalfa and ladino pasture in Indiana. Hampshire sows were mated to a Montana No. 1 boar. (Courtesy *The Farm Clinic*)

erysipelas, gastroenteritis, anemia, leptospirosis, and necrotic enteritis losses have been especially severe.

The fact that farmers can get in and out of hog production in a comparatively short time may prove disadvantageous at times. When hog-corn price ratios are wide, 15 to 1 or above, farmers flock in and the increased production may crowd the market.

Another disadvantage of the hog enterprise is that farmers produce too many lardy hogs. This disadvantage, like those mentioned previously, can be overcome by use of good breeding, feeding, and marketing practices.

Efficiency in Pork Production

The profit in producing hogs is determined largely by the efficiency of the grower in production and marketing practices. It has been estimated that the average farmer loses at least 25 per cent of the pigs farrowed. The cost of maintaining a brood sow from breeding time until the pigs are weaned is about the same regardless of the number of pigs farrowed and weaned.

The loss of pigs due to disease is great, since hogs are subject to a large number of diseases. Some animals die; others are weakened. Considerably more feed is required to feed out diseased hogs, additional time is necessary to get them on the market, and they cannot be sold when the market is high. Often the carcass of the animal must be condemned entirely or in part, and sometimes the packer must offer a lower price for the diseased animals. The efficient producer uses practices which prevent disease outbreaks.

Care must be taken also to prevent losses due to swine parasites. Worms and mange probably cause some loss on most farms.

The efficient producer of hogs must be very careful in the selection of breeding stock and in the breeding of these animals. Prolificness is inherited, as are growth rate and carcass quality. Good feeding and disease control cannot entirely offset losses due to poor quality breeding stock or the use of poor breeding methods.

The efficient producer selects feeds carefully and feeds them in proper balance. He makes adequate use of home-grown grains and forages, and uses protein supplements, minerals, antibiotics, and vitamins to supplement the home-grown feeds.

It is possible to produce profitably but at the same time to market inefficiently. Markets are better in some seasons than they are in others. Packers pay higher prices for hogs of certain weights than they do for others. Some packers pay higher prices for hogs of high quality than do other buyers. Through careful planning it is possible to have ready for market the kind and weight of hogs that will top the market.

Summary

Hog production is big business in this nation, especially in the Corn Belt States. Iowa, Illinois, Indiana, Ohio, Missouri, and Minnesota produced 66 per cent of the nation's hog crop in 1957. Iowa alone produces more hogs than the 39 low-producing states.

The number of hogs produced annually is affected by the hog-corn price ratio, the feed supply, the supply of hogs at the markets, consumer demand, world economic conditions, supplies of meats which compete with pork, price, and the swine disease situation.

The average person in the nation consumed in 1957 a total of 190 pounds of meat, of which 62 pounds was pork. The per capita lard consumption was 12 pounds.

Lard represents 15 per cent of the weight of a live hog, but only ten cents of each dollar spent for pork products is spent for lard.

A hog-corn price ratio represents the relationship between the two, based upon the number of bushels of corn that can be bought for the price of 100 pounds of pork. A break-even hog-corn price ratio is 13.5 to 1.

Hog production is a profitable enterprise which requires a comparatively small investment, and the returns come rather quickly. Hogs are efficient converters of feed into food for human consumption.

The market for lard has not kept pace with the market for pork. Pork producers must find a way to produce hogs with more lean meat and less fat.

Profitable hog production is dependent upon how well farmers do the following: (1) use sound methods in selection and breeding; (2) be efficient in feeding and management; (3) control diseases and parasites; and (4) use good judgment in marketing operations.

• Questions

1. What percentage of the income on your farm is derived from the sale of hogs?
2. What percentage of the grains produced on your farm are fed to hogs?
3. What percentage of the farm income in your state is obtained from the sale of hogs?
4. About how much meat is consumed in a year by the average American? How much of this amount is pork?
5. What are the leading states in hog production?
6. What do you think can be done to decrease the lard produced on our farms without reducing the production of high-priced pork cuts?
7. What are the advantages and disadvantages of hog production on your farm?
8. What are the essentials of a profitable swine enterprise? Explain.

• References

Anderson, Arthur L., *Swine Management*, J. B. Lippincott Company, Philadelphia, 1957.

Bundy, Clarence E., and Ronald V. Diggins, *Swine Production*, Prentice-Hall, Inc., Englewood Cliffs, New Jersey, 1956.

Ensminger, M. E., *Swine Husbandry*, The Interstate Printers and Publishers, Danville, Illinois, 1952.

Selection of Breeding and Feeding Stock

The pork producer must make a number of decisions before he obtains his breeding stock. He must first decide what type of hogs to raise; then he must determine which breeding program to follow. He usually has at least three plans to consider. He can start with grade or crossbred sows and upgrade them, selling the offspring as market hogs, or he can start with purebreds and maintain a purebred herd, selling the offspring to other breeders for breeding purposes or disposing of them as market hogs. His third possibility is to start with grade, crossbred, or purebred sows and follow a plan of crossbreeding in producing hogs for the packer market.

The third decision to be made is usually a difficult one. What breed or breeds should he grow? There are numerous breeds of swine available. Which of them is best suited to the breeding program that he plans to follow? The breeding program and the breed

51

Figure 6-1. A champion Poland China boar at the Iowa State Fair about 1920. (Courtesy *Wallaces' Farmer and Iowa Homestead*)

or breeds of hogs are both determined in part by the methods he plans to use in marketing his hogs.

A number of factors must be considered in selecting a breed, and the selection of desirable breeding animals within the chosen breed involves additional problems. What body conformation is desired? Shall the producer use proven sows and sires or select young, untried breeding stock? In selecting animals, how much importance should he place on rate of gain, economy of gain, prolificacy, and freedom from disease?

Good breeding stock is essential for the most profitable hog production enterprise. It is sometimes possible for a hog producer to overcome, in part, the lack of good breeding stock by efficient feeding, good management, and disease control. For maximum returns, however, it is necessary that he start out with the right kind of breeding animals.

The factors to be considered in selecting breeding and feeding stock are enumerated in this chapter, and suggestions are offered to aid the reader in making wise decisions when choosing animals for the home farm enterprise.

Meat-type Hogs

The type of hog produced in this country has varied from time to time during the past century. Originally there were two types. The lard type, as the name implies, was a thick-bodied hog, which in market condition carried a large amount of fat. The bacon-type hog was imported from England and the Scandinavian countries, where it was developed to meet consumer demand for "Wiltshire Sides" of bacon.

Figure 6-2. The present-day meat-type hog. (Moore photo. Courtesy American Yorkshire Club, Inc.)

Figure 6-3. A crossbred barrow which cut 7.27 square inches of loin eye at the 1957 National Barrow Show. (Courtesy *National Hog Farmer*)

A

Figure 6-4. (A) This meat-type gilt produced a 29.5 inch carcass with 1.5 inches of back fat. (B) This barrow produced a 28.25 inch carcass with 2.1 inches of back fat. (Courtesy Rath Packing Company)

B

The competition of vegetable fats on the market has de-emphasized the value of lard, and hog breeders are now trying to develop a hog which will yield a carcass high in lean meat, but comparatively low in lard. Regardless of the breed of hogs which is being raised, the average farmer is trying to produce a *meat-type* hog.

Meat-type Hog Defined. While there is not complete agreement among swine producers as to what is meant by the term meat-type hog, they generally will agree to the following specifications:

1. The hog will yield when slaughtered 50 per cent of its live weight in the primal cuts: ham, loin, picnic, and butt.
2. The animal will weigh about 200 to 210 pounds at 5 to 5½ months of age.
3. The 200 to 210 pound carcass will be 29½ to 31 inches long at about 5 months of age.
4. The back fat thickness will not exceed 1.5 inches.
5. The ideal carcass should yield about 19 per cent ham, 15.2 per cent bacon, 15.8 per cent loin, 9.7 per cent picnic, and 6 per cent Boston butt.
6. The animal will have a feed conversion ability of 1 pound of gain from three to three and one-half pounds of feed.
7. The females will produce litters of eight to nine pigs raised to market weight.

Comparison of Meat-type and Lard-type Hog Carcasses. The two pigs shown in Figure 6-4 came from the same farm and ran to the same self-feeder. They were 5½ months old and each weighed 200 pounds alive. The meat-type gilt is trim in the jowl, has smooth and firm shoulders, is well-muscled along the loin, has a deep plump ham, and is trim and firm in her middle. She produced a carcass 29.5 inches long with 1.5 inches of back fat.

The barrow produced a carcass which was 28.25 inches long and had 2.1 inches of back fat. While he weighed the same as the gilt, he was 1.25 inches shorter and had 0.6 inch more back fat. The area of the loin muscle on the meat hog was 3.53 square inches. The fat hog had only 2.15 square inches.

In Figure 6-5 are shown the cross sections of the hams of the two hogs. The meat hog had a ratio of one square inch of fat to every 3.8 square inches of muscling. The fat hog had a ratio of one square inch of fat to every 2.4 square inches of muscling.

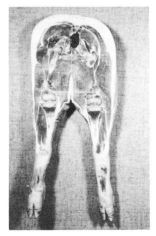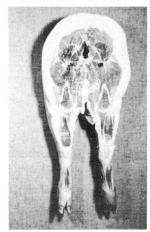

Figure 6-5. Cross-sections of the hams of the two carcasses. Note difference in muscling, lard content, and fullness. (Courtesy Rath Packing Company)

Meat-type Hogs Make Rapid and Economical Gains. Some hog producers, remembering their experiences with the leggy, "hamless wonder" hogs raised in the 1920's, have questioned the rate and economy of gain of meat-type hogs. However, tests have proven that meat-type hogs can be produced as rapidly and as economically as fat-type hogs.

Packers Pay More for Meat-type Hogs. Most packer buyers are now bidding from 25 cents to $1.00 per hundredweight above the current market price for uniform loads of meat-type hogs. Some interior markets are buying hogs on the basis of carcass grade and yield. Some farmers have received as much as $1.80 more per hundredweight by selling meat-type hogs according to their carcass value.

Breeding Systems

We have already pointed out that farmers select breeding stock to meet the demands of the breeding programs which they are following. Most growers produce hogs for slaughter. It is estimated that less than 4 per cent of all growers are raising purebred hogs to be sold for breeding purposes.

The breeding programs followed by producers of purebred hogs are often quite different from those followed by producers

Figure 6-6. Typical litters of crossbred pigs. (Courtesy Kent Feeds)

55

of market hogs. These breeders mate purebred boars and sows of the same breed. Some breeders do inbreeding or line breeding. Most breeders of commercial hogs follow upgrading, crossbreeding, or criss-crossing methods, which may involve two or more breeds. A description of each of the various swine-breeding systems may be found in the following paragraphs.

Upgrading. The system of mating purebred boars with grade sows of the same breed is called *upgrading*. A *purebred* is an animal that is registered or eligible for registration by a breed association. A *grade* animal is one whose sire is a purebred but whose dam or mother is not eligible for registration. The use of a purebred Chester White boar on a grade sow herd of the same breed is an example of upgrading.

Use of this method has resulted in much improvement of our grade herds in type and productiveness. The development and maintenance of many herds of purebred swine has provided farmers with sources of boars for the production of market hogs.

Purebred Breeding. In the breeding of purebreds, purebred boars are mated to purebred sows of the same breed. The mating of purebred Hampshire boars with purebred Hampshire sows is an example of purebred breeding. Breeders of purebreds must produce boars for use by their neighbors who raise market hogs; they must also produce purebred animals for use by other breeders of purebreds. Breeders have attempted to improve their herds through careful selection. For many years much of the improvement had to do with type factors, but recently considerable attention has been given to production factors, such as number of pigs farrowed and weaned, weight of litter at weaning time, rate of gain, economy of gain, and carcass quality.

Crossbreeding. The mating of purebred or inbred boars of one breed with purebred or grade sows of another breed is called *crossbreeding*. From studies made of the hogs received at the packing plants, it was found that from 60 to 80 per cent of the hogs possessed the characteristics of more than one breed. A large percentage of commercial hog producers are crossbreeding or are criss-crossing their hogs. An example of this system of breeding is the mating of a Duroc boar with Tamworth sows.

In tests conducted at Iowa State College over a 10-year period, it was found that fewer pigs were born dead among the crossbreds and slightly more of the crossbred pigs lived to weaning age than

TABLE 6

CROSSBRED AND PUREBRED PIGS*

(*Miami County, Ohio, Experimental Farm*)
A—Two-breed crossbreds; B—Three-breed crossbreds; C—Cross-breds of subsequent generations

	A		B		C	
	Duroc	P.C. and Duroc	Duroc	Hamp. and P.C. & D.	Duroc	Crossbreds from Sows of Sub. Gen.
Litters from gilts	10	12	2	4	15	18
Litters from sows	19	21	5	3	16	12
Average gestation (days)	114.5	114.3	113.5	113.3	115.0	113.5
Live pigs per litter at birth	9.3	9.1	9.9	9.9	10.3	9.7
Dead pigs per litter at birth	0.4	0.3	0.4	0.4	0.5	0.4
Total pigs per litter at birth	9.7	9.4	10.3	10.3	10.8	10.1
Pigs per litter at weaning	6.4	6.4	6.4	7.4	7.0	8.1
Average adjusted wt. at 56 days	31.2	36.2	32.3	31.6	36.8	36.9
Per cent live pigs lost before weaning	31.7	29.8	34.8	24.6	31.9	16.4
Per cent live pigs lost after weaning	2.6	0.7	0.0	1.4	2.8	1.7
Pigs per litter at 180 days	6.1	6.4	6.4	7.3	6.7	8.0
Average daily gain, birth to 180 days (lbs.)	.99	1.11	1.10	1.05	1.06	1.13
Average weight per pig at 180 days (lbs.)	178.3	200.3	197.1	188.4	191.4	203.8
Average weight per litter at 180 days (lbs.)	1,094.5	1,274.6	1,267.3	1,372.8	1,290.6	1,623.9

*Bulletin 675, Ohio Agricultural Experiment Station, Wooster, Ohio, 1948.

did the purebred pigs. The crossbred pigs weighed an average of nearly four pounds more at weaning time than did the purebreds. The crossbreds gained more rapidly from weaning to market and reached market weight of 225 pounds about ten days earlier than did the purebreds. Between 25 and 30 more pounds of feed were required to bring the purebreds up to 225 pounds than were required for the crossbreds.

The crossbred sows were good mothers when bred back to a boar of either of the parent breeds or to a boar of a third breed. The pigs produced compared favorably with the first-cross pigs in rate and economy of gain.

In Ohio tests, pigs produced by crossing purebred Durocs and Poland Chinas weighed 22 pounds more at 180 days than did purebred Duroc pigs. The daily gain was .12 of a pound more, and the litter weight at 180 days was 180.1 pounds heavier. The best gains in the Ohio tests were made by pigs produced by mating the Duroc-Poland-Hampshire crossbred gilts with purebred boars of the same breeds. A summary of the Ohio tests is shown in Table 6.

Criss-crossing. In this system purebred boars of one breed are mated with grade or purebred sows of another breed (as in cross-breeding); then the gilts produced from the first mating are mated with a boar of the same breed as the original sows. The gilts produced from this cross are mated the next year with a boar of the same breed as the boar used in making the first cross. Boars of the parent breeds are then used in alternate years thereafter. A farmer who breeds a group of Spotted Poland China gilts to a Duroc boar and then alternates the use of boars of these two breeds in the following years is using the criss-cross method.

Rotation Breeding Swine specialists in several states are now recommending the use of boars of three or four breeds of hogs in rotation. This method is especially recommended when inbred boars are used in producing commercial hogs. The use of four carefully selected breeds maintains the hybrid vigor desired in hog production. The boars used in this system of breeding may be purebreds, inbreds, or crosslines. Crosslines are the progeny resulting from the crossing of two inbred lines of the same breed.

An example of this method follows: A farmer has a Duroc sow herd which he mates to a Poland China boar. The gilts from this cross are mated the next year to a Montana No. 1 or Hamprace

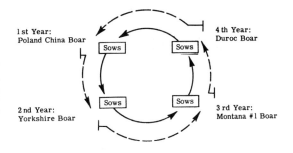

Figure 6-7. An example of a rotation system of breeding using Poland China, Yorkshire, Montana No. 1, and Duroc boars. (Drawing by David C. Opheim)

1st Year: Poland China Boar

Sows

Sows

4th Year: Duroc Boar

2nd Year: Yorkshire Boar

Sows

Sows

3rd Year: Montana #1 Boar

boar. During the third year he uses a Spotted Poland China boar, and in the fourth year he uses a Duroc boar. The rotation system is then repeated. A rotation involving Duroc, Poland China, Yorkshire, and Hampshire boars has produced excellent results. A diagram of rotation breeding is shown in Figure 6-7.

Inbreeding. The mating of boars with sows of the same breed which are closely related is called *inbreeding*. The mating of brothers with sisters and of sires with daughters are examples of inbreeding. Purebred and commercial producers have frowned upon inbreeding because usually the offspring are inferior to the parent in growth ability and in prolificacy. After several years of inbreeding, however, it is possible to obtain lines which produce uniform offspring. The crossing of two or more of the inbred lines results in hybrid vigor which is greater than that obtained when two noninbred purebred lines are crossed.

Line Breeding. Line breeding involves the mating of purebred boars of one line or family with sows of the same line that are not so closely related as those used in inbreeding. The mating of second cousins is an example of line breeding. Many breeders of purebred hogs have used line breeding to intensify the desirable characteristics of certain blood lines in their herds. An examination of the pedigrees in most herds will produce many examples of line breeding. This method is rarely used in producing market hogs.

Crossline Breeding. When this system is used, inbred boars of one line are mated to inbred sows of another line of the same breed. This method has been used extensively at the U.S.D.A. Agricultural Research Center at Beltsville, Maryland, at the Regional Swine Breeding Laboratory, and at cooperating state agricultural experiment stations.

The crossing of two distinct lines of a breed produces a type of hybrid vigor similar to, but in smaller amounts than, that resulting from the crossing of two breeds. Hybrid vigor is increased

Selection of Breeding and Feeding Stock • 59

from about 12 to 15 per cent as a result of the crossing of two inbred lines. By crossing four lines, as is done in producing hybrid corn, the hybrid vigor is further increased. By crossing lines of different breeds, it is possible to obtain higher levels of performance than can be obtained by crossing two lines of one breed.

Factors in Selecting a Breed of Hogs

Because we have a number of breeds of hogs in this country, it is difficult to determine the breed or breeds which will do best in a breeding program. Each breed has a loyal group of supporters, and there is rivalry between the producers of the various breeds. Each of the breeds has desirable characteristics, yet all of them have some weaknesses. Usually there are as many differences among the individuals within a breed as there are between breeds.

Certain factors are important in selecting a breed of hogs for a given program, as other factors are important in buying a tractor or in purchasing seed corn. The goal in hog production is to produce large litters of pigs which can be grown out rapidly and economically, and when sold, will command the top market price. Pork producers must decide which breed or breeds will fit best in their breeding programs.

The following factors must be given careful consideration in the selection of a breed of hogs: (1) availability of breeding stock, (2) prolificacy, (3) growth ability, (4) temperament, (5) carcass quality, (6) nicking ability, (7) market demand, (8) disease resistance, (9) feeds available, (10) personal likes and dislikes of the grower.

Classification of Breeds

Up to a few years ago, swine breeds were classified either as *lard type* or as *bacon type*. Most of the hogs produced in this country were of the lard type. We had a ready market for lard. Conditions have changed. Our lard market is partly gone since we have vegetable fats competing with lard on the shortening market. As a result, swine breeders have focused their attention on the production of *meat-type* hogs.

While we can no longer classify hogs as lard type or as bacon type, we find a considerable variation both within and between breeds to the extent that they produce carcasses high in the lean cuts and low in lard and fat cuts. Since the animals within a breed vary in this respect, it appears better to classify the breeds on physical characteristics and recentness of origin.

Shown in Table 7 is a classification of the most popular old established breeds and of the new breeds according to the predominant color of hair and type of ears.

The American Landrace is listed as a new breed since the Landrace bloodlines obtained originally from Denmark, Norway, and Sweden have now been recorded by the American Landrace Association, one of the new swine record associations.

TABLE 7

PHYSICAL CHARACTERISTICS OF BREEDS

Breed	Predominant Color of Hair	Type of Ears
Old Established Breeds:		
Berkshire	Black with white feet, face, switch	Erect
Chester White	White	Drooping
Duroc	Red	Drooping
Hampshire	Black with white belt	Erect
OIC	White	Drooping
Poland China	Black with white on face, feet, legs, and switch	Drooping
Spotted Poland China	Black-and-white spotted	Drooping
Tamworth	Red	Erect
Yorkshire	White	Erect
New Breeds:		
Beltsville No. 1	Black with white spots	Drooping
Beltsville No. 2	Light red	Erect
American Landrace	White	Large, slightly drooping
Maryland No. 1	Black with white spots	Erect
Minnesota No. 1	Red	Slightly erect
Minnesota No. 2	Black with white spots	Slightly erect
Montana No. 1	Black	Slightly drooping
Polouse	White	Slightly erect to drooping
San Pierre	Black and white	Erect

Several other breeds of hogs have been raised in small numbers for many years. The Kentucky Red Berkshire, the Hereford, the Essex, and the Mulefoot breeds are still being produced, and record associations are maintained for the recording of pedigrees.

Breed Differences in Carcass Quality

The market hogs exhibited at the National Barrow Show held annually at Austin, Minnesota come from many states and represent the bloodlines of the respective breeds. The data obtained from the carcasses of the slaughtered live show winners, and from the entries in the carcass contest give some indication of the ability of the various breeds to produce desirable carcasses.

Shown in Table 8 is a summary of the data obtained from the

TABLE 8

CARCASS RESULTS
1957 NATIONAL BARROW SHOW

Breed	No. Hogs Slaughtered	Average Live Weight	Average Yield	Average Length	Average Backfat	Average Loin Eye	Average Live Weight Value
		pounds	per cent	inches	inches	inches	dollars
Hampshire	35	209.5	71.04	29.9	1.33	3.94	20.30
Yorkshire	14	213.1	71.50	31.3	1.44	3.61	20.24
Crossbred	16	212.9	71.85	29.9	1.44	4.27	20.24
Berkshire	20	210.6	71.00	30.3	1.36	3.66	20.12
Chester White	11	209.3	71.20	29.5	1.47	3.44	19.99
Poland China	12	214.1	69.68	29.1	1.32	4.55	19.94
Landrace	7	212.4	69.16	32.3	1.28	3.94	19.86
Duroc	12	218.1	70.50	29.8	1.46	3.45	19.83
Spotted Poland China	12	215.3	71.13	29.5	1.46	3.92	19.82
Tamworth	10	211.1	70.13	30.6	1.70	3.10	19.20

carcasses of the 149 market hogs which were slaughtered in connection with the 1957 National Barrow Show.

Origin and Characteristics of the Old Established Breeds

Six of the nine old-established breeds of swine raised in the United States originated in this country. They are the Chester

White, Duroc, Hampshire, OIC, Poland China and Spotted Poland China. The three breeds which are not native to this country are the Berkshire, Tamworth, and Yorkshire. They were imported from England.

Berkshire. This English breed is one of the oldest breeds of swine. For many years the Berkshire was considered the best of the meat breeds because of the excellent carcasses which it produced. The champion barrows and carlots of barrows at national shows often carried Berkshire breeding. During recent years the other breeds have been improved, so that now there is less difference in the quality of the carcasses. The Berkshire still rates high, however, as a producer of a good carcass.

The Berkshire is an extremely long animal and in form and fleshing conforms to the ideal meat-type hog. The breed is black, with white markings usually on the feet, head, and tail; it has long been characterized by a short snout and a wide, dished face. The "pug nose" of the Berkshire of years ago has been well refined through breeding.

Berkshires are slightly smaller than some of the other meat-type breeds at maturity. Mature boars will weigh 900 pounds or more. In 1957 there were 17,517 Berkshire swine recorded in this country. This breed has had general use in crossbreeding programs with excellent results.

Chester White. The Chester White breed had its origin in Chester and Delaware counties in Pennsylvania. The parent stock used to produce the breed included English Yorkshire, Cheshire, and Lincolnshire bloodlines. The Chester White Swine Record Association was established in 1908.

The Chester White has white hair and skin. Small flecks in the skin are not discriminated against, but black or other than white hair is objectionable. The Chester White is intermediate in size and mature boars weigh 900 pounds and over.

Barrows of the Chester White breed have made excellent records at state and national shows in both on-foot and carcass tests. This breed has been popular with farmers in some areas. The sows produce and raise large litters which grow out rapidly and make good gains.

There were 13,383 purebred animals registered by the Chester White Swine Record Association in 1957.

Selection of Breeding and Feeding Stock • 63

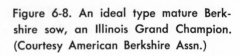
Figure 6-8. An ideal type mature Berkshire sow, an Illinois Grand Champion. (Courtesy American Berkshire Assn.)
←

Figure 6-9. A beautiful Chester White mature sow—a state fair champion. (Moore photo. Courtesy The Chester White Swine Record Assn.) →

Figure 6-10. The Grand Champion Gilt at the 1958 National Duroc Congress. (Moore photo. Courtesy *National Hog Farmer*)
←

Figure 6-11. An All-American Hampshire junior spring boar. (Courtesy American Hampshire Assn.) →

Figure 6-12. A National Champion OIC boar. (Courtesy OIC Swine Breeders' Assn., Inc.)
←

Figure 6-13. A Grand Champion Poland China boar at the Iowa State Fair. (Moore Photo. Courtesy The Poland China Record Assn.) ➡

Figure 6-14. A Junior Champion Spotted Poland China gilt. (Courtesy *The National Spotted Poland China Record and Bulletin*) ⬅

Figure 6-15. A State Fair Champion mature Tamworth boar. (Moore photo. Courtesy Tamworth Swine Assn.) ➡

Figure 6-16. A Grand Champion Yorkshire sow at the Iowa State Fair. (Moore photo. Courtesy Cerney Brothers) ⬅

Figure 6-17. Grand Champion Gilt at the 1958 National Landrace Type Conference. (Moore photo. American Landrace Assn., Inc.) ➡

65

Duroc. The ancestry of this breed is not entirely known, but the Jersey Reds of New Jersey, the red Durocs of New York, and the red Berkshires of Connecticut have contributed to the formation of the breed. The breed was first called the Duroc-Jersey. Standards were established for the breed in 1885, and although the type has changed several times during the past 75 years, the color standards are still adhered to.

The Duroc is red in color, with the shades varying from a golden to a very dark red. A medium cherry red is preferred. Black flecks may appear in the skin, but large black spots, black hair, and white hair are objectionable. The Duroc is large, with excellent feeding capacity and prolificacy. In type and conformation, the Duroc is similar to the Chester. White and the Poland China. The sows are good mothers, with good dispositions, producing large quantities of milk. Farmers have found the breed to be excellent for use in crossbreeding programs.

For the year ending November, 1957, there were 60,146 purebred Durocs recorded by the United Duroc Record Association. More Durocs were recorded in 1957 than hogs of any other breed. This was also true in 1955 and 1956. A total of 92,090 animals were recorded in 1954 by the United Duroc Record Association of Peoria, Illinois.

Hampshire. The Hampshire breed was developed in Boone County, Kentucky, from hogs probably imported from England in the early 1800's. The foundation stock, known as the *Thin Rinds* and *Belted Hogs*, had been raised in the New England States.

The breed association was organized in 1893, and although the breed is one of the youngest, it has become very popular. In 1957, when 53,797 were recorded, Hampshires ranked second to Durocs.

The Hampshire is a black hog with a white belt encircling the body and including the front legs. The back legs are usually black, and no white should appear above the hock. The head and tail are black, and the ears are erect. No white can appear on the head.

The Hampshire is smaller than some of the other meat-type breeds. It has been bred for refinement, quality, and prominent eyes. The sows of the breed are very prolific and are good mothers. The Hampshire is a good rustler, doing well on pasture and following cattle in the feed lot.

It is usually shorter-legged than are most breeds but sound on its feet and legs in most cases. The breed has been used extensively in crossbreeding because of its quality, fleshing, and prolificacy.

OIC. This breed was originated by L. B. Silver in Ohio about 1865 from foundation stock obtained in Chester and Delaware counties in Pennsylvania, the same counties which produced the Chester White breed. The breed was first called the Ohio Improved Chesters. The OIC Swine Breeders Association, Inc., was organized in 1897.

The OIC breed resembles the Chester White in color. The sows are good mothers and milkers. There were 2,234 animals recorded in 1957.

Poland China. For many years the Poland China has been considered the largest of the American breeds. Today it is similar in size, type, and conformation to the Duroc, Chester White, and Spotted Poland China.

The breed was originated between 1800 and 1850 in Warren and Butler counties in Ohio. The white Byfield hog, imported from Russia, and the White Big China hog were used with native hogs in producing the Warren County Hog. The use of the Berkshire on the Warren County Hogs and later the use of boars imported from Ireland produced the Poland China breed.

Since about 1875, the Poland China has been a black hog with six white points, the feet, face, and tip of tail. Mature boars weigh up to 1,000 pounds. The typical Poland China has thick, even flesh and is free from wrinkles and flabbiness. The breed has good length and excellent hams. The head is trim, and the ears are drooping.

Poland Chinas produce excellent carcasses. Barrows of this breed have been winners in both on-foot and carcass contests.

There were 20,019 Poland Chinas recorded in 1957. The sows of this breed are good mothers, but the breed has been best used in crossbreeding. The Poland China crosses excellently with the Duroc, Hampshire, and Chester White.

Spotted Poland China. Early in the development of the Poland China breed, many of the hogs were spotted, and some breeders preferred this color. They were reluctant to adhere to the color standards set up for the Poland China breed, and many continued to grow spotted hogs. Some of these hogs were crossed with the black

Poland China and some with Gloucester Old Spots which had been imported from England.

The formation of the National Spotted Poland China Record Association came about in 1914.

The Spotted Poland China resembles the Poland China in type and conformation. It is a large breed, and the animals are good feeders. To be eligible for registration the color on the body must be between 80 and 20 per cent white, but the desired color is 50 per cent black and 50 per cent white.

This comparatively new breed has become quite popular. In 1957 the breed association recorded 14,972 animals.

Tamworth. The Tamworth is red in color, with the shades varying from light to dark. The head is long and narrow, with a long snout and erect ears. The body is also long and narrow, and the sides are smooth. Usually the Tamworth has a strong back and thin shoulders. The carcass produces bacon of the best quality.

Sows of this breed are prolific and are excellent mothers and foragers. Mature boars weigh up to 700 or 800 pounds. In 1957, 8,887 purebred animals were recorded. Tamworth bloodlines were used in producing the Minnesota No. 1 breed of swine.

Yorkshire. During the time that our American hogs were classified as *bacon* or as *lard* type, the Yorkshire was considered by many as the best bacon type breed. The breed is raised in large numbers in Canada, England, Scotland, and Ireland. It is a native of northern England, and was imported to this country early in the nineteenth century.

The Yorkshire is white in color, but occasionally there are black pigment spots in the skin. These spots are objectionable but do not disqualify the animal in the show ring or from recording. The ears are erect. Mature boars weigh from 700 to 1,000 pounds.

The Yorkshire is extremely long and deep, and is firm fleshed.

The American Yorkshire Club, Inc., of Lafayette, Indiana, recorded 20,064 animals in 1957. The popularity of the breed has increased greatly since 1952. It has had wide use in crossbreeding.

Origin and Characteristics of the New Breeds

A number of new breeds of swine have been developed during the past twenty years in an attempt to produce one which is prolific, will gain rapidly, will make efficient use of feed, will produce a carcass high in lean and low in fat cuts, and has a strong constitution.

Most of the breeds that have been developed to date have had their origin at the U.S.D.A. Agricultural Research Center at Beltsville, Maryland, or at cooperating state agricultural experiment stations. A number of inbred lines of various existing breeds have also been developed.

In the development of new breeds, an attempt has been made to produce animals which possess the desirable characteristics of two or more parent stocks. The Danish Landrace, Yorkshire, and Tamworth have been used in various combinations with other long-established breeds. Following is a description of the most promising results.

American Landrace. Landrace hogs originated in Denmark and were first imported to this country in 1934 for experimental crossbreeding purposes. By government agreement it was not possible at that time to produce and release Danish Landrace stock in this country as purebreds. They were used extensively in crossbreeding, and as a result of this practice many of the new breeds carry Landrace breeding.

In 1957, 23,571 Landrace hogs were recorded by the American Landrace Association, Inc. This organization was incorporated in December, 1950, with headquarters at Noblesville, Indiana. In addition to the importations from Denmark, a number of Landrace hogs have been brought in from Norway and Sweden.

The Landrace has white hair, and the skin is usually white. Small black spots, however, are common. The breed is extremely long, deep-sided, and well-hammed. Usually the animals are flat and sometimes low in the back. The ears are very large and cover much of the face. Many of the Landrace breed have weak pasterns. The breed is prolific, and is efficient in the use of feed. In addition, the carcass of the Landrace hog is meatier than that of most of our American breeds.

New Breeds Developed from Inbred Lines. A summary of the new breeds of swine which have been developed is presented in Table 9. Animals of these breeds are recorded by the Inbred Livestock Register Association of St. Paul, Minnesota. None of the new breeds is produced in large numbers, yet they have played important parts in the development of crossbreeding programs for commercial hog production.

TABLE 9

NEW BREEDS OF SWINE DEVELOPED FROM INBRED LINES

Breed	Parent Stock	Color	Developer	Number Recorded 1957
Beltsville No. 1	Landrace 74% Poland China 26%	Black and white spots	U. S. D. A.	924
Beltsville No. 2	Yorkshire 58% Duroc 30% Landrace 6% Hampshire 6%	Light red	U. S. D. A.	5
Maryland No. 1	Berkshire 38% Landrace 62%	Black and white spotted	U. S. D. A. Maryland Agri. Exp. Sta.	84
Minnesota No. 1	Tamworth 45% Landrace 55%	Red	Minn. Agri. Exp. Sta.	1,072
Minnesota No. 2	Yorkshire 40% Poland China 60%	Black with white spots	Minn. Agri. Exp. Sta.	400
Minnesota No. 3	Gloucester Old Spot Welch pig, English Large White, Beltsville No. 2 and others	Red	Minn. Agri. Exp. Sta.	293
Montana No. 1	Hampshire 45% Landrace 55%	Black	U. S. D. A. Mont. Agri. Exp. Sta.	812
Palouse	Chester White Landrace	White	Wash. Agri. Exp. Sta.	41
San Pierre	Berkshire Chester White	Black and white	Gerald Johnson, Indiana	67

Inbred Livestock Register Association

Figure 6-18. This litter of hybrid pigs was named Grand Champion at an Iowa market hog show. (Courtesy Farmers Hybrid Hogs)

Hybrid Hogs

Hybrid Defined. A hybrid is produced by crossing two or more inbred lines. Most commercial hybrid seed corn is a result of a double-cross process involving four inbred lines. Line A is crossed with line B (A x B), and line C is crossed with line D (C x D) during one growing season. The next year the progenies of the two crosses are crossed (AB x CD). The corn produced from the latter cross is sold as commercial seed corn.

Hybrid hogs are produced in much the same manner as is hybrid corn. Lines of hogs are inbred for several generations and then crosses are made of the inbred lines. The extent that the hybrid hog is more productive than the parent stock is dependent upon the genetic make-up of the various lines, and upon how well they supplement each other when they are brought together.

Hybrid Hog Production. There is no set pattern in the production of hybrid hogs in this country. The hybrid is produced by crossing two or more inbred lines, usually from different breeds. Many farmers and breeders do not understand the true meaning of the term "hybrid" and as a result some hogs are called hybrids incorrectly.

Hybrid hog production is a complicated procedure and one that involves careful planning and management. Producers of hybrid hogs must understand genetic laws and be able to apply them. Usually there is quite an outlay in breeding stock and equipment. Hybrid hog production has been until recently in the experimental stage. The number of producers of hybrid hogs is small. However, some of them do produce large numbers of hogs.

Selection of Individual Boars and Gilts

The factors to be considered in selecting boars and sows for the breeding herd are much the same regardless of the breeds and breeding programs which are involved. It is very important that hog producers select carefully the animals which are to be used in the breeding herd, because it is difficult to grow hogs profitably when inferior breeding stock is being used.

Parts of a Hog. Farmers, breeders, and packers use much the same terms in describing hogs. Since these terms will be used repeatedly in the following paragraphs, the reader should become familiar with them. Figure 6-19 shows the various parts of a hog body.

The Ideal Type and Conformation. Breeders of purebreds and commercial pork producers usually have some ideal in mind in selecting breeding and feeding stock. Usually they do not find animals which possess all the characteristics that they are looking for, and must select those that are nearest their ideal.

The ideal type changes from time to time with changes in market demands. More attention is usually given to quality of carcass when hogs are plentiful than when hogs are grown in smaller numbers. Factors associated with prolificness may be given more emphasis when the price of pork is high than when pork is cheap.

Producers select animals to be mated with other animals. Quite often the animal selected is not the ideal in several respects, but it is sufficiently outstanding to mate well.

Ideal Type of Market Hog. The ultimate goal in all hog production is to produce efficiently and profitably a hog which will yield when slaughtered a carcass high in the cuts of pork desired by the consumer. The Duroc barrow shown in Figure 6-20 is considered by many to approach the present-day concept of the ideal meat-type hog. For illustrative purposes, a similar animal could have been selected from each of the other meat-type breeds. It is the goal of the farmer and hog breeder to select breeding stock which will produce market hogs with the muscling, conformation, and carcass quality.

This barrow has good length and width of body. He carries his depth uniformly from front to rear, and he is deep- and smooth-sided. He is especially good in the ham. Note the plumpness and depth of ham. This barrow gives evidence of being firm-fleshed. There are no signs of flabbiness and he is well-muscled, with a trim head and jowl.

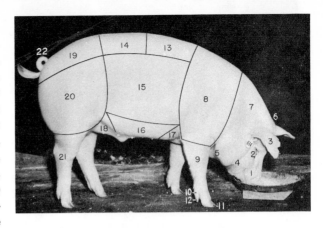

Figure 6-19. Parts of a hog. (1) snout, (2) eye, (3) ear, (4) cheek, (5) jowl, (6) poll, (7) neck, (8) shoulder, (9) foreleg, (10) pastern, (11) toes, (12) dew claw, (13) back, (14) loin, (15) side, (16) belly, (17) fore-flank, (18) hind flank, (19) rump, (20) ham, (21) hind leg, (22) tail. (Abernathy photo. Courtesy Chester White Swine Record Assn.)

Figure 6-20. The Grand Champion Barrow over all breeds at an Illinois State Fair. (Courtesy United Duroc Record Assn.)

This barrow should produce an excellent carcass and yield a 71 per cent dressing percentage or better. *Dressing percentages* refer to the percentage of the live weight of the hog found in the carcass after the animal has been slaughtered. Lard-type or exceedingly fat hogs may yield dressing percentages of 75 per cent or more. In the meat-type hog a carcass with a high dressing percentage is desired, but it must also be a carcass high in the choice cuts: ham, loin, Boston butt, and picnic shoulder. This barrow should produce a high percentage of lean cuts and a minimum of back fat and lard.

The carcasses of three barrows of different types are shown in Figure 6-21. The carcass on the left is from the intermediate or meat-type hog. It is the type of carcass which we would expect to get from the barrow pictured in Figure 6-20. Note the thickness of the layer of fat over the back and compare it with the back fat on the carcass in the center, which is from a chuffy hog. There is nearly twice as much back fat on the carcass from the chuffy hog as there is on the carcass from the intermediate hog. It has been found that

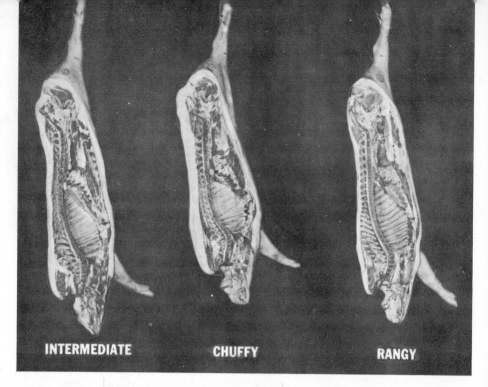

INTERMEDIATE CHUFFY RANGY

Figure 6-21. Carcasses of hogs intermediate, chuffy, and rangy in type. Note the differences in length, meatiness, and back fat thickness. (Courtesy Wilson and Company)

the percentage of lean cuts in a carcass is closely related to the back fat thickness.

The carcass on the right is from a rangy barrow. It has a very thin layer of back fat, but the ham and loin are undeveloped. A higher percentage of the carcass is in the form of bone and skin. Usually, rangy hogs require more time in being finished for market, and they are marketed at heavier weights.

Today the ideal market hog is the intermediate, middle-of-the-road, meat-type hog. Breeders and packers shy away from both the chuffy and the rangy animals. The chuffy hog produces too much back fat and lard; the rangy hog requires too much time to be properly finished and produces a heavy carcass.

Ideal Type of Breeding Animal. The breeder, knowing what type of market hog he wants to produce, can determine the type, conformation, and other qualities desired in the boars and sows which will produce this kind of pig. The kinds of feeds given and the methods

Figure 6-22. This Hampshire sow was All-American as an aged sow as well as being an 8-star P. R. sow. (Moore photo. Courtesy *American Hampshire Herdsman*)

of feeding also influence the growth rate, the economy of gain, and the quality of the carcass produced. Good feeding practices are of little value unless he has the right kind of breeding stock to begin with.

Selection of Females. The mature sow shown in Figure 6-22 possesses many of the characteristics desired in a brood sow. She has a medium-long body and a strong, well-arched back. She is deep-sided and has the capacity of the chest and middle that insures good feeding quality and vigor. Note her well-developed, deep, full hams. This sow is good on her feet and legs. She has ample bone, strong but medium-length legs, and short, straight pasterns. A brood sow must have good feet and legs; an inactive or clumsy sow usually is unable to raise a good litter.

This sow has a trim head and jowl. She is feminine and has a prominent eye. Coarse-headed and heavy-jowled sows should not be kept in the herd. Femininity and a reasonable amount of refinement are desirable in brood sows.

This brood sow is smooth in the shoulders, has a wide, well-muscled loin, and an excellent hair coat. The refinement of the head and ear, shoulder, and hair coat are important items in selecting female herd material.

The udder of the sow should be well-developed with twelve or fourteen sound teats. The teats should be prominent and well-spaced. The sow shown in Figure 6-22 has an excellent udder.

Most hog producers select young animals as replacements in their herds. This is especially true in making replacements in the sow herd. Most farmers select gilts that are six to eight months of age.

Selection of Boars. The selection of the herd boar is a major undertaking for most farmers. The boar genetically represents one-half of

Selection of Breeding and Feeding Stock • 75

Figure 6-23. The Junior Champion boar at the 1958 National Duroc Congress. (Moore photo. Courtesy National Hog Farmer)

the herd. It has been through the use of good boars that much of the progress has been made in swine improvement, since one boar can be mated to a large number of gilts.

Boars should show masculinity and breed-character. They should show cleanness and firmness of jowl, wide open eye, and the neck should blend in well with the shoulders. The shoulders should be smooth and the back strong. The width should be uniform from front to rear with no tendency to be narrow at the loin or ham.

The tail setting should be high and there should be no fat around it. The hams should be deep and full. The lower ham should be smooth and firm. The side should be smooth with a trim middle but good depth at both the fore and rear flank.

Boars should be big for their age, medium long and rugged. They should have strong bone and stand squarely on all four legs. The pasterns should be short and the legs should be set out on the corners. Shown in Figure 6-23 is an outstanding herd boar prospect.

A boar must have a good constitution. He should have width and depth in the heart area. He should have well-developed sex organs. The testicles should be of equal size and prominent.

Underlines. Bidders on boars and gilts in purebred sales usually inspect the teats or rudimentaries on the animal being sold. The teats on boars are called *rudimentaries* or rudimentary teats. Sometimes a teat on a sow is not connected with a milk gland and will not produce milk. This is called a *blind teat.* A teat which has an inverted nipple is more serious. These teats usually do not come down and produce milk. Boars and sows will pass this characteristic on to their offspring. Figure 6-24 shows a normal and an inverted nipple.

Tests for Carcass Lean and Fat. It is possible to take much of the guesswork out of selecting meat-type breeding stock by using

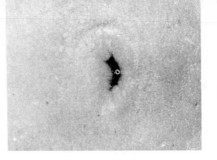

A

B

Figure 6-24. (A) Normal nipple (B) Inverted nipple
(Courtesy Dr. Roy Kottman, Iowa State College)

one of two tests which have been developed by swine research specialists.

Back Fat Probe. A small incision is made in the skin of the animal with a sharp knife. The incision is made to one side of the exact center of the back and just behind the shoulders. A small metal ruler is carefully pushed through the incision into and through the fat until it reaches the back muscle. The depth of back fat can be read on the ruler. By repeating the process over the loin it is possible to get a good idea of the thickness of fat carried by the animal. The probe does not injure the animal and there is little danger of infection.

Figure 6-25. Dr. F. N. Andrews of Purdue University using the Lean-Meter in making a measurement of back fat. (Courtesy F. N. Andrews, R. M. Whaley, and Duncan Electric Mfg. Co.)

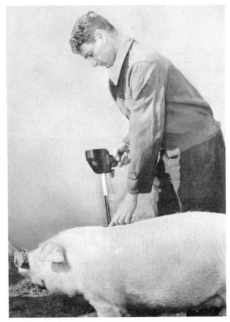

Selection of Breeding and Feeding Stock • 77

Purdue Electric Lean-Fat Meter. Purdue University researchers have developed an electronic device which will tell the difference in the proportion of lean and fat inside the loin, ham, shoulder, or bacon side of live hogs. This procedure involves no more injury or pain to the animal than the skin-prick of a needle.

The needle on the instrument is part of an electrical circuit. When flesh completes the circuit, a high current in lean and low current in fat result. The needle is set for depth, then pushed into the flesh. The meter, which is a part of the instrument, then shows whether the needle is in fat or lean.

Other Factors in Selecting Breeding Stock. Although type and carcass quality are important, there are other factors which should be considered in selecting breeding stock. In selecting both boars and gilts, age, pedigree, performance or production records, health, and disposition should be given consideration.

Age. The use of boars and sows which have proven themselves as producers eliminates the risk encountered in using untried animals. Mature sows usually produce more and larger pigs per litter than do gilts, and are usually better milkers. However, they become large, heavy, and more clumsy than gilts. They require more feed to maintain themselves and need larger farrowing pens. Mature boars usually settle more sows and are more dependable during the breeding season. They do not get the "flu" as easily as do young boars, and are usually in better health during the breeding season.

Most farmers and breeders, however, use young boars and gilts in their breeding operations. The young animals require a smaller investment, need less feed to maintain themselves, and less space in housing. When a young animal dies, there is less loss than there is when a mature animal is lost. The young animal gains in weight during the production period, and can be sold at a good price after it is no longer useful in the herd.

Pedigree. Every animal has a pedigree, but only the pedigrees of purebred animals can be recorded by a breed association. A pedigree is merely a record of the bloodlines of the ancestors of the animal. The pedigree is very important in the breeding of purebreds, but the breeder of commercial hogs is more concerned with the production record of the sire and dam of the litter than with their pedigrees.

Performance or Production Records. It is possible to judge the performance of a mature animal by the size of the litters produced, by the conformation of the pigs, and by the weight of the pigs at 56 days or at 150 to 180 days of age. Most breeders prefer breeding stock from litters of eight or more pigs raised. They want the pigs to average 40 to 50 pounds at 56 days, and 200 to 225 at five or five and a half months of age. By ear-marking the pigs at birth and weighing them at 56 days, or at 150 to 180 days, it is possible to select breeding animals from the most productive litters.

All of the breed associations have production registry programs. The production of the ancestors is recorded on the pedigree in the same way as production records of dairy cows are reported on the pedigrees of cows. The National Association of Swine Records has developed a production record plan based upon the number of pigs farrowed in the litter and the weight of the litter at 56 days of age. A litter qualifies for production registry when there are eight or more pigs farrowed and raised by a mature sow to a 56-day weight of at least 320 pounds. A first litter gilt must raise the same number of pigs to a 56-day weight of at least 275 pounds.

Sows qualify for production registry after producing two production registry litters. Boars must sire five qualified daughters, or 15 daughters which have produced one production registry litter, to qualify as production registry sires.

Litter testing of the home herd can help materially in the improvement of the productiveness of the herd. It is good practice to purchase breeding stock from a breeder who has maintained production records.

Health. Breeding animals which are large and heavy for their age usually are in good health, but the best policy is to buy only animals which have been vaccinated for cholera and leptospirosis and tested for brucellosis. In some areas it may be desirable to buy animals vaccinated for erysipelas. The herd from which the animals come should be inspected, and breeding and feeding stock should be purchased only from disease-free herds.

Careful hog producers inspect the herds and the farms on which they are raised before buying breeding stock. Many breeders will not buy breeding or feeding animals which have been marketed through public sales barns or stockyards. The policy of buying only disease-free stock and keeping them away from other hogs for two or three weeks is a sound one.

Disposition. The disposition of a sow may materially affect the number of pigs she will save at farrowing time. A sow that is nervous and easily disturbed is more likely to lie or step on pigs than is a sow with a quiet disposition. Quiet animals and those that like to be scratched usually have good dispositions and are good gainers. A good brood sow should permit you to enter the pen at any time, even during farrowing.

The disposition of a boar is equally important because the boar will be the sire of the next year's sow herd. A boar should be friendly in disposition, active, and a good rustler. Inactive boars are usually slow breeders.

Feeder Pigs

The number of farmers who buy feeder pigs has increased in recent years. Cattle feeders have always purchased large numbers of feeder pigs to follow cattle in fattening lots because it is easier for them to buy the pigs as they are needed than it is to maintain a breeding herd. But we now have a new group of buyers. Many farmers who have been unsuccessful in raising pigs because of disease losses are now buying pigs in fairly large numbers.

It has been estimated that any farmer who cannot raise an average of 6½ pigs per litter on his farm will find it to his advantage to buy pigs rather than to try to produce them himself. The average number of pigs weaned per litter in this country is rarely above 6½ to 6¾ pigs.

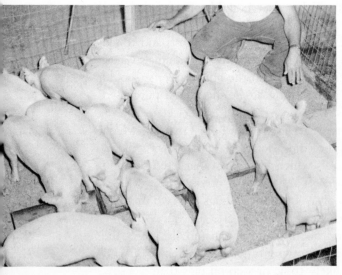

Figure 6-26. This Yorkshire litter had a combined weight of 947 pounds at 56 days of age. Raised by Eugene Wagner, Newton, Illinois (Courtesy Paul Walker)

Figure 6-27. A group of thrifty feeder pigs sold at a Maryland market. (Courtesy National Hog Farmer)

Feeder pig production has become a profitable business especially in areas where feed is not available to grow out the pigs for market. It is estimated that about 800,000 feeder pigs are sold annually in Wisconsin. Some 350,000 pigs are imported from other states into Indiana each year. Missouri farmers sold approximately 173,000 feeder pigs to Iowa producers in 1957.

Selection of Feeder Pigs. Regardless of the source, extreme care must be taken in the selection and purchase of feeder pigs. The reputation of the breeder, the breeding stock used in producing the pigs, the type and conformation, the health of the animals, and the purchase price must be carefully considered.

Price of Feeder Pigs. How much is a feeder pig worth? There is no one answer to this question. The price varies with the needs of the prospective buyer, the availability of the pigs, the price of farm grains, the market outlook for pork products, and the crop outlook. In 1958 40-pound feeder pigs which were vaccinated, wormed, and castrated were selling for $15 per head delivered to the farm. The top price on No. 1 market hogs at that time was $21.50 per hundredweight. Efficient producers could then raise their own feeder pigs for less money. The inefficient producers, and those without breeding stock and facilities, purchased the pigs at $15 per head and felt that they had made a good buy.

Summary

Good breeding stock is essential for the most profitable hog enterprise. Lard-type hogs are out of the picture. We must grow meat-type hogs.

A meat-type hog is one which will yield 50 per cent of its carcass in the primal lean cuts—ham, loin, picnic and Boston butt. It will weigh 200 pounds in five to five and one-half months and have a carcass which is 29½ to 31 inches long and a maximum of 1½ inches of back fat. It will produce a pound of pork on 3 to 3½ pounds of feed. The litters will average from eight to nine pigs raised.

Tests indicate that meat-type hogs made as rapid and as economical gains as the fat or chuffy type of hog.

There is no one best breed of hogs. The differences among the animals within a breed may be greater than those between breeds. The following factors should be considered in selecting a breed: availability of good breeding stock, prolificness, growth rate, temperament, carcass quality, nicking ability, market demand, disease resistance, feeds available, and personal likes and dislikes.

Of the ten old established breeds, the Duroc and Hampshire are most popular among farmers.

The Berkshire, Hampshire, Tamworth and Yorkshire have erect ears. The Chester White, Duroc, Herefore, OIC, Poland China and Spotted Poland China hogs have drooping ears.

The Beltsville No. 1, Beltsville No. 2, Maryland No. 1, Minnesota No. 1, Minnesota No. 2, Montana No. 1, and San Pierre are new breeds developed in this country by crossing two or more of our existing breeds or by crossing Danish Landrace hogs with one or more of our old-established breeds.

The American Landrace breed is an outgrowth of importations of Landrace hogs from Denmark, Norway, and Sweden. It has been used extensively in the production of new breeds.

We need to develop longer hogs with trimmer jowls and heads. Boars and gilts should be selected from large uniform litters. Breeding animals should be large for their age, have good length, uniform width and depth, and be firm-fleshed. There should be no signs of wasteness or wrinkling. The feet and legs should be set out on the corners and be straight. Sound underlines with 12 or more nipples are preferred. Good eyesight and a good disposition are musts.

• Questions

1. What breeds of hogs are most common in your community?
2. Why do you raise the breed of hogs which you have on your farm?

3. What factors should be considered in selecting a breed?
4. What use can be made of the new breeds of hogs in your community?
5. What kind of a production testing program should you use on your farm to improve the productiveness of your herd?
6. Describe the type and conformation of the kind of barrow which will top the market.
7. What are the advantages of crossbreeding over upgrading and breeding of purebreds?
8. Describe the factors that you would consider and what you would look for in selecting open gilts.
9. What additional factors would you consider in selecting bred sows?
10. Outline the qualities you would seek in selecting a young boar for use in your home herd.
11. What is the difference between a blind and an inverted nipple?
12. In selecting breeding and feeding stock, how can you be certain that the animals are from a disease-free herd?

● *References*

Anderson, Arthur L., *Swine Management,* J.˙B. Lippincott Company, Philadelphia, 1957.

Bundy, C. E. and R. V. Diggins, *Swine Production,* Prentice-Hall, Inc., Englewood Cliffs, New Jersey, 1956.

Ensminger, M. E., *Swine Husbandry,* The Interstate Printers and Publishers, Danville, Illinois, 1952.

7

Feeding and Management of the Breeding Herd

The profit or loss from a swine-breeding herd is often determined by the number of pigs weaned and marketed per sow. An average of five or six pigs marketed per sow is usually necessary to come out even. For profitable hog production we need to increase the number of pigs farrowed, weaned, and marketed.

It has been estimated that out of 100 pigs farrowed only 65 will live to be weaned, and only 55 will be marketed. Tests conducted at Iowa State College indicated that when 11 pigs were weaned per litter, the average cost of each eight-week-old pig was about $10.45. When nine pigs were weaned the cost was $12.01 per pig. Pigs from litters of seven weaned cost $14.52, and pigs from litters of five cost $17.92 at weaning time. These figures would indicate that unless we

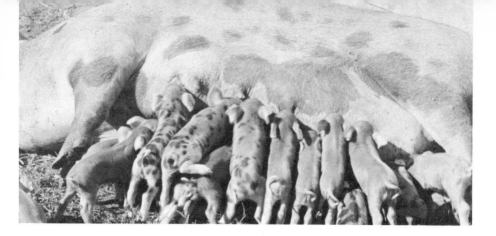

Figure 7-1. Good management during the breeding and pregnancy periods produces large litters of healthy pigs. (Courtesy Farmers Hybrid Hogs)

can save seven or more pigs per sow we should consider buying feeder pigs, or anticipate little profit from the enterprise.

The feeding and management of the herd at breeding time and during the gestation period can greatly influence the number of pigs farrowed and weaned. Good production methods will result in the following:

1. More pigs being farrowed per sow
2. Larger and healthier pigs at birth
3. Fewer dead pigs, runts, and abnormal pigs per litter
4. Better production of milk by the sows
5. More and heavier pigs weaned per litter

Feeding and Care During the Breeding Season

A farmer may decide that the small litters produced are due to the lack of prolificacy in his breeding stock. Usually he is wrong in making this assumption. Small litters are very often a direct result of carelessness in the feeding and management of the herd at breeding time.

Age to Breed. Gilts should be bred to farrow when they are 11 to 13 months of age if they have been well grown out. The maturity of the gilt is more important than its age. Most gilts which have done well reach puberty and come in heat when they are five to

Figure 7-2. The boar and gilts should be well grown out before breeding, especially when lot breeding is practiced. (Courtesy Kent Feeds)

six months of age. It is not a good policy to breed gilts during their first heat periods. Larger litters usually result from gilts bred during their third or fourth heat periods.

Gilts should be well grown out and weigh from 200 to 250 pounds at breeding time. Boars should be a little heavier if they are to receive heavy service. Some breeders prefer to use mature animals, fall boars, or early spring boars in their breeding programs. The older boars are more dependable, especially in settling mature sows.

Heat Period. The heat period, which usually lasts two or three days, is the time during which the sow will accept the boar. It is better to breed the sow during the second or third day of the heat period than during the first day. Sows that are in heat are usually restless and frequently mount other sows. The vulva is usually enlarged and inflamed. Sows that are not bred will usually come in heat at intervals of about three weeks.

Gestation Period. The period of time between the breeding of the sow and the farrowing of the litter is known as the *gestation* or *pregnancy period*. The length of period varies somewhat with sows but is usually from about 112 to 115 days. Breeders quite often figure 114 days as the gestation period. Older sows usually have longer gestation periods than gilts.

Time to Breed. Farmers plan their breeding operations to have the pigs farrow when the temperature, housing, pasture, and labor conditions are favorable. They also plan farrowings so that the pigs can be grown out and ready for a desirable market. Nearly one-half of the hog producers in the Corn Belt raise but one litter per sow per year. These men breed the sows so that they farrow in the spring.

October, November, and December are the months during which most sows are bred.

TABLE 10

SWINE BREEDING AND FARROWING DATES

Date Bred	Date Due to Farrow	Date Bred	Date Due to Farrow
January 1	April 24	July 1	October 22
January 15	May 8	July 15	November 5
February 1	May 25	August 1	November 22
February 15	June 8	August 15	December 6
March 1	June 22	September 1	December 23
March 15	July 6	September 15	January 6
April 1	July 23	October 1	January 22
April 15	August 6	October 15	February 5
May 1	August 22	November 1	February 22
May 15	September 5	November 15	March 8
June 1	September 22	December 1	March 24
June 15	October 6	December 15	April 7

Farmers who produce two litters of pigs per sow, or who produce litters in both the spring and the fall, breed their sows to farrow in August and September as well as in February and March. Table 10 shows the dates of breeding swine and the corresponding farrowing dates, based upon a 114-day gestation period.

Flushing. The condition of the sow or gilt at breeding time affects the regularity of the heat period, the number of eggs or reproductive cells produced, and the conception or the settling of the sow at the first service. *Flushing* is the feeding of the sows to insure their good health and a gain of from one to 1½ pounds per day from about two weeks before breeding until after they are bred. Gilts or sows which are recovering from "flu" at the time of breeding seldom produce good litters. It is better to flush these sows and breed them for a later litter.

The ration to be fed during the flushing period will vary with the age and condition of the sow and with the feeds and pastures available. It is important that the ration be well balanced and fed in the proper amounts. Plenty of proteins, minerals, vitamins, and forages are desired. Gilts usually should receive 2½ to three pounds of feed daily per 100 pounds of live weight, whereas mature sows may need less than two pounds daily for each 100 pounds of live weight. Usually a ration consisting of one-half to three-quarters of a pound of a balanced protein and mineral supplement, one pound of oats, and enough corn or other grains fed each day to produce daily gains of about 1½ pounds will meet the needs of a sow during the flushing period. Sows which are not on pasture should be self-fed alfalfa hay or should receive from one to two pounds of alfalfa meal daily. Sows and gilts should not become overfat.

A recent breeding experiment at the Ohio Agricultural Experiment Station showed that sows fed alfalfa before breeding produced more eggs during the critical heat period. Alfalfa and other legume pasture or high-quality alfalfa hay should be fed to both the boar and the sow previous to breeding time.

Feeding and Management of the Boar. Normally, if the boar is in good, thrifty condition and is well managed, he will not affect unfavorably the size of the litters which he sires. If his vitality is too low or if he is used very heavily, the sperms, or male reproductive cells, may be so weak that only a part of the eggs produced by the female will be fertilized, and small litters may result.

On some farms the boar is a neglected individual. He is purchased at breeding time and placed in a pen in the hog house. He may have been used previously by other farmers. He is in poor physical condition. Quite often he is fed too little protein, mineral supplement, and vitamins. Such a boar will be low in vitality and a poor breeder.

The boar should receive about the same kind of a ration as fed to the gilts during the flushing period. He should not be fattened but kept in good, thrifty condition. The following rations are suggested:

RATION 1		RATION 2	
(*Boar or sow on pasture*)		(*Boar or sow in dry lot*)	
	Pounds		*Pounds*
Corn, ground barley, or grain sorghums	73	Corn, ground barley, or grain sorghums	60
Ground oats or wheat	15	Ground oats or wheat	15
Meat scraps	5	Meat scraps	7
Soybean meal	6	Soybean meal	7.5
Mineral	.5	Ground alfalfa	10
Salt	.5	Salt	.5
	100		100

The boar should be given a lot of from about one-quarter to one-half acre, which has been seeded to alfalfa, red clover, ladino clover, or some other forage crop. A movable house should be provided at one end, and the boar should be fed and watered at the other end of the lot. Exercise is important in caring for a boar.

Yearling and other mature boars can be mated to 50 or 60 gilts during a breeding season if properly managed. An eight-month-old boar should not usually be expected to service more than 20 to 30 sows unless he is very carefully managed.

Pen- Versus Lot-Breeding. It is usually better to bring the boar to the sow or the sow to the boar at the time of service rather than to permit the boar to run with the sows. One good service is normally sufficient, and a record can be kept of the breeding date. If gilts are mated during their first heat period, they should be bred twice at 12- to 24-hour intervals. A young boar turned in with a large number of sows may be punished and become shy. This is especially true if mature sows are involved.

A mature boar should not be mated to more than three sows during one day, and a young boar should not serve more than two sows per day. Some farmers who practice pen-breeding bring a sow to the boar in the morning and another sow during the evening. Breeders of purebreds often space services six or eight hours apart and breed as many as four sows to an outstanding sire in one day. This plan cannot be followed throughout the entire breeding season.

Ranty and Inactive Boars. Some boars are very active during the breeding season and pace back and forth along fences or go through the fence. They may be difficult to manage, but are excellent breeders. Some breeders place a barrow or a bred gilt with the boar with excellent results. A better practice is to keep the boar in a lot at some distance from the sows.

Other boars are inactive—quite often because of improper feeding and management—and are slow breeders. It is a good idea to try out a boar a month or so before the breeding season begins to make certain the boar will serve and settle a sow. If he does not serve or does not settle the sow, the situation can be remedied before time to breed the main herd.

A boar may be inactive because he has become too fat or has not had sufficient exercise. Many so-called *non-breeders* are boars of this type. Be certain your boar is in good breeding condition. It is a good policy to turn two boars together in case one is inactive. The boar

Figure 7-3. Boars should have exercise pens, pasture, shade, and houses with high doors.

should be familiar with his surroundings because quite often a boar will not service a sow in new quarters. Some boars will not serve a sow when humans or other hogs are around. Pen-breeding is preferable from this standpoint.

Some boars breed only at night or early in the morning. It is a good idea to try out the boar and bring gilts to him at the time of day when he is most active. It is not a good idea to start a young boar by mating him to mature sows. It is much better to mate him to gilts of his own age and size.

A breeding crate also may be helpful in getting a boar to serve a sow. This is especially true in mating mature boars with young gilts. It is possible to make a temporary crate of straw bales and panel gates, or a commercially made crate may be used.

A number of products are sold as remedies for the inactivity of boars, but in most cases they are not effective. A veterinarian should be called in if it is necessary to use drugs or hormones.

Breeding Records. A record of the breeding dates for the sows in the herd is very helpful in checking upon the ability of the boar to settle sows and in selecting sows to be kept in the herd. It is also helpful in selling bred sows. The buyer will need to know when to expect the sows to farrow.

The breeding record is helpful at farrowing time in deciding when to pen up the sows. It is a good practice to mark the gilts as they are bred by use of ear tags or by clipping hair on the hip or back and to record the mark and the date of breeding.

Multiple Farrowing

Packers and marketing specialists have encouraged farmers to follow a multiple farrowing system of breeding in order to make economical use of the capital invested in breeding stock and equip-

Figure 7-4. A group of Duroc gilts that are in excellent breeding condition. (Courtesy Gregor Vaske)

ment and to distribute the marketing of hogs throughout the year. At one time a large percentage of the hogs produced in this country were farrowed in the spring and sold during the following fall and winter. The supply during the marketing period exceeded the packer demand, and low prices resulted. The tendency during the past several years has been to increase the number of fall litters and to decrease the number of spring litters. More producers are now raising two litters from each sow each year. As a result we have a more uniform price of hogs throughout the year.

There are now about as many fall pigs farrowed in Indiana and Ohio as there are spring pigs, whereas in Iowa the number of spring pigs farrowed is considerably larger than the number of fall pigs.

Two Litters Per Sow Multiple-farrowing Program. It has been pointed out that most sows are bred to farrow during two periods of the year—the spring period from February to May, and the fall period from August to November. As a result there are big seasonal runs on the markets, which result in lower prices. This problem is being solved by a number of farmers by splitting the sow herds into three, four, or five groups and having each group farrow twice each year.

Three Litters Per Sow Per Year. The use of pre-started pig rations has made it possible to wean pigs when from three to ten days of age. As a result, it is possible to rebreed sows and raise almost three litters from each sow each year.

Feeding and Care During Gestation

The vigor of the pigs and the number produced in the litter at farrowing time are determined by the number of eggs fertilized by

Feeding and Management of the Breeding Herd • 91

Figure 7-5. This litter weighed 810 pounds at 56 days. The Landrace sow owned by Howard A. Cowden farrowed 49 pigs in her last three litters in 351 days. (Courtesy *National Hog Farmer*)

the boar at the time of breeding and by the methods used in feeding and managing the sows during pregnancy. Not all eggs fertilized at breeding time produce live, healthy pigs at farrowing time. Some of the fertilized eggs produce embryo pigs which die early in the pregnancy period and are absorbed. Others die later, and are farrowed as dead pigs. Those that live but are weak are sometimes called "squealers."

The ration fed the sow has much to do with the type of litter which she will farrow. The methods used in feeding, exercising, and housing the sow also influence the number of healthy pigs which she will farrow. The kind of litter that we should strive to produce is shown in Figure 7-5. Note both the number and the health of these pigs. Tests have shown that a three and one-half-pound pig at birth has a six times better chance to reach weaning than a one and one-half-pound runt.

Rations for Bred Sows and Gilts. Bred sows use feed to maintain their bodies and also to produce litters of pigs. Young gilts also need feed to grow and become mature sows. If the rations are inadequate, the sows will be ineffective in maintaining themselves and in producing strong litters. Weak pigs may result. Young sows may remain small or stunted in growth and be poor milkers. The feeding of a balanced ration in adequate amounts during pregnancy is a must in profitable pork production.

The age and condition of the sow determine the amount and kind of a ration which she should receive. Thin sows require more feed than do sows in good flesh. Large sows need more feed than do small sows, and young sows must have more feed per hundred pounds of live weight than must mature sows. The stage of pregnancy also must be considered.

Nutritional Allowances. Pregnant sows should receive rations containing 14 to 15 per cent protein, .9 per cent calcium, .6 per cent phosphorus, 2,600 units of vitamin A, and 400 units of vitamin D per pound, and the following milligrams per pound of the B-vitamins and antibiotics: riboflavin, 1.5; niacin, 15; pantothenic acid, 5; and antibiotics, 5 milligrams. In addition the ration should contain about .5 per cent salt and 5 micrograms of vitamin B_{12} per pound.

Gain Desired. A gain of 100 to 125 pounds in gilts during pregnancy will allow for the growth of the gilt and her litter. Mature sows should gain from 75 to 100 pounds during gestation. These figures can be reduced somewhat if the litter is to be weaned when from one to three weeks of age.

Amount of Feed Required. Up to about 1953, we assumed that a thin mature sow would require from one to one and one-quarter pounds of feed daily, and a young gilt would need from one and one-half to two pounds daily, for each hundred pounds of live weight. Recent tests, however, indicate that we can reduce the amounts of concentrates by feeding an abundance of legume hay, corn, or grass silage, or by providing adequate pasture.

Hand-Feeding versus Self-Feeding. Swine producers must control the rate of grain of bred sows and gilts. They can be fed by hand the right amounts of feed daily or self-fed a bulky ration. Either method may be used successfully. The self-feeding method requires less labor, and hand-feeding usually takes less feed.

Figure 7-6. Pasture, silage, or hay can make up the greater share of the ration for bred sows during first months of gestation. (Courtesy American Berkshire Assn.)

When the sows gain too rapidly, the amount of corn or grain in the ration is reduced and ground alfalfa is added.

Bred sows and gilts should receive about one-half to one pound of supplement each day.

Rations. The ration best suited to your farm must be based upon the kinds of feeds and forages available and the prices of these feeds in your community. The key to feed efficiency is the use of high-quality, cheap farm-grown feeds, properly supplemented with proteins, minerals, vitamins, and antibiotics.

Following are rations recommended by various swine specialists. Grain sorghum may be substituted for corn, oats, or barley in the rations, but it should be ground. Rye may be fed in small quantities, but it cuts down the palatability of the ration.

RATION 1

Dry Lot Ration for Sows, Hand-fed

(Purdue University)

Ground corn	530 lbs.
Ground oats	250
Alfalfa meal	150
Protein (45%) supplement	70
	1,000 lbs.

RATION 2

Dry Lot Ration for Sows, Self-fed

(Purdue University)

Ground corn	300 lbs.
Ground oats	300
Alfalfa meal	300
Protein (45%) supplement	100
	1,000 lbs.

RATION 3

Complete Gestation Ration for Self-feeding Sows on Dry Lot

(Iowa State College)

Ground corn	550 lbs.
Ground oats	600
Alfalfa meal	600
Sow Supplement	250
	2,000 lbs.

Sow Supplement (32% P.):

Meat and bone scraps	400 lbs.
Soybean meal	750
Wheat middlings	300
Dehydrated alfalfa meal	400
Vitamin-antibiotic premix	30
Defluorinated phosphate (30% Ca, 18% P.)	70
Iodized salt	40
Trace mineral premix	15
	2,005 lbs.

Pasture. Sows that have access to alfalfa, ladino, rape, or other good pasture need little or no grain during the first half of the pregnancy period. They will need only about one-half as much grain during the latter part of the pregnancy period as they would have needed had they been in dry lot. While on pasture sows should receive from one-third to one-half pound of protein supplement per head daily and have free access to mineral.

Silage. Corn or grass silage can be fed to bred sows. Corn silage should be supplemented with 1½ pounds of a good protein supplement per sow per day. Grass silage should be supplemented with one pound of protein supplement and two pounds of corn daily. Sows will consume from 10 to 14 pounds of silage daily.

Water. Plenty of water should be fed to sows during pregnancy, either in the form of slop feeds, in troughs twice daily, or provided in automatic waterers. Water is especially important during the summer when the temperature is high. Fresh water should be available to the sows at all times.

Exercise. During the early stages of gestation it is desirable to have the sows forage in the cornstalk fields or in the pasture. Brood sows need exercise, and if they do not rustle out into the fields themselves, they should be fed at a distance of from 10 to 15 rods from their housing quarters. It is not a good policy to feed brood sows in the hog house or just outside their housing quarters.

Shelter. During the summer months pregnant sows need only a wooded area, open sheds, or shades to protect them from the sun and rain. Portable houses with open doors or straw sheds are satisfactory during the winter months in many areas. In the northern Corn Belt warmer houses may be necessary. Several sows may sleep in one house, but they should not be crowded. Bred gilts should have 11 to

14 square feet of shelter per head in cold weather and 15 to 22 square feet of shade per head in warm weather. Mature sows need 16 to 20 square feet of shelter per head in cold weather and 20 to 30 square feet of shade per head in warm weather.

Sows should not be kept in the same lots or buildings with other types of livestock. Sows heavy with pig may be injured by cattle or horses, or may injure themselves by crowding or by going up steep inclines, under creeps, or in low doors. Sows should not be in the cattle feed lots.

Summary

It is usually more profitable to raise two litters from each sow each year. By early weaning it is possible to obtain five litters from a sow in two years.

Gilts should be bred to farrow when they are from 11 to 13 months of age. It is usually best to breed gilts during the second day of the third or fourth heat period. The gestation period is 114 days.

Boars and sows should be in gaining condition but should not be fat at breeding time. Rations high in protein, minerals, and vitamins are important during the flushing or prebreeding period. Legume pasture or high-quality legume hay should be provided.

Pen breeding is preferred and breeding records should be kept. Not more than one or two sows should be mated to a young boar in one day. Mature boars may be mated to three or four sows in one day if matings are properly spaced.

Gilts should gain from 100 to 125 pounds and sows 75 to 100 pounds during pregnancy if they are to suckle litters for six to eight weeks.

With limited forage sows need from one to 1¼ pounds of feed per head and gilts 1½ to two pounds daily. Sows and gilts on good pasture need little or no feed during the first part of pregnancy. Sows and gilts should not be permitted to get fat.

Sows and gilts may be hand-fed grain and supplement in amounts necessary to keep them in good condition. Alfalfa hay may be self-fed.

Pregnant sows and gilts may be self-fed a bulky ration. It should contain from 25 to 35 per cent alfalfa.

Gilts may be fed from eight to 12 and sows ten to 15 pounds of corn or grass-legume silage.

Alfalfa and ladino clover pastures will provide for most of the nutritional needs of bred sows and much of the needs of bred gilts.

It is good practice to separate bred sows and gilts from other hogs and livestock.

Sows and gilts should be fed at some distance from sleeping quarters, or be allowed to glean a cornstalk field or good pasture.

From 11 to 20 square feet of dry, draft-free housing should be provided for each sow during winter. From 15 to 30 square feet of shade per animal should be provided during the summer.

- ## Questions
    1. How often will gilts come in heat?
    2. When in the heat period is the best time to breed gilts?
    3. Which is better on your farm, a one-litter-per-year or multiple-litter breeding program? Why?
    4. When should sows and gilts be bred to farrow litters in February and March?
    5. What care and management should be given the boar during the breeding season?
    6. Plan a good ration for flushing a group of 225-pound gilts.
    7. What nutritional allowances are recommended for bred sows and gilts during gestation?
    8. How much gain should sows and gilts put on during pregnancy?
    9. Describe the best methods of making effective use of silage in feeding pregnant sows and gilts.
    10. How much alfalfa hay should be included in a self-fed ration for pregnant sows?
    11. What are the grain and supplement needs of sows and gilts on alfalfa and ladino pasture during gestation? Explain.
    12. Describe the methods that you would use in managing the sow herd on your home farm to provide adequate rations, exercise, housing, and protection from injury.

- ## References

Catron, Damon, et al., Balanced Swine Ration Formulas, Iowa State College, Ames, Iowa, 1957.

Hollanbeck, Richard, Raising Hogs in Indiana, Ext. Cir. 429, Purdue University, Lafayette, Indiana, 1957.

Meade, R. J., et al., Nutrients, Feeds, and Example Rations for Swine, E. C. 253, University of Nebraska, Lincoln, Nebraska, 1957.

National Research Council, Nutrient Requirements for Swine, National Academy of Sciences, Washington, D. C., 1953.

Feeding and Management of Market Hogs

Critical periods in hog production occur at farrowing time, during the suckling period, at weaning time, and during the period from weaning until the pigs have been marketed. The successful producer plans carefully the practices which will be followed during each of these periods. If he fails to care for his hogs properly during any one of the periods, serious losses may take place. He may have fewer pigs per sow at weaning or at market time; the pigs may be unthrifty and require a long period of time and a large quantity of feed to get them ready for market; or the quality of the hogs produced may be so poor that they cannot be sold as No. 1 hogs.

Care and Management at Farrowing Time

Time of Farrowing. Some farmers have been successful in producing only one litter of pigs per sow per year by having the sows farrow in late May or June in timber areas or on legume pasture with

Figure 8-1. The Doane-designed multi-use 12-sow hog house. (Plan No. 52. Courtesy Doane Agricultural Service, Inc.)

temporary shelters or houses. They give the sows little or no attention at farrowing time, but plan on saving fewer pigs per litter, and keep a few more sows than if they were to give them more attention. Sows need less attention during warm weather than during the winter or early spring. Whether this practice is economically sound depends upon a number of factors: the price of hogs, the capital and facilities available, the labor supply, and the feed situation. Many farmers now plan on two or more litters per year, which usually necessitates having sows farrow during the cold months of January, February, and March, and again during the hot months of July, August, and September. With the latter system, special care of the sows and litters at farrowing time is necessary.

Housing. The portable hog houses or the pens in the permanent, central-type house should be cleaned and ready for use several days before the sows are due to farrow. The sow should be penned up a few days before farrowing so that she will be familiar with the surroundings and less likely to be nervous. The size of pen needed will vary with the age and size of the sow, and whether or not guard rails, pig brooders, or farrowing stalls are used. Pens seven or eight feet wide and from eight to ten feet long are preferred. In central-type houses the short side of the pen should be next to the wall or alley.

The house should be clean, dry, relatively warm, and well ventilated. The floors of movable houses should not be drafty due to cracks. It is sometimes a good policy to bank the sides and ends of movable houses with baled straw or with earth.

Feeding and Management of Market Hogs • 99

Figure 8-2. A 20-pen farrowing house owned by John W. Simpson, Edgerton, Missouri. Pens are 7½ x 8 feet. The center alley is 9 feet wide. A 12-foot concrete apron has been laid on each side and a 24- x 52-foot apron with loading dock is provided at one end. (Courtesy John W. Simpson)

Some farmers raise the front side of the movable hog house about six to eight inches so that the sow will lie in the pen with her back toward the door. Fewer pigs are lain upon by use of this method. Some breeders have tilted floors in permanent hog houses. A floor slope of one inch to the foot is recommended.

Most movable houses have openings at the ends for ventilation. Windows in movable houses are not necessary from the standpoint of providing light, and are not satisfactory as means of ventilation.

Whether a large central-type house for farrowing purposes should be built is questionable on some farms. The movable houses may be pulled up to the farmstead where electricity is available for use at farrowing time and then moved to the pasture to house the pigs during the summer. The investment is much less when movable houses are used, and desirable housing is available during the summer months. Some producers use both permanent and movable houses.

Sanitation. Losses due to swine diseases and worms can be avoided in part by properly cleaning the farrowing pen before it is used. All dust, dirt, and litter should be removed, and the floors and walls from 1½ to two feet from the floor should be scrubbed with boiling lye water. One pound of lye should be added to each 20 gallons of water. After the pen has been cleaned, it should be sprayed with a good disinfectant. Commercial disinfectants or a mixture of one pint of cresol solution to about four gallons of water may be used. The lye water loosens the dirt and kills the worm eggs while the disinfectant kills the germs of diseases. Equipment used in the pen should also be cleaned and sprayed.

Figure 8-3. These farrowing quarters are being scrubbed with hot soap and lye water. (Courtesy John W. Simpson)

The sides, underline, feet, and legs of the sow should be brushed and washed with soap and warm water before she is placed in the farrowing pen. Any dirt left on the sow may contain worm eggs which, if eaten by the pigs, could produce worm infection and runty pigs. In moving the sows or the pigs from one lot to another, it is best to haul them so that worm eggs or disease germs will not be picked up enroute.

Bedding. Coarse ground corncobs, wood shavings, fine straw, or sawdust may be used for bedding. Too much bedding or coarse hay and straw bedding may result in the loss of pigs. A deep depression in a heavily bedded pen will cause the pigs to lie too closely to the sow and will hinder them in getting away from the sow when she moves. A bushel basket or two of bedding in a pen is much better than a four-inch layer covering the entire pen. The bedding should be kept clean, dry, and well distributed. Removing the sow from the pen each morning and evening, for brief exercise, helps to keep the pen clean and dry.

Figure 8-4. Comfortable, clean, and roomy farrowing quarters are essential. (Courtesy John W. Simpson)

Guard Rails. A number of devices have been developed to keep sows from lying on the pigs. A simple device is the guard rail which is placed on the back three sides of the pen about eight to ten inches from the wall and eight to ten inches from the floor. These may be made of metal pipe, native poles, or 2 x 4's. In any case, they should be installed several days before the sow is due to farrow so that she will be used to them. They permit the pigs to get back of the sow without being crushed between the sow and the wall.

Heat Lamps or Brooders. The temperature in the farrowing house should range from about 50 to 60 degrees. When the temperature drops below 50 degrees, the little pigs chill and may take cold. The use of heat lamps or pig brooders is recommended for the first week or so after farrowing when the weather conditions are unfavorable. The heat lamp or brooder not only provides heat but also attracts the pigs away from the sow where they will be less likely to be stepped or lain upon.

The infra-red heat lamp type of brooder usually consists of a drop cord with a mechanical support, a socket, a heat bulb, and a protective reflector with screen over the end of the reflector. The bulb should be a 250-watt lamp. The hard pyrex heat-resisting bulb is preferred. In using heat lamps, care should be taken to avoid fire. The cord should be heavy and rubber-covered and have a lock-type connector. The socket should be porcelain and keyless, and the lamp should be supported by a chain, wire, or bracket. The electric cord should never be used to support the heating unit.

Figure 8-5. A properly placed heat lamp. (Courtesy Kent Feeds)

102

The unit should be placed about 30 inches above the top surface of the bedding, and care should be taken that water cannot drip down on the heat lamp. To prevent the sow from getting into contact with the brooder, a barrier made of 2 x 4's should be built in the corner of the pen with room enough only for the pigs to get under the lamp for heat. The barrier should be pen height or 36 inches.

The hover-type brooder has had general use for several years and is an effective means of providing heat and protection. The brooder is usually built in the corner of the pen so that only the little pigs can crawl underneath.

The top of the shelter should be 12 inches from the litter. It is solid with the exception of a 12- to 14-inch hole in the middle where the reflector and bulb are placed. Usually a 75- to 100-watt bulb is adequate. A bulb larger than 150 watts should never be used. One-fourth-inch hail screen should be placed over the opening in the top of the shelter to prevent injury to the bulb and the pigs. A barrier should be constructed to prevent the sow from coming in contact with the bulb assembly.

In wiring a building for pig brooders, provide a permanent and separate circuit with a maximum of 1,500 watts on each circuit protected by a 15-ampere fuse. The wire should be No. 12 size or

Figure 8-6. What *not* to do. Note unprotected drop cord and heat lamp, and absence of guard rails.

Figure 8-7. A farrowing stall in use. Note that the pigs can be on either side of the sow. (Courtesy Kent Feeds)

heavier. The extension cords to the brooders should not be longer than six feet, and each pen should have a separate outlet. The pig brooder, like the guard rails, should be installed several days before time for the sows to farrow.

Farrowing Stalls. The farrowing stall in Figure 8-7 shows the use of both guard rails and heat lamps, which is the most effective means of providing heat and protection for the pigs. It is estimated that farmers can save at least one more pig per litter by using these stalls.

In using farrowing stalls, the sow is confined in the stall, which is 24 inches wide, except when she is let out for feed, water, and exercise. The little pigs can run around the sow and under heat lamps on either side. Each heat lamp may be used by two litters at the same time, since a divider is provided to keep the litters separated.

The stall should be at least six feet long, but a length of eight feet is preferred. A 2 x 4 across the back of the stall may be used to regulate length. The partition panels should be from ten to 12 inches above the floor, depending upon the size of the sow. The same precautions should be taken in the use of heat lamps as were discussed previously in this chapter.

Sows may be left in the farrowing stall for just a few days or for several weeks. By moving the sows to regular pens after two or three days, it is possible to use the same stall for several litters. The sow should be removed from the stall each morning and evening for exercise, feed, and water.

Feeding and Management. *Rations at Farrowing Time.* The sow should be fed a bulky, laxative ration in moderate amounts just previous to farrowing. She should receive all the water that she can drink, but cold water should be avoided. It is usually best to reduce the ration just before farrowing and to give her no feed for 12 hours after farrowing, unless she is nervous and appears hungry.

The following rations are recommended for sows at farrowing time:

RATION 1

(University of Illinois)	
Ground shelled corn	300 lbs.
Ground oats	300
Wheat bran	300
Dry lot sow supplement	100
	1,000 lbs.

RATION 2

(Purdue University)	
Ground oats	600 lbs.
Wheat bran	150
Alfalfa meal	150
Protein supplement	100
	1,000 lbs.

The sow may be fed the same ration after farrowing as before. It is usually best to feed about a half ration the first day and to increase the ration gradually until she is on full feed. Heavy milking sows should be hand-fed for the first week after farrowing. Other sows may be self-fed.

Assistance at Farrowing Time. Although most sows do not need assistance at farrowing time, it is a good policy to be on hand. Sows become nervous as they approach farrowing time and may pace the pen and scrape up bedding materials. Most sows farrow within 24 hours after milk develops in the nipples, but some sows will have milk in the nipples for two days or longer before farrowing.

Feeding and Management of Market Hogs • 105

If the pen is cold at farrowing time you may need to dry the pigs and place them under the brooder or heat lamp as they are farrowed. If the pen is not equipped with a brooder or heat lamp, the pigs may be placed in a box or basket and taken to the house, or a jug of warm water or heated bricks may be placed in the middle of the basket. The pigs should be returned to the sow to suckle as soon as possible. Pigs normally will suckle each two or three hours. If pigs are removed from the sow, they should be returned each two or three hours for nourishment. Some pigs may not show interest in nursing even though they are a day or two old. These pigs may respond to a hand-fed solution of half sirup and half water.

A good hogman has worked with his sows so that they are not nervous when he is present at farrowing time. If they are nervous, it is best to leave them alone or to work very quietly.

Generally speaking, when sows have difficulty farrowing, it is best to have a veterinarian render assistance. Many instruments are on the market for use in helping sows at farrowing time, but they must be used with caution, or serious injury to the sow may result.

A man with a small hand may straighten out a pig which a sow has been unable to deliver; however, under no conditions should one attempt to do this without the use of a rubber glove, which has been coated with vaseline. Brucellosis in hogs is readily transferable to man, and undulant fever may result.

Navel Cord. Sometimes the navel cord is long, and it is impossible for the pig to move about freely. The cord should be cut, and the navel daubed with a tincture of iodine solution. The latter should be used on all pigs regardless of the length of the cord.

Needle Teeth. The clipping of needle teeth is a controversial issue. Some hogmen do not clip the teeth because they believe that the mouth and gums may be injured, allowing infectious organisms to enter the body. The practice, if done properly, will not cause disease infections. It may even prevent them, because, when fighting, pigs will not be able to inflict wounds about the face that would permit necrotic and rhinitic organisms to enter the body.

There are four of these tusk-like teeth on each jaw. Clipping should be done with a pair of cutters in such a way that there is a clean, smooth break with no injury to the gums and no jagged edges. Many hog breeders have developed skill in clipping needle teeth and make it a regular practice.

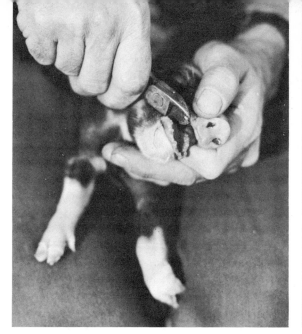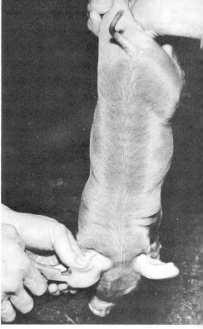

Figure 8-8. Clipping points of upper and lower incision teeth of a pig. (Courtesy U.S.D.A. Bureau of Animal Industry)

Figure 8-9. Ear-notching a pig shortly after birth is recommended. (Hufnagle photo. Reprinted from *Successful Farming*)

Ear-Notching. The notching of the pigs' ears at farrowing time is a universal practice among breeders of purebred hogs and among many commercial producers. It is the most practical method of identifying the pigs of a litter so that the productiveness of a sow can be determined and considered in the selection of breeding stock. All sow-testing programs begin with the ear-notching of the pigs.

Often in the fall farmers select the largest gilts to keep as brood sow replacements. The gilts may have been large because there were only three or four pigs raised in the litter. Unless the litters are marked, there is no way of knowing the kind of a litter the gilts came from. The marking of the pigs should be done as they are farrowed, giving all of the pigs of one litter the same ear notch.

Most producers number the litters in the order in which they are farrowed. The first litter farrowed is No. 1, the second litter farrowed is No. 2, and so forth. The notches may be made by using a notching instrument or scissors. It is also a good practice to weigh the pigs as they are being ear-notched.

Although there are numerous marking systems, the following is most commonly used:

Standard Ear- notching System

One notch in the lower right ear is 1
One notch in the lower left ear is 3
One notch in the upper right ear is 10
One notch in the upper left ear is 30

EXAMPLES:

Litter No. 2—Two notches in the lower right ear.
Litter No. 14—One notch in the upper right ear, one notch in the lower left ear, and one notch in the lower right ear.

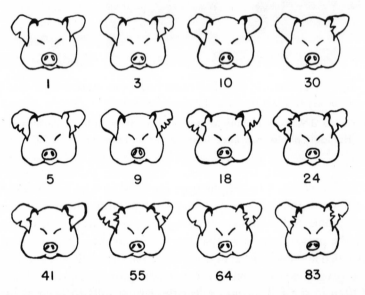

Figure 8-10 Standard ear-notching system. (Drawings by Francis G. Telshaw)

Purebred breeders and swine research specialists may wish to mark each pig so that it can be identified by litter number and by number within the litter. This is accomplished by using a dual system of ear notching. One system is used to identify the litter while the other is used to identify the various pigs of the litter. Shown in Figure 8-11 is a description of the system used in the Wisconsin Swine Selection Program.

Figure 8-11. The ear-notching system used in the Wisconsin Swine Selection Program. Notches in pig's right ear indicate litter. Notches in pig's left ear indicate pig's number in litter. (Courtesy University of Wisconsin)

Management During the Suckling Period

The weight of the pigs at weaning time is a good indication of the inherited growth ability of the pigs, and of the ability of the sow to produce milk. It has been estimated that from 25 to 30 per cent of pigs that are farrowed fail to reach a weaning age of eight weeks. Although many of the pigs die because they are lain upon, injured, diseased, or chilled, we know that many of them die because they do not receive sufficient milk and other feeds. The ration given the sow, the ration provided for the pigs, the pasture available, and the management given the sow and litter determine whether or not we save a high percentage of the pigs in the litter and have them at a heavy weight at weaning time.

Feeding. *Feeding the Sow.* A sow, when fed a good ration, may produce from six to eight pounds of milk per day. When the size of litter is small, five or six pounds of milk may be sufficient. Sows, however, which are nursing from ten to 12 pigs must produce the maximum of milk to meet the needs of the pigs satisfactorily. As we increase the size of the litters produced by our sows, we must also improve the rations fed to both the sows and their litters. A sow's milk contains about 81 per cent water, nearly 6 per cent fat, slightly more than 6 per cent protein, about 6 per cent lactose sugar, and about one per cent ash or mineral. The sow must receive feeds containing these nutrients in sufficient amounts to produce the milk required by the litter.

The bulky, laxative ration recommended for the sow at farrowing time is usually continued for several days after farrowing. The amount is increased daily. Sometime during the second week after farrowing the sow should be on full feed. By that time the pigs require large amounts of milk, and usually changes must be made in the ration. Most sows by this time can, and should, be self-fed a ration containing about 15 per cent protein.

The condition of the sows, the number of pigs being nursed, and the type of pasture available influence the amount and kind of a ration which should be fed. The following rations are recommended for sows during the suckling period.

COMPLETE LACTATION RATION

(Iowa State College)

Ground yellow corn	872 lbs.
Ground oats	300
Wheat middlings	300
Meat and bone scraps	100
Soybean oil meal	150
Dehydrated alfalfa meal	200
Distillers dried solubles	50
Vitamin-antibiotic premix	10
Ground limestone	6
Dicalcium phosphate	8
Iodized salt	10
Trace mineral mix	4
	2,010 lbs.

LACTATION RATION

(Michigan State University)

Ground corn	600 lbs.	Supplement No. 1 (38% P.)	
Ground oats	200	Soybean meal	580 lbs.
Supplement No. 1	200	Meat scraps	150
	1,000	Fish meal	50
		Alfalfa meal	150
		Dicalcium phosphate	40
		Trace mineralized salt	30
		Irridiated yeast	1 million units
		Antibiotics	30 grams
		B-vitamins (use commercial concentrate according to directions)	
		B_{12}	25 mg.

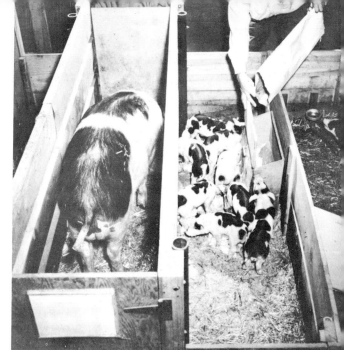

Figure 8-12. An excellent far-rowing stall and feeder for young pigs. (Courtesy Eli Lilly and Company)

Iodized Casein. The feeding of iodized casein to nursing sows during the first week after farrowing increases milk production. Iodized casein contains thyroxine, a natural hormone produced by animals. It should be fed at the rate of 100 milligrams per pound of total ration from the 110th day of gestation through the first weeks of lactation.

Creep-Feeding Young Pigs. Pigs will begin to nibble at feeds when a few days old and can consume considerable feeds by the time they are two or three weeks old. The milk production of the sow usually declines after the third week, and it is important that the little pigs be fed a palatable ration in ample amounts. This is especially true when sows are suckling large litters, and when the sows are in poor condition.

The little pigs need a more palatable ration, higher in protein and in antibiotics and lower in fiber content, than do their mothers. As a result, the feeding of the pig starters or creep rations are recommended. These rations should be fed in a trough or feeder in a pen separate from that of the mother. The gates may be adjusted so that the pigs can get in but the sows cannot.

The use of pre-starters and creep rations is very important if the pigs are to be weaned from the sows at an early age.

Feeding and Management of Market Hogs • 111

There have been a number of important developments in the creep feeding of pigs during the past few years. A common practice among hog producers has been to feed young pigs which were suckling their mothers rations of rolled or hulled oats, cracked wheat, or cracked corn.

A few years ago much research was done in developing synthetic milk rations in hope that pigs could be weaned from the sows when only a few days old. While excellent feeds were developed, they required more exacting procedures than the average farmer. was willing or had the time to use, and the cost of the feeding program was high.

Swine nutritionists next concentrated their efforts on building dry pig starters which were more palatable and better fortified with vitamins, minerals, and antibiotics than creep rations previously recommended. A number of excellent rations have been developed.

Baby Pig Feeding Program. Shown in Table 11 is the Iowa State College baby pig feeding program, which involves the feeding of three creep rations.

TABLE 11

BABY PIG FEEDING PROGRAM

Age of Pig (Days)	Approximate Weight of Pig (lbs.)		Kind of Feed		Amount of Feed Needed (lbs.)	Feed per Pound of Gain (lbs.)
	At Beginning	At End	Protein	Name		
7 to 14	5*	to	8 or 10	20-25%	Pre-starter	3 to 5	1.0 to 1.25
14 to 35	8	to	25	18%	Starter	25	1.2 to 1.5
35 to 56	25	to	40	16%	Grower	50	2.0 to 2.25

*Minimum. Pig weight and feed consumption, by periods, not age, are the best management guides.

Iowa State College, 1957

Pre-Starter Period. Shown in Table 12 are formulas of two I.S.C. pre-starter rations. No more than ten pigs should be penned together and the pigs should be of the same size. Approximately six square feet of floor space per pig should be provided and floor drafts should be avoided. Solid pen walls should be used. Heat lamps or brooders should be provided and the bedding should be kept clean and dry. Young pigs will need plenty of fresh water. Automatic fountains are preferred and they should be clean and sanitary at all times.

Ration 1 contains no *pepsin*. In Ration 2 pepsin has been added, the quantity of milk has been reduced, and the amount of soybean meal increased. Pepsin is an enzyme which aids in the digestion of protein. Pigs under five weeks of age cannot produce enough pepsin to digest all of the vegetable proteins that they consume.

TABLE 12

PIG PRE-STARTER RATIONS

(For Pigs Weaned from 2 to 4 Weeks of Age)

Ingredient	Revised ISC Pre-Starter 75	Low Milk Plus Pepsin
	Pounds	Pounds
Ground yellow corn	191	127
Cane or beet sugar	200	200
Dextrose or corn sugar	100	100
Dried whey (70% lactose)	50	300
Dried skim milk	800	400
Solvent soybean oil meal	350	600
Condensed fish solubles	50	50
Stabilized lard	100	50
Corn steep water	20	20
Dried brewers yeast	20	20
Dried beet pulp	40	40
Vitamin-Antibiotic premix	50	50
Calcium carbonate	3	6
Dicalcium phosphate (26% Ca, 18% P)	12	18
Iodized salt	10	10
Trace mineral premix	4	4
Pepsin (proteolytic enzyme, 1:3000)	—	5
Total	2,000	2,000

Iowa State College

Saccharin. Preliminary tests indicate that pigs prefer saccharin to sugar and that they make more rapid gains on rations containing saccharin during the hot summer months than when fed rations containing sugar. Saccharin is much cheaper as an appetizer than sugar. It has no food value, however. Pigs gain more rapidly during cool weather on rations containing sugar. When one pound of saccharin is substituted for 300 pounds of sugar in a starter ration, the energy producing feeds in the ration must be provided in increased amounts to replace the energy previously provided in the form of sugar.

Starter Period. As the pigs reach eight to ten pounds in weight, the ration is shifted from the pre-starter to a highly fortified starter feed which has been pelleted. The formulas of starter rations for weaned and unweaned pigs are shown in Table 13.

TABLE 13

PIG STARTER RATIONS
(Complete Rations for Pigs up to 25 Pounds—About 5 Weeks of Age)

Ingredient	18% Protein	16% Protein
	Pounds	Pounds
Ground yellow corn	558	656
Rolled oats	200	200
Cane or beet sugar	300	300
Dried whey	200	200
Dried skim milk	100	100
Soybean oil meal	500	400
Condensed fish solubles	50	50
Vitamin-antibiotic premix	50	50
Calcium carbonate	8	8
Dicalcium phosphate	34	36
Iodized salt	10	10
Trace mineral premix	4	4
	2,014	2,014

Iowa State College

Figure 8-13. Pigs like pellet feeds. (Courtesy Eli Lilly and Company)

114

Pigs like pellets better than meals or crumbled feeds. Dusty or finely ground feeds are not eaten readily. It has been found that pigs will consume nearly twice as much feed in pellet form as in the form of meal.

In feeding the starter ration, the pigs should not be crowded. At least four inches of feeder space should be provided for each two pigs. An adequate supply of fresh water should be available at all times.

Grower Ration. The grower ration may be fed to weaned or unweaned pigs. Weaning is a normal process if the pigs are provided adequate amounts of the creep fed rations.

Shown in Table 14 are the formulas of two grower rations. These rations, like the starter rations, may be purchased from reputable feed manufacturers as a mixed feed or can be mixed at the local elevator.

TABLE 14

16% PIG GROWER RATIONS
(Complete Ration)

Ingredient	Ration 1	Ration 2
	Pounds	*Pounds*
Ground yellow corn	1,380	1,250
Ground oats (hulled preferred)	—	200
Soybean oil meal	450	400
Meat and bone scraps	—	50
Condensed fish solubles	50	—
Dried whey	50	50
Vitamin antibiotic premix	25	25
Dry vitamin A (2 million I. U./lb)	.5	.5
Calcium carbonate	11	6
Dicalcium phosphate	39	28
Iodized salt	10	10
Trace mineral premix	4	4
	2,019.5	2,023.5

Iowa State College

It is best to sort pigs according to size and to feed not more than 20 pigs in one lot if they are confined. Each pig should have eight square feet of floor space if confined. Fresh water and adequate housing quarters are essential.

Figure 8-14. Sod is provided to prevent anemia. (Courtesy Rath Packing Company)

Pre-weaning Management

Anemia Control. Small pigs which have had little exercise and no opportunity to pick up iron and copper from the soil may develop anemia. Anemia in pigs is a blood condition usually caused by a lack of copper and iron. A large number of pigs die each year because of this trouble.

The anemic pigs usually show a loss of appetite, become weak, have trouble breathing, and sometimes have a swollen condition around the head and shoulder. Sometimes they "thump."

There are at least three ways of preventing anemia. First, pigs which are raised in the late spring or summer and have access to earth and sod do not get anemia. The little pigs get enough iron and copper from the sod to satisfy their needs. Second, if the pigs are confined and cannot get sod, bring it to them. Get the sod from a disease-free field or from along the roadside.

The third method of controlling anemia is to use drugs obtained from the drug store or veterinarian. Iron and copper pills, which can be given each pig when about five days old and weekly thereafter, are available. Pigs may be given an injection of a solution of copperas (ferrous sulfate), which can be purchased at any drug store. Some hogmen mix copperas with the feed given the sow during pregnancy and nursing periods.

Castration. Pigs should be castrated when they are from two to three weeks of age. They recover from the operation very quickly at this age. Under no conditions should the pigs be castrated, wormed, vaccinated, or weaned at the same time. These operations should be spaced at two-week intervals.

Unless heat is provided by use of brooders or heat lamps, pigs should be castrated when the weather is warm. The hog house and pen should be clean, dry, and well bedded.

Two persons are usually needed in castrating—one holds the pig while the other operates. The pig may be held by a front and a hind leg on opposite sides with its back on the floor, or by the hind legs with its head and shoulders between the assistant's knees. The scrotum should be washed with a mild antiseptic solution or with soap and water. The sharp knife used in castrating and the operator's hands or rubber gloves should be carefully disinfected.

The incision may be made over each testicle, or in between the testicles, parallel to the middle line of the body. The incision should pass through the skin near the top of the testicle and through the testicle covering. The testicle is pulled slowly through the incision, and the attachments are separated with little bleeding. The second testicle is removed in the same manner.

Care should be taken to make the incision fairly long and low so that it will drain well. As much of the cord should be removed as possible. Usually there is no need to apply disinfectant or healing oil after the operation.

When mature boars are castrated, it is usually necessary to throw them and tie their legs. The operation is similar to that on pigs but there is more danger of bleeding.

Sometimes pigs are ridglings or "originals." They have but one testicle in the scrotum. It is often best to turn over these pigs, as well as those that are ruptured, to a veterinarian.

Vaccination. In most hog producing areas it is advisable to vaccinate pigs for cholera, leptospirosis, and erysipelas. These diseases are discussed in a later chapter. Usually only healthy pigs should be vaccinated and the three vaccinations should be made separately about two weeks apart. Some veterinarians begin the vaccinations

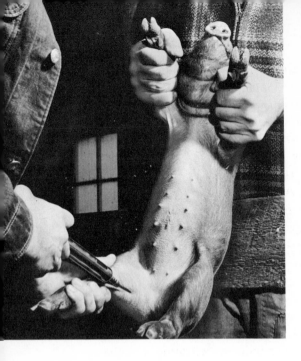

Figure 8-15. Vaccinating a pig for hog cholera about two weeks before weaning time. (Hufnagle photo. Reprinted from *Successful Farming*)

when the pigs are from six to seven weeks of age; others wait until they are eight to ten weeks of age. Only the modified live virus, crystal violet, or BTV cholera vaccines should be used.

Antibiotics. The practical level of feeding antibiotics in pig starters seems to be from 20 to 40 grams of antibiotics per ton of total ration or from 10 to 20 milligrams per pound. (A pound equals 453.6 grams, and a gram equals 1000 milligrams.) Experimental work indicates that aureomycin, terramycin, and penicillin are equally effective in increasing rate of gain and in protecting pigs from disease.

Pasture. Most hog producers like to move the sows and litters to clean legume pasture as soon as possible after the pigs are a week or two old. Because of cold weather and the required electricity it may be necessary to postpone the moving of the litter. Pigs can be raised efficiently while confined, but care must be taken to provide sanitary quarters, and a ration which contains the minerals, vitamins, and proteins which are provided by pasture crops.

Care should be taken in moving pigs to pasture so that no infections are picked up enroute. It is better to haul the sow and litter than to drive them. On some farms concrete runways have been provided for this purpose. They can be cleaned easily and permit the pigs to travel back and forth from the farrowing house to the pasture without picking up infections in old lots.

Weaning. With the use of fortified pig starter rations it is possible to wean pigs in advance of the usual age of eight weeks. Following are weaning pointers.

1. Pigs less than ten days of age should not be weaned from the sow unless adequate equipment, heat, labor, and highly fortified rations are available.
2. The tendency among hogmen is to wean pigs when they are from three to five weeks of age.
3. It is a good idea to wean pigs by weight rather than by age. Wean the larger pigs from the litter first.
4. Avoid making any changes in the ration at weaning time.
5. The sows should be moved from the pigs rather than taking the pigs from the sow at weaning time.
6. Care should be taken to make certain that feed and water are fresh and plentiful.
7. Comfortable quarters are essential. Warm, dry, well-ventilated quarters are necessary during winter months. Shade and cool and well-ventilated quarters are important in hot weather.
8. It is best to separate pigs by weights and keep not more than about 20 pigs of the same size in a pen at weaning time.

Production Registry. The weight of the pigs at 56 days determines quite accurately the productiveness of the individual sows and the effectiveness of the breeding, feeding, and management programs. The litter weights are very helpful in planning rations for the pigs after weaning and for the sows to be used in producing the next crop of pigs. The selection of gilts and sows to be retained in the herd should be based upon the litter weights. The tried sows to be kept over for second and third litters should be those which produce the best litters. Untried breeding animals are always a risk. By selecting gilts from litters which were heavy at 56 days, much of this risk can be removed.

A bathroom scale, or a scale supported by a tripod, may be used in weighing. A good litter should average 40 to 50 pounds at 56 days of age, and there should be at least eight pigs weighed. Some producers weigh the pigs at 35 days rather than at 56 days of age.

Figure 8-16. Paul Walker, Vocational Agriculture Instructor at Newton, Illinois, assisting a member of the Jasper County Herd Improvement Association weigh his pigs at 56 days. (Courtesy Paul Walker)

Feeding and Management from Weaning to Market

Approximately one-third of the total cost of producing a 220-pound market hog is involved in raising the pig to weaning age. It takes the remaining two-thirds of the total cost to grow out the pig from weaning time until it is ready for market. From the production standpoint, the period from weaning to market is an important one, since more than twice as much capital is involved in this period as is involved in producing weaning pigs. Serious losses can occur during this period as a result of poor feeding and management, or of a disease outbreak.

The efficient hog raiser plans carefully his production program. He provides adequate rations and feeds them in the proper amounts. He uses the methods of feeding best suited to his farm situation. He provides pasture of good quality in the desired amount. He is efficient in housing his hogs and in controlling diseases and parasites. The profit from the enterprise can be judged by the cost of production and by the selling price. Usually he can influence the cost of production more easily than he can the selling price.

Worming. Most farms are contaminated with round worms, which are injurious to swine. This parasite is discussed fully in another chapter, but we wish to mention here the need for worming most pigs when they are placed on pasture.

Figure 8-17. Chester White pigs on excellent rotated pasture. (Courtesy The Chester White Swine Record Assn.)

Round worms may be controlled by the use of rotated pastures, but we are never certain that the mature animals in the herd are free from the parasites. The only safe way is to treat the pigs for worms even though we have used the McLean County clean-ground system of rotated pastures.

Many drugs and other materials for worming purposes are sold commercially. Among the best wormers are hygromycin and the piperazine compounds which are safe, convenient, and control more kinds of worms than other wormers now on the market. The instructions on the label should be carefully followed.

Pasture Versus Dry- lot Feeding. Each farmer must evaluate his facilities and resources to decide whether he should grow his pigs on pasture or in dry lot. Most farmers prefer to use pastures in their production programs. Following are the advantages of the two systems.

Kinds of Pasture Crops. A number of pasture crops have been tested and their value for swine has been determined. Shown in Table 15 is a summary of tests conducted by the Missouri Agricultural Experiment Station.

According to the Missouri tests, alfalfa proved superior to all other crops in pounds of pork produced per acre and in value of pork produced. Red clover and rape ranked second and third.

Birdsfoot trefoil ranks with alfalfa in palatability, in feed value, and in ability to stand drouth. It does well seeded with bluegrass

TABLE 15

Crop	Number of Days Pastured	Number of Hogs per Acre	Pounds of Pork per Acre of Forage	Value per Acre with Pork @ $20 per Cwt.
Alfalfa	163	10	592	$118.40
Red Clover	130	12	449	89.80
Rape (Dwarf Essex)	82	23	395	79.00
Sorghums	87	15	275	55.00
Bluegrass	136	12	274	54.80
Soybeans	25	17	175	35.00
Cowpeas	32	13	149	29.80

* The rations of the pigs were limited to one-half to two-thirds of a full feed.
Source: Pork Production in Missouri, Bulletin 587, University of Missouri, Columbia, Missouri, 1952.

as a permanent pasture crop. Often two to three years are required to get a stand, but it will last for many years. The usual rate of seeding is from four to five pounds of inoculated seed per acre.

The nonleguminous crops, oats, rape, brome grass, sudan grass, and rye, should be used only as emergency crops when the legumes winter-kill or when new seedlings do not survive dry weather. Rye provides a very early pasture in the spring but dries up in the early summer. Rape does not provide an early pasture but does make an excellent late pasture.

Figure 8-18. A healthy group of Hampshire sows and litters on pasture. (Courtesy *American Hampshire Herdsman*)

Ladino clover, a comparatively new clover which resembles white Dutch clover, is rated in several states as the best pasture for swine. In Purdue tests, it was found superior to alfalfa as a pasture for full-fed hogs, as indicated by a more rapid gain and a 40 per cent saving in protein supplement. The feed cost of 100 pounds of gain was $9.35 on the ladino pasture and $10.42 on the alfalfa.

Advantages of Pasture

1. Pork can be produced on clean hog pastures with 15 to 30 per cent less concentrates than can be done on dry-lot feeding.
2. The protein-supplement feed bill can be cut one-third to one-half by using good legume pasture.
3. There is less chance for diseases and parasites to cause losses when pigs are on "clean" legume pasture.
4. The equipment necessary to feed and manage hogs under sanitary conditions is less when they are on pasture than when they are confined.
5. There is no bedding problem during the summer months.
6. Hogs on pasture will spread their own manure. Less labor is involved.
7. Most tenants must rely upon use of pastures in growing out hogs. Few landowners will provide desirable facilities for dry-lot feeding programs.
8. One man can take care of more pigs that are on pasture than are confined.
9. Pasture-fed pigs usually produce better carcasses and have less back fat.
10. It takes less know-how to grow pigs on pasture than on dry lot.

Advantages of Dry-lot Feeding

1. It may not be economical to use land valued at $300 an acre or more as hog pasture.
2. More rapid gains can be produced when pigs are in dry lot if adequate rations and good management are provided.
3. Dry-lot facilities can be used during more months of the year than can pasture facilities.

4. There is usually less labor used in hauling and handling feed when pigs are confined.
5. There is less labor and difficulty in providing an adequate supply of water.
6. Fence problems will be minor as compared to pasture feeding.
7. The dry-lot method is best for the man who wishes to grow out a large number of hogs on a small farm.

Pasture Management. The management given the pastures, and the hogs which graze them, may greatly influence the effectiveness of the pastures in hog production programs. Many good pastures are not managed properly.

Rotated Pastures. In order to prevent disease and parasite outbreaks, it is desirable to provide a new pasture area each year. Farmers who make new seedings each year have a new pasture area for each crop of pigs.

Farmers who use permanent or semi-permanent pastures accomplish the same result by dividing the pasture area into three or four parts, and then rotating the use of the divided areas.

Figure 8-19. Duroc pigs on pasture. Note the excellent location of feeders, waterers, and housing. (Courtesy United Duroc Record Assn.)

Pigs per Acre. The number of pigs or hogs per acre depends upon the kind of pasture, fertility of the soil, weather conditions, and whether a full or limited feeding program is followed. An acre of legume or legume-grass pasture should provide adequate pasture for 20 to 30 growing-fattening pigs on full feed. Frequent clipping of pastures during the summer months is recommended if the pigs do not keep the growth down.

Location of Feeders and Waterers. Considerable labor may be saved by locating the feeders and waterers near the fence so that they may be filled by use of power equipment without driving into the field. Large feeders which are protected from the weather are recommended.

Tests conducted at the South Dakota Station indicate that the feeders and waterers should be located close together. When they were located more than 300 feet apart the average daily gain decreased.

Ringing Pigs. It is sometimes necessary to nose-ring pigs to keep them from rooting the sod in the pasture. The feeding of

Figure 8-20. One man can care for a large number of hogs if large self-feeders and modern feed hauling and elevating equipment are available. (Courtesy Dodgen and Company)

Feeding and Management of Market Hogs • 125

balanced rations containing animal proteins and minerals tends to reduce rooting. Care should be taken in ringing pigs to avoid injury to the bone structure of the nose.

Feeding Pigs on Pasture. Most rapid and economical gains are usually brought about by full-feeding pigs which have access to good legume pasture. When feeds are high in price or scarce in quantity, it is sometimes desirable to feed a limited ration and make more effective use of the pasture. Each hog raiser must decide which of the two systems will be more profitable on his individual farm.

Methods of Feeding. Pigs may be hand-fed or self-fed. Self-feeding saves labor and usually produces more rapid and economical gains than does hand-feeding.

Self-feeding promotes sanitation and provides large feed storage space. Self-feeders, however, are expensive and are sometimes neglected by irresponsible caretakers. Sometimes the use of the self-feeders decreases the effect of good pasture because the appetites of the pigs are satisfied while they are at the feeders. Some farmers prefer to hand-feed their pigs. They can watch them more closely and can give types of feeds which cannot be self-fed, such as ear corn and slop feeds.

It is possible to get pigs to consume more feed by mixing it with water or milk, providing it is fed as a wet mash rather than as a thin slop. Slop or wet mash feeding also encourages the pigs to consume more water.

If pigs are to be hand-fed, give only the amount of feed that they will clean up in an hour or two. This is especially important if slop or wet mash feeding is practiced. Stale feed in the trough is not only wasteful but unappetizing, and decreases the amount of feed that the pigs will consume.

Self-feeders. A good self-feeder should make available to the pigs a supply of clean, dry feed at all times. It should be solidly constructed, and protect the feed from wind or rain. It should be large enough to store amounts of feed which will last the pigs for several days. It should have an adjustable throat or opening, and some type of agitator, so that various types of feeds will feed down in desired amounts. The trough should be constructed in such a manner that little feed will be wasted. Doors or lids over the troughs are desirable. If the ration is fed as a complete mixed

Figure 8-21. A walk-in type of self-feeder. (Courtesy Doane Agricultural Service, Inc. Plan No. 10)

ration, only one feeder will be needed. If feeds, such as shelled corn, ground oats, and supplement, are fed separately, separate feeders will be needed, or separate compartments in a large feeder may be used.

The use of large feeders which will handle 250 bushels of shelled corn and 1,500 pounds of supplement will cut down the cost of feeding equipment and will save labor.

There should be one foot of feeder space for each three to four hogs. If supplement is fed separately, from 15 to 25 per cent of the total feeder space should be reserved for supplement. Heavier hogs require less supplement and less feeder space.

Rations. Farm grains should make up the main part of the ration. Corn, when available, produces the most rapid and economical gains. Barley, wheat, oats, and grain sorghums may be fed, but should be ground. These feeds produce slower gains but may produce better carcasses.

A common practice in the Corn Belt is to feed rations made up largely of corn supplemented with tankage and soybean oil meal, or with a mixed protein feed. From 10 to 30 per cent of the ration may be made up of grains other than corn.

In areas where corn is not obtainable, it is possible to build good rations by using ground barley or ground grain sorghums.

Since the grains and pasture cannot provide all the proteins, vitamins, and minerals necessary, we must supply sufficient feeds to meet the nutritional needs of the pigs. Protein and mineral supplements which have been fortified with vitamins and antibiotics must be added.

Proteins. It has been pointed out that proteins are made up of amino acids and that ten of these amino acids are essential for animal health. Corn, which is the basic grain fed to hogs in much of the Corn Belt, is low in two of these essential amino acids, lysine and tryptophan. Therefore, it is necessary to supplement corn with protein feeds rich in these two amino acids. Most proteins of plant origin are deficient in lysine. The exception is soybean oil meal, which is a good source of lysine. Animal proteins, such as tankage, meat scraps, and fish meal, are also good sources of this amino acid. A good protein supplement, then, should contain soybean oil meal or a meat origin protein, or both.

Plant proteins, in general, are good sources of tryptophan, whereas meat and bone scraps, if fed alone with corn, will not provide an adequate amount of this amino acid for maximum growth. Most mixed protein and mineral supplements contain several protein feeds of plant origin which provide an adequate supply of tryptophan.

Value of Protein Supplements. Numerous tests have been conducted to determine the value of protein supplements in feeding pigs. In general, protein feeds are more important for pigs weighing from 45 to 85 pounds than for those weighing 100 pounds and over. Light pigs fed corn alone will gain less than ⅓ pound per day. The same pigs fed a protein supplement will gain more than a pound a day. Heavier pigs fed corn alone will require about 200 pounds more feed to produce 100 pounds of gain than will pigs fed corn and a protein supplement. Tests show that 100 pounds of tankage may save from 500 to 600 pounds of corn.

Protein feeds are more important in feeding pigs in dry lot than in feeding those on pasture. The use of good legume pastures can reduce the amount of protein concentrates by nearly 50 per cent.

Until the discovery of vitamin B_{12}, it was necessary to provide rations containing from 18 to 20 per cent protein for weanling pigs. By adding B_{12}, we can reduce this to 14 per cent, providing the ration is well balanced. The amount of protein necessary for heavier hogs can be reduced proportionally by the addition of this vitamin. Pigs weighing from 75 to 150 pounds require 12 per cent protein rations; heavier hogs, from 150 to 200 pounds, require 10 per cent if the rations are balanced and vitamin B_{12} has been added. The addition of B_{12} in the ration can reduce the amount of protein supplement to the extent of about 80 to 110 pounds of 40 per cent supplement saved per 240-pound market hog. Be certain that you feed a protein supplement containing vitamin B_{12}.

Following are examples of recommended protein supplements for pigs on pasture and on dry lot:

Dry Lot			Pasture		
Purdue Supplement 5 45% Protein			Purdue Supplement C 47% Protein		
Meat and bone scraps	200 lbs.		Meat and bone scraps	200 lbs.	
Fish meal	200		Fish meal	200	
Soybean oil meal	400		Soybean oil meal	400	
Cottonseed meal	100		Cottonseed meal	100	
Alfalfa meal	100		Linseed oil meal	100	
	1,000 lbs.			1,000 lbs.	

Iowa Supplement 3 35.7% Protein			Iowa Supplement 2 35.4% Protein		
Meat and bone scraps	300 lbs.		Meat and bone scraps	300 lbs.	
Solvent soybean oil meal	1,150		Solvent soybean oil meal	1,200	
Condensed fish solubles	100		Condensed fish solubles	100	
Dehydrated alfalfa meal	100		Dehydrated alfalfa meal	100	
Vitamin antibiotic premix	40		Vitamin antibiotic premix	30	
Ground limestone	102		Ground limestone	103	
Defluorinated phosphate	110		Defluorinated phosphate	112	
Iodized salt	40		Iodized salt	50	
Trace mineral premix	10		Trace mineral premix	5	
	2,002 lbs.			2,000 lbs.	

Antibiotics and minerals are discussed later in this chapter. It is suggested that these materials be mixed with the protein supplement and be self-fed. A hog will balance his own ration if given an opportunity. For pigs weighing from 75 to 150 pounds, 86 pounds of corn and 14 pounds of 40 per cent protein supplement will make the recommended 12 per cent protein ration. For pigs weighing more than 150 pounds, 92 pounds of corn and eight pounds of 40 per cent supplement will make a 10 per cent ration. The amounts of protein supplement and corn needed to make up rations of different levels of protein are shown in Table 16. We are indebted to Dr. Damon Catron of the Iowa State College for this information.

TABLE 16

(Shelled Corn Only Figured at 8.5% Protein)

% Protein in Supplement		% Protein in Total Ration			
		10	11	12	13
30	Grain (lb.)	1,860	1,767	1,674	1,581
	Suppl. (lb.)	140	233	326	419
	Lb. grain per 1 lb. suppl.	13.3	7.6	5.1	3.8
31	Grain (lb.)	1,867	1,778	1,689	1,600
	Suppl. (lb.)	133	222	311	400
	Lb. grain per 1 lb. suppl.	14.0	8.0	5.4	4.0
32	Grain (lb.)	1,872	1,787	1,702	1,617
	Suppl. (lb.)	128	213	298	383
	Lb. grain per 1 lb. suppl.	14.6	8.4	5.7	4.2
33	Grain (lb.)	1,877	1,796	1,714	1,633
	Suppl. (lb.)	123	204	286	367
	Lb. grain per 1 lb. suppl.	15.3	8.8	6.0	4.4
34	Grain (lb.)	1,882	1,804	1,725	1,647
	Suppl. (lb.)	118	196	275	353
	Lb. grain per 1 lb. suppl.	15.9	9.2	6.3	4.7
35	Grain (lb.)	1,887	1,811	1,736	1,660
	Suppl. (lb.)	113	189	264	340
	Lb. grain per 1 lb. suppl.	16.7	9.6	6.6	4.9
36	Grain (lb.)	1,891	1,818	1,745	1,673
	Suppl. (lb.)	109	182	255	327
	Lb. grain per 1 lb. suppl.	17.3	10.0	6.8	5.1
37	Grain (lb.)	1,895	1,825	1,754	1,684
	Suppl. (lb.)	105	175	246	316
	Lb. grain per 1 lb. suppl.	18.0	10.4	7.1	5.3
38	Grain (lb.)	1,898	1,831	1,763	1,695
	Suppl. (lb.)	102	169	237	305
	Lb. grain per 1 lb. suppl.	18.6	10.8	7.4	5.6

14	15	16	17	18	19	20
1,488	1,395	1,302	1,209	1,116	1,023	1,070
512	605	698	791	884	977	930
2.9	2.3	1.9	1.5	1.3	1.0	1.2
1,511	1,422	1,333	1,244	1,156	1,067	1,022
489	578	667	756	844	933	978
3.1	2.5	2.0	1.6	1.4	1.1	1.0
1,532	1,447	1,362	1,277	1,191	1,106	1,021
468	553	638	723	809	894	979
3.3	2.6	2.1	1.8	1.5	1.2	1.0
1,551	1,469	1,388	1,306	1,224	1,143	1,061
449	531	612	694	776	857	939
3.5	2.8	2.3	1.9	1.6	1.3	1.1
1,569	1,490	1,412	1,333	1,255	1,176	1,098
431	510	588	667	745	824	902
3.6	2.9	2.4	2.0	1.7	1.4	1.2
1,585	1,509	1,434	1,358	1,283	1,208	1,132
415	491	566	642	717	792	868
3.8	3.1	2.5	2.1	1.8	1.5	1.3
1,600	1,527	1,455	1,382	1,309	1,236	1,164
400	473	545	618	691	764	836
4.0	3.2	2.7	2.2	1.9	1.6	1.4
1,614	1,544	1,474	1,404	1,333	1,263	1,193
386	456	526	596	667	737	807
4.2	3.4	2.8	2.4	2.0	1.7	1.5
1,627	1,559	1,492	1,424	1,356	1,288	1,220
373	441	508	576	644	712	780
4.4	3.5	2.9	2.5	2.1	1.8	1.6

TABLE 16   (Continued)

(Shelled Corn Only Figured at 8.5% Protein)

% Protein in Supplement		% Protein in Total Ration			
		10	11	12	13
39	Grain (lb.)	1,902	1,836	1,770	1,705
	Suppl. (lb.)	98	164	230	295
	Lb. grain per 1 lb. suppl.	19.4	11.2	7.7	5.8
40	Grain (lb.)	1,905	1,841	1,778	1,714
	Suppl. (lb.)	95	159	222	286
	Lb. grain per 1 lb. suppl.	20.1	11.6	8.0	6.0
41	Grain (lb.)	1,908	1,846	1,675	1,723
	Suppl. (lb.)	92	154	215	277
	Lb. grain per 1 lb. suppl.	20.7	12.0	8.3	6.2
42	Grain (lb.)	1,910	1,851	1,791	1,731
	Suppl. (lb.)	90	149	209	269
	Lb. grain per 1 lb. suppl.	21.2	12.4	8.6	6.4
43	Grain (lb.)	1,913	1,855	1,797	1,739
	Suppl. (lb.)	87	145	203	261
	Lb. grain per 1 lb. suppl.	22.0	12.8	8.9	6.7
44	Grain (lb.)	1,916	1,859	1,803	1,746
	Suppl. (lb.)	84	141	197	254
	Lb. grain per 1 lb. suppl.	22.8	13.2	9.2	6.9
45	Grain (lb.)	1,918	1,863	1,808	1,753
	Suppl. (lb.)	82	137	192	247
	Lb. grain per 1 lb. suppl.	23.4	13.6	9.4	7.1

Antibiotics. The feeding of antibiotics to pigs from weaning time to market weight will normally result in an increase in gain from 10 to 20 per cent, will save 20 pounds of feed in producing each 100 pounds of gain, will reduce the problem of scours in young pigs, will result in more uniformity of pigs in the litter, and will have the added advantage of almost eliminating the runt-pig problem.

Experimental work at the Iowa and Illinois Experiment Stations indicates that aureomycin, terramycin, and penicillin antibiotics

14	15	16	17	18	19	20
1,639	1,574	1,508	1,443	1,377	1,311	1,246
361	426	492	557	623	689	754
4.5	3.7	3.1	2.6	2.2	1.9	1.7
1,651	1,587	1,524	1,460	1,397	1,333	1,270
349	413	476	540	603	667	730
4.7	3.8	3.2	2.7	2.3	2.0	1.7
1,662	1,600	1,538	1,477	1,415	1,354	1,292
338	400	462	523	585	646	708
4.9	4.0	3.3	2.8	2.4	2.1	1.8
1,672	1,612	1,552	1,493	1,433	1,373	1,313
328	388	448	507	567	627	687
5.1	4.2	3.5	2.9	2.5	2.2	1.9
1,681	1,623	1,565	1,507	1,449	1,391	1,333
319	377	435	493	551	609	667
5.3	4.3	3.6	3.1	2.6	2.3	2.0
1,690	1,634	1,578	1,521	1,465	1,408	1,352
310	366	422	479	535	592	648
5.5	4.5	3.7	3.2	2.7	2.4	2.1
1,699	1,644	1,589	1,534	1,479	1,425	1,370
301	356	411	466	521	575	630
5.6	4.6	3.9	3.3	2.8	2.5	2.2

Swine Nutrition, A. H. Dept., Iowa State College

have yielded the best results, and are almost equal in increasing the rate of gain and the efficiency of feed utilization in growing and fattening pigs. There is insufficient research evidence of the value of feeding antibiotics in combination compared to the feeding of single antibiotics. Bacitracin, however, seems to be ineffective when fed alone, yet when fed with penicillin produces a significant growth increase.

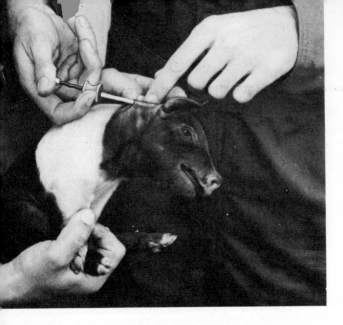

Figure 8-22. Implanting an antibiotic pellet behind the ear of a pig. (Courtesy *Wallaces' Farmer and Iowa Homestead*)

Whereas the feeding of antibiotics will increase the rate of gain in healthy pigs by 10 to 20 per cent, it will increase the gain in unhealthy pigs by as much as 100 per cent. The higher the disease level, or the more infection present, the greater the value of feeding antibiotics.

Approximately 5 milligrams of aureomycin, terramycin, or penicillin per pound of total ration should be fed pigs from weaning to market. The feeding of antibiotics during this period may be your insurance against disease.

The feeding of antibiotics to ·healthy pigs is good insurance against scours and intestinal diseases, and some increases in gains will result. Antibiotics fed to young pigs on high-disease-level farms will produce maximum results. Tests show also that antibiotics can be effective only when fed with a balanced ration.

Antibiotics may be purchased in the form of vitamin-antibiotic premixes in 10-, 25-, and 50-pound packages. It is possible to add them to the other feeds included in the mixed ration. The directions of the manufacturer, or distributor, should be followed closely, and care should be taken to mix the materials uniformly with the other feeds.

A popular and easy way to obtain feeds containing antibiotics is to buy a ready-mixed feed. Most feed companies have fortified their rations with both antibiotics and vitamins.

A ↑   B ↓

Figure 8-23. Effect of feeding vitamin B$_{12}$ and antibiotics to pigs. (A)
Pigs received no vitamin B$_{12}$ or antibiotics. (B) Pigs received vitamin
B$_{12}$ and aureomycin in addition to basic ration. (Courtesy U.S.D.A.
Bureau of Animal Industry)

Vitamins. Pigs require thiamine, riboflavin, niacin, pantothenic
acid, pyridoxine, biotin, folic acid, vitamin B$_{12}$, and choline for
normal health. These are water-soluble vitamins.

In addition to the water-soluble vitamins, pigs require vitamins
A, D, and E, which are fat-soluble. Yellow corn and green hays
and pastures supply adequate amounts of vitamin A. Sunlight provides vitamin D. Cereal grains and green hays or pastures provide
vitamin E.

Some of the water-soluble vitamins are available to the pigs
in farm grains and forages. Thiamine or vitamin B$_1$, pyrodoxine,
biotin, and folic acid are available in cereal grains or in forage
crops, and need not be provided from other sources. The other
water-soluble vitamins must be provided from sources other than
the normal farm feeds.

Feeding and Management of Market Hogs • 135

Figure 8-24. The result of a ration low in vitamin A. (Courtesy U.S.D.A. Bureau of Animal Industry)

Riboflavin should be provided at the rate of 1.5 milligrams per pound of ration for pigs weighing under 100 pounds, and 1.4 milligrams per pound for pigs weighing over 100 pounds. Niacin, or nicotinic acid, is required at the rate of 15 milligrams for young pigs under 100 pounds in weight, and ten to 15 milligrams per pound of ration for heavier pigs.

Pantothenic acid is required by growing pigs at the rate of five milligrams per pound of ration. Much of the choline may be supplied by feeding corn which contains 200 milligrams per pound, and oats, wheat, and barley, which contain about 450 milligrams per pound. Meat scraps, fish meal, and soybean meal are excellent sources of this vitamin.

Vitamin B_{12} was discovered to be an important part of APF (animal protein factor), and is a by-product in the manufacture of antibiotics. About nine micrograms (1,000 micrograms equals one milligram) of vitamin B_{12} are needed per pound of dry ration for the most rapid gains of young pigs.

The best means of providing the vitamins which cannot be supplied by farm grains, protein supplements, and forages is to give them in the form of a vitamin-antibiotic premix, which can be mixed with the protein supplement or with the complete ration, or to buy a ready-mixed supplement which contains the needed vitamins and antibiotics.

136 • *Feeding and Management of Market Hogs*

The information on the tag or carton should be checked carefully for the content of the mix and for the cost.

Minerals. Pigs on good legume pasture which receive skim milk or meat and bone meal usually need little additional mineral feeds. Pigs which are fed plant proteins on poor pasture need considerable mineral. Because cereal grains are very low in mineral content, it is a good idea to self-feed a mineral mixture or a protein supplement to which minerals have been added. Calcium, phosphorus, and salt, the most important mineral materials in feeding hogs, are easily obtained. Ground limestone is an excellent source of calcium, and steamed bone meal supplies both calcium and phosphorus. A low-fluorine calcium phosphate may also be used, but an excess of .4 per cent of fluorine is toxic to the pigs.

Swine rations should contain about one-half pound of salt per 100 pounds. In tests conducted at Purdue University a penny's worth of salt saved 287 pounds of feed. Salt may be fed free choice in a feeder, it may be mixed with the mineral, or it may be mixed with a complete ration. Usually it is mixed with the mineral which is fed free choice.

Small quantities of so-called "trace minerals" should also be supplied in the mineral mixture. Iodine, iron, copper, zinc, manganese, and cobalt are considered most important, and they are most easily provided by purchasing trace mineral premixes, or by purchasing ready-mixed mineral feeds or ready-mixed protein and mineral supplements.

Mineral mixtures which have been recommended are as follows:

No. 1	Pounds	No. 2	Pounds
Steamed bone meal	40	Ground limestone	50
Ground limestone	40	Dicalcium phosphate	30
Salt	20	Salt	20
	100		100

No. 3	Pounds	No. 4	Pounds
Steamed bone meal	38	Ground limestone	600
Ground limestone	38	Steamed bone meal	900
Salt	20	Iodized salt	400
Trace mineral premix	4	Trace mineral mix	100
	100		2000

Arsenicals. Arsenicals act like antibiotics in stimulating gains and increasing feed efficiency in pigs, especially when pigs are fed on dry lot or under high disease level conditions. In Iowa tests in 1957 arsenilic acid added to the rations of pigs on dry lot resulted in a 7 per cent increase in daily gain and a 7 per cent saving in feed. Pigs on dry lot fed 3-Nitro gained 16 per cent more quickly on 3 per cent less feed than a control group of pigs. For growing pigs on pasture, 3-Nitro increased average daily gains and reduced feed per pound of gain, both 5 per cent. Arsenilic acid, when fed to pigs on pasture, reduced feed consumption 4 per cent but failed to increase the rate of gain. Similar results have been obtained in Minnesota and Texas tests.

Arsenicals should not be fed for a period of seven to ten days before the hogs are to be marketed. This period of time permits the arsenic to disappear from the liver and muscle tissue of the animal. The directions of the manufacturer should be followed closely in feeding arsenicals.

Complete Ration for Growing and Fattening Hogs. There are two common systems of feeding pigs from weaning to market: (1) self-feeding corn or other grains and a balanced supplement, free-choice; and (2) self-feeding a complete mixed ration.

The first system is easy to follow and requires less work than other systems, but its efficiency varies with the palatability of the grain, supplement, and pasture. Undereating or overeating of supplement is common. As a result the cost and rate of gain may vary.

It is possible to formulate a complete ration which will provide for the food nutrient needs of the pigs by mixing ground corn, or other grains, and a balanced supplement in proper proportions. According to several swine specialists, this is the recommended system of feeding pigs, whether on pasture or in dry-lot. Recommended complete rations are shown in Table 17.

Water. If you want your pigs to make fast and economical gains, they must have plenty of fresh water available at all times. A pig needs from one-half gallon to 1½ gallons of water daily for each 100 pounds of live weight. Eighty pigs weighing 150 pounds on pasture in July may consume as much as 80 to 150 gallons of water in one day. Young pigs and sows nursing litters have high water requirements, and more water is needed during the hot months of the summer than during the winter.

TABLE 17

"LEAST-TIME" GROWING-FINISHING RATIONS

(Complete "tailor-made" rations for pigs from 50 pounds to market weight)

	Dry Lot			Pasture		
	50– 100	100– 150	150– 200	50– 100	100– 150	150– 200
Ingredients	lbs.	lbs.	lbs.	lbs.	lbs.	lbs.
	lbs.	lbs.	lbs.	lbs.	lbs.	lbs.
Ground yellow corn	1,620	1,727	1,825	1,618	1,775	1,875
Meat and bone scraps	50	50	50	50	50	50
Solvent soybean oil meal	250	150	50	300	150	50
Dehydrated alfalfa meal	50	50	50	–	–	–
Vitamin-antibiotic premix	5	5	5	5	5	5
Ground limestone	9	11	10	12	13	11
Defluorinated phosphate	21	12	14	20	12	14
Iodized salt	10	10	10	10	10	10
Trace mineral premix	2	2	2	2	2	2
Totals	2,017	2,017	2,016	2,017	2,017	2,017
Protein %	14.0	12.3	10.5	14.7	12.1	10.3

Iowa State College

Although water may be supplied in the form of skim milk or buttermilk, and slop feeds, it is preferable that the pigs have access to automatic waterers. Hand-feeding of water in clean troughs is satisfactory if done often enough, and if the pigs can be kept out of the troughs. Slats may be nailed across the trough to accomplish this purpose. The labor necessary to provide a sufficient amount of water by hand is usually not available.

Figure 8-25. Tank hog waterer with water piped to the pasture. (Courtesy Iowa State College)

Shade. The use of rotated pastures during the summer months makes it necessary to provide some form of shade to protect the pigs from the hot sun. Pigs in wooded areas or those which have access to the farm buildings usually need no other shade unless the pasture area is at some distance from the buildings.

The shades should be from four to five feet above the ground to permit circulation of air and should be located on high ground. A 10-by-12-foot shade will accommodate 10 to 20 pigs, depending upon their size. The sunshades may be temporary structures or they may be pieces of equipment which can be moved from field to field.

Tests conducted at Davis, California showed that 100-pound pigs did best when the temperature was around 70 degrees. Some hog producers have found it profitable to install cooling devices in central-type hog houses used during the summer months.

Hog Wallows. Sanitary wallows may be used during the summer months to aid in keeping the pigs cool and in maintaining health. Portable wallows of the type shown in Figure 8-27 may be constructed.

Feeding and Management of Pigs on Dry Lot. An increasing number of pigs are being produced on dry lot. The development of complete and fortified rations has made it possible to provide growing pigs with the nutrients, vitamins, and minerals commonly supplied by pasture. Vaccination and the feeding of arsenicals and antibiotics have aided materially in the control of disease. "Pig parlor" pig production has made rapid strides and large numbers of pigs are produced on dry lot. Some producers have invested heavily in housing and equipment. Others, especially in the South, are growing pigs in confinement with very little invested in housing and equipment.

Summer and Fall Pigs. Most summer and fall pigs are well beyond the weaning stage by the time the pastures dry up in the fall. The pigs will weigh from 75 pounds upward, and can be fed the rations recommended for dry-lot feeding in Table 17. Dry-lot rations contain more supplement than do pasture rations. The supplement recommended for dry-lot feeding contains more animal protein, more alfalfa, more vitamin supplements, and less mineral than that recommended for pasture feeding.

The use of self-feeders and automatic waterers is recommended in dry-lot feeding as in pasture feeding. The big problems in dry-

Figure 8-26. A cheap but effective type of summer shade. (Courtesy *American Hampshire Herdsman*)

Figure 8-27. A portable pig wallow. (Courtesy *Wallaces' Farmer and Iowa Homestead*)

Figure 8-28. Sanitation and adequate equipment are necessary if pigs are to be fed in confinement. (Courtesy Kent Feeds)

Feeding and Management of Market Hogs • 141

Figure 8-29. Hogging down corn. (Courtesy U.S.D.A. Bureau of Animal Industry)

lot feeding, aside from nutritional problems, have to do with providing adequate and sanitary quarters. It is much more difficult to care for a large number of pigs in a hog house, on a feeding floor, or in a small lot than it is to manage pigs on pasture. Bedding, ventilation, and sanitation problems are often troublesome.

Feeding Floors. A paved feeding floor is the answer to many of the sanitation problems in dry-lot feeding. Concrete feeding floors can be cleaned quite easily, and the pigs do not have to use their energy in wading through mud during the wet fall and spring seasons. Considerable labor and feed are saved in feeding and in managing hogs on feeding floors. More of the fertilizer value of the manure is saved, and more sanitary conditions can be maintained. A good feeding floor is almost a "must" in dry-lot feeding, especially during the wet weather.

Most hog producers like feeding floors or strips of concrete at least ten feet wide. A 150- to 200-pound hog requires 10 to 15 square feet of area. A feeding floor 10 by 60 feet will provide space for 40 to 60 hogs weighing 150 to 200 pounds, or for about 80 younger pigs.

A strip of concrete the width of the portable house and 10 to 12 feet deep is usually considered adequate for a sow and litter.

142 • *Feeding and Management of Market Hogs*

Hogging Down Corn. The practice of hogging down corn is less popular today than it was a few years ago. With the multiple-litter system of breeding, the spring pigs are farrowed in February and March and are marketed before the new crop of corn is ready for hogging down. The fall pig crop may be large enough to glean a field following the corn picker, but the pigs are usually too small to break down the stalks in the hogging-down process.

In hogging down corn, best results are obtained by using thin, active pigs weighing from 90 to 150 pounds. Heavier hogs waste more corn and do not make economical gains.

An early maturing variety of corn is best for hogging down, and the pigs should be turned in after the corn is well dented. A protein-mineral supplement and water should be available at all times.

Garbage Feeding. Most states have passed ordinances prohibiting the feeding of raw garbage to hogs. The cooking of garbage kills disease organisms, but it is costly and the cooked garbage is less palatable to the pigs.

A ton of raw garbage used to produce 50 to 80 pounds of pork. With the changes that have come about in kitchen and restaurant management, a ton of garbage today may produce only from 20 to 30 pounds of pork. Unless considerable grains are fed with the garbage, a poor carcass will be produced.

Garbage-fed hogs were responsible for the rapid spread of vesicular exanthema during the past few years, and many cases of trichinosis have been prevalent in some communities where raw garbage is fed to hogs. In feeding garbage, extreme care should be taken to maintain sanitary quarters. Concrete feeding floors are recommended, and the yards should be thoroughly cleaned and disinfected regularly. Thorough cooking of pork products is necessary to kill any disease organisms which may be prevalent in the meat.

Summary

From 25 to 30 per cent of the pigs farrowed never reach weaning age, and 80 to 90 per cent of death losses occur shortly after farrowing time.

Sows should be penned up two or three days before farrowing time. The farrowing pen or stall should be thoroughly cleaned and disinfected. Farrowing stalls are recommended over farrowing pens and guard rails. Heat lamps should be provided on each side of the sow. Farrowing quarters should be bedded lightly with dust-free dry material.

A bulky, laxative ration in moderate amounts should be fed just prior to farrowing. Fresh chill-free water should be available. It is good practice to be on hand at farrowing time. The navel cord should be clipped and treated with tincture of iodine. Pigs should be ear-marked at birth to facilitate record keeping.

Needle teeth may be clipped in case pigs are inclined to fight.

Sows should be fed lightly after farrowing but brought to full feed in about a week or ten days.

Pigs should be fed a 24 per cent protein, highly fortified pre-starter feed during the second week. During the third, fourth, and fifth weeks they should be fed an 18 per cent protein starter feed. After 35 days they should be fed a 14 per cent grower ration.

Pigs like and do better on pellet feeds than on meals. Creep feeds should contain from 5 to 15 per cent sugar and be highly fortified with vitamins, minerals, and antibiotics.

Anemia may be controlled by providing clean sod or by use of iron and copper pills or by injection fluid, which should be given each pig once each week. Boars should be castrated by the time they are two to three weeks old.

Vaccination for cholera, leptospirosis, and erysipelas should be done during the first eight weeks. Vaccination, castration, and weaning should not be done at the same time.

Weaned pigs should be wormed before moving them to clean ground. Pigs can be raised profitably in dry lot if adequate rations and sanitation are provided.

Farm grains must be supplemented in feeding growing-fattening hogs. Protein, mineral, vitamin, and antibiotic feeds are essential. Corn in the Corn Belt and grain sorghum in the Southwest are usually the best grains. A mixed protein is considered better than a single protein feed. Pigs weighing from 75 to 150 pounds require rations containing from 12 to 14 per cent protein. Heavier hogs need rations with 10 to 12 per cent protein.

Pigs weighing from 100 to 200 pounds will show an increase of about 5 per cent in gains when antibiotics are fed. Pigs doing poorly will show greater increases.

A mixture of steamed bone meal (38 pounds), limestone (38 pounds), salt (20 pounds), and trace mineral premix (4 pounds) will meet the mineral needs of growing-fattening hogs.

Pastures are used by most hog producers. They save 15 to 30 per cent of concentrates used by pigs on dry lot. Rotated pastures aid in controlling diseases and parasites.

Dry-lot feeding may·be more economical on very high-priced land and when large numbers of hogs are produced on small farms. Rations for pigs fed in dry lot must be more highly fortified than for pasture feeding.

Ladino clover and alfalfa are the two best legume pastures. Ladino is superior to alfalfa.

It pays to self-feed a complete ration to growing fattening pigs. A "least-cost" ration should be fed when a stable market is anticipated. When a lower market is anticipated, it may pay to feed a "least-time" ration in order to market the hogs before the break in price.

Shades and wallows should be used during hot weather. Pigs do better when the temperature is from 60 to 70 degrees. Fresh water should be available at all times; each pig will consume a half gallon to 1½ gallons per day per 100 pounds live weight.

• Questions

1. Outline the plan which you should use on your home farm in caring for brood sows at farrowing time.
2. Make a diagram of an economical and serviceable farrowing stall.
3. What attention should be given pigs at farrowing time?
4. Outline a system which you can use on your farm in earmarking the pigs.
5. Contrast prestarter, starter, and grower rations.
6. Which antibiotics should be fed to young pigs and in what amounts?
7. At what age should pigs be castrated? vaccinated for erysipelas? for cholera? for leptospirosis?
8. How can anemia be controlled in young pigs?
9. Outline a program of feeding and management of the sows and litters on your farm through the weaning period.
10. Which is the better system of feeding hogs on your home farm, in dry lot or on pasture? Why?

11. What should be the protein content of rations for 50- to 100-pound pigs? 100- to 150-pound pigs? 150- to 200-pound pigs?
12. Outline a good protein mixture for use in balancing the rations for the growing-fattening hogs on your farm.
13. What is the place of antibiotics in feeding growing-fattening hogs? Explain.
14. Which of the vitamins needed by growing-fattening hogs must be provided in the form of vitamin premixes?
15. Outline a simple mineral mixture which will meet the mineral requirements of growing-fattening hogs.
16. Outline a program which will provide adequate hog pasture for the swine enterprise on your home farm.
17. Outline a complete balanced ration which you could use as a "least-time" ration on your farm.

● *References*

Bundy, C. E. and R. V. Diggins, *Swine Production,* Prentice-Hall, Inc., Englewood Cliffs, New Jersey, 1956.

Hollandbeck, Richard, *Raising Hogs in Indiana,* Ext. Cir. 429, Purdue University, Lafayette, Indiana, 1957.

Meade, R. J., et al., *Nutrients, Feeds and Example Rations for Swine,* Ext. Cir. 253, University of Nebraska, Lincoln, Nebraska, 1957.

Morrison, F. B., *Feeds and Feeding,* The Morrison Publishing Company, Ithaca, New York, 1957.

Disease and Parasite Control

Swine diseases and parasites are responsible for losses amounting to millions of dollars each year. It is estimated that one-third of the pigs farrowed die before they are weaned, and another one-third are stunted or are unprofitable because of diseases or parasitic conditions. Only about one-third of the pigs farrowed are grown out as healthy pigs. On many farms the profit or loss from the enterprise is determined largely by the extent to which disease and parasite losses have been controlled.

Prevention Is Better Than a Cure

Most diseases, ailments, and parasitic conditions of hogs may be prevented, and preventative measures are much more effective than are cures. The treating of diseased pigs is expensive because of medicine and veterinarian costs and because feeds are wasted when fed to unthrifty pigs. A stunted or runty pig requires a long feeding period and a large amount of feed to get him ready for market. It is cheaper to prevent the unhealthy condition than it is to remedy it.

147

Figure 9-1. Sanitation is important in disease and parasite control. (Courtesy U.S.D.A. Bureau of Animal Industry)

Farmers who raise large numbers of hogs year after year, on the same lot, usually have disease and parasite losses. The control of diseases and parasites is largely a matter of sanitation. The use of disease- and parasite-free breeding stock, rotated legume pastures, clean and disinfected houses, and good balanced rations, fortified with vitamins and antibiotics, can do much to reduce losses. Some diseases and parasites, however, must be controlled by vaccination and medication.

Swine Diseases

There are a large number of infectious diseases of swine and their prevalence varies from community to community, and from year to year. Cholera, erysipelas, necrotic enteritis, black scours, atrophic rhinitis, brucellosis, flu, vesicular exanthema, anemia, leptospirosis, baby-pig disease, and gastroenteritis produce most of our disease problems.

Hog Cholera. Losses in the United States due to hog cholera vary from $10 million to $60 million annually, and these losses occur even though biological products have been developed and are effective in preventing the disease.

Cause. The disease is caused by a small virus which cannot be seen under a microscope. It is present in the blood and body tissues of an infected animal, and is spread through the urine and feces, as well as through nose and mouth secretions. Contaminated feed and water cause the infection, which spreads through the hog's body by way of the digestive system.

Young hogs are more susceptible to the disease than are older hogs. The virus is usually introduced by bringing new animals to the herd, or by the carrying of virus to the farm on the shoes of attendants. It can be spread also by trucks, by birds, and by streams.

Symptoms: The incubation period is usually from three to seven days. Infected animals first show fever and loss of appetite. Later the eyes become filled with a sticky discharge, and the hogs prefer dark quarters. They lose weight, and the underside of the neck and abdomen may show dark red or purple coloration. Infected animals cough and have difficulty breathing.

Usually the first cases which appear are in acute form, and the animals die in from three to seven days. Chronic cases last longer. Some hogs do not die but make only partial recoveries.

Treatment and Prevention. There is no drug treatment for the disease, but some benefit may result if large doses of anti-hog-cholera serum are given the hogs in the early stages. Vaccination is recommended. Four methods of immunization are used.

1. A *double treatment* was the standard method used in the Corn Belt for years. It involves the injection of *anti-hog cholera serum* and *live virus* into different parts of the body. This usually produces immunity for life. The use of a live virus brings the disease onto the farm. This method is being outlawed in some states.

2. A *single treatment of serum* will protect healthy pigs from cholera for a 20- to 30-day period. This treatment is generally used only when animals pass through public yards or sales where state laws require vaccination.

3. Crystal violet and BTV are single-treatment vaccines that become effective about three weeks after vaccination and provide protection for five to seven months. While immunity is temporary, the disease is not brought onto the farm.

4. The modified live virus "rabbit" vaccine has become very popular in the Corn Belt. Nearly 90 per cent of the pigs vaccinated in some areas are given this treatment. It is less severe than the double treatment and the immunity is more permanent than the crystal violet or BTV treatments.

Pigs may be vaccinated at any age, but the cost increases with the increased weight of the pig. Pigs usually should be vaccinated when they are from four to ten weeks old, depending upon treatment used.

Erysipelas. Hogs may contract this disease in the acute form and die quickly, or they may have the chronic form, which causes swelling of the joints in the legs and general stiffness. It is sometimes called the "diamond-skin" disease.

Cause. The disease is produced by a microorganism or bacteria similar to those which cause arthritis in some animals. Diseased animals, and others which carry the disease, pass off the organism in urine and feces, and other hogs pick it up by eating contaminated feed or water.

Symptoms. Hogs with the acute form have a high body temperature and may have a redness of skin as in cholera. They may die within 24 hours to three or four days. Those with the less acute form run high temperatures for a couple of days. When the temperature drops, red diamond-shaped patches, which disappear in time, show on the skin. Mortality from this form is low.

Those that have the chronic form are stiff in the joints and lame. They become sluggish and are easily fatigued. Often they rest on their haunches or on their breastbones.

Treatment and Prevention. In treating erysipelas an injection of anti-erysipelas serum in the early stages of the disease is helpful. Exceptionally good results have been obtained when penicillin was in-

Figure 9-2. An animal infected with swine erysipelas. (Courtesy U.S.D.A. Bureau of Animal Industry)

jected with the serum in both the acute and chronic forms. Since the disease is difficult to identify, it is best to rely upon the local veterinarian for diagnosis and treatment.

Sick animals should be segregated from the herd immediately, and the healthy animals moved to clean ground. As a preventative, the entire herd may be vaccinated with the serum and penicillin.

One means of preventing the disease is to double-treat the pigs at five to seven days of age with live-culture erysipelas vaccine and anti-swine-erysipelas serum. When bringing new animals to the herd, insist that they come from disease-free herds or from herds which, as pigs, were double-treated for erysipelas. However, pigs thus vaccinated, can give the disease to unvaccinated animals.

Erysipelas Bacterin. Killed vaccine bacterins have been developed which may be used in controlling erysipelas without danger of spreading the disease or contracting of the disease by humans.

Necrotic Enteritis or Necro. This disease is often associated with other diseases and with wormy pigs. It is the cause of large losses of pigs each year, as well as the cause of a large number of runt pigs. It produces an inflammation of the intestines, and is very infectious, easily spread, and chronic.

Cause. The disease is caused by a microorganism which is highly virulent in the presence of hog cholera.

Symptoms. Necro usually begins with a rise in temperature, a decrease in appetite, and diarrhea. The temperature drops after a few days, and the pigs begin to eat again. They remain unthrifty, however, and fail to gain normally. They are usually weak, remain thin, and have rough hair coats.

Treatment and Prevention. The feeding of antibiotics and arsenicals to pigs weighing under 75 to 100 pounds appears to aid materially in controlling necro. The feeding of pig starters and milk, recommended in an earlier chapter, will also aid in controlling the disease. Forty to 80 milligrams of aureomycin, terramycin, or penicillin per pound of total ration are recommended in feeding young pigs which are infected with necro.

Sanitation is important in controlling necrotic infections. Rotated pastures, sanitary quarters, and the isolation of any sick pigs will help prevent losses.

Black Scours. This disease is sometimes called "bloody scours" or "swine dysentery," and may be confused with necrotic enteritis and with trichinosis. It is almost always associated with unsanitary conditions.

Cause. The cause is unknown, but black scours is recognized as a specific disease. Healthy pigs fed feeds contaminated with materials from the intestines of diseased animals become infected.

Symptoms. This disease is very acute and infectious, and the main symptom is a bloody diarrhea or black feces. The animals may or may not go off feed. They have some fever, but it is not high. Some pigs die within a few days; others linger for several weeks or longer. It is more serious in young pigs than in older pigs. The disease affects the caecum and the colon, which becomes inflamed and bloody.

Figure 9-3. (A) & (B) Pigs with twisted and distorted snouts due to atrophic rhinitis. (Courtesy M & M Livestock Products Co.) (C) A pig infected with bull nose. (Courtesy University of Illinois)

A

Treatment and Prevention. The feeding of 3-Nitro, or other arsenicals, has proven helpful in controlling scours. Recent Kentucky tests indicate that nf-180 furazolidone is also effective in stopping scouring in swine. A veterinarian should be called and directions followed closely when commercial treatments are used.

The isolation of sick animals and the moving of healthy pigs to clean ground is recommended, as in the control of necro.

Atrophic Rhinitis. This disease, though prevalent for somewhat longer, has caused most losses since 1950. It is now widespread among herds of both purebred and commercial hogs. It is quite often confused with *bull nose.* Rhinitis is very infectious, whereas bull nose is not contagious.

Cause. The disease is caused by infectious organisms which get into wounds or scratches in the mouth or nose of the pig. It spreads from one pig to another through contaminated feed or water or by body contact.

Symptoms. The infection seems to start when the pigs are a few days or a few weeks old. They first show signs of sneezing, which becomes more pronounced as they grow older. At from four to ten weeks of age the snout begins to wrinkle and may bulge or thicken. Sometimes the snout becomes twisted or dis-torted.

The hair coat is usually rough, and infected pigs are poor doers. Quite often there is a discharge from the nose which may be clear and thick or pus-like and bloody. Some pigs develop a short, deformed snout similar to that of the early Berkshires.

Treatment and Prevention. There is no known cure for the disease, but several practices are recommended as control measures.

1. Gilts and boars from litters in which there are pigs with rhinitis should not be saved for breeding purposes.

2. The dams of infected pigs should be sold as soon as possible.

3. Bred gilts or sows showing outward signs of rhinitis should be sold in advance of farrowing.

4. Early-weaned pigs fed highly fortified prestarter and pig-starter rations will be less likely to pick up atrophic rhinitis infection.

5. Tests indicate that rations high in vitamins and antibiotics will aid materially in rhinitis control.

6. Boars, gilts, and bred sows purchased and brought on to the farm should come from rhinitis-free herds and be kept in isolation for at least 30 days.

Brucellosis. This disease has been known as *contagious abortion of swine* and as *Bang's disease*. Surveys indicate that 1 to 3 per cent of the hogs in the United States are infected, and each year many persons become infected with brucellosis. In man the disease is known also as *undulant fever* and as *Malta fever*.

Losses caused by brucellosis in swine herds are due to the abortion of pigs, pigs born weak, sterility or infertility in sows and gilts, and sterility in the boar when the reproductive tract becomes infected.

Cause. The disease is caused by an infectious organism, *Brucella suis*, and is spread from animal to animal through contact, and by contaminated feed, water, and after-birth.

Symptoms. There are no symptoms which can be easily recognized with certainty. Many animals carry the disease but appear to be normal in every respect. Symptoms which may appear are premature abortion of litters, sterility, and inflammation of the uterus or womb, testicles, and joints. Small litters may also be a symptom, but they often result from other causes.

The only sure way to determine whether or not your herd is infected is to have the entire herd blood-tested. A herd of swine may be considered free from infection when, on two tests made from 30 to 60 days apart, no animal reacts, no previous evidence of infection (such as abortion and weak pigs) exists, and no new stock has been added to the herd during the past three months.

Treatment and Prevention. There is no treatment. The herd should be tested and all reactors marketed. Re-tests should be made every 30 to 90 days until the herd is free from the disease.

Breeding and feeding stock should be selected from brucellosis-free herds and isolated for at least four weeks after purchase.

Vesicular Exanthema. In June, 1952, a load of raw garbage containing uncooked pork chops was carried out of California on the diner of a train and set off at Cheyenne, Wyoming. A hog raiser at Cheyenne fed the raw garbage to pigs which were later shipped to a hog-cholera serum firm in Nebraska. Those Wyoming pigs apparently became infected with V. E. (vesicular exanthema) from the garbage and carried it to Nebraska. From the serum firm it was carried to the Omaha stockyards. By the close of 1952 it had shown up in thirty-six states.

Cause. Vesicular exanthema, like foot-and-mouth disease, is caused by a sub-microscopic germ of the virus group. It is extremely contagious and spreads rapidly from animal to animal. It also may be spread by contaminated carrier or objects.

Symptoms. The chief symptom of V. E. disease is the formation of blisters on the lips, tongue, and snout, and above and between the claws of the feet. There is usually a rise in body temperature and a loss of appetite. The blisters often break and ulcers form. Pigs may show lameness and they may lose their hoofs. The mortality rate is high in young pigs, but the disease is seldom fatal in older hogs.

Treatment and Prevention. There is no known vaccination for V. E. disease, and in most states infected animals are quarantined and later slaughtered. No treatment is available. Since the disease may be spread through raw garbage, most states have passed laws to prohibit the feeding of raw garbage.

Flu. In a survey made in one state 16 per cent of the farmers interviewed said that their hogs had had flu during the past year. Very few animals die with the flu, but it can take the profit out of the hog business.

Cause. Flu in hogs, much like flu in humans, is caused by a virus. It is passed readily from one animal to another. It is most likely to show up when the resistance of hogs has been lowered by fatigue, exposure to temperature changes, changes in feeds, or movement to new quarters. Hogs confined in a poorly ventilated building may become overheated and may chill when exposed to the air. Drafty and extremely cold sleeping quarters can cause just as much trouble as buildings which are too hot.

Symptoms. Infected pigs usually go off feed and become listless and inactive. They appear to be distressed, and breathing is difficult. There may be a discharge from the eyes and a cough. At later stages, the cough is deep and loud. Infected hogs have fever for a few days. The sickness usually lasts less than a week if permitted to run its course, but treatment may shorten this time.

Treatment and Prevention. Veterinarians can inject drugs which may aid in the control of flu, but there is no effective vaccine or serum for the disease. Hogs should be provided with warm, clean, well-ventilated quarters and plenty of fresh water. Healthy pigs fed good rations are less likely to get the flu.

Anemia. This disease was discussed in the previous chapter.

Transmissible Gastroenteritis. Outbreaks of this disease have caused mortality as high as 100 per cent among pigs in some localities.

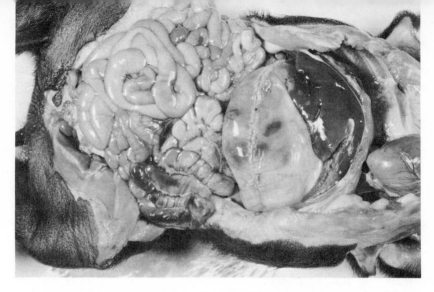

Figure 9-4. The stomach and intestinal tract of a pig infected with transmissible gastroenteritis. (Courtesy University of Illinois)

Infected older animals suffer a short-lived diarrhea, which is followed by loss in weight, but they recover in a few days.

Cause. Research indicates that the disease is caused by a virus or some other filterable organism which can spread from pig to pig by direct and indirect contact. The incubation period is very short, 18 to 24 hours.

Symptoms. The infected pigs vomit and have diarrhea. The feces appear to be partially curdled milk. The pigs become thin and die within three or four days. Postmortem examinations of the pigs show inflammation of the stomach and intestines.

Treatment and Prevention. While no treatments have been proven, some experimentation indicates that early weaning of the pigs and the use of pre-starters, very highly fortified with antibiotics and arsenicals, may be the best treatment for T.G.E. (transmissible gastroenteritis).

The best means of prevention is to scatter the farrowing places over a wide area. Sows should be moved to clean ground away from other hogs. Any bred sows brought onto the farm should be isolated, and sanitation, as recommended for the control of other diseases, should be practiced.

Sows which contract T.G.E. during gestation and have recovered two to three weeks before farrowing will farrow litters which usually are immune or resistant to the disease. These sows should be kept for future breeding purposes.

Multiple farrowing will aid in the control of T.G.E. In most cases the virus causing the disease will disappear during the interval between farrowings if this involves two months or more.

The disease spreads rapidly. Visitors should not be permitted on or near the hog lots.

Leptospirosis. This disease is a very important one to all livestock farmers because it affects cattle, swine, sheep, horses, and man. In Illinois tests it was found that nearly 29 per cent of swine herds had infected animals.

Cause. The disease is caused by species of bacteria known as *Leptospira*. The organism may be found in the kidney or urinary tract.

Symptoms. Diagnosis of the disease is difficult because the symptoms resemble those of cholera and erysipelas. The disease causes fever, loss of appetite, loss in weight, jaundice, anemia, abortion, and reduced milk flow. Abortions, as well as high percentages of dead pigs are common. Pigs that are farrowed and live may show signs of anemia and scouring. Many may die during the first two weeks.

Treatment and Prevention. A veterinarian should be called in as soon as symptoms are apparent. Blood and tissue tests should be made. If abortion has taken place, tests for Bang's disease should also be made.

The test for leptospirosis is not accurate. Some animals are infected but do not react to the test. They serve as carriers. Terramycin when fed at a rate of 500 grams per ton of feed for a 14-day period is effective in eliminating the carrier state of leptospirosis in swine and controls the acute infection.

Vaccination is the best method of fighting leptospirosis. Breeding animals should be vaccinated with L. pomona bacterin two or three weeks prior to breeding and pigs to be kept for breeding purposes should be vaccinated at weaning time.

Parakeratosis. This disease is seldom fatal but has caused hog farmers much concern during the past few years.

Cause. Improper balance of calcium and zinc in the ration.

Symptoms. First symptoms are a skin reddening and pimple-like formations. The shoulders, backs of front legs, underside of belly, and hocks are first affected. In later stages the skin becomes thick and crusted. A dark serum is secreted. The entire body may be affected.

Treatment. The feeding of zinc in the rations constantly will prevent and control the disease. The zinc may be purchased commercially in trace mineral feeds or may be obtained separately. Zinc sulphate heptahydrate should be fed at the rate of .9 of a pound per ton of feed. Zinc carbonate may be fed at the rate of .4 of a pound, or zinc oxide at the rate of .3 of a pound per ton of ration. The zinc compound should be carefully mixed with the feed. Mange oils and treatments tend to aggravate rather than cure the disease.

Swine Parasites

A parasite is something which lives on, and gets its food from, some other plant or animal. Hogs have a number of parasites. Some live on or under the skin and are called *external parasites.* Others live within the organs of the body and are called *internal parasites.* The latter group of organisms are most injurious to swine.

Roundworms. Large intestinal roundworms, or ascarids, cause hog raisers heavy losses every year. These losses are due to stunting, development of a pot-belly, general weakness, and sometimes death of the pigs.

Figure 9-5. Life cycle of the large swine roundworm. (Courtesy U.S.D.A. Bureau of Animal Industry)

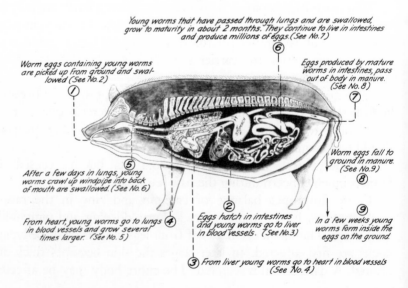

Young worms that have passed through lungs and are swallowed, grow to maturity in about 2 months. They continue to live in intestines and produce millions of eggs. (See No. 7)
⑥

Worm eggs containing young worms are picked up from ground and swallowed (See No. 2)
①

Eggs produced by mature worms in intestines, pass out of body in manure. (See No. 8)
⑦

After a few days in lungs, young worms crawl up windpipe into back of mouth are swallowed. (See No. 6)
⑤

Worm eggs fall to ground in manure. (See No. 9)
⑧

From heart, young worms go to lungs ④ in blood vessels and grow several times larger. (See No. 5)

Eggs hatch in intestines and young worms go to liver in blood vessels. (See No. 3)
②

In a few weeks young worms form inside the eggs on the ground.
⑨

③ From liver young worms go to heart in blood vessels (See No. 4)

In tests conducted by the U. S. Department of Agriculture, it was found that worm-free pigs fed a well-fortified ration gained an average of 161 pounds in 169 days. Littermate worm-infested pigs fed the same ration gained an average of only 119 pounds.

Life History. The roundworm is a large, thick, yellow or pink worm, about the size of a lead pencil. The adult normally lives in the small intestine. The female produces thousands of eggs daily, which are eliminated from the body in droppings. Pigs become infested with roundworms by swallowing the eggs with feed or water. The eggs are abundant in old hog lots and pastures. The young worms hatch out in the pig's intestines. They penetrate the wall of the intestine and travel in the bloodstream to the liver, and on to the lungs. From the lungs, they move up to the mouth where they are swallowed. They return to the intestine where they mature in about two to two and one-half months.

Damage. The roundworms in the intestine consume nutrients which the hog needs and cause digestive disturbances. Worms are more injurious to pigs on poor rations than to pigs on good rations. During the time that the young worms are in the lungs, the pig has difficulty breathing, and if exposed to dust or changes in weather, is subject to pneumonia. The liver is also damaged by the worms, and it can function only in a limited capacity. The worms weaken the pigs, making them susceptible to the many swine diseases.

Treatment and Prevention. Hygromycin and *piperazine compounds* are the best wormers now in use. Hygromycin is an antibiotic

Figure 9-6. Round worms in the intestine of a pig. (Courtesy Eli Lilly and Company, Inc.)

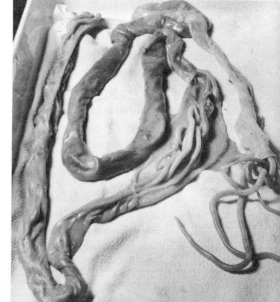

and should be fed continuously in the ration from the time the pigs start eating until they are marketed. It controls all three major hog worms—roundworms, whipworms, and nodular worms.

Piperazine compounds should be fed at the rate of one-fifth of an ounce of anhydrous piperazine per 100 pounds of animal weight. The pigs should be wormed at weaning time and at 50-day intervals until marketed. Both hygromycin and piperazine compounds may be used in worming pregnant sows.

The preventive measures for controlling worms have been described in previous chapters.

Lungworms. These worms are long, slender, and whitish in color, from half an inch to two inches long, and threadlike in diameter. They are found in the windpipe, more often in the two branches of the lower windpipe, and in the lungs.

Life History. The female lungworm produces large numbers of eggs, which are coughed up, swallowed, and eliminated with the droppings. The lungworm eggs are swallowed by angleworms. They hatch and develop in the angleworms, and the pigs become infested when they eat the angleworms while rooting. In the intestines of the pig, the lungworm penetrates the intestinal wall and follows the bloodstream to the heart and back to the lungs.

Damage. Lungworms weaken the pigs and cause them to cough, to breathe with difficulty and to grow more slowly. Severe infestations may cause death. Infected animals are susceptible to other diseases and to other parasites.

Treatment and Prevention. There is no known treatment for lungworms once they are in the lungs. Sick animals should be isolated from the herd and fed highly fortified, balanced rations.

Lungworms can be controlled quite well by the use of rotated pastures and by the use of sanitary practices during farrowing time and until the pigs weigh 75 pounds.

Mange. Mange is a highly contagious skin disease, and although very few animals die as a result of mange, it is the most serious of the external parasites.

Cause. Mange is caused by a very small mite which spends its entire life on the hogs. It feeds on the tissues of the skin and blood and burrows into the skin, causing a dry, rough, scaly hide.

Damage. Hog mange causes intense itching, which motivates the hog to bite and rub itself. The infection usually starts around the eyes and ears and along the underline where the skin is tender. It may spread until the entire body is covered with a red rash or heavy, scaly hide.

Treatment and Prevention. The mite can live in infested quarters for several weeks. Control measures must include a thorough cleaning of the shelters and houses. All manure should be removed. All surfaces should be disinfected with chemicals or with boiling water.

The chemicals lindane and benzene hexachloride are excellent for use in controlling mange. Lindane should be mixed at the rate of two pounds of 25 per cent wettable powder to 25 gallons of water. Benzene hexachloride should be mixed at the rate of four pounds of 12 per cent gamma isomer to 25 gallons of water. About half a pound of detergent such as Dreft or Vel should be added to the solution. The pigs should be sprayed with this solution at the rate of about two to four quarts per animal. Sows and pigs should be sprayed when it is warm. Brood sows should be sprayed several weeks before farrowing so that the young pigs will not become infested.

When nursing sows are sprayed, they should be thoroughly dry before the pigs are allowed to nurse.

Lice. Hog lice, by their blood-sucking habits, cause some loss to swine producers, and they may be responsible for the spread of infection.

Figure 9-7. Pig being sprayed with lindane for mange. (Gordon photo. Courtesy *Wallaces' Farmer and Iowa Homestead*)

The louse is about one-quarter inch long and grayish brown in color. During the winter months it may be found in the ears, in folds of skin around the neck, and around the tail.

The female lays several eggs a day during the winter. These eggs are attached to the hair, and hatch in two to three weeks. They mature in another two weeks.

Treatment and Prevention. The lindane and benzene hexachloride treatments for mange will also kill the hog lice. If there is no need for mange control, the hogs should be dusted with a DDT powder or sprayed with a 0.5 per cent DDT solution. One pound of 50 per cent DDT wettable powder mixed with 12½ gallons of water, and one-quarter pound of wetting agent will produce a satisfactory solution. The hogs should be treated as often as necessary.

Summary

Swine diseases and parasites can take much of the profits out of the hog business. Cholera, erysipelas, brucellosis, necro, scours, rhinitis, gastroenteritis, leptospirosis, flu, anemia, and roundworms cause the heaviest losses. Gastroenteritis and leptospirosis are the newest diseases and are proving real problems to swine producers.

Hog cholera, erysipelas, and leptospirosis can be controlled best by vaccination. The rabbit-adapted hog cholera vaccines appear to be the best treatments for cholera. Vaccination of the gilts and sows for erysipelas before breeding and the erysipelas bacterin vaccination of pigs after weaning is recommended.

The feeding of arsenicals, antibiotics, highly fortified pig starters, and milk products is the best means of controlling necro. Sanitation and rotated pastures are essential in controlling the diseases of the digestive tract.

Rhinitis and brucellosis may be prevented by the isolation of diseased animals and by careful selection of breeding and feeding stock. All swine-breeding stock should be tested for brucellosis, and only animals which have been negative on two tests, given at least 30 days apart, should be kept.

Scours in pigs can be controlled by feeding 3-Nitro or other arsenicals.

Flu in hogs can best be controlled by the feeding of well-balanced rations and by proper housing. There is no treatment for gastroenteritis, but it can be controlled, in part, by the isolation of new animals brought onto the farm, and by dividing the herd and pasturing them in areas apart from other hogs.

When abortion or dead pigs occur, the breeding animals should be tested for leptospirosis as well as for brucellosis. Infected animals should be sold. It is possible to vaccinate for leptospirosis.

Hygromycin or piperazine compounds should be used in treating pigs for roundworms. Rotated pastures and sanitary practices are effective in preventing both roundworm and lungworm losses.

Mange and hog lice can be controlled by dipping or spraying with lindane or benzene hexachloride.

• Questions

1. Which hog cholera treatment is best suited to the farm situation? Why?
2. What would you do if erysipelas was discovered in your home herd?
3. How does atrophic rhinitis differ from bull nose?
4. How does black scours differ from necrotic enteritis?
5. What has been done to control vesicular exanthema in the United States?
6. How can transmissible gastroenteritis losses be controlled on the farm?
7. What is the extent of losses in your community due to leptospirosis and how may they be reduced?
8. Outline a plan for controlling roundworms on your farm.
9. What methods are best in controlling mange?
10. Outline a disease and parasite control program for your farm.

• References

Dykstra, R. R., Animal Sanitation and Disease Control, The Interstate Printers and Publishers, Danville, Illinois, 1949.

Schwartz, Benjamin, Internal Parasites of Swine, Farmers' Bulletin No. 1787, U. S. Department of Agriculture, Washington, D. C., 1952.

Seiden, Rudolph, Livestock Health Encyclopedia, Springer Publishing Company, Inc., New York, 1951.

Stamm, G. W., Veterinary Guide for Farmers, Windsor Press, New York, 1950.

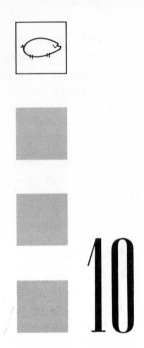

Marketing Hogs

The efficient hog raiser tries to plan his breeding and feeding operations so that he will have hogs of the weight and conformation desired by the packer and consumer ready for market when the price is most favorable. With feed and pasture available, and no serious disease problems, it is possible to have hogs ready for market in 4½ to 6 months. By planning breeding operations and allowing a 4½ to 6-month growing-out period, it is possible to plan the time the hogs will be ready for market.

We are not always able to predict so accurately the season when the price will be best. Hogs of certain weights sell better during some months than during others. The number of hogs going to market varies seasonably, and when hogs are plentiful, the price goes down. When few hogs are being marketed, the price is higher. Farmers who follow the markets from year to year are usually able to anticipate the best time to market their hogs.

Most farmers find it necessary to make changes in their breeding and feeding methods in order to have their pigs at marketable

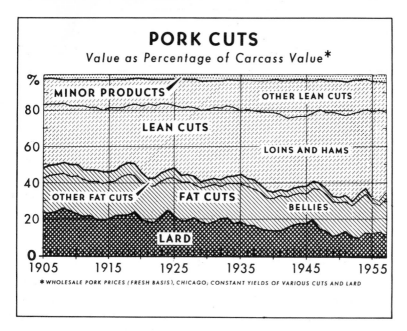

PORK CUTS
Value as Percentage of Carcass Value*

%
80
60
40
20
0

MINOR PRODUCTS
OTHER LEAN CUTS
LEAN CUTS
LOINS AND HAMS
OTHER FAT CUTS   FAT CUTS
BELLIES
LARD

1905   1915   1925   1935   1945   1955

*WHOLESALE PORK PRICES (FRESH BASIS), CHICAGO; CONSTANT YIELDS OF VARIOUS CUTS AND LARD

Figure 10-1. The hams, loins, and other lean cuts account for about 60 per cent of the carcass value of a hog. (Courtesy U.S.D.A. Agricultural Marketing Service)

weights at the time when the price is best. At times it is necessary to decide whether the increased selling price of the hogs will offset the costs of the changes in production. Each farmer must analyze his swine enterprise and decide upon the production and marketing program best suited to his farm.

Swine producers, through breeding and feeding practices, can control the type, quality, and finish of the hogs which they produce. A check of the prices paid by packers for various grades and weights of hogs will indicate the kind of hog which will bring the most money. The efficient hog raiser produces the kind of hog desired by the packer and by the consumer. He plans ahead. He has the desired type of hog at the preferred weight when the packer and consumer need it.

Changes in the Hog Market

It was pointed out in a previous chapter that the consumer today is buying less lard and fat pork than he purchased a few years ago. The housewives who buy meat are guiding farmers in the production of quality pork. They are demanding leaner cuts. They bypass pork chops with an inch of fat for lean chops, or they buy poultry or beef instead. As a result the demand for pork has been reduced.

With 96.8 million head of beef cattle on our farms on January 1, 1959, we can expect beef to be plentiful the next few years. This supply spells cheaper beef and more competition for pork.

The fast-growing broiler industry provides another area of competition. In 1940 about 816 million pounds of live birds were produced. More than one and a half billion pounds were produced in 1950 and nearly five billion pounds of broilers were produced in 1957. A total of 80.6 million turkeys were raised in 1957.

Pork products are on a competitive market. The future of the enterprise is in part dependent upon the quality and quantity of pork products produced and the methods used in merchandising.

The Lard Problem. At one time, lard sold wholesale for more than live hog prices. This was before vegetable fats and oils entered the picture. The situation has changed. Wholesale lard during the past years has been selling for considerably less than the price of live hogs. The prices of lean cuts of pork have advanced, and the prices of fats have declined.

In 1957, the retail selling price of pork chops was nearly four times the retail selling price of lard. Table 18 shows the retail

TABLE 18

AVERAGE RETAIL PRICES OF PORK CUTS AND LARD
1940-1955

Year	Pork chops	Ham (whole)	Bacon (sliced)	Lard
	Cents per lb.	Cents per lb.	Cents per lb.	Cents per lb.
1940	27.9	24.3	27.3	9.4
1942	41.4	37.4	39.5	17.2
1944	37.3	35.4	41.1	18.7
1946	48.5	47.8	53.3	26.3
1948	77.2	68.0	76.9	29.6
1950	75.4	62.0	63.7	19.1
1952	80.3	65.2	64.9	18.4
1954	86.3	70.0	81.7	26.2
1955	79.3	60.5	65.8	20.8

U.S.D.A. *Livestock Market News Statistics and Related Data, 1956.*

prices of various pork products from 1940 to 1955. In 1949 the average cost of hogs in Chicago was $18.40 per 100 pounds. Lard at that time sold for $12.03 per 100 pounds.

Hog raisers and packers have a joint responsibility in making available to the consumers a better-quality pork product. Hogs with more lean meat must be produced, and they must be marketed at a reasonable weight. We need lean meat, but we must reduce lard production. There are two ways of doing this: (1) producing a better-muscled, meat-type hog, and (2) marketing our hogs at lighter weights.

The Meat-type Hog

The meat-type hog is being developed to meet the changes in demand for pork products. It is not necessarily a new breed. We have meat-type hogs in all of our standard breeds.

Many farmers believe that it costs more to produce a heavily muscled meat-type hog than it does to produce a hog carrying more lard. This is not true. In tests conducted at Iowa State College, hogs with less than 36.9 per cent lean cuts and 26.4 per cent fat cuts weighed 229 pounds at five months of age and used 340 pounds of feed to produce 100 pounds of gain. Pigs which had more than 41 per cent of lean cuts and 22.9 per cent of fat cuts weighed 227 pounds at five months, and used only 333 pounds of feed to produce 100 pounds of gain.

Time to Sell

Two pig crops are normally produced each year. One is far-rowed in the spring and is ready for market in the fall. The other is farrowed in the late summer, and is sold in the spring. The bulk of the year's hog production is marketed during these two periods. A large share of the full-farrowed pigs are marketed in March, April, and May; the bulk of the spring pigs are marketed in October, November, and December. The supply of hogs during the two marketing periods is such that packers can buy hogs at lower prices than they can during other seasons.

Season Price Variations. The variation in the monthly prices of hogs of different weights at Chicago during the five-year period 1953 to 1957 is shown in Figure 10-2. The highest prices paid for top U. S. No. 1 and for light weight butchers occurred during

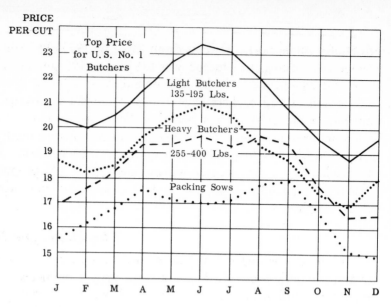

Figure 10-2. Monthly prices of hogs of different weights on the Chicago market during 1953 to 1957 period. (U.S.D.A. Agricultural Marketing Service)

the months of May, June, and July. Lowest prices were paid for these grades of hogs during October, November, and December. The spread between the top price paid for U. S. No. 1 hogs in June and November was $4.44 per hundredweight.

Since more pigs are produced in the spring than in the fall, there is less variation in the prices received for fall pigs. During the 1953 to 1957 period, the best time to market fall pigs was during the months of January, March, and April. Pigs farrowed in late July, August, and September can easily be fed out in time to get them on the high market. The spread in prices paid for hogs between January and April was about $1.20 per hundred.

Weight to Sell

The consumer wants smaller and leaner cuts of pork and less lard, and the consumer must be satisfied if pork is to meet the competition of other meats. Consequently, farmers must grow meatier hogs and market them at lighter weights; hog raisers will have to produce more litters per year to feed out home-grown grains and to realize the same gross income as in the past.

Heavy Hogs Are Discounted. Roughly speaking, there is nearly twice as much lard in the carcass of a 300-pound hog as there is in the carcass of a 200-pound pig. A 200-pound live hog will produce about 30 pounds of lard and backfat. A 300-pound hog will yield about 55 pounds.

Following are the average prices paid in the nation in 1957 for butcher hogs of various weights, according to U. S. D. A. data:

160-180 pounds	$17.32
180-200 pounds	18.60
200-220 pounds	18.93
220-240 pounds	18.87
240-270 pounds	18.55
270-300 pounds	18.17

Light Hogs Make Cheaper Gains. Swine producers are interested in economical use of feed, and it is known that young animals make cheaper gains. Tests conducted at the University of Minnesota indicated that lighter hogs used less feed and made cheaper gains than did heavier hogs. Their data were as follows:

Weight of Pigs (in Pounds)	Feed for 100 Pounds Gain
Birth-100	304 lbs.
100-200	359 lbs.
200-300	415 lbs.
300-400	470 lbs.
400-500	510 lbs.

These data applied to 1958 prices show the cost of feed in producing the 200-pound hog to be $9.26 per hundredweight. The cost in producing the 300-pound hog would be $10.12 per hundredweight.

Market Classes and Grades of Hogs

Market hogs are classified in terms of sex, use, weight, and value. Classes are provided for barrows and gilts, sows, stags, and boars. Animals are classified according to use, as slaughter hogs, slaughter pigs, stockers, and feeders. The weights vary with the classes according to sex and use.

Two systems of grading are in use. The standard system classifies animals as choice, good, medium, and cull. On September 12, 1952, the United States Department of Agriculture

TABLE 19

Use	Sex	Weights (pounds)	Grades
HOGS:			
Slaughter hogs	Barrows and gilts	Under 180 180-240 240-300	U. S. No. 1 U. S. No. 2 U. S. No. 3 Medium Cull
	Sows	300 and over 270-300 300-330 330-360 Fat Type 360-400 Meat Type 400-450 450-500 500-600 600 and over	Choice Good Medium Cull
	Stags Boars Unclassified	All weights All weights All weights	Ungraded Ungraded Ungraded
Feeder and stocker hogs	Barrows and gilts	120-140 140-160 160-180	Choice Good Medium Common
PIGS:			
Slaughter pigs	All classes	Under 30 30-60 60-80 80-100	Ungraded Ungraded Good Medium Cull
	Barrows and gilts	100-200	Choice Good Medium Cull
Feeder pigs	Barrows and gilts	Under 80 80-100 100-120	Choice Good Medium Cull

announced new grade standards for barrows and gilts. The five grades recommended were Choice No. 1, Choice No. 2, Choice No. 3, Medium, and Cull. The names of the five grades were later changed to No. 1, No. 2, No. 3, Medium, and Cull.

A systematic grading procedure makes it possible for hogs to be marketed according to the value of their carcasses or according to the value of the animals as stockers or feeders. Market grades of hogs serve the same purposes as grades of corn or grades of butter. Prices are quoted for the various grades, and it is possible for both the buyer and the seller to make comparisons before making market transactions.

Shown in Table 19 are the market classes and grades of hogs and pigs. Variations in weight and grade classifications among markets are common.

U. S. D. A. Hog Grades. The five grades established by the U. S. Department of Agriculture apply to hogs on foot and on the hook. The degree of finish, the quantity and the quality of the lean meat, and the percentage of fat determine the grade. The three top grades are numbered from one to three according to the percentage of lean meat in the carcass. The other two grades, "medium" and "cull," are so called because of underfinish and poor quality of lean-meat cuts. The use of these grades is voluntary.

The thickness of backfat in relation to the length, weight, and dressing percentage of the carcass serves as the basis for determining the grade. A summary of the U. S. hog carcass grades is shown in Table 20.

TABLE 20

U.S. HOG CARCASS GRADES

Dressed Weight or Carcass Length	Average Backfat Thickness (Inches) by Grade				
	No. 1	No. 2	No. 3	Medium	Cull
Under 120 pounds or under 27 inches	1.2 to 1.5	1.5 to 1.8	1.8 or more	0.9 to 1.2	Under 0.9
120 to 160 pounds or 27 to 29.9 inches	1.3 to 1.6	1.6 to 1.9	1.9 or more	1.0 to 1.3	Under 1.0
165 to 209 pounds or 30 to 32.9 inches	1.4 to 1.7	1.7 to 2.0	2.0 or more	1.1 to 1.4	Under 1.1
210 pounds or more or 33 or more inches	1.5 to 1.8	1.8 to 2.1	2.1 or more	1.2 to 1.5	Under 1.2

The five grades and the qualifications for both the live animals and carcasses follow:

U. S. No. 1. These hogs have the minimum of finish necessary for high-quality pork cuts. The carcasses have a high ratio of lean to fat, and the hams, loins, picnics, and Boston butts make up about 50 per cent of the carcass weight. The carcass of a 200-pound No. 1 hog is nearly 30 inches long and has from 1.3 to 1.6 inches of backfat. The loin eye should total 3.75 or more square inches in cross-section area.

U. S. No. 2. These hogs produce high-quality pork, but are slightly overfat. The carcasses are the same length as No. 1, but usually the backfat is from 1.6 to 1.9 inches thick. The carcasses yield from about 45 to 47 per cent of their weight in the four lean cuts.

U. S. No. 3. This grade designates hogs which possess high-quality pork but which are decidedly overfat. Their carcasses yield less than 45 per cent of their weight in the four lean cuts. For example, the backfat on a 200- to 240-pound shoat will be 1.9 inches or more.

Medium. These hogs are slightly underfinished. The cuts are flabby and soft. The proportion of lean to fat may be high, but the carcasses are poorly marbled. The backfat on a 200-pound hog will usually be less than 1.3 inches.

Cull. Hogs of this grade are decidedly underfinished. The cuts are inferior even though the ratio of lean to fat is high. The backfat may be only about an inch thick.

Selling Hogs According to Carcass Weight and Grade

The government grades represent an attempt to satisfy hog producers who have felt that packers were not paying for quality hogs. Market quotations have usually been based upon the weight of the hogs rather than upon quality. It is difficult to grade hogs on foot, and most packers have preferred to buy them by the pound in droves or loads. There has been little incentive for hog breeders to improve the carcass quality of their hogs, for they all sold at the same price.

Figure 10-3 (A) U. S. No.1 market hogs. (B) U. S. No. 2 market hogs.

A

B

(C) U. S. No. 3 market hogs. (D) Medium grade market hogs.

C

D

E

(E) Cull grades market hogs. (Courtesy University of Wisconsin, Wisconsin State Board for Vocational Education, and Oscar Mayer & Co.)

173

Figure 10-4. Hams (A), loins (B), and sides of bacon (C) from No. 1, No. 2, and No. 3 market hog carcasses. (Courtesy Rath Packing Company)

Advantages of Selling Hogs by Carcass Grade. Selling hogs on the basis of carcass grade and weight will encourage farmers to produce quality hogs and will eliminate the wasteful practice of "filling" hogs to get the maximum market weight. Selling by carcass grade should provide the producer with an unbiased evaluation of the quality of his hogs, and it will also permit the tracing of diseased, injured, and inferior pork carcasses to the producers who are responsible.

Hogs have been sold by carcass grade in Denmark, Sweden, Great Britain, and Canada, and the method has proved efficient and practical. Some packing plants in the Corn Belt have purchased hogs on this basis for several years. In general, breeders with high-quality hogs profit by selling their hogs on a carcass-grade basis, whereas hog producers with below-average hogs profit by selling them in the traditional manner.

Disadvantages of Selling Hogs by Carcass Grade. One of the chief reasons for delay in selling hogs by carcass grade is that the packer buyers have had neither the facilities nor the personnel to do the job. Buying by carcass grade is less flexible than the present system. There is less opportunity for both the buyer and seller to bargain. Quite often the grading is done in the absence of the seller, who may later question the results. Many farmers are not sufficiently informed in regard to carcass quality to accept the packer's judgment. Another objection to the system is that the seller must wait until the hogs have been slaughtered and processed before he can receive his check.

Future of Merit Buying of Hogs. Most interior packers in this nation are now buying hogs on a live-grade or grade-and-yield basis. While the carcass value increases about $1.00 per hundredweight, the average packer is paying a premium of 40 to 50 cents for each increase in grade. The spread between the price paid for U. S. No. 1 and U. S. No. 3 hogs is too narrow to encourage producers to improve their breeding and feeding methods. Merit and grade-and-yield buying will increase rapidly as packers become equipped and have personnel qualified to do the job.

Figure 10-5. A packer buyer inspecting a pen of hogs at the Chicago Stockyards. (Abernathy photo. Courtesy Swift and Company)

Choosing a Market

Let us assume that, during early March, you have 34 fall-farrowed pigs ready for market as U. S. No. 1 slaughter hogs. Where should you sell them? Several times each year almost every hog raiser is confronted with this or a similar problem regarding the best hog market. The answer depends upon where you are located.

Markets Available. In every community we have local hog buyers, dealers, and livestock auctions. In many communities we can consign our hogs and sell through a cooperative shipping association. Some meat packers have concentration yards or buying plants in our communities. We can truck our hogs to interior packing companies located 20 to 50 miles away, or we can put our hogs with the neighbors' and truck or ship them by rail to public stockyards at a central market, such as Chicago or Kansas City. We can ship direct to the packer, or we can sell them through a commission firm. Which is best?

Factors in Choosing a Market. A number of factors are involved in the selection of a market. Distance, transportation problems, shrinkage, methods of grading, handling and selling charges, dependability, and price quotations are perhaps the most important.

To market effectively you need to know the price at each available market of the grade you have to sell. You may have a half-dozen or more markets to choose from. The U. S. Department of Agriculture Market News Service, the various cooperating radio stations, and the newspapers supply market information. At times a telephone call may result in several dollars more in profits.

In addition to the price at the various markets for the kind of hogs that you have to sell, you need to know the cost of transporting them and the shrinkage you may expect. If you consign to a terminal market, there will be a commission or handling charge. This may amount to from 20 to 30 cents per hundredweight. The transportation cost will vary with the number of hogs to be transported and with the distance to be covered. The shrinkage and loss due to injury or death will vary with the method of transporting and the distance. These losses may be as little as 10 cents or as large as 60 cents per hundredweight.

A large percentage of the hogs produced in this country are sold directly to the packing plant and not through a public market.

Care in Marketing Hogs

A study recently completed by Livestock Conservation, Inc., indicated that 8.06 per cent of the hogs which arrived at packing plants in 1954 were bruised. The average loss in dollars per animal bruised was $1.05. The swine industry's 1954 loss due to bruises was estimated at $5,192,215.

Location of Bruises. Nearly one-half of the bruises were on the hams, the source of one of the highest-priced cuts. More than one-fourth of the bruises were on the back and loin, the source of rib and loin chops. Figure 10-6 shows a bruised ham with the bruised section removed. Hams and loins that have been trimmed because of the removal of bruised sections cannot be sold at the prices received for unbruised cuts.

A   B

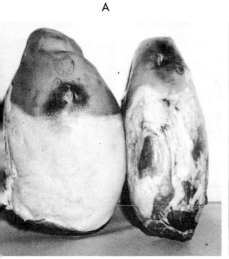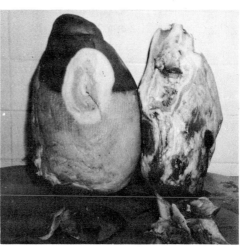

Figure 10-6. (A) & (B) Hams showing bruises and the removal of the bruised sections. (Courtesy Rath Packing Company)

Cripples and Dead Animals. Surveys indicate that about 13 hogs in each 1,000 are dead on arrival at the market. It is estimated that besides this loss, nearly 13 hogs in each 1,000 marketed arrive as cripples.

Prevention of Losses. Care in preparing animals for shipment, in loading, and in handling hogs in shipment will greatly reduce losses due to bruises, cripples, and dead animals. Following are suggestions for the proper handling of hogs at market time:

1. Do not feed hogs heavily before shipping.
2. Allow 3½ square feet of floor space in the truck for each 225-pound hog.
3. Clean truck or car before loading.
4. Use sand for bedding in hot weather and straw, or sand and straw, during cold weather.
5. Separate heavy from light hogs in truck or car.
6. Wet hogs and bedding during hot weather.
7. Remove all boltheads and nailheads and other obstructions from the loading chute and truck.
8. Have adequate loading equipment.
9. Handle hogs quietly and with care.
10. Use canvas slappers in loading.
11. Do not put too few or too many hogs in a truck.
12. Separate hogs from other types of livestock when being transported in the same truck.
13. Move hogs at night in hot weather.
14. Close side openings and put cover over truck during cold weather.
15. Drive carefully and avoid sudden stops.

Summary

Your breeding and feeding operations should be planned carefully in order to have U. S. No. 1 hogs ready when the market is best. A leaner, better-muscled market hog should be produced and sold when it weighs from 200 to 225 pounds. Because our market for lard has declined, we should produce less of it. A 300-pound hog produces nearly twice as much lard as does a 200-pound hog.

A meat-type hog can be produced more cheaply than can a lard-type hog. Light hogs produce 100 pounds of gain on less feed than do heavy hogs. Heavy hogs sell for from $1 to $3 less on the market than do 200-pound hogs.

To get the best price, spring pigs should be sold in July, August, and September and fall pigs in January, March, and April. The difference between high and low markets may be as much as $3 to $4 per hundredweight.

The U. S. D. A. grades are N
and Cull. Hogs should be sold as th
U. S. D. A. grades are based largely
fat percentage, length of carcass, fi
by grade will encourage farmers t
w'ich they produce.

Packers who buy hogs accordi
pay higher prices for choice hogs a
than do buyers who do not grade

A market should be chosen ca
transportation, shrinkage, and othe
the determining factor.

More than 8 per cent of the h
in 1954 were bruised. About 13 ho
the plant crippled and 13 arrived

Care in trucking and shipping w
bruises. The truck should be caref
not be underloaded or overloaded.
have three and one-half square feet of
be separated from light hogs, and I
other types of livestock in the truck

• *Questions*

1. Why does the packer pay
   225-pound hog than for a
2. What percentage of the car
   four primal cuts—hams, loin
3. What is the difference betw
   the old grading system?
4. What goes to make up a U.
5. Which will make the most
   pig, a 200-pound hog, or c
6. Does it cost more to produc
   hog?
7. In which months should spr
   most money? When should
8. How much variation occurs
   the year?
9. How will you select the ma
   your hogs? What factors wi

ou need to take in transporting market

ll hogs by carcass grade or by weight?

the income from your home hog enter-
marketing practices?

al, *Yearbook of Figures of the Livestock*
llinois.

ure, *Livestock Market News Statistics and*
shington, D. C., June, 1957.

ure, *Official United States Standards For*
ine, Agricultural Marketing Service, Regu-
o. 172, Washington, D. C., 1954.

ure, *Official United States Standards For*
es, Agricultural Marketing Service, Regu-
o. 171, Washington, D. C., 1954.

BEEF PRODUCTION

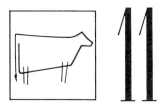

The Beef Production Industry

"We're having steak for dinner." These words seldom have to be repeated to bring an American family to the dinner table. Beef is one of the more important meats in the American diet. It is high in nutritional value, and many people consider it first in flavor. We consumed an average of 84.3 pounds of beef per person during 1957.

With our ever-expanding population, there will be an even greater demand for beef in the future. Beef producers must meet this challenge. They must produce at a profit more beef per acre of farm land, and they must furnish beef to the consumer at a price he can afford to pay.

Opportunities in Beef Production

Opportunities in beef production are numerous. Almost any young man with a love for livestock, an eagerness to learn, and a willingness to work can find a life of satisfaction in some phase of the beef production industry.

181

Figure 11-1. This is a typical scene from the range country where most feeder cattle are produced. (Courtesy American Hereford Assn.)

Classes of Beef Cattle Producers

The three main divisions of the beef cattle production industry that one may enter are: (1) the production of feeders, (2) the production of fat or slaughter cattle, and (3) the purebred beef cattle industry. It is also possible under certain conditions to develop a program combining two or more of the above phases of the beef industry.

Production of Feeders. The production of feeders is carried on primarily by producers located on lands that are generally not suitable for heavy crop production other than grass.

These farmers and ranchers maintain herds of cows to produce calves. The calves are usually dropped in the spring and run with the cows on the pasture or the range during the grass season. In the fall the calves are weaned from their mothers and sometimes sold as feeder calves or they may be carried through the winter on hay, pastured the next summer, and sold as yearlings to be fattened for slaughter.

It is not necessary to have grain for feed in feeder cattle production. The cow herd may be successfully maintained on pasture in summer and on hay or pasture during the winter; therefore, such a program is well adapted to land areas not suitable for rotation crops.

Cattle can grow and produce on rations containing mostly roughages. This makes it possible to develop a profitable business on what may otherwise have been waste land.

Many young farmers with capital too limited to purchase high-priced crop land may find opportunities in the purchase of low-priced grass land which can be used in the production of feeder cattle. Successful feeder cattle production depends largely upon having a good supply of cheap forage crops available.

Production of Fat or Slaughter Cattle. Farmers who make a business of buying feeder cattle and fattening them for market are called "cattle feeders." Since grain is usually essential in finishing high-quality beef, most cattle feeders are located in a feed grain area.

Profits from fattening cattle come from two sources: (1) the selling price over purchase price, which is known as *margin,* and (2) the value of the increased weight over the cost of the feed. If a feeder buys cattle weighing 700 pounds at $18 per hundred weight and sells them after fattening for $20 per hundred weight, he has made a margin of $2 on each 100 pounds of original weight, or a total margin of $14 per head. If the cost of the feed and other expenses of the feeding operation amounts to $17 per 100 pounds of gain, then the feeder has made a profit of $3 per 100 pounds of

Figure 11-2. Most of the cattle produced on the western range go into feed yards in the midwestern Corn Belt area where they are finished for slaughter. (Courtesy American Hereford Assn.)

gain. If he increases the weight of these cattle to 1100 pounds, which represents a gain of 400 pounds per animal, his profit on gain is $12. His marginal profit is $14, giving a total profit of $26 per head.

The principal reasons cattle feeders have for buying and fattening cattle are: (1) to receive a higher price for their grain when sold as beef, and (2) to increase soil fertility by spreading the manure on the land. If the manure is properly handled, a large part of the plant food removed by the crops may be returned to the soil. Farms that have had a cattle-feeding program over a period of years are generally high in fertility.

The Purebred Beef Cattle Industry. The breeder of purebreds produces high-quality bulls and cows to improve the breed and to provide bulls for use by the producers of feeder cattle. He maintains a pedigreed herd of breeding stock. He sells to feeder cattle producers and to other breeders. Quality purebred animals usually bring premium prices. Commercial cattlemen turn to the breeder for bulls, and occasionally for females, for use in improv-

Figure 11-3. Purebred herds are found throughout the U. S. This fine Angus herd was produced on a Massachusetts farm. (Courtesy American Aberdeen-Angus Breeders' Assn.)

ing their herds. The breeder of purebreds can rightfully claim most of the credit for the improvement of the beef cattle breeds.

More skill, knowledge, and patience are probably required for success in the purebred business than for any other phase of beef production. The breeder of purebreds must know the type of cattle that are in demand. He must keep in mind the kind that will make the most money for the producer and the feeder, and the type that will cut a carcass to suit the consumer.

More capital is needed per animal for purebred production than for any other phase of the beef cattle business. Foundation stock is usually high in price, and equipment needs per animal are greater than for feeder or slaughter cattle production. Improvement is slow, and it may be many years before a herd of quality animals is developed. Before the breeder can reap substantial returns for his effort he must have both quality and quantity of animals to sell. Although it is not essential, experience in growing and fattening commercial cattle may be helpful before attempting to develop a purebred herd.

Large amounts of grain are not essential in purebred production. Bulls and females that are being fitted for shows probably need grain in order to produce the finish necessary to bring out the type and quality of the animal. Animals carrying a good finish are usually more attractive to prospective buyers; therefore some fattening grains may be desirable.

Combining Two or More Enterprises. Under certain circumstances, two or more beef enterprises may be combined profitably. An example might be the program on a half-section farm with 160 acres of land capable of producing good grass, but too hilly for rotation cropping; the other quarter-section may be level land, in rotation crops. A herd of stock cows may be kept to consume the pasture and part of the hay, but there will not be enough corn to feed out the calf crop. Some of the calves may be sold as feeders and the remainder placed in the feed lot and fattened.

Summary

There are three major divisions of the beef cattle industry:
1. The production of feeders.
2. The production of fat or slaughter cattle.
3. The purebred beef cattle industry.

Lands which are not suitable to rotation crops but which will produce grass are best adapted to feeder cattle production. Feeders are generally sold to Corn Belt or grain-producing farmers, who fatten them for slaughter. The farmer who fattens cattle depends upon the difference in the price of beef over feed and operating costs, or the difference in the buying and selling price (margin) for his profit.

The breeder is responsible for furnishing improved stock for commercial cattlemen and for other breeders. Breeders of purebreds generally need a higher capital outlay per animal than do ranchers or cattle feeders. Breeders require considerable knowledge of type and mating if they are successful. Income from purebred herds may be high because quality animals usually bring premium prices. Farms producing a combination of grain and grass in quantity may be suited to two or more beef enterprises.

• Questions

1. Which beef cattle enterprise is best adapted to your farm? Why?
2. What type of land or farm is best suited for developing each of the three types of beef cattle enterprises? Why?
3. Give an example of how two beef enterprises could be combined successfully on one farm.
4. Why is more knowledge and skill required for success in breeding beef cattle than in the other beef production programs?
5. Which program requires the most capital per animal? Why?
6. What determines the profit in each type of the beef production enterprises?

•· References

Diggins, Ronald V., and C. E. Bundy, *Beef Production,* Prentice-Hall, Inc., Englewood Cliffs, New Jersey, 1956.

Ensminger, M. E., *Beef Cattle Husbandry,* The Interstate Printers and Publishers, Danville, Illinois, 1951.

Snapp, Roscoe R., *Beef Cattle,* Fourth Edition, John Wiley and Sons, Inc., New York, 1952.

Williams, D. W., *Beef Cattle Production in the South,* The Interstate Printers and Publishers, Danville, Illinois, 1950.

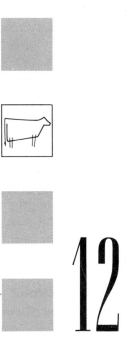

Selection of Breeding
and Feeding Stock

Upon entering the beef cattle business one must decide which breed of cattle to produce. The term breeder generally applies to one who produces improved purebred animals for breeding purposes. Most of the early developmental work on beef cattle breeds was started in the 18th century by British breeders. During this period, British cattle breeds were imported into the United States and until about 1900 were the only important breeds used in the improvement of cattle in this country. Since 1900, importation of cattle from India and France has been made for the purpose of developing breeds that could be adapted to certain sections of the United States.

Selecting the Breed

Careful consideration should be given the following before a start is made on a cattle breeding program of either purebred or grade animals: (1) personal likes, (2) availability of breeding stock, (3) outlet for surplus animals, and (4) environmental conditions under which the animals will be raised.

Personal Likes. Most cattle breeders develop a liking for certain breeds of livestock. Unless other conditions make it inadvisable to select a breed of personal choice, one should give that factor due consideration before making a start in breeding cattle.

Availability of Breeding Stock. The cattle breeder must be continually on the lookout for animals he can bring into his herd for the purpose of improving his own cattle. Other breeders of the same breed are his main source of supply. If they are few and far between in his particular area, the cattle breeder will have to travel over long distances in order to obtain replacement animals at greater cost.

Outlet for Surplus Animals. The breeder of purebreds depends upon the other purebred and commercial or non-purebred breeders for the sale of bulls and surplus females. It is important that one consider the demand before selecting a breed.

Grade herd producers generally find cattle feeders their best market outlet. Although cattle feeders are less concerned about breed than are cattle breeders, certain areas tend to show partiality for certain breeds. If the producer of commercial cattle has a good market in a certain locality, he will be wise to give consideration to the breed that is most popular among feeders in that particular area.

Environmental Conditions. Weather, grazing, disease, and insect conditions are important factors in selecting a breed of cattle. The Brahman cattle, for example, are able to make good use of poor forage, are not particularly bothered by flies, ticks, or mosquitoes, and are resistant to Texas fever, which make them and their crosses especially valuable in certain Southern areas. The Hereford is noted for hardiness and foraging ability where certain diseases and insects are not prevalent. The Shorthorn and Angus have special merits under certain circumstances. Cattle best adapted to the conditions under which they will be raised should be considered by the prospective producer.

Breeds of Beef Cattle Developed in Europe

Aberdeen-Angus. The Aberdeen-Angus is one of the most popular breeds of beef cattle in the United States. They originated in northern Scotland under cool damp climatic conditions. The first importations of these Scottish cattle, to play an important part in the United States, was made in 1873 by George Grant, a native of Scotland then living in Victoria, Kansas. Many more importations were made during the latter part of the 19th century and have continued up to the present time. However, as the breed became well established in America, importations gradually declined. Today most of the great sires of the breed in the United States were produced in this country.

The Aberdeen-Angus cattle are black; white is not permitted except on the underline behind the navel and there only to a moderate extent. The breed is polled (no horns), which has contributed to Angus popularity among many breeders. The polled characteristic in Angus cattle is so well established that when Angus are crossbred with horned breeds most of the first cross offspring are polled. Angus cattle have shown more resistance to certain eye diseases, particularly cancer eye and pinkeye, than have some of the other breeds. Calves from Angus cows are usually smaller at birth than are calves from other breeds, but the weaning weights

Figure 12-1. This Angus bull is of the correct type. He would improve any herd. (Courtesy American Aberdeen-Angus Breeders' Assn.)

are equal to or greater than that of other breeds. The smaller calves at birth cut down calving difficulties, and there are fewer cow and calf losses at this time.

The body form of Angus cattle is smooth, broad, low-set, blocky, compact, and well-muscled.

Red Angus. Occasionally a red animal crops out from a herd of black Angus even though both parents are black. This is because many black Angus carry a red gene. (See Chapter 36.) Red Angus have existed for years but it is only recently that a group of breeders have been organized for the purpose of breeding Red Angus in the United States. The Red Angus breeders have adapted high standards for registration. Each animal must be inspected by a committee and approved before registration.

The general characteristics are similar to those of the black Aberdeen-Angus (since they have the same ancestry), except for color. The Red Angus have a deep red color that is very attractive.

Galloway. Galloway cattle are native to Scotland. This breed is considered one of the oldest of the British breeds. They were probably introduced into the United States about 1860. For a period following their introduction they became popular through the North Central states. However, probably because of the slower development of the Galloway, the breed has steadily declined in the United States.

Galloways are good rustlers and extremely hardy, able to stand cold weather conditions. They are the smallest of the beef breeds, black in color with long, curly hair. The breed is polled, has short legs, and is blocky and compact in type.

Hereford. Hereford cattle are native to England. They originated in the county of Hereford, which lies in the fertile valley between the Severn River and the eastern boundary of Wales.

The first breeding herd of Herefords to play an important part in establishing the breed in the United States was that of William H. Sotham and Erastus Corning of Albany, New York, in 1840. The Hereford breed grew rapidly in the United States. Today there are more Herefords than any other breed in this country. The breed is popular from coast to coast and constitutes, by far, the largest percentage of the cattle found on the Western range.

Hereford cattle are easily distinguished by their red-colored bodies and white faces. The accepted color is a rich red with white

Figure 12-2. A beautiful Red Angus bull. (Courtesy *Capper's Farmer*)

Figure 12-3. A typical Galloway bull. (Abernathy photo)

Figure 12-4. An excellent type Hereford bull. (Courtesy American Hereford Assn.)

face. The white is found on the flank, underline, breast, crest, tail switch, and below the hock and knees on both fore and hind legs. They are often referred to as "white-faced cattle."

In form Hereford cattle are low-set, muscular, compact, broad, and smooth. They are well developed in the regions of valuable cuts —the back, loin, and hind quarters or round.

The Hereford breed is well known for its vigor and foraging ability.

Polled Herefords. In 1900, Warren Gammon of Iowa wrote to nearly every breeder of Herefords in the United States asking if they had any cattle which did not develop horns. He succeeded in securing 13 head of purebred Herefords that were polled. From this small beginning the polled Hereford breed was established.

The breed has become very popular among breeders who desire the Hereford form but dislike the horns. Polled Herefords that originated from registered Hereford stock may be registered in both breed associations.

In form and characteristics, the polled Herefords closely resemble their ancestors, the Herefords. The main distinguishing difference is the absence of horns.

Shorthorns. The Shorthorns originated in northeastern England in an area which includes the counties of Durham, Northumberland, and York.

The breed, introduced in 1783 by Miller and Gough of Virginia, was the first to be established in America. These cattle gained rapidly in popularity, and are found throughout the United States today. They represent one of the three most popular breeds.

In form, the Shorthorn is large, rectangular, and compact. They range in color from red to white and all combinations of these colors, such as spotted or roan. Shorthorns are well liked by many commercial cattlemen for crossing on other breeds for the production of feeder cattle.

Polled Shorthorn. The Polled Shorthorns were developed by a cross and from naturally polled Shorthorns found in the breed. Most present-day Polled Shorthorns are descendants of purebred Shorthorn cattle, and are eligible for registration in the American Shorthorn Breeders' Association herd books.

In form and color the Polled Shorthorns are similar to the Shorthorn except for the polled characteristic.

Figure 12-5. A polled Hereford bull of excellent type. (Courtesy *Polled Hereford World*)

Figure 12-6. A fine example of a Shorthorn bull. (Courtesy American Shorthorn Breeders' Assn.)

Figure 12-7. The absence of horn combined with shorthorn conformation has made the polled Shorthorn popular among many cattlemen. (Abernathy photo. Courtesy American Shorthorn Breeders Assn.)

Selection of Breeding and Feeding Stock • 193

Figure 12-8. The Charolais combine scale with excellent beef qualities. (Courtesy American Charolais Breeders' Assn.)

Charolais. The Charolais originated in France and is one of the most important breeds of French cattle. Only a small number of Charolais cattle have been imported to the United States. Most of the breed brought into this country have gone to Texas, Louisiana, and Florida, where they have been used for crossing purposes, especially with Brahmans.

Charolais are light creamy-colored and are one of the largest of all beef breeds. They are quite compact in body form, but lack the smoothness of the British breeds.

Scotch Highland. The Scotch Highland breed of beef cattle was developed in the Hebrides, a group of islands near the west coast of Scotland.

Figure 12-9. A Silver Highland herd owned by Ray Carr, Valentine, Nebraska. (Courtesy *Capper's Farmer*)

The breed has not been popular in the United States. However, a few have been imported from time to time.

Scotch Highland cattle are small but exceedingly hardy. They have a long, coarse outer hair coat and a soft, thick undercoat which gives them natural body protection against severe weather conditions. Acceptable colors are black, brindle, red, light red, yellow, dun, and silver.

They have recently found favor among some ranchers in the northern plains for crossing on other breeds to produce animals more capable of withstanding the long, hard winters.

Breeds of Beef Cattle
Developed in India

Brahman. Several breeds of cattle exist in India. Most of them have been named after the Indian province in which they have been developed. In Europe and South America, they are known as Zebu, and in the United States are called Brahman. They are the oldest existing breed of domestic cattle.

The first cattle of this breed to play a part in the development of Brahman cattle in this country were two bulls given to Richard Barrow of Louisiana in 1854.

In recent years, considerable interest has been shown in the development of Brahman cattle in the South. A number of Brah-

Figure 12-10. A Brahman bull, a breed that has done much for the improvement of cattle in the South. (Courtesy Brahman Breeders' Assn.)

man crossbred feeder cattle have reached Midwest feed lots and have given good results as fattening cattle.

Brahman cattle are characterized by a large hump over the shoulders and loose skin in the area of the dewlap. They have drooping ears, and instead of the "moo" of other cattle they produce a sound resembling a grunt. The most prevalent color is some shade of grey, although red is very acceptable.

In form the Brahman cattle are more upstanding and less compact, and lack the smoothness of the other breeds.

Brahman cattle are resistant to Texas fever, can stand heat well, and are bothered little by flies, ticks, and mosquitoes. They are able to produce beef when grazing on poor-quality forage on which many other breeds would fail. These characteristics have made Brahman and crossbred strains, developed by using Brahman on other breeds, very popular in areas of the Southern part of the United States. These crossbred calves have produced gains and carcass quality equal to those of any of the other breeds. Like the Angus, they show resistance to cancer eye and pinkeye.

Breeds of Beef Cattle Developed in the United States

Several breeds of beef cattle have been developed in the United States. All of these breeds were developed by using Brahman crosses on European breeds. The objectives were to combine the Brahman ability to graze poor quality forage and their resistance to insects and heat with the smoother, more compact qualities of the European breeds.

The need for beef cattle that could withstand the hot, humid climate, the pests, and diseases prevalent in many sections of the South was the primary factor in creating an interest among Southern farmers, ranchers, and experiment stations toward the development of new breeds. These breeds have played an important part in changing much of Southern agriculture from a one-crop system to a cropping and livestock program. The results have been: improved soil fertility, conversion of the forage of untillable land into beef, and increased income to the farmers and ranchers of the South.

Santa Gertrudis. This breed was developed on the Santa Gertrudis division of the King Ranch in Southwest Texas.

Figure 12-11. Santa Gertrudis bull. (Courtesy American Santa Gertrudis Breeders' International)

It resulted from crossing Brahman beef-type bulls on beef-type Shorthorns.

The Santa Gertrudis is approximately three-eighths Brahman and five-eighths Shorthorn. They are large beef animals with mature cows attaining weights of 1600 pounds and mature bulls 2000 pounds on pasture. They are solid cherry-red in color and horned. The ears are somewhat pendulant. They are smoother and more compact than the Brahman, but retain the loose hide and underline skin folds characteristic of their Brahman ancestry.

The breed is especially adapted to subtropical climates and semi-arid grazing conditions. They are noted for their ability to make large gains on grass and to rustle for a living on areas of sparse forage, and for their tolerance to heat and insects.

Other breeds developed from Brahman and European crosses are the Brangus (Brahman x Angus), Beefmaster (Brahman x Hereford x Shorthorn), Charbray (Brahman x Charolais), and Braford (Hereford x Brahman).

Crossbred Cattle. For commercial cattle, crossbreeding has brought out some definite advantages over purebreeding or straight-breeding.

Experimental work of the United States Department of Agriculture has shown that a rotation system of crossing three breeds results in somewhat heavier calves at weaning time and faster feed-lot gains.

Selection of Foundation Breeding Stock

After having decided upon the breed, the problem of selecting individual animals for foundation stock must be considered. Good and inferior animals exist in all breeds. Regardless of the breed, certain general characteristics that contribute to beef production should be understood and used as a basis of selection. The breeder of purebreds will be concerned with individual breed characteristics which animals must have if they are to be eligible for registration. This information can be secured from the breed associations.

The producer of grade animals is usually less concerned about breed disqualifications, but should carefully consider those factors that contribute to economical beef production.

The building of a good herd of breeding cattle is a long-time proposition. It should be remembered that the cost of feeding and managing an inferior herd is equal to that of a good herd. While the initial cost of superior foundation animals may be high, the long-time cost, in relation to income from the herd, will be less than that from inferior foundation stock. It is better to buy a few good animals than a large number of poor ones, if the goal is the establishment of a high-quality herd.

In selecting foundation stock, the breeder should consider two sets of factors: (1) those he can see in sizing up the individual animal and (2) those in which he must rely upon production records for his information.

Determining Desirable Body Conformation. One can judge desirable conformation by closely inspecting the animal in question. If possible a similar inspection should be made of the sire, dam, sisters, brothers, and other closely related animals. By inspecting close relatives of the animal being considered for foundation stock, one can determine, to some extent, whether the line breeds true to type. It is not uncommon to find an attractive animal from a strain in which few good ones exist. Such an animal may be disappointing in the quality of his or her offspring. Since animals may inherit poor qualities from ancestors several generations back, it is important to observe as many representatives of the line as possible to determine to what extent undesirable qualities are cropping out.

Figure 12-12. (A) A near ideal type from a side view. (B) Note the excellent development of the hind quarters, the great width over the back and loin, and the uniformity of the animal from end to end. (Courtesy American Shorthorn Breeders' Assn.)

Points to Consider. Fast-growing animals are important to economical production. A foundation animal should be at least average in size for its age and breed.

In type, it should be reasonably low-set, blocky, and compact. Does the shoulder blend smoothly into the body? Is the heart girth full? Is the neck short and thick? Does the tail-head blend smoothly into the rump? Is the rump long and level? Does the animal have good depth with a well-sprung rib? Is the top and underline straight? Does the animal move freely and with style? Are the legs straight and out on the corners? Is the bone clean cut, dense, and moderate in size?

Selection of Breeding and Feeding Stock • 199

The hind quarters should be wide, plump, and well developed in proportion to the rest of the animal. The thighs should be thick, carrying flesh down to the hocks. The twist (distance between hind legs to the top of rump) should be deep, not cut up between the hind legs. In looking over the top of the animal, observe if it is broad over the back, loin, and rump. On cows or heifers of calving age the udder should not be fleshy. It should extend well forward and well up behind, with teats squarely placed, well apart, and of good size.

The desired head is broad, short, slightly dished, and clean cut. The eyes are full and expressive with good width between them. Distance from the eyes to nostrils should be of moderate length. The muzzle should be wide and flaring and the nostrils open. The shoulders should be smooth, compact, and broad on top. The brisket must not be too prominent, and must be wide, moderately deep, and free from flabby flesh and wrinkled skin. The forelegs should be wide apart, allowing for good width on the chest floor. Bulls should possess pronounced masculinity with a well-developed crest. Females should show refinement and should give indication of being good producers.

As a final step in breeding stock selection step close to the animal, keeping the hand flat, and feel down over the back, loin, and ribs. This procedure will tell the amount and uniformity of fleshing

Figure 12-13. This Angus is highly desirable from a front view. (Courtesy American Aberdeen-Angus Breeders' Assn.)

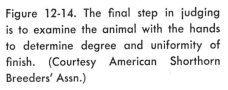

Figure 12-14. The final step in judging is to examine the animal with the hands to determine degree and uniformity of finish. (Courtesy American Shorthorn Breeders' Assn.)

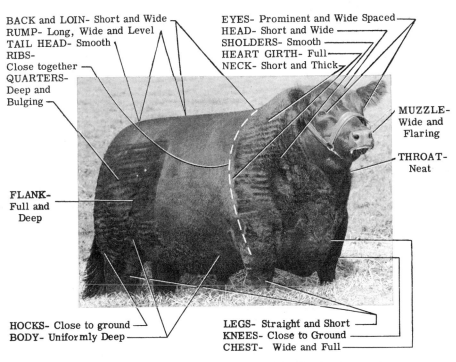

BACK and LOIN- Short and Wide
RUMP- Long, Wide and Level
TAIL HEAD- Smooth
RIBS-
Close together
QUARTERS-
Deep and
Bulging

EYES- Prominent and Wide Spaced
HEAD- Short and Wide
SHOLDERS- Smooth
HEART GIRTH- Full
NECK- Short and Thick

MUZZLE-
Wide and
Flaring

THROAT-
Neat

FLANK-
Full and
Deep

HOCKS- Close to ground
BODY- Uniformly Deep

LEGS- Straight and Short
KNEES- Close to Ground
CHEST- Wide and Full

Figure 12-15. It is necessary to know the parts of an animal before one can become a successful judge. Study the above figure carefully. (Courtesy American Aberdeen-Angus Breeders' Assn.)

over the region of valuable cuts. Breeding cattle do not necessarily need to be in exceptional condition, unless they are to compete for premiums in a show ring. However, the covering should be uniform and free from patches and lumps. Animals that carry

Selection of Breeding and Feeding Stock • 201

good flesh, as compared to others being given the same feed and management, usually indicate easy keepers and are desirable breeding stock prospects. The hide should be pliable and of medium thickness and the hair should be fine and soft.

Passing Final Judgment on Breeding Stock. Remember there is no perfect animal. However, after carefully considering all points listed here, if the animal has scored well compared to the average of the breed, then we may be sure the general type is satisfactory.

It is important to try to correct weaknesses that exist in the herd. For example, if one is buying a bull to breed cows that are rough in the tail head, then he should select a bull that will help to correct this fault. Many times to correct a herd fault one may have to compromise on other characteristics in buying additions to the breeding herd. It is also important to evaluate good and bad points.

Most cattlemen will agree that type, development in the regions of the most valuable cuts, size for age, health, and vigor should receive the most emphasis when buying breeding stock for commercial herds. Breeders of purebreds will have to give special consideration to characteristics that may disqualify an animal for registration. The other factors mentioned should be considered but are secondary to those that have most to do with economical beef production.

Selection Based Upon Production Records. Research work shows there is little association between body conformation of an animal, and ability to grow and fatten. While conformation is important, it should not be the sole means by which a cattleman selects his breeding stock. Conformation characteristics and gaining ability are inherited. However, an animal that has inherited outstanding body conformation may not necessarily have inherited good gaining ability. The growing ability must be largely determined by progeny and production records. The outward body conformation of the live animal does not always indicate the amount of muscling or the proportion of lean meat to fat.

Progeny and production records will reveal the following information: (1) inherited growth ability, (2) milking qualities of the cows, (3) fertility record of the herd, (4) percentage of lean to fat, and (5) quality of carcass.

The term *progeny testing* means the testing of the offspring from certain breeding animals. Since the bull contributes half the characteristics inherited by the calf crop, most progeny testing has been done on herd sires. The purpose is to determine the ability of a bull to produce fast-growing calves with desirable body conformation.

The birth weight of calves has been found to be a fairly accurate method of determining their growth rate and also the ability of a sire to transmit this desirable quality to his offspring. By selecting at random at least five calves all sired by the same bull from different cows, and recording their rate and efficiency of gain, a fairly accurate record of the growth transmitting ability of a sire can be determined. A combination of both birth weight and growth records of the progeny of a bull will give sufficient evidence to prove or disprove his value as a sire of fast-gaining calves. When sufficient evidence has been obtained as to the ability of a bull to sire fast-growing calves with desirable body conformation, he is known as a "proven sire." When the services of a proven sire cannot be secured, young animals sired by a proven bull are next best.

The weaning weight of calves is a good indication of the milking ability of the dams. If feeding and environmental conditions are uniform, calves that are the heaviest at weaning time indicate growth ability and good milking qualities of the mother. The fertility record of the herd and individuals in the herd is important in selection.

Dwarfism

Dwarfs are usually compact and stocky, but very much undersized. They generally develop a large stomach and heavy shoulders. Later they may become sway-backed and develop crooked legs. Dwarfs represent an almost 100 per cent loss economically.

Cause of Dwarfs. The condition leading to dwarfism is inherited. The parents may be perfectly normal but, when mated, produce a dwarf. The problem is to determine which animals in the herd are dwarf carriers. When a bull, normal in appearance, but

Figure 12-16. Dwarf calves. Note the sway back and large middles. These calves have reached their maximum growth. (Courtesy U.S.D.A. Bureau of Animal Industry)

a dwarf carrier, is mated to a similar cow, on the average one calf in four will be a dwarf. Of the remaining three calves, two will be carriers of the dwarf factor, but will appear normal, and one will be free of the dwarf factor. As an example of how great the loss would be, let us suppose that in a herd of 16 cows eight were dwarf carriers. If the eight dwarf-carrying cows were mated to a dwarf carrying bull, one could expect two dwarf calves per year. Of the remaining six calves, four would carry the factor and, if kept in the herd, might produce more dwarf calves. In addition, the non-dwarf carrying cows if bred to the same bull would produce an average of four calves carrying the dwarf factor, although they would be normal in appearance. To produce dwarf calves both parents must be carriers of the factor.

Prevention of Dwarfism. To purge the herd of dwarfs is not simple. If a dwarf results from any mating, both parents carry the factor, and they should be eliminated. This does not tell us how many more cows may be carriers. The ratio of dwarf calves from parents that are carriers is one in four. This is only a ratio based on large numbers, and it is conceivable that a carrier cow mated to a carrier bull for ten years may never produce a dwarf.

After having disposed of the carrier bull, one is confronted with the problem of securing a replacement that is not a carrier. If the prospective bull has been in service and has not sired any dwarfs, that is some indication he may be free of the factor. If replacement animals are selected from a herd where the record has shown no dwarfism, they probably do not carry the factor.

At present, scientists are busy trying to perfect methods whereby dwarf carriers may be detected before going into service and contaminating cattle herds. Prospects of new discoveries in detection methods such as X-rays and other devices are promising, but it is too early to come to any definite conclusions.

Selection of Feeder Cattle

Feeder cattle are those that are unfinished or that do not carry enough condition to make the slaughter grade of which they are capable. Such cattle are usually purchased from the range by cattle feeders and put into the feed lot to be fattened. The feeder depends upon margin and value of the gain over feed costs and other expenses for his profits.

Feeder cattle vary considerably in age, weight, body conformation, ability to make rapid gains, and amount of condition they carry. Heifers and steers will vary in their performance in the feedlot. These large variations in feeder cattle create a number of problems for the purchaser of cattle for fattening. There will be price variations depending upon weight, quality, and sex, but the prices will not vary in the same proportion each year.

Certain weights and quality of cattle may be better adapted to the amount and kinds of feed available. Also the future market outlook must be considered. The cattle feeders' problems are many, and only those with good judgment are likely to succeed financially over a long period.

Classes and Grades of Feeder Cattle

Feeder cattle are classified and graded according to age, sex, weight, and conformation.

Age. Cattle are classified according to age as calves, yearlings, two-year-olds, cows, bulls, and stags. All cattle are designated as calves until they are one year old. Between the ages of one year and two years they are classified as yearlings. Animals over a year but less than 18 months old are sometimes referred to as short-yearlings, whereas the term long-yearlings is applied to animals over 18 months, but under two years of age. Two-year-olds are cattle between the ages of two and three years. Cattle three or more years of age seldom enter the feeder trade, except for cows, bulls, and stags.

Sex. Cattle are classified as steers, heifers, heiferettes, cows, bulls, and stags.

Steer. A steer is a male animal that was castrated at an early age and before he reached sexual maturity.

Heifer. A heifer is a female animal that has not developed the mature form of the cow and has not had a calf. Usually females under three years of age are classed as heifers. Heiferettes is a term often used in the cattle trade. It refers to young cows, usually those that have not had more than one calf.

Cow. A cow is a mature female that has had one or more calves. A barren female (one that fails to get with calf) that has reached maturity is also classed as a cow.

Bull. A bull is an uncastrated male of any age.

Stag. A stag is a male animal castrated after he has developed the physical characteristics of a mature bull.

Weight. Steers and heifers are classified as heavy, medium, and light on a weight basis. There is no weight classification for cows, bulls, and stags. The weight class a steer or heifer falls in is determined by the age of the animal. For example, a steer calf to be classified as heavy would need to weigh from 450 to 500 pounds. A heavy yearling feeder steer would weigh from 700 to 800 pounds, whereas a heavy two-year-old feeder steer would weigh around 1100 pounds. The amount of condition is important in determining the weight classification of feeder cattle. Some cattle have a frame large enough to classify as heavies, but owing to a short feed supply may be thin and not classify heavier than medium or in extreme cases as light weights. Heavy calves could be heavier than light yearlings. This is especially true if the yearlings are thin. Cattle have attained most of their growth by the time they are two and a half years old. Weight beyond a 1000 pounds is largely due to finish. Yearlings on good pasture could be as heavy as two-year-olds that have less abundant grazing conditions.

Grade. Steers and heifers are graded according to quality into six grades. They are fancy, choice, good, medium, common, and inferior. For cows, bulls, and stags the highest grade is choice, with a total of only five grades.

Fancy Cattle. The term fancy is applied to only a small percentage of feeder steers and heifers. Those grading fancy show exceptional smoothness and body conformation. Such cattle, especially the steers, are in demand by showmen who fatten them out for exhibition at the fat cattle shows. They usually sell for too high a price to be profitable for commercial feeders.

Choice Cattle. Choice is the highest practical grade of feeder cattle. They are superior in conformation, natural finish, and quality. They are blocky, compact, wide, and deep. They are straight in their top and underlines and well-developed in the quarters, showing evidence of having only high-grade or purebred ancestry of strictly beef cattle breeds. One who buys choice young cattle can expect them to finish into high choice or prime slaughter grades and bring the higher price paid for the top grade of fat cattle.

Good Cattle. Cattle grading good must show evidence of having ancestry mostly from the beef breeds, but show less compact-

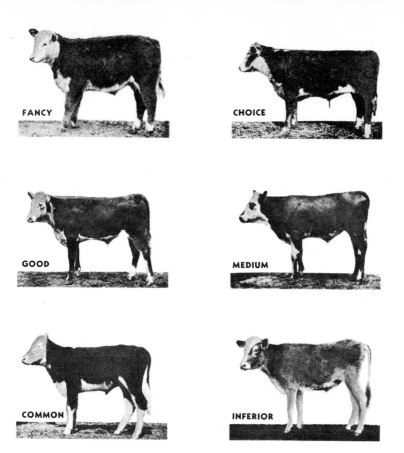

Figure 12-17. The grades of feeder cattle. (Courtesy U.S.D.A.)

ness and be more upstanding and not as smooth as the higher grades. They lack in the development of the more valuable cuts such as the back, loin, and hind quarters. Feeder cattle grading good can be expected to finish into good to choice fat cattle.

Medium Cattle. Medium grade cattle are upstanding, and uneven in the top and underlines. The hip bones are prominent and they are somewhat narrow over the back, and light in the hind quarters. They may show evidence of some dairy breeding. Medium steers cannot be expected to grade higher than good as slaughter cattle.

Common Cattle. Common steers show a lack of thrift and constitution. They are upstanding, narrow-chested, narrow over the back and loins, light in the hind quarters, shallow-bodied, long-necked, and prominent in the hips. They are not straight in the top and underlines and are usually steep in the rump. In type they resemble the dairy breeds more than the beef breeds of cattle. Many of the feeder cattle lots grading common are dairy breeds of steers. Medium slaughter steers are about as high as they can be expected to grade after fattening.

Inferior Cattle. This is the lowest feeder grade. In addition to having all the faults of common grade cattle they are apt to be unhealthy, stunted, and extremely unthrifty. See Table 21.

Cows, Bulls, and Stags. Cows, bulls, and stags do not make up a large percentage of the feeder cattle trade. However, when cows become old or nonproductive, they go to market. Some cattle

TABLE 21

CLASSES AND GRADES OF FEEDER CATTLE

Sex	Age	Weight	Grades
Steers	Calves	Heavy Medium Light	Fancy, choice, good, medium, common, and inferior
	Yearlings	Heavy Medium Light	Fancy, choice, good, medium, common, and inferior
	2-year-olds	Heavy Medium Light	Fancy, choice, good, medium, common, and inferior
Heifers	Calves	Heavy Medium Light	Fancy, choice, good, medium, common, and inferior
	Yearlings	Heavy Medium Light	Fancy, choice, good, medium, common, and inferior
	2-year-olds	Heavy Medium Light	Fancy, choice, good, medium, common, and inferior
Cows	All ages	Any weight	Choice, good, medium, common, and inferior
Bulls	All ages	Any weight	Choice, good, medium, common, and inferior
Stags	All ages	Any weight	Choice, good, medium, common, and inferior

feeders make a practice of buying cows. They fatten them to improve the slaughter grade, thereby increasing the per pound value. The profit on cows usually comes from margin because cows are not very efficient users of feed.

Bulls usually come to the market as singles, and are sold by breeders and commercial producers when they can no longer use them for breeding. A certain percentage of the bulls are castrated, fattened, and sold as stags.

Selecting the Class and Grade of Feeder Cattle

The kind of cattle to buy depends upon so many factors that only a few can be considered here. However, the more important considerations are: (1) kind and amount of feed available, (2) price of feed, (3) spread in prices between feeder and slaughter cattle, (4) future market outlook, and (5) the length of time they are to be fed.

Feed. If high-quality slaughter beef is to be produced, the use of liberal amounts of feed grains and good-quality forage is usually essential. A cattle feeder with his bins full of feed grains and a barn full of good hay may well consider buying choice grades. Since young beef grading prime generally tops the market, choice heavy calves or choice light yearlings which can be marketed at from 1000 to 1200 pounds in weight should be considered.

These cattle may be either steers or heifers. If heifers are purchased, the price must be less than that of steers in the same grade. Heifers finish somewhat faster on the average than steers, but will not equal steers in dressing percentage. The market price of fat heifers is usually lower than that of steers in the corresponding grade.

It takes both quality cattle and quality feed to produce top beef. Low-grade feeders, regardless of how well fed, will not make high-grade slaughter cattle. If an abundance of low-quality roughage, such as corn fodder, sargo fodder, and hay that is coarse or stemy, is available, the problem of using this forage profitably may be solved by feeding it to cattle. Cattle may be bought in the fall and used to clean up a corn field behind the picker or run out on the pastures as long as there is sufficient feed. Medium-to-heavy yearlings, weighing from 600 to 750 pounds, and medium-to-common grades would be well suited for this purpose. After the rough feed in the fields has been eaten up, the cattle may be put in the feed lot and full-fed roughage with enough protein to meet the animals' need. Grain should be limited to from three to five pounds per day until the last 30 to 60 days of the feeding period. A full feed of grain may be used the last month or so. These cattle will market as standard-to-good slaughter steers and will not require more than 15 to 25 bushels of grain.

It is important that lower-grade cattle be bought at a price considerably under the price of choice grades. Such cattle will not make top-grade slaughter animals, and the cattle feeder will receive less for them on a hundredweight basis. They do offer an opportunity to convert low-quality feed into a marketable product. High-grade cattle fed on low-quality feed will generally not produce the highest grade of beef. The loss in margin usually results in a financial loss when cattle are not fed according to grade. The kind of feed available should determine to a large extent the grade of cattle to buy.

Feed Prices. When prices of feed are high in proportion to finished beef and when feeder prices are low, the cattle feeder generally expects to make his profit on the margin rather than on the gain in weight. Under these conditions heavy cattle weighing from 800 to 1000 pounds may be the best. These cattle will be ready for market after a gain of from 200 to 300 pounds. The purpose of the gain is to finish the cattle to meet the requirements of their slaughter grade and to bring the feeder an increased price per hundred over the cost of the feeders. If he makes a marginal profit of from $2 to $3 per hundredweight, he has a profit of from $16 to $30 per head if he can break even on the gain. If the reverse is true—that is, low-priced feed and high-priced feeders—then the chance for profit is greater on the gain than on the margin. When feed is cheap, light yearlings or calves weighing from 300 to 500 pounds will cost less. With low-priced feed the feeder may put from 600 to 800 pounds of gain per head on the cattle. His profit will result from the gain rather than from the margin.

Spread in Feeder and Slaughter Cattle Prices. If the price of feeders is low compared to the price of slaughter cattle, again the margin is important. Heavy cattle will usually bring in the most profit.

Future Market Outlook. Price prospects for fat cattle are important in determining which weights and grades of feeders to buy. If the immediate future outlook is good, but the long-time outlook is very uncertain, then heavy cattle, which will meet the grade most in demand for fat cattle, are more certain to make a profit. Such cattle may be short-fed from 90 to 120 days and moved before the expected price break.

Length of Feeding Period. The amount of feed available usually determines the length of time cattle are fed. Cattle feeders with feed they desire to market as beef generally desire light animals of a grade that will correspond to the quality of feed available.

These cattle are often calves bought in the fall, wintered to gain a pound a day, which is only a good growth gain, and turned on pasture the next spring. Some grain may be fed to the cattle while on grass. The second fall they are put into the feed lot and finished according to their grade.

Summary

A cattle breeder is one who produces animals either for breeding purposes or the feed lot. However, the term breeder generally refers to one who tries to improve the breed and produces purebred animals primarily for breeding purposes.

British breeders are credited with most of the early developmental work on beef cattle breeds.

When selecting a breed, the prospective breeder must consider personal likes, availability of breeding stock, outlet for surplus animals, and environmental conditions.

The most important breeds of cattle in the United States are three British breeds, Aberdeen-Angus, Hereford, and Shorthorn.

Other European breeds found in the United States include the Galloway, a British breed, and the Charolais, a French breed.

Brahman cattle are native to India. The breed differs considerably from European cattle, being more upstanding and less compact, and having drooping ears. They are resistant to many insects and diseases affecting European breeds and can graze and produce on forage too scant for the survival of many other breeds.

The Brangus, Charbray, Beefmaster, Santa Gertrudis, and Braford are all breeds developed in the United States, most of them in the south. They were developed by blending Brahman blood with Angus, Charolais, Hereford, and Shorthorn cattle. These breeds are credited by their supporters with having exceptional vigor, more size, fast growing ability, a tolerance to extremes in climatic conditions, insects, and diseases. They are good rustlers and can forage over areas of scant vegetation and survive.

Crossbred cattle have shown some advantages in gaining ability over straight bred cattle.

Foundation stock should be selected on the basis of conformation, progeny, and production records.

Dwarfism is an inherited abnormality that has caused considerable economic loss in many herds. Dwarf calves come from mating animals where both the male and female carry the factor

Feeder cattle are unfinished cattle that are generally either sold to cattle feeders or put into the feed lot by the producers and finished for market.

Feeder cattle vary considerably as to age, weight, and grade Most feeder cattle are steers or heifers. The weight classes are light medium, and heavy. The age classes are calves, yearlings, and two-year-olds. Steers and heifers are graded fancy, choice, good, medium, common, and inferior. Feeder cows, bulls, and stags have a top grade of choice.

In selecting feeder cattle one should give careful consideration to the available feed, feed prices, spread in feeder and slaughter cattle prices, future market outlook, and length of the feeding period.

● Questions

1. Define the term "cattle breeder."
2. List the important decisions a prospective cattle breeder must make.
3. Describe the European breeds of beef cattle found in the United States.
4. What are the three most popular breeds of cattle in the United States?
5. How does the Brahman differ from the European breeds of beef cattle?
6. List the breeds of beef cattle developed in the United States.
7. How were the breeds listed in question 6 developed?
8. Tell how you would proceed to obtain breeding stock.

9. Describe what you would look for in breeding stock.
10. What information will production records reveal?
11. Discuss the cause and prevention of dwarfism.
12. What are feeder cattle?
13. What are the age classifications of feeder cattle?
14. What are the weight classifications of feeder cattle?
15. List the grades of heifers, steers, cows, bulls, and stags.
16. Describe the choice feeder steer.
17. What are the chief factors that determine the grades of feeder cattle?
18. Give an example when heavy cattle would be a good buy. Light cattle.
19. Under what conditions would you recommend the purchase of choice feeders? The plainer grades?
20. What are the important factors one should consider in determining the weight and grade of cattle to buy?

References

Baker, Marvel L., Leslie E. Johnson, Russell L. Davis, *Beef Cattle Breeding Research at Fort Robinson*, Miscellaneous Publication 1, Agricultural Experiment Station, University of Nebraska, Lincoln, Nebraska, 1952.

Beef Cattle Feeding and Breeding Investigations, Reports 37, 38, 40. 1950-53, Kansas Agricultural Experiment Station, Kansas State College, Manhattan, Kansas.

Feeding and Breeding Test With Beef Cattle, Reprinted from Miscellaneous Publication No. MP-34, Feeders' Day Report, Oklahoma Agricultural Experiment Station, Oklahoma A & M, Stillwater, Oklahoma, 1954.

Gregory, P. W., W. C. Rollins, F. D. Carroll, *Heterozygous Expression of the Dwarf Gene in Beef Cattle*, Reprint from the Southwestern Veterinarian, Volume 5, No. 4, pp. 345-349, Summer, 1952.

Livestock Breeding Research at the U. S. Range Livestock Experiment Station, U. S. Department of Agriculture, Agriculture Information Bulletin No. 18.

Roubreck, C. B., N. W. Hilston, S. S. Wheeler, *Progeny Studies With Hereford and Shorthorn Cattle*, Wyoming Agricultural Experiment Station, Bulletin 307, University of Wyoming, Laramie, Wyoming, 1951.

Williams, D. W., *Beef Cattle Production in the South*, The Interstate Printers and Publishers, Danville, Illinois, 1950.

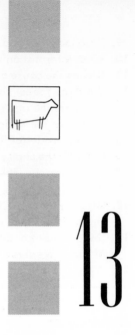

Feeding and Management of the Breeding Herd

The breeding herd must be properly fed and managed if a good calf crop is to be attained. The percentage calf crop, the vigor and size the calves attain by market time, and the feeding efficiency largely determine the profit realized.

Recent studies and research in cattle nutrition have shown that cows can utilize an amazingly large amount of low-quality roughage when properly balanced with minerals, vitamins, and protein, and still produce a strong, healthy calf crop.

Feeding the Herd on Pasture

When an ample amount of good pasture is available, summer feeding problems of the breeding herd are easily solved. Young growing plants are generally high in most food nutrients and represent a fairly well-balanced ration for two-year-old heifers and cows.

Studies reveal that cattle will spend not much more than eight hours a day grazing. Whenever a pasture fails to provide, in eight

Figure 13-1. Cows can utilize a large amount of low-quality roughage when properly supplemented with vitamins, minerals, and proteins. (Courtesy Rath Packing Company)

hours of grazing, sufficient forage to satisfy the animal's requirements, additional feed should be provided.

Supplementing the Grass. Whenever the pasture is insufficient to provide adequate nutrients to meet the needs of the cattle, it will be necessary to supplement the pasture with additional feed for best results. Ten pounds of good legume hay, 30 pounds of legume silage, or 20 to 25 pounds of sorghum or corn silage will replace about one-half the pasture requirements for mature cattle. When a lower quality forage is used, the amount will need to be increased. If available, silage is an excellent supplement when the grasses are

Figure 13-2. When plenty of good pasture is available summer feeding problems of the breeding herd are pretty well solved. (Courtesy *Farm Journal & Country Gentleman*)

dry or mature. Dry forages are generally considered superior when the pasture grasses are green and succulent.

Many farmers use extra forage to supplement the pasture early in the season to prevent the cattle from cropping the grass too short. When it is known that the amount of pasture is insufficient as the sole forage for cattle during the season, it may be extended by feeding additional forage from the start of the pasture season.

Grain may be used to replace part of the pasture requirements for breeding cattle. Three to five pounds of corn, barley, wheat, or sorghum grain, will replace about one-half the pasture requirements for mature breeding cattle. If oats are used it will require from five to seven pounds.

Salt should be within easy reach of the cattle at all times. As an insurance against mineral starvation and since mineral mixtures are relatively cheap, a good mineral mixture should be kept before the cattle at all times. Following are some good mineral mixtures recommended for various sections of the United States.

Mineral mixtures for areas where only additional salt, calcium, and phosphorus need to be provided.

(1) 200 pounds steamed bone meal
100 pounds common salt

(2) 200 pounds steamed bone meal
50 pounds ground limestone
100 pounds common salt

Mineral mixtures for areas where one or more trace minerals, in addition to salt, calcium, and phosphorus, may be deficient.

(1) 50.0 pounds iodized salt
25.5 pounds ground limestone
100.0 pounds steamed bone meal
25.0 pounds red oxide of iron
2.5 pounds pulverized copper sulfate
1.0 ounce cobalt sulfate

(2) 40 pounds iodized trace mineral salt
18 pounds ground limestone
40 pounds steamed bone meal
2 pounds iron (ferric oxide)

(3) 40 pounds common salt
     22 pounds ground limestone
     35 pounds steamed bone meal
    * 3 pounds trace mineral mixture

(4) 30 pounds common salt
     25 pounds ground limestone
     40 pounds steamed bone meal
    * 5 pounds trace mineral mixture

* Trace minerals can be purchased as a trace mineral mixture and added
to the other ingredients.

It is seldom necessary to supplement good pasture with any vitamin supplement. Vitamin A and D are the only ones ever likely to be deficient in the rations of cattle a month or more of age. Green plants, containing an abundance of vitamin A and sunlight, will provide the D requirements. Cattle can store vitamin A in abundant quantities and can draw upon this reserve for several months. Only when cattle have been grazed for several months on poor-quality, dry pastures is there a danger of a vitamin A deficiency.

Cattle suffering from a vitamin A deficiency show an inability to see in dim or subdued light, staggering gait, and excessive running of the eyes and nose. If a vitamin A deficiency is suspected, they may be fed one pound per day of fresh, dehydrated alfalfa meal or two pounds of high-grade alfalfa hay. When these feeds are not available a vitamin supplement, prepared commercially, containing 3,000 international units of vitamin A per gram, may be fed at the rate of one-fourth pound per animal per day. If this supplement is fed over a period of from ten to 15 days, enough vitamin A will be provided to correct the condition. After that one or two feedings per week should prevent a recurrence of the trouble.

When an ample amount of green pasture forage is available, mature breeding cattle seldom need additional protein. If the pasture is short or if poor-quality and low-protein forage is used to supplement the pasture, then from one-fourth to one pound per head of protein concentrate such as cottonseed cake or meal, soybean, linseed, or peanut oil meal will be needed to balance the ration.

The practice of using salt mixed with the protein supplement, as a means of controlling the intake of protein when the mixture is self-fed to cattle, is gaining in popularity among ranchers in some sections of the range country. The salt-protein mixture permits the self-feeding of protein, which reduces labor and provides for a more even consumption of the supplement and more uniform grazing of the range than does hand feeding. It is necessary to have plenty of water available when a salt-protein mixture is fed. Constant adjustment of the salt-protein ratio is necessary to provide for the correct intake of protein. As the salt is increased or decreased in proportion to the protein meal, consumption of the mixture increases or decreases. The salt is used to govern the protein intake. The amount and quality of the pasture determines the needed level of protein intake.

In tests carried out by the Oklahoma Agricultural Experiment Station, daily consumption of protein meal by 700-pound cattle was held to two pounds per day by mixing seven-eights pound of salt with each two pounds of meal. California tests showed that by shifting the salt content from 10 to 30 per cent in a ration made up of equal parts of cottonseed meal and barley, consumption could be controlled.

Water. Water is usually the cheapest and most essential element in livestock nutrition. The need for plenty of fresh, clean water within easy reach of the cattle cannot be overestimated. Cattle make faster gains and utilize feed more efficiently when plenty of water is available. Range cattle tend to feed more in the vicinity of the watering place. When watering facilities are too far apart the range is grazed unevenly. Some areas will be grazed so closely that the grass will be destroyed and will be replaced by undesirable weedy plants.

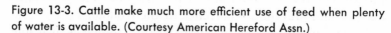

Figure 13-3. Cattle make much more efficient use of feed when plenty of water is available. (Courtesy American Hereford Assn.)

218

Pastures Compared. There is a wide variety of pasture plants. Weather, soil, and moisture conditions determine the pasture crops best adapted for each locality. Pasture crops are divided into two general classes: legumes and grasses.

Legumes. Legumes have the ability to use atmospheric nitrogen. Since nitrogen is important in the building of proteins, legumes are usually higher in protein than are the grasses. Legumes are heavy feeders on phosphorus and calcium and, when grown on land well supplied with these elements, are rich in these essential minerals. Legumes are usually higher in total food value than are grasses. In general, legumes are very palatable to cattle. When legumes are used alone as a pasture crop, there is danger of bloat. The loss from bloat has been so great that straight legume pastures cannot be safely recommended. Scientists are studying the cause of bloat and some information has been revealed. Prospects appear bright that a method of bloat prevention may soon be discovered. However, for the present, legumes should be grown in combination with grasses when used for pasture. Legumes should not make up more than one-half of the plant stand, and care should be used in seeding to get an even mixture of the two types of plants. If the seeding is uneven, cattle may graze where the heavy stand of legumes occur, and bloat will result.

Wherever legumes are adapted, they should make up part of the pasture mixture. Experiments conducted at several stations have shown that when a legume and grass pasture is used, it is superior to grass alone. Some of the advantages of legumes used in conjunction with grasses are: (1) faster gains, (2) longer grazing season, and (3) greater carrying capacity of the pastures.

Some of the more common pasture legumes are: alfalfa, alyce clover, alsike clover, trefoil, crimson clover, kudzu, ladino clover, lespedeza, red clover, sweet clover, vetch, and white Dutch clover. Most areas of the United States have one or more legumes adapted to the particular region. Legumes do not grow well under arid or semi-arid conditions. In the drier sections they may be grown on irrigated land as hay or pasture crops.

Grasses. As with legumes, there are many types of pasture grasses. Various areas have a number of grasses adapted to their climatic conditions. In selecting grasses for permanent pasture seeding, those that will produce the most forage over an extended period and that are palatable to livestock are recommended. Some of the better grasses to be used in mixtures for temporary and semi-permanent pastures in the midwest are: bluegrass, bromegrass, tall fescue, orchard grass, redtop, perennial rye grass, sudan grass, and timothy. All of these grasses are perennials except sudan grass, which is an annual.

There are many combinations of legume and grass seed mixtures used for seeding pastures. The length of time a pasture is expected to last is important in selecting a mixture.

There are such wide varieties of soil and climatic conditions prevailing in the United States that no attempt will be made to give recommended pasture seed mixtures for all areas. This information may be secured from the local vocational agriculture instructor, the county extension director, or the agricultural college. Some recommended mixtures for the Midwestern states that have wide adoption in other sections are listed in Table 22 on page 221.

For economical beef production, plans should be made to pasture the cattle as much of the year as possible. Studies at Purdue University showed that 55.4 per cent of the feed cost for an entire year occurred during a 127-day wintering period. The cost of wintering rations was 2½ times as much as the cost of pasture per day.

Nutrient Value of Pasture Varies. The nutrient value of pasture crops does not remain the same during the season. (As plants become more mature, the fiber content increases and the protein and vitamin content decreases.)The same is true when the growth of plants is retarded because of dry weather. Many pastures that have provided the entire ration successfully during one part of the season will need to be supplemented with considerable amounts of additional forage and grain at other times. Young pasture grass will average from 18 to 22 per cent protein and 70 to 80 per cent total digestible nutrients on a dry matter basis (water removed), compared to about 5 to 9 per cent protein and 40 to 50 per cent total digestible nutrients for matured grasses. Young pasture grass contains more protein and is of a highly digestible nature.

Cutting and Hauling Pasture Forage. Green-lot feeding is a term applied to the practice of cutting and hauling pasture to the cattle that are confined to a dry lot. Experiments conducted at several stations show that one can expect to produce from 20 to 30 per cent more beef per acre than can be produced from grazing.

TABLE 22

GRASS AND LEGUME MIXTURES RECOMMENDED FOR THE MIDWEST

Seeding Rate per Acre in Pounds

ROTATION PASTURES

1.	Alfalfa	6-8	Smooth brome grass	5-10
2.	Alfalfa	6-8	Meadow fescue	6-8
3.	Alfalfa	6-8	Smooth brome	6	Meadow fescue	2
4.	Alfalfa	6-8	Smooth brome	4-5	Timothy	1-2
5.	Alfalfa	7-8	Red clover	3	Orchard grass	6
6.	Alfalfa	5-6	Ladino	½	Smooth brome	8
7.	Alfalfa	3	Ladino	½	Red clover	3	Smooth brome	8
8.	Alsike	3	Ladino	½	Red top	2-4	Timothy	2-3
9.	Red clover	6-8	Timothy	4-6

PERMANENT PASTURES

1.	Birdsfoot trefoil	4-6	Bluegrass	3-4	Smooth brome	6-8	Timothy	2
2.	Birdsfoot trefoil	4-6	Alfalfa	3-4	Smooth brome	6-8	Timothy	1-2

EMERGENCY PASTURES

1.	Sudan grass	15-25	Soybeans	60-80
2.	Sudan grass	5-10	

221

Figure 13-4. More beef can be produced per acre of pasture when the green forage is cut and hauled to the cattle. (Courtesy University of California)

Figure 13-5. Unloading fresh green forage from a self-unloading wagon. (Courtesy University of California)

In addition to more carrying ability of the pastures and faster gains on the beef cattle, fences may be eliminated and bloat is seldom a problem.

Forage should be cut daily and in an amount that will be consumed by the cattle in a twenty-four hour period. Larger amounts will mold and result in waste. The taller legumes and grasses have shown considerable increase in total yield from green-lot feeding. The shorter crops have shown little if any increase. The practice of green-lot feeding is more adaptable to legume and grass pastures grown in rotation than to permanent pastures. This system is more adapted to the high-priced crop land than to permanent pasture areas.

While there are the advantages mentioned in the preceding paragraphs, there are also many disadvantages to green-lot feeding. Some of the more important disadvantages are: (1) the job must be done each day, creating a labor problem; (2) considerable investment is needed in machinery, wagons, and other equipment; (3) rainy spells and wet spots are a problem with heavy machinery. One must carefully weigh the advantages and disadvantages before he changes from a grazing system to green-lot feeding. The large operator may consider the possibility of hauling pasture to his cattle. It is doubtful that the small herd owner would find the extra investment and labor needed to be economically sound.

Feeding the Herd in Dry Lot. Dry lot feeding of the breeding herd, such as is necessary in areas of the United States too far north for winter pastures, presents more problems than pasture or summer feeding.

Danger of Nutritional Deficiencies. Deficiencies in protein, vitamin A, and minerals may occur in cattle confined to a dry lot, especially when low-quality forages are used without supplements. However, breeding cows can utilize large quantities of corncobs, corn stalks, and other low-quality feeds if they are properly supplemented, and still produce a good calf crop.

If the roughage used is at least one-half good legume hay or legume silage and the cows are fed liberal amounts, they will go through the winter in good condition and produce a strong calf with no extra feed except for a mineral mixture and salt self-fed. Legume hay or silage is high in protein, vitamins, and most of the minerals.

When low-quality roughages, such as corncobs, corn stalks, or coarse, stemy hay is fed as the only roughage, some high-energy feed such as molasses or grains, and a complete supplement that contains the needed vitamins, minerals, and proteins, are needed to properly balance the ration.

Experiments conducted at Purdue University show that cows receiving 14.5 pounds of ground corncobs, one pound of dehydrated alfalfa meal, 3.5 pounds of Purdue Cow Supplement (fed daily), and a mineral mixture (fed free choice) wintered and produced as good a calf crop as did cows receiving 20 pounds of alfalfa-brome-timothy hay plus minerals. The Purdue Supplement used in the cow-feeding trials consisted of 636.8 pounds of soybean meal, 285.8 pounds of 45 per cent molasses feed, 51.4 pounds of bone meal, 17.2 pounds of iodized salt, and 2.5 pounds of vitamin A concentrate.

Recent work at the Iowa station has shown that if corn is picked when it is about 30 per cent moisture and the stalks are harvested and made into silage, the corn stalk silage will provide good cattle feed, if properly supplemented. Cows receiving daily two pounds of grain and five pounds of good legume hay, plus a full feed of corn stalk silage and minerals fed free choice, could be expected to winter well and produce a good calf crop.

If corn or sorghum silage (grain included) is used as the only roughage, the addition of one to two pounds of cottonseed, soybean, linseed, or any good 30 to 40 per cent cattle supplement plus a mineral mixture will provide adequate nutrients for the herd. If five to seven pounds of good legume hay is added to the silage ration, the protein concentrate may be eliminated.

Grass silage when used as the only feed for wintering bred cows has not proven as economical as grass silage plus the addition of a small amount of dry roughage. The dry roughage need not be of high quality. Four to five pounds of ground corncobs or other low-grade roughage will produce good results. Cows receiving 40 pounds of alfalfa-oats silage and 4 pounds of corncobs, plus a mineral mixture, gained an average of .36 pounds per head daily and produced a good calf in a recent Iowa trial.

Ordinarily, during the winter cows should gain weight equal to the weight gain of their unborn calf, fluids, and membranes of the advanced gestation. This would equal about one-third pound per day.

Cows should have a wintering ration that will range from 8 to 10 per cent protein (air-dried basis) plus adequate minerals and vitamin A. Following are several rations for cows in dry lots during the winter.

TABLE 23

Ration	Feed	Pounds Fed Daily
1.	Legume hay	15-20
	Mixed minerals	Free choice
2.	Legume hay	5-10
	Oat straw	10-15
	Mixed minerals	Free choice
3.	Corn or sorgo silage	20-30
	Legume hay	5
	Oat straw	5-7
	Mixed minerals	Free choice
4.	Ground corncobs	14-15
	Dehydrated alfalfa meal	1
	Purdue Cow Supplement	3.5
	Mixed minerals	Free choice
5.	Corn or sorgo silage	30-40
	Chopped dry cornstalks	5-10
	Cottonseed, linseed, or soybean meal	1
	Mixed minerals	Free choice
6.	Legume and grass silage	25-30
	Corncobs	4-5
	Mixed minerals	Free choice
7.	Cornstalk silage	30-40
	Legume hay	5-10
	Grain	2
	Mixed minerals	Free choice
8.	Cornstalks in field	Graze at will
	Legume-grass hay	10
	Mixed minerals	Free choice
9.	Dry winter range	Graze at will
	30-40% protein supplement	2
	Mixed minerals	Free choice

Note: Mineral mixtures are the same as those recommended for cattle on pasture; salt should be fed free choice in addition to the mineral mixture.

Feeding and Management of the Breeding Herd • 225

Mating

The period of heat or oestrum is the time when the female will be receptive to the bull and the act of mating will occur. The duration of the heat period will vary from 12 to 30 hours with individual cows. The average heat period is from 12 to 18 hours. The time between heat periods will vary from 17 to 26 days, with an average of about 21 days.

The time from conception until the cow calves is known as the gestation period. Most authorities agree that 283 days is about the average length of the gestation period.

Age to Breed Heifers. Heifers that have made a good growth for their breed may be bred successfully as yearlings to calve as two-year-olds. Heifers should weigh at least 850 pounds when bred. Unless they are this heavy, small, stunted cows may result from early calving. The size rather than the age should determine when heifers are bred.

Age of the Bull. Under range conditions a bull should be two years old before he is turned with the herd. Bulls past seven years old may not be depended upon to meet the strenuous conditions of the range and breed their quota of cows. Where they may be properly cared for, many bulls will breed when 12 or more years old.

Under small herd conditions where the number of cows a bull serves can be regulated, a young bull 15 months old, can be depended upon to breed 10 to 15 cows.

Figure 13-6. A vigorous, healthy range bull in good breeding condition. (Courtesy American Hereford Assn.)

Figure 13-7. A strong, healthy calf is the first step in the profitable production of cattle. (Courtesy American Hereford Assn.)

Time for Calving. When warm housing is available, early calving is recommended. Calves that are two to three months of age when the pasture season arrives will utilize more grass and the feed cost will be reduced.

Shelters. When cows calve during cold weather, it is a common practice to keep the calves shut up in pens located in barns or sheds as protection against the cold. The calves are turned with the cows morning and night so that they may nurse. This practice permits the cows to graze the cornstalk field or winter pasture without exposing the young calves to severe cold. Most cattlemen prefer to leave the cow and calf together continuously for the first two or three days. After that the cow may be turned out and the calf transferred to a group pen.

Well-lighted, well-ventilated, clean, dry pens, adequately bedded and free from drafts, are essential to the successful raising of calves born during cold weather.

It is important to avoid overcrowding the pens and to group the calves according to size and age. Calf pens should be equipped with a feed box, a hay rack, and watering facilities. Feed boxes should be about ten inches wide, six inches deep, and long enough to provide two feet of feeding space for each calf. They should be 20 inches from the floor and away from the waterer. The hay rack should be constructed so as to prevent waste and provide at least one foot of feeding space per calf.

Dehorning

While horns that have been well trained and polished add to the attractiveness of show cattle of the horned breeds, commercial beef cattlemen should remove the horns.

Advantages of Dehorned Cattle. Cattle should be dehorned for the following reasons:

1. More room is needed for horned cattle in sheds, barns, and lots.
2. Cattle with horns inflict more damage on equipment.
3. There is more danger to the operator in handling cattle with horns.
4. Horned cattle that are inclined to fight will keep others away from the feed.
5. Cattle with horns inflict bruises on each other that may result in heavy economic losses.

When to Dehorn. The age to dehorn calves depends upon the conditions and the method used in performing the operation. Generally, the sooner it can be done the less inconvenience is suffered by the calf.

Methods of Dehorning. There are a number of methods that may be employed for dehorning cattle. The age of the calf to be dehorned and facilities available determine which one is best.

Chemical Method of Dehorning. The horn buttons may be prevented from growing by burning with chemicals. This method is most successful if done before the calf is ten days old. The chemicals that are commonly used are caustic potash or caustic soda. They come in a white stick about the size of blackboard chalk, or in a commercially prepared dehorning paste. Care should be used in handling them to prevent serious burns to the operator. The hair should be clipped around the horn button and a ring of heavy grease applied to the clipped area to prevent the burning action of the chemical from spreading too far. If using the caustic stick, dip the end in water to moisten it and rub with a rotary motion on the horn button. If the paste is used, it may be smeared on with a swab or flat wooden spatula. In a few days, a heavy scab forms over the horn; the scab drops off in about ten days. The calf suffers little inconvenience, and there is no open wound to become infected.

While removing horns by chemicals is effective in eliminating the horns, there is a tendency for the face to appear longer as the animal matures. This is due to the frontal bone becoming somewhat oval in outline and extending above the point where the horns would normally have been. For this reason, the use of caustic for dehorning is objected to by those who desire to show their animals at fairs and other shows.

Figure 13-8. Dehorning with a dehorning tube and branding of a western produced calf. (Courtesy Tony Fellhauer, University of Wyoming)

Hot Iron. Burning the horn button with an electric dehorner or hot iron is a method being used on some farms for dehorning young calves. Calves should not be over three months old, if burning is to be effective in preventing horn growth. The electric dehorner has an automatic control that maintains the temperature at about 1000°F. Applying the electric dehorner to the horn button for ten seconds is sufficient to destroy the cells and prevent growth of the horn.

Spoons and Tubes. There are a number of instruments, such as spoons and tubes, on the market for dehorning. Up to 3½ months of age, horns are only skin appendages and may be gouged or scooped out with a tube which is cylinderical in shape with a hand grip on one end and a sharpened edge on the other. After the age of 3½ months the horns become fastened to the skull and tubes are not an effective means of removing them.

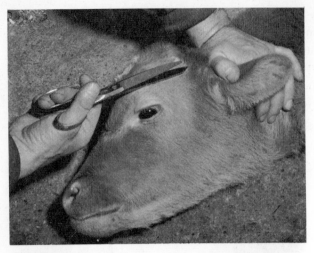

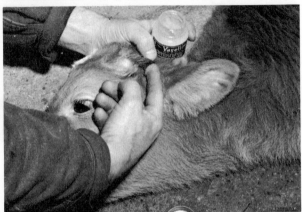

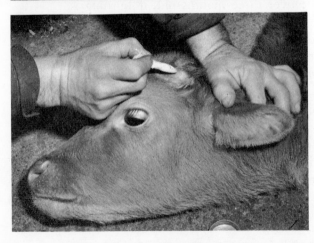

Figure 13-9. Dehorning with caustic potash. (top) Clipping the hair around the horn button. (center) Applying vaseline to the area where the hair has been clipped. (bottom) Rubbing the horn button with caustic potash. (Courtesy Michigan State College)

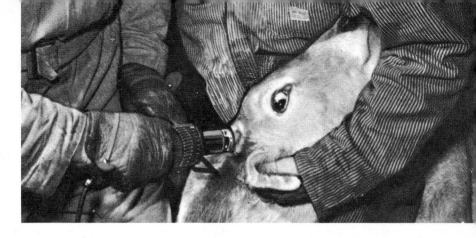

Figure 13-10. Dehorning with the electric hot iron. (Courtesy Sunbeam Corporation)

Dehorning tubes come in several sizes varying from three-fourths of an inch to one and one-eighth inches in diameter. Since the horn sizes vary with individual calves several different sizes of tubes should be made available. In using tubes, (1) select a sharp tube of the proper size to fit over the horn base; (2) place the cutting edge straight down over the horn; (3) push and twist both ways until a cut of from one-eighth to three-eighths of an inch deep has been made. Calves nearing three months of age will require the deeper cut. Do not go deeper than necessary to cut through the skin, as excessive bleeding will result; (4) turn the tube down to a 45-degree angle and lift the horn button out.

An open wound results from the use of either tubes or spoons and therefore it is better to perform the operations in cool weather. Otherwise use a good fly repellent on the wound.

Clippers and Saws. When older cattle are to be dehorned, especially designed clippers or saws are used. A considerable amount of bleeding may follow the operation. To prevent bleeding, the main horn artery should be tied off with a cotton or silk thread. This may be done by sliding a sewing needle under the artery to pull thread in place before tying. It is necessary, when sawing or clipping the horns, to take about one-half inch of skin in order to get the horn roots. An open wound results; therefore, it is better to perform the operation during cool weather when there are no flies. In warm weather, a good fly repellent should be smeared over the wound.

Feeding and Management of the Breeding Herd • 231

Castration

All male calves not to be used for breeding should be castrated.

Castrating should be done in cool weather to prevent screw worm infestation or other infections. Between the ages of one and three months is probably the ideal time to perform the operation, although many cattlemen prefer to castrate when the calves are one to two weeks of age. Generally speaking, the younger the calf is, the less inconvenience it suffers.

Methods of Castrating. Pulling downward on the scrotum and cutting off the lower one-third, exposing the testicles from below, is a common method of castrating. For show cattle where a well-developed cod is desired, one testicle is pulled down at a time and held firmly with the left hand so that the skin of the scrotum is tight over the testicles. An incision is then made on the outside of the scrotum next to the leg, both through the scrotum and the membrane surrounding the testicle. The pressure exerted by the left hand will expose the testicle so that it may be grasped and held in the right hand. The left hand may be used to separate it from the supporting tendons. While holding the testicle with the left hand, the tendons should be cut close to their lower attachments. The spermatic cord should now be stripped of all surrounding membranes and severed by scraping rather than cutting, as less bleeding will result. As much of the spermatic cord as possible should be removed. This may be accomplished by pulling downward on the testicle, drawing the cord out as far as possible before it is severed.

A specially constructed instrument, known as the Burdizzo or castrating pincers and designed to crush and destroy the spermatic cord and the blood vessels that supply the testicles, leaving the testicles to dry up and be absorbed, has found some favor in the South. The operation is bloodless and no open wound is left for infestation by screw worms or infection. However, unless it is used by a skilled operator the cord and blood vessels will not be completely destroyed. The result will be a calf known as a "slip," which will show stagginess when about a year old.

Marking

Marking is essential to good management. It permits identification of animals as to ownership and breeding.

Ear notches are easy to identify and may be used for ownership as well as breeding records. One of the best marks for permanent identification of cattle is that of tattooing the inside of the ear with indelible ink.

Figure 13-11. (A) These calves have just been branded. Note the horse-shoe-shaped brand. (Courtesy American Aberdeen-Angus Breeders' Assn.) (B) Ear tattoo and ear tag. (Courtesy University of Wyoming) (C) Neck chains with metal numbers attached are a good means of identification. (Courtesy American Aberdeen-Angus Breeders' Assn.) (D) Horn brands are sometimes used for identification. (Courtesy American Hereford Assn.)

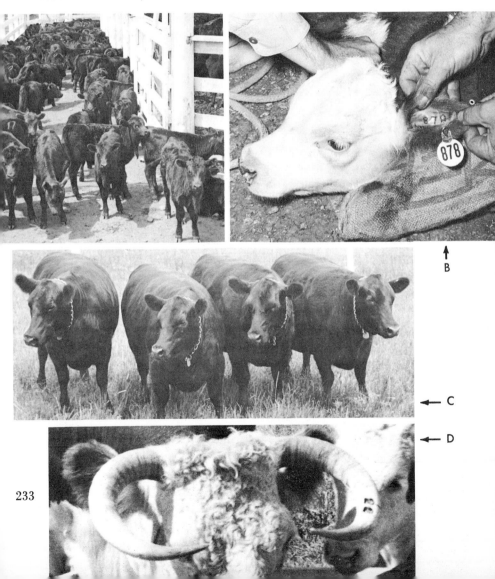

B

← C

← D

233

Horn brands may be used as easily identifiable marks on mature horned cattle. Metal ear tags or buttons with letters and numbers may be inserted in the ear as a means of identification of calves.

Leather neck straps or neck chains with a number plate attached make an easy method of identification.

Feeding Suckling Calves

Beef cattlemen usually follow the practice of letting the calves nurse the cows. Whether or not it will be profitable to feed concentrates to suckling calves will depend upon the pasture conditions, age that calves will be marketed, the cost of the supplemental feed, and whether the calves will be sold as feeders or kept in the herd for breeding purposes. The feeding of concentrates to calves that are to be sold as yearling feeders may not be profitable where pastures are good and there is plenty of good roughages for winter feeding.

Creep-Feeding Calves. The practice of creep-feeding calves has the following advantages: (1) the calves will have more weight at weaning time; (2) the cows are less suckled down; (3) calves will not miss their mothers as much at weaning time; (4) calves will be more uniform in size as creep-feeding helps to make up for the difference in milking ability of the cow; (5) calves that are to be fattened will be in better condition when they go into the feed lot, and the fattening period will be shortened; (6) heifers and bulls that are to be kept or sold as breeding animals will have more growth; (7) fat is a good seller even of feeder calves. Creep-fed calves are usually fatter than other calves and therefore will sell better, either as feeders or for breeding purposes.

Feeds for Suckling Calves. A large variety of feeds may be successfully fed to suckling calves. Availability and price should largely determine those that are selected.

Figure 13-12. A good calf creep. (Courtesy *Successful Farming*)

234

Corn, oats, barley, sorghum grain, or wheat are all good grains for self-feeding suckling calves. The price per pound of digestible nutrients should be the determining factor in making a selection. If a good mineral mixture is available for the cow herd, and is fed in a place easily accessible to the calves, it may not be necessary to provide a mineral supplement in the creep ration. However, many good cattlemen reserve a small section of the creep where a mineral supplement is placed separately for the calves.

Antibiotics for Suckling Calves. Experiments conducted at Purdue University showed a marked reduction in scouring among suckling calves, plus a growth stimulation, when aureomycin was fed at the rate of 24 milligrams per 100 pounds live weight.

Judging from these experiments and similar results from other agricultural experiment stations, it seems advisable to include aureomycin in the creep rations.

Rations for Suckling Calves. The accompanying table lists some suggested rations for creep-feeding calves.

TABLE 24

SUGGESTED RATIONS FOR CREEP-FEEDING SUCKLING CALVES

With good pasture or legume hay		Poor pasture, low protein forage, or poor milking cows	
(1) Ground oats	1000 lbs.	(1) Ground oats	1000 lbs.
Ground corn	1000 lbs.	Ground corn	800 lbs.
*Antibiotics		Linseed, soybean, or	
		cottonseed meal	200 lbs.
(2) Ground oats	1000 lbs.	*Antibiotics	
Ground barley	1000 lbs.		
*Antibiotics		(2) Ground oats	1000 lbs.
		Ground barley	850 lbs.
(3) Ground barley	1000 lbs.	Corn gluten meal,	
Ground sorghum		soybean, cottonseed,	
grain	1000 lbs.	or linseed oil meal	150 lbs.
*Antibiotics		*Antibiotics	
(4) Ground oats	500 lbs.	(3) Ground sorghum	
Ground wheat	500 lbs.	grain	1000 lbs.
Ground corn	500 lbs.	Ground barley	800 lbs.
Ground sorghum		40% commercial	
grain	500 lbs.	protein	200 lbs.
*Antibiotics		*Antibiotics	

* An antibiotic supplement which will provide 40 grams of aureomycin per ton of feed.

Feeding Replacement Heifers

After the replacement heifers have been weaned, it is important to feed them separately from the cows. Heifers need a better quality ration than do mature cows, if they are to reach normal size at breeding time.

Whenever it is possible, during the first and second winters, breeding stock should receive at least five pounds of good legume hay, plus additional amounts of sorgo or corn silage in the colder regions. In the South, if good winter pastures are available, additional forage is not essential.

Unless a roughage that will supply some grain like sorghum silage or corn silage is fed, grain in addition to good forage will speed up the growth and maturity of heifers. It is important to raise the replacement heifers as cheaply as possible without sacrificing growth and development.

Antibiotics for Growing Heifers. Experimental results reported at Kansas State College and Purdue University indicate that antibiotics fed to calves receiving a ration consisting largely of roughage, after weaning and up to 18 to 20 months of age, will increase gains and efficiency of feed utilization.

The level of aureomycin fed daily is important. Purdue scientists recommend a level of about 10 milligram to 100 pounds of live weight. When greater amounts are fed, the antibiotics have a depressing effect on the appetite of the cattle.

Feeding Young Bulls

The feeding of young bull calves up to the time they will be put into service does not differ greatly from that of replacement heifers. Because their growth is more rapid, their feed requirements are greater. The grain ration should be increased over that recommended for heifers. In addition to an unlimited amount of good cured roughage or pasture, young bulls should receive about a pound of grain per hundred pounds live weight daily. If the roughage is of a low protein nature one half to one pound of protein supplement should be fed daily in addition to the grains. A mineral supplement should be available free choice.

Young bulls about to be put in service should be in good flesh but not overly fat. Bulls in service will usually stay in condition on the same rations fed to the cows, unless they are used exceptionally heavily over a considerable length of time. If so, an additional amount of concentrates will be required to maintain them.

Beef Cattle Housing and Handling Equipment

Well-planned buildings, lots, feed bunks, and handling facilities are essential to a successful beef cattle enterprise.

Housing for Beef Cattle. Beef cattle are not especially sensitive to changes in weather conditions. Warm and expensively-built barns are not needed except when the cattle program calls for cows to calve during severe cold weather.

The reproducing herd may be successfully wintered without any shelter even in the Northern regions where winters are cold. However, a good windbreak will reduce the amount of feed necessary to winter the herd and provide additional comfort for the cattle. Trees, a high board fence, or a natural windbreak provided by a hill or a similar wind barrier will provide ample protection except under the most severe conditions.

Figure 13-13. (A) A combination of open shed for older cattle and closed shed for calves. (B) Fattening cattle can get along with only a windbreak even in cold regions. (Courtesy George Hormel and Company)

In the Northern areas, when the cattle production plan calls for calving during the cold months, warm housing will need to be provided during the calving period. Feeder cattle need little more than a wind break.

Under no conditions is it necessary to provide more than a shed open on the South for fattening cattle or those being wintered for later fattening.

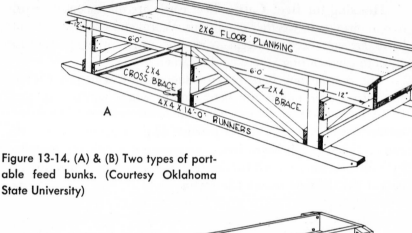

Figure 13-14. (A) & (B) Two types of portable feed bunks. (Courtesy Oklahoma State University)

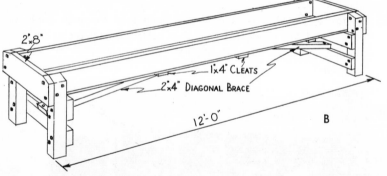

Young growing cattle or cattle being fattened on grass will make more rapid gains during the hot part of the summer if they have access to shade. When natural shade such as trees is not available, artificial shades will prove profitable.

Feeding and Other Equipment. Stationary bunks may be constructed along one side of the cattle lot. This type may be built close to the feed supply and of a heavy material such as concrete. If properly constructed, they are very durable and maintenance costs are small.

Figure 13-15. A portable manger for feeding hay from a stack. (Courtesy American Hereford Assn.)

Portable feed bunks have the advantage of being easily moved from one lot to the next or onto the pastures if desired. They are usually less durable than well-constructed permanent type bunks.

Hay Mangers. As with grain feed bunks, hay mangers may be of the fixed type for feeding along one side of the feed lot or of the portable type. Portable mangers may be of two types: those designed for feeding hay or silage directly from a stack or haybarn, and those that are designed to be moved easily from lot to lot or onto the pasture.

Self-Feeders. Self-feeders reduce labor in feeding cattle. They are especially valuable for feeding concentrates to cattle that are on pasture.

Mineral Feeders. Mineral feeders, built to protect the mineral mixture from rain or snow, should be placed in an area where it

Figure 13-16. Cattle stocks are useful to confine animals for dehorning and other operations. (Courtesy American Aberdeen-Angus Assn.)

239

will be easy for the operator to fill them and where the cattle can get at the minerals conveniently. The best place to locate mineral feeders is usually near the watering facilities.

Loading Chutes. Every cattleman needs a loading chute. These may be portable or of the fixed type. If a fixed type chute is being used, it should be located so that both large and small trucks and trailers can reach it conveniently any time of year.

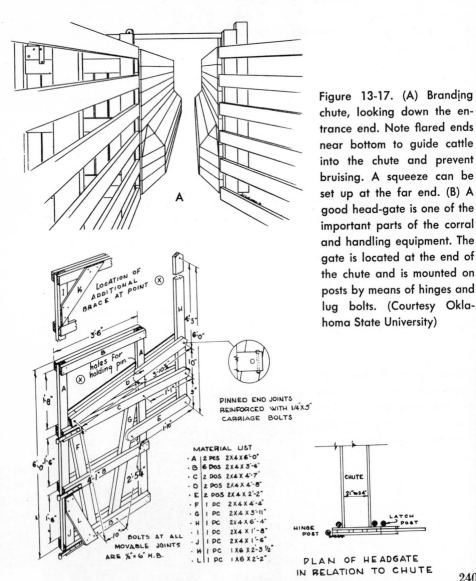

Figure 13-17. (A) Branding chute, looking down the entrance end. Note flared ends near bottom to guide cattle into the chute and prevent bruising. A squeeze can be set up at the far end. (B) A good head-gate is one of the important parts of the corral and handling equipment. The gate is located at the end of the chute and is mounted on posts by means of hinges and lug bolts. (Courtesy Oklahoma State University)

PINNED END JOINTS
REINFORCED WITH 1/4 X 5"
CARRIAGE BOLTS

MATERIAL LIST
· A | 2 PCS 2X4X6'-0"
· B | 6 POS 2X4X3'-6"
· C | 2 POS 2X4X4'-7"
· D | 2 POS 2X4X4'-8"
· E | 2 POS 2X4X2'-2"
· F | 1 PC 2X4X4'-4"
· G | 1 PC 2X4X3'-11"
· H | 1 PC 2X4X6'-4"
· I | 1 PC 2X4X1'-8"
· J | 1 PC 2X4X1'-6"
· K | 1 PC 1X6X2-3½"
· L | 1 PC 1X6X2'-2"

ALL BOLTS AT ALL MOVABLE JOINTS ARE ½"X6" M.B.

CHUTE

21"-24"

HINGE POST

LATCH POST

PLAN OF HEADGATE
IN RELATION TO CHUTE

240

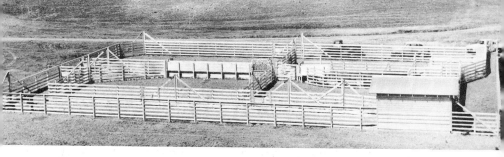

Figure 13-18. A good corral for handling cattle, including all necessary equipment arranged for convenience. The corral may be adapted for large or small size ranches or farms by reducing or increasing the size. (Courtesy University of California)

Restraint Equipment. It is necessary to secure cattle for hoof trimming, dehorning, and other similar operations. Stocks and squeezes are used for these purposes.

Cattle Yards and Lots. Well-planned corrals and lots make handling of stock easier and save labor. Paved lots are ideal, especially in the more humid regions. They keep cattle out of the mud, make it easier to work with them, and save manure. Paved lots are easy to clean. If the lots are not paved, they should be located on well-drained areas.

Fences. Feed lot fences need to be strong. A good fence can be made by combining plank and woven wire, with posts set not more than ten feet apart. While it is more expensive, a plank fence made by bolting two-inch planks to wooden posts makes a very durable fence. Cattle confined to small lots subject fences to considerable punishment.

Figure 13-19. A simple but safe loading chute constructed from old railroad ties and earth. (Courtesy Livestock Conservation, Inc.)

Feeding and Management of the Breeding Herd • 241

Mechanized Feeding Systems. One who is anticipating the building or remodeling of a cattle feeding plant will profit by making a study of various labor-saving systems that have been devised by many cattle feeders. By using properly constructed bins, mechanical augers, and feed conveyers, it is possible with very little hand labor, to mix feed and deliver it into the bunks for the cattle.

Since labor is always an expensive part of any farm or feeding enterprise, labor-saving equipment that will reduce the number of man-hours necessary for carrying on any farming program should be considered. Lack of capital may prevent the operator from completely developing the plant at one time. However, a complete plan that is adapted to the conditions should be made, and each building or piece of equipment added should fit in with the general plan.

Summary

Cows should be fed as cheaply as possible without reducing the percentage and vigor of the calves or sacrificing any of the productive life of the cows.

Plenty of roughage is the key to economical production of calves. An ample amount of pasture will maintain the herd except for minerals and salt, which should be provided at all times during the pasture season. Inadequate pastures should be supplemented.

Legumes grown in combination with grasses provide excellent grazing of a highly nutritious nature. Wherever they are adapted, legumes should be grown as part of the pasture crop.

There is a danger of mineral, vitamin, and protein deficiencies when cattle are fed in dry lots unless proper precautions are taken in formulating the ration.

Mature cattle can utilize large quantities of low-quality roughages such as cornstalk silage, corn cobs, and straw, if a supplement containing protein, minerals, and vitamins is provided. When good legume hay, or legume hay and silage, is fed as the major part of the ration, bred cows can be expected to winter well and produce a calf with little else except salt and minerals self-fed. Bred cows should normally gain about one-third pound per day.

The heat period for cows will average from 12 to 18 hours. The time between heat periods will vary from 17 to 26 days, with an average of about 21 days. The gestation period is about 283 days, with some variation between breeds and individual animals.

Heifers that are well grown out may be bred to calve as two-year-olds, but under most conditions it is recommended that they drop their first calves when three years of age.

When hand-mated, a young bull 15 months of age may be used to breed up to 15 cows. Bulls should be at least two years old and not more than seven when turned on the range. Older bulls, when properly handled, may be used for limited service up to 12 years of age.

Calves should come as early in the spring as conditions will permit. Calves two to three months old will utilize more grass and be heavier in the fall.

During cold weather clean, dry, well-lighted, and well-ventilated pens should be provided for the calves. Pens should not be overcrowded and calves should be grouped according to age and size. Pens should be equipped with hay racks, feed boxes, and watering facilities.

The operator will need to give more attention to sanitation conditions when calves are confined to pens than when they are on pasture.

The commercial cattlemen should dehorn their cattle. Dehorning may be accomplished by chemicals, hot iron, dehorning spoons and tubes, saws, or clippers. The method used will depend upon the age of the calf and the experience of the operator.

Calves may be castrated any time after they are a few days old. Most experienced cattlemen prefer to perform the operation when they are from two to three months of age.

Hide brands, ear notches, and tattooing will provide permanent marks that will not be lost. Other methods include horn brands, neck chains, or straps, and ear tags.

Suckling calves will grow quite satisfactorily on milk and grass or other good forage. However, growth and weight gains will be faster if a concentrate ration is provided in a creep.

Antibiotics have increased the rate of gain and reduced the incidence of scours among suckling calves.

Replacement heifers need a better ration than is ordinarily necessary for mature cows. When the ration is made up primarily of roughage, antibiotics will increase the rate of growth of young stock up to 18 to 20 months of age.

Young bulls may be fed the same as replacement heifers except they will require more feed.

Well-planned equipment is essential to the successful handling of beef cattle. Housing need not be elaborate or expensive for beef cattle unless cows calve during cold weather.

Feeding equipment may consist of either fixed or portable type grain bunks and hay racks or both.

Loading chutes and restraining equipment are an essential part of the cattlemen's equipment.

Lots and corrals should be either paved or located on well-drained land. Lots should be planned for convenience in sorting, loading, and handling cattle.

Mechanized feeding systems will reduce labor and should be considered before building or remodeling a cattle feeding plant.

• *Questions*

1. What are the important considerations in feeding the cow herd?
2. Under what conditions will it be necessary to supplement pasture?
3. Give several examples showing how, when, and what kind of additional feed you would provide for cows on pasture.
4. Give some mineral mixtures that could be used under various conditions.
5. How may additional vitamin A be provided for cows on pasture?
6. How do grasses and legumes compare as pasture plants?
7. Why should grasses and legumes be grown in combination?
8. List the common pasture legumes.
9. Give some pasture mixtures suitable to your area.
10. Develop a pasture program suitable to your area.
11. Explain how the nutrient value of pastures will vary.
12. How should pastures be managed in your area for greatest production?
13. Why is there more danger of nutritional deficiencies when cattle are fed in dry lots?
14. Explain how one can utilize successfully various quality roughages.
15. Give several rations that can be depended upon to winter beef cows successfully.
16. What is the duration and length of time between heat periods?

17. What is meant by the gestation period and what is the average length of the gestation period?
18. When should heifers be bred? Explain.
19. How old should bulls be before being put into service?
20. When should cows calve? Why?
21. What steps would you take to provide sanitary conditions for young calves?
22. Describe the type of pens you would recommend for young calves housed in barns or sheds.
23. Why should calves be dehorned?
24. Describe the kind of protection needed for beef cattle on your farm. Describe where beef cattle are kept on the average farm in your community.
25. Make a list of equipment needed for the handling of beef cattle on your farm.
26. Make a sketch of a plan for beef cattle yards or corrals that would meet the needs of the average cattleman in your area.
27. What advantages do paved lots have?
28. Make a plan for a mechanized cattle feeding plant.

• References

Albaugh, Reuben, C. F. Kelly, H. L. Belton, *Beef Handling and Feeding Equipment,* Agricultural Experiment and Extension Service Circular 414, University of California, Berkeley, California, 1952.

Beef Cattle Housing in the North Central Region of the United States, Agricultural Experiment Station Bulletin 382, Committee on Housing of Beef Cattle and Sheep, South Dakota State College, Brookings, South Dakota, 1946.

Beeson, W. M., T. W. Perry, *Chopped Forage Vs. Pasture for Feeding Cattle,* Agricultural Experiment Station, Mimeo A. H. 122, Purdue University, Lafayette, Indiana, 1953.

Lindgren, H. A., *Feed Requirements and Values for Livestock,* Extension Bulletin 639, Oregon State System of Higher Education, Corvallis, Oregon, 1951.

Smith, Harry, and Ford C. Daugherty, *Beef Production in Colorado,* Extension Bulletin 389-A, Colorado A. & M. College, Fort Collins, Colorado, 1950.

Totusek, Robert, E. C. Hornback, T. W. Perry, and W. M. Beeson, *Corncobs for Wintering Beef Cows,* Mimeo A. H. 94, Purdue University, Lafayette, Indiana, 1952.

14

Feeding and Management of Stockers and Fattening Cattle

In addition to the initial cost of the cattle, the feeder has his feed tied up in his cattle. If his feeding operations go wrong, through mistakes in judgment, he will lose heavily.

Figure 14-1. These cattle have been moved from the range to a rural concentration point for weighing and sorting before shipment into the Corn Belt fattening yards. (Courtesy Union Pacific Railroad)

Figure 14-2. Manure constitutes an important source of profit in terms of increased crop production. It should be conserved. (Courtesy Deere and Company)

Sources of Profit from Feeding Cattle

Profits from Margin and Gain. Unless there is a general price decline in cattle, or conditions that have created unusually high prices for feeder cattle, the feeder can reasonably expect to sell his finished cattle for a higher price per hundred pounds than he paid. This increase in price is known as margin. To assure himself of getting a margin, he will generally need to finish his cattle to meet the market grade they are capable of making.

Profits from gain result from receiving a greater total price from the increased weight than it cost to put on the gain.

Profits Resulting from Manure Value. The value of the manure is indirect and more difficult to determine than are margin and gain profits. Manure value must be determined in terms of increased crop production, as a result of the fertilizing value of the manure, and in the amount of commercial fertilizer replaced by the manure.

Dry Roughages for Stocker and Fattening Cattle

Cattle feeds are many and varied. The rations used depend upon the kind of cattle to be fed, and the cost and availability of feeds.

Roughages should make up a large part of the cattle ration. They are economical and, when properly fed, decrease the cost of gain. Roughages vary considerably in feeding value.

Legume Hays. High-quality legume hay is recognized as the best roughage from a nutritional standpoint. It is high in proteins, minerals, and vitamins.

Grass Hays. Most of the grasses are excellent roughages but low in protein and minerals compared to legumes. One pound of a 40 to 45 per cent protein supplement is usually all that is needed when legume hay is used as the entire roughage. If grass hay is fed as the only roughage, an increase of one-half to one pound of protein supplement will be required to balance the ration. More attention will need to be given the mineral and vitamin content of the ration to make up for the roughage deficiency. Feeding a mineral mixture free choice and one or two pounds of dehydrated alfalfa meal per head daily will compensate for the mineral and vitamin deficiencies of the grass hays.

Mixed Hays. The term mixed hay usually applies to a mixture of grasses and legumes. The food value of mixed hay will be between that of legume and grass hay, depending upon the percentage of legumes in the mixture.

Beet Tops. Fresh beet tops have a very high feeding value but lose much of this if left too long in the field. They should be harvested and stored to conserve their feeding value, or they should be made into silage.

Dehydrated Hays. Dehydrated hays are the result of harvesting green plants and artificially drying them. This process saves the leaves and results in a higher protein and vitamin A content. However, since vitamin D is absorbed by the hay from the sunshine while curing in the field, sun-cured hay is higher in vitamin D.

Cattle that are exposed to direct sunshine are not likely to suffer from a vitamin D deficiency. Therefore, the vitamin A content of forage is more important than the vitamin D content.

Dehydrated alfalfa meal or pellets have been a consistent gain booster when added to cattle rations that did not include legume hays, or where the legume was of poor quality. Alfalfa apparently has growth-stimulating qualities that have not been duplicated in other feeds. When the crop is cut at the proper stage and artificially dried, few nutrients are lost.

Corncobs and Dry Chopped Corn Stalks. Corncobs have been used successfully, when properly supplemented, for growing and fattening cattle. Cobs are high in fiber and very low in protein, vitamins, and mineral content.

Corn stalks, as well as corncobs, when properly supplemented, will produce substantial gains on fattening cattle.

The bacteria that are responsible for the ability of cattle to digest high-fiber feeds must be supplied with enough energy, protein, mineral, and vitamin nutrients for their own growth. Unless these bacteria are well fed, ruminants fail to get enough food value from cobs, corn stalks, and similar feed to survive and produce gains.

Silage. Silage is produced by putting feeds containing a high percentage of moisture into one of several types of silos, or by packing the feed in a compact stack known as a silage stack.

When alfalfa, brome grass, oats, and other legumes, grasses, or small grain crops are made into silage, it is generally referred to as grass silage; actually it would be more correct to refer to silage made from legumes as legume silage, that from grasses other than small grains as grass silage, and that made from small grains as small grain silage.

These crops all vary considerably in their nutrient content. Silage made from legumes will contain more protein than that made from grasses.

Figure 14-3. Hay and silage will cheapen cattle gains.

249

Corn and the sorghums make excellent silage. The silage from these crops will be lower in protein than legume or legume and grass mixed silage, but higher in carbohydrates.

Corn stalk silage is made from the stalks after the ears have been harvested. Water may be needed to increase the moisture as the stalks are usually too dry for silage when the corn is ready for harvest. The addition of molasses as a preservative improves the feeding value and prevents possible spoilage.

Recent feeding trials using corn stalk silage have revealed that a considerable amount of food value, especially carbohydrates, is present in corn stalks.

TABLE 25

COMPARABLE VALUE OF ROUGHAGES WHEN ALFALFA
IS WORTH $20 PER TON

Roughage	Value	Roughage	Value
Alfalfa hay	$20.00	Legume and grass silage	$7.50
Red clover hay	18.00	Corn silage	8.00
Soybean hay	16.00	Sorghum silage	7.50
Lespedeza hay	15.00	Corn stalks (dry chopped)	6.00
Brome grass hay	13.00	Corn stalk silage	3.00
Timothy hay	12.00	Corn cobs (ground)	6.50
Prairie hay	13.00	Oat straw	5.00
Sudan grass hay	12.00		

Grains and Grain Substitutes for Stocker and Fattening Cattle

The grains are the most important concentrates used for fattening cattle. Corn, barley, sorghum grain, wheat, and rye are the major grains.

Corn. Corn is the standard fattening grain, and all other grains or grain substitutes are compared to corn in determining their value. Corn may be fed shelled, cracked, or as ground ear corn. Shelled or cracked corn furnishes more nutrients per pound than does ground ear corn, and will produce faster gains when full fed. It takes more experience to feed shelled or cracked corn because there is greater danger of the cattle overeating and going off feed. Although gains will be somewhat slower, ground ear corn can be fed more safely and has the advantage of utilizing the cob. Unless hogs follow the cattle to utilize the undigested corn, it will pay to grind it.

Recent experiments show that high moisture corn, such as corn ensiled or stored in air-tight storage facilities containing up to 32 per cent moisture, produced cheaper gains than dry corn. Cattle consume from 12 to 15 per cent less feed per pound of gain when high moisture corn is used. This has resulted in approximately a 3 per cent less cost per pound of gain.

Barley. Barley may be substituted for corn. Barley has about 85 per cent of the value of corn for cattle feed. Feeding tests show that from 12 to 15 per cent more pounds of barley are used per 100 pounds gain. Barley should be crushed or ground for greatest feed efficiency.

Wheat. Wheat may replace all or any part of the corn fed pound for pound, but it is better when it does not exceed 50 per cent of the ration.

Oats. Oats are better for young calves than for older fattening cattle. They are considered more of a growing feed than a fattening feed. Oats provide bulk when added to corn. If cattle are to be fed on shelled or cracked corn, adding oats to equal one-half of the ration at the start and continuing to use from two to three pounds of oats in the daily ration will eliminate part of the danger of cattle going off feed from overeating. When used as a fattening ration, they are low in food value compared to corn.

Rye. Rye is not palatable to cattle, and if fed in large quantities for a long period, it may slow down feed consumption, resulting in slower gains. Rye should not exceed 25 per cent of the grain ration. It can be used as a corn saver if the price is right.

Grain Sorghums. Grain sorghums can replace corn in the cattle fattening ration, and will produce nearly equal results. Because grain sorghums are hard, grinding improves them for cattle feed.

Molasses. Molasses is well liked by cattle and is often used as an appetizer. When unpalatable feeds, especially low-quality roughages, are fed, cattle may be induced to eat them by sprinkling molasses over the feed. Molasses is not a protein but a carbohydrate feed and a partial replacement for grains. Liquid molasses has a feeding value equal to about 70 per cent of corn pound for pound. Because of its palatability, its chief value is in increasing feed consumption. Molasses may be purchased in liquid or dry form. Mixed protein supplements, designed to be fed in conjunction with low-quality forages, often contain molasses as a source of high energy feed to stimulate bacterial growth in the rumen. Rumen organisms require carbohydrates in order to digest roughages.

Animal Fats. Animal fats, such as tallow and lard, are often surplus products of the packing industry. Considerable research is now in process to determine to what extent these products may be used in livestock feeds. Experiments at Nebraska University and Texas Agricultural Experiment Station indicate that animal fats may be successfully used in livestock feed. At the University of Nebraska, the addition of 5 per cent tallow to a high roughage cattle ration brought cattle to market weight with about half as much corn.

Since fats must be heated to 150° to 160° F. to be mixed with other feed substances, this process requires special mixing facilities. Cattlemen should follow the research and make use of new developments in the feeding of animal fats.

TABLE 26

COMPARATIVE FEED VALUE ON A PER-POUND BASIS OF GRAINS
AND GRAIN SUBSTITUTES FOR FATTENING CATTLE

Feed	Bushel Weight (lbs.)	Value Compared to Corn (%)	Approximate Quart Weight (lbs.)
Shelled corn	56	100	1.7
Corn (ear, ground)	70	85	1.4
Barley (ground)	48	85–90	1.1
Wheat (cracked)	60	100	1.7
Oats (ground)	32	70–75	.7
Rye (cracked)	56	70–80	1.5
Sorghum grain (ground)	50–60	95	1.4–1.5
Molasses (liquid)		70	3.0

Proteins and Protein Substitutes for Stocker and Fattening Cattle

There are a large number of protein concentrates suitable for cattle feeding. The cost per pound of protein should be the chief consideration in making a selection.

Soybean Oil Meal. Soybean oil meal is equal or higher in percentage of protein than other protein meals. With the increase in soybean acreage, it is often cheaper than other similar feeds.

Linseed Oil Meal. Linseed oil meal has long been a favorite source of protein among cattle feeders. It gives cattle a sleek hair coat and is especially popular among cattlemen who fit animals for fairs and shows. Many feeders use a mixture of protein meals, including linseed oil meal.

Cottonseed Meal. Cottonseed meal is a widely used protein supplement. It is especially popular as a cheap source of protein among cattlemen in the Cotton Belt. It is not considered as good as linseed or soybean oil meal for calves under four months of age. It may prove toxic to young calves if fed in too large a quantity.

Dehydrated Alfalfa Meal or Pellets. Dehydrated alfalfa meal or pellets will range from 17 to 20 per cent protein and therefore closely approach what we may term a protein concentrate. Dehydrated alfalfa may be used to replace a part of the protein in the cattle ration. It is also a rich source of carotene and several essential minerals.

Peanut Oil Meal. Peanut oil meal is about equal to cottonseed, soybean, and linseed oil meal for fattening cattle. In some experiments, it was slightly inferior but, for all practical purposes, may be used as a protein supplement for cattle. The price per pound of protein is the deciding factor.

Soybeans. Ground soybeans provide a good source of protein. Generally, the price is too high to make them an economical feed. However, if soybeans are a cheaper source of protein than the other common protein feeds, they provide a good home-grown protein supplement.

Tankage, Fishmeal, and Other Animal Proteins. Animal proteins may be used to make up a part of the protein content of the rations, if they are more economical than the vegetable proteins. Experiments show they have no other advantage over the vegetable proteins in rations for cattle over three months of age.

Urea. Urea is a nitrogen compound. Cattle can convert a certain amount of urea to protein. This is accomplished through the bacterial action which takes place in the rumen. Protein is made by combining the urea nitrogen with carbohydrates into the correct chemical combination. It is essential that some good source of carbohydrates be fed, if urea is contained in the ration. Molasses or grains are usually recommended. It should be remembered that urea is not a protein. The feeding form of urea is known as 262 for it has a protein equivalent of 262 per cent. In other words, one pound of urea will combine with the carbohydrates to make 2.62 pounds of protein. When urea is fed, one pound mixed with six pounds of grain will replace seven pounds of the oil seed meals. Urea may be mixed with soybean or linseed meal and fed as a protein supplement. When mixed, 0.1 pound of urea plus 0.75 pounds of linseed oil meal are equal to 1.5 pounds of linseed oil meal, or 1760 pounds of linseed oil meal plus 240 pounds of urea are equal to 4000 pounds of linseed meal in protein equivalent. If soybean oil meal is used with urea, 0.1 pound of urea plus 0.65 pounds of soybean oil meal equals 1.25 pounds of soybean oil meal.

If urea is mixed with one of the common proteins, as with linseed oil meal, the following example will serve to show how the percentage of protein equivalent of the mixture may be calculated.

1900 lbs. Linseed oil meal = 35% protein   = 665 lbs. protein
100 lbs. Urea feed = 262% protein equivalent = 262 lbs. protein equivalent
_____
2000 lbs. total feed   927 lbs. protein equivalent

927 ÷ 2000 = 46.35% protein equivalent

Precautions in Feeding Urea. It should be remembered that urea, if fed in too great quantities, will cause considerable difficulty. It is toxic if overfed; it will make cattle sick and could possibly be fatal. It is important to have urea evenly mixed with grain or protein supplement; therefore, good mixing facilities are required. Urea should not exceed 1 per cent of the total dry matter in the ration, 3 per cent of the concentrate mixture, or 5 per cent of a high protein supplement. The maximum safe limit is 0.3 pounds of urea per day per animal over 800 pounds, 0.2 pounds for animals between 500 and 800 pounds, 0.1 pound for those between 300 and 500 pounds, and smaller animals should not be fed urea. The protein supplement, containing more urea than the recommended 5 per cent, may be safely fed, if the maximum daily allowance per animal is observed.

Urea has no advantage, except as an economy measure, over other recommended protein concentrates. Its value should be determined in terms of replacing the protein value of other feeds. Urea has no energy, mineral, or vitamin value. This should be considered, if urea is to be fed. Urea should not be mixed with raw soybeans or untoasted soybean oil meal. These feeds contain an enzyme that causes urea to become toxic to the animal.

Mixed Supplements. There is a variety of mixed cattle supplements designed for various types of feeding programs. Where good-quality forage is used as the primary roughage, almost any of the protein meals that have been discussed will prove satisfactory. When low-quality roughages are used, a protein supplement reenforced with additional vitamins and minerals is recommended. If urea is to be used to replace part of the protein in the ration, it is usually fed in a mixed supplement. Following are some mixed supplements that are especially designed to be fed with low-quality roughages but may be used in any ration.

Mixed Supplements Containing
30 to 35 Per Cent Protein or Protein Equivalent

1. PURDUE CATTLE SUPPLEMENT WITH UREA

Feed	Pounds
Soybean oil meal	400.5
Molasses feed (50% molasses)	280.0
Corn or its equivalent	208.0
Urea	40.0
Bone Meal	52.0
Salt (mineralized)	17.0
*Vitamin A & D concentrate	2.5
	1000.0

2. PURDUE SUPPLEMENT A

Feed	Pounds
Soybean oil meal	650.5
Molasses	140.0
Alfalfa meal	140.0
Bone meal	52.0
**Salt with cobalt	17.0
*Vitamin A & D concentrate	.5
	1000.0

* Vitamin A & D concentrate contains 2250 I. U. of A and 300 I. U. of D per gram.

** One ounce of cobalt sulfate added to each 100 pounds of salt.

Feeding and Management of Stockers and Fattening Cattle • 255

Mixed Supplement Containing
48 to 52 Per Cent Protein Equivalent

IOWA SUPPLEMENT

Feed	Pounds
Linseed oil meal	666
Distiller's grains	666
Molasses	268
Urea feed	214
Bone meal	134
Iodized salt	36
Trace mineral mixture	8
Vitamin A & D oil (2250-300)	8
	2000

Purdue cattle researchers developed a supplement designed to be fed with grass silage. Since grass silage is relatively high in protein and vitamins, the Purdue Supplement G is lower in protein, and the vitamin A and D concentrate was not included.

PURDUE SUPPLEMENT G

Feed	Pounds
Alfalfa meal	400
Molasses	329
Dried brewer's grains	132
Bone meal	105
Salt with cobalt	34
	1000

The Iowa Experiment Station has developed an economy supplement consisting of 10 milligrams of stilbestrol per pound, 10 per cent urea, 10 per cent minerals, 15 per cent molasses and the balance a cheap carrier such as ground corncobs. The supplement is known as 10-10-10-15. Following is a list of the ingredients used per ton.

IOWA ECONOMY SUPPLEMENT

Feed	Pounds
Carrier (ground corncobs)	1250
Molasses	300
Urea	200
Dicalcium phosphate	110
Limestone	75
Salt	40
*Stilbosol	20
Trace mineral premix	5

* Stilbosol is a stilbestrol premix carrying 1000 milligrams of stilbestrol per pound.

On the basis of several experiments, this table can be expected to compare favorably with all other supplements, when fed to cattle weighing 500 pounds or more, at the rate of one pound to at least four pounds of corn and three pounds of good legume hay per head daily. It is not recommended for cattle under 500 pounds. This supplement depends upon the nitrogen in the urea combining with the carbohydrates furnished by the other ingredients to provide the necessary protein. Since the farmer cannot purchase the stilbestrol premix, he would have to get a feed company licensed to buy and mix stilbestrol to prepare the Iowa economy supplement.

Minerals and Vitamins for Stockers and Fattening Cattle

Minerals. A mineral mixture for cattle recommended for the area (see Chapter 13), fed free choice, will generally meet the mineral requirements of stocker and fattening cattle if a high-quality roughage, such as legume hays, is fed to the extent of five pounds or more per day. Where the roughage consists mostly of low-quality materials such as corn cobs and corn stalks, a supplement containing minerals is recommended as assurance that the animal will consume enough needed minerals for proper nutrition.

Vitamins. Usually vitamins A and D are all that need concern the cattle feeder. When high-quality forage is used to make up 50 per cent or more of the roughage part of the ration, and the cattle are exposed to sunshine, these vitamins will be supplied in sufficient quantities. When low-quality roughage is used almost exclusively, a supplement containing vitamin A and D concentrate is recommended.

Hormones for Fattening Cattle

Recent experimental work at the Iowa Agricultural Experiment Station has revealed that stilbestrol, when fed in small quantities to fattening cattle, has resulted in considerable feed savings and a higher rate of gain.

What Is Stilbestrol? Stilbestrol is a manufactured chemical that will produce effects similar to those of the hormone, estrogen estradiol, which is secreted by certain glands in the animal body. Stilbestrol is incorporated in the feed for fattening cattle or implanted in pellet form at the base of the ear. Liveweight gains may be stimulated as much as 30 per cent on high-grain fattening rations. Cattle being fed high-roughage rations gained from 10 to 15 per cent more quickly when stilbestrol was added to the ration or implanted. Feed costs have been reduced 10 to 20 per cent when stilbestrol was used.

Stilbestrol is a highly potent chemical and must be fed with caution. The recommended level for feeding stilbestrol is 5 to 20 milligrams per day.

Stilbestrol Premix. Stilbestrol premix varies in content but usually contains 10,000 milligrams of stilbestrol incorporated into 10 pounds of soybean meal and vegetable oil. This premix is then incorporated into a cattle supplement.

Supplements containing 2½, 5, 7½, and 10 milligrams of stilbestrol are now available. The feeder may feed from one to four pounds of supplement and not go over the 20 milligrams level of stilbestrol.

The recommended feeding level is not less than five milligrams and not more than ten milligrams daily, until the last two to three months of the feeding period. Recent experiments indicate that faster gains and greater feed savings resulted when the level of feeding stilbestrol was increased to 20 milligrams during the last three months of the feeding period. Some authorities recommend a lower level not to exceed 7½ milligrams for the early part of the feeding period and up to 10 milligrams the last three months for cattle fed on pasture. The reason given is that fresh grasses apparently contain hormone-like substances which may cause difficulty, if too high a level is fed to cattle on grass. Heifers have shown nearly as much increase in gain as steers from the feeding of stilbestrol. However, prolapsed uteri, excessive teat and udder development, and other undesirable effects have been noted when amounts in excess of 10 milligrams were fed to heifers. For this reason 10 milligrams is the maximum amount recommended for heifers.

Implanting Hormones. Stilbestrol pellets may be implanted at the base of the ear with an instrument especially designed for this purpose. Cattle are placed in a squeeze chute and from 24 to 36 milligrams of stilbestrol is implanted in pellet form. Each pellet contains 12 milligrams. The lower level is used for pasture feeding or for short fed cattle and the higher level for dry lot cattle. The pellets are absorbed over a period of 120 to 180 days. The gains of implanted cattle compare favorably with those made by animals fed stilbestrol. The cost of implanting is less than that of feeding stilbestrol. However, the labor and equipment necessary for implanting must be considered before deciding whether to feed or implant the hormone. More undesirable effects, explained on page 258, have resulted from implanted heifers than from those fed stilbestrol.

Precautions in Feeding Stilbestrol. Unless research proves differently, stilbestrol should not be fed to any animals that are to be kept for breeding purposes. Breeding swine should not be allowed to follow cattle receiving stilbestrol in their rations.

A number of experiments are in progress to determine whether stilbestrol will adversely affect bred heifers, or bred sows following cattle that are being fed stilbestrol. Cattlemen should watch closely the results of these tests.

Recent experiments indicate that young growing cattle may benefit from the feeding of stilbestrol. However, the work up to the time of the writing of this book has not been sufficient to warrant a recommendation. Ranchers and farmers are advised to follow closely the results of further experiments which will determine to what extent it may be advisable to use the drug in rations of young growing cattle.

Antibiotics for Fattening Cattle

Experiments have indicated recently some increased rate of gain and feed efficiency when antibiotics, especially aureomycin and terramycin, have been fed to fattening cattle. Cattle receiving a comparatively low-quality ration have shown the greatest percentage of gain, while those receiving a high-energy ration consisting of full grain feeding and high-quality roughage have shown lower rate of gain. Most of the advantage from antibiotic feeding came during the first three or four months of the feeding period.

The addition of an antibiotic premix to the supplement, to provide 50 to 80 milligrams of aureomycin or terramycin daily for cattle on a high roughage ration, would probably be profitable in view of the results of recent feeding trials.

Tapazole. Tapazole, trade name for a product known chemically as 1-methyl 2-mercaptoimidazole, is a white powder in its pure state. It has a blocking effect upon the thyroid gland in animals. While Tapazole shows promise as.a gain booster *it has not been approved by state and Federal authorities*. Therefore, no recommendation can be made for its use until further experiments have been made and approval granted. It looks promising, however, and cattlemen should follow the research results.

Dynafac. Dynafac, a trade name for a chemobiotic (see Chapter 1) has given inconsistent results as a growth stimulator. Some experiments have shown beneficial results, while others have indicated it is of little value. Further testing of the product will be necessary before accurate recommendations can be given.

Rations for Fattening Cattle. Using the feeds that have been discussed, a large variety of fattening rations may be developed. Many areas produce feeds, not included here, that may be successfully substituted. It is important to use rations that will supply needed nutrients as cheaply as possible. The following are some suggested rations for finishing cattle for market.

RATIONS FOR CATTLE THAT ARE INTENDED
TO MAKE CHOICE OR PRIME GRADES

Feed	*Pounds*
1. Legume hay	½ lb. per cwt. live weight daily
Corn	850
Oats	100
Linseed, soybean, or cottonseed meal or a 30 to 35% protein mixed supplement	50
2. Legume hay	½ lb. per cwt. live weight, daily
Ground ear corn	900
Linseed, soybean, cottonseed meal or 30 to 35% protein mixed supplement	100
3. Legume hay	½ lb. per cwt. live weight, daily
Corn	500
Barley	450
Any recommended protein meal or 30 to 35% protein mixed supplement	50

Feed	Pounds
4. Legume hay	½ lb. per cwt. live weight, daily
Legume and grass silage	2 lb. per cwt. live weight, daily
Sorghum grain	600
Barley	350
Protein meal or 30 to 35% protein	
mixed supplement	50
5. Legume hay	½ lb. per cwt. live weight, daily
Legume-grass silage	2 lb. per cwt. live weight, daily
Corn	500
Sorghum grain	450
Protein meal or 30 to 35% protein	
mixed supplement	50
6. Legume-grass hay	½ lb. per cwt. live weight, daily
Corn	825
Oats	100
Protein meal or 30 to 35% protein	
mixed supplement	75
7. Legume-grass hay	½ lb. per cwt. live weight, daily
Ground ear corn	875
Protein meal or 30 to 35% protein	
mixed supplement	125
8. Grass hay	½ lb. per cwt. live weight, daily
Sorghum or corn silage	2 lb. per cwt. live weight, daily
Corn or sorghum grain	850
Protein meal or 30 to 35% protein	
mixed supplement	150

Note: If cattle are implanted with stilbestrol pellets, it should not be included in the feed. When a stilbestrol supplement is used, the amount of stilbestrol fed daily can be better regulated by hand feeding the protein. This can best be accomplished by sprinkling the supplement over the grain portion of the ration. The amount of stilbestrol should not exceed the level previously recommended. Aureomycin or terramycin may be mixed with the supplement to provide up to 80 milligrams per head daily. The Iowa economy supplement 10-10-10-15, with or without antibiotics, may be substituted at the rate of one pound per head daily for the above protein supplements.

If the feeder has an abundance of low-quality forage, he may desire to buy plain grades of cattle and utilize this roughage. Such cattle may not be expected to grade as high as cattle full-fed grain, but his gains will not be expensive. Following are some suggested rations using low grades of roughages.

Feed	Pounds Fed Daily
1. Chopped corn stalks	10–12
Mixed hay	2–3
Cracked shelled corn	4.5
Purdue Supp. A or a similar commercial	
supplement with stilbestrol and antibiotics	3.5
2. Corn stalk silage	Full feed
Mixed hay	2.0
Cracked shelled corn	7.0
Iowa economy supplement with or	
without antibiotics	2.5
3. Ground corn cobs	11–12
Mixed hay	2
Cracked shelled corn	5.25
Iowa Supp. with or without antibiotics	2.25
4. Ground corn cobs	11–12
Liquid molasses	2–4
Cracked shelled corn	2–3
Iowa Supp. with stilbestrol and antibiotics	2.75

Rations for Wintering Feeders. Feeders who have an abundance of pasture which they wish to utilize, often buy 400 to 600 pound calves or yearlings in the fall, carry them through the winter on a growing ration, and turn them on grass in the spring. Young cattle that are wintered should be fed a ration that will produce from one to 1½ pounds gain per day which is considered a normal growth rate. Following are some suggested rations for wintering feeders intended to be fattened at a later period.

WINTERING RATIONS FOR FEEDER CATTLE

Feed	Pounds Fed Daily
1. Legume-grass hay	Full feed
Minerals	Free choice
2. Ground corn cobs	10–14
Purdue Supp. A	3–3.5
3. Legume-grass hay	5
Corn or sorghum silage	15–25
35–40 protein meal	½
Minerals	Free choice
4. Legume-grass hay	5
Legume-grass silage	15–25
Minerals	Free choice

5. Legume-grass hay	5–8
Corn and cob meal	2–3
Minerals	Free choice

Note: Recent experiments conducted by Iowa State College indicate that stilbestrol will save feed and increase gains when fed to cattle being wintered for later fattening. When stilbestrol was discontinued there was no decrease in gains, beyond the gain expected from other recommended rations that do not include stilbestrol.

Preparing Feed for Cattle. The common method of feeding dry feeds to cattle has been to grind the grains and feed the hay or fodder either chopped or long. Grinding the grains increases their digestibility and reduces the amount of undigested material that passes through the digestive system.

Pelleting Dry Feeds. Recently a great deal of interest has been shown in the use of complete pelleted rations except for silage or other succulent feeds. When this system is used, the dry roughage, grain, supplement, and molasses (if molasses is included in the ration) are ground and run through a pelleting machine.

In experiments conducted by the Illinois Agricultural Experiment station, cattle fed a complete pelleted ration consisting of 65 per cent ground ear corn, 5 per cent blackstrap molasses, 10 per cent soybean meal, and 20 per cent hay gained 100 pounds on 729 pounds of pellets while cattle fed the same ration as meal required 845 pounds of feed for 100 pounds gain and gained 22 pounds less during the feeding period.

Pelleting is especially recommended for self-feeding since the intake of grain and roughage can be controlled. However the cost of pelleting must be considered before deciding whether to feed pellets. If the feed saving and other advantages will offset the cost of pelleting, it will be more economical.

Pastures for Feeders and Fattening Cattle. Good pastures are essential for maximum growth and fattening of cattle on grass. Like breeding cattle, feeders make greater gains on legume-grass pasture than on straight grasses. The pasture mixtures discussed in Chapter 12 are applicable for feeders and fattening cattle.

Factors Influencing Gains on Grass. Several factors, such as age, weight, and condition affect the gains cattle will make on grass.

Age and Weight. Big, thin cattle have more frame on which to put fat and a greater capacity for grass consumption. They can be

Figure 14-4. Self-feeding grain to cattle on grass saves labor when cattle are to be fattened while on pasture.

expected to improve most quickly in condition. Yearlings would rank second in total pounds gain, and calves would be last. However, in proportion to starting weight, calves will make greater gains per hundred pounds original weight than older cattle.

Condition. Cattle that have been wintered well, and are in high condition, will need grain while on grass if they are to continue to gain. It is not economical to turn cattle carrying too good a condition on grass without including grain in the ration. Such cattle will lose weight rather than gain. Cattle that are intended for grass during the pasture season, to be further grown out and fattened the following fall and winter, should not be wintered to gain more than 1½ pounds per day.

Concentrate Rations for Cattle on Grass. The kind and amount of concentrates fed cattle on grass depend upon the gains expected, the amount of pasture and the grains available, and the time cattle are to be marketed. Cattle can be expected to make greater total gains if fed grains on pasture than cattle receiving pasture only. However, when concentrates are fed, less gain due to grass alone will result. It may be more economical not to feed grain to cattle that are on pasture, when the grass is abundant and the feeder expects to finish them in a dry lot at the end of the pasture season.

Cattle receiving concentrates while on pasture may be fed the same grain mixtures, except for roughage, as those in dry lots. The roughage will be provided by grass. If the pasture is from 20 to 50 per cent legumes, the amount of protein supplement may be reduced to one-half the amount generally recommended for dry lot rations in which legumes, such as hay or silage, are fed.

When pastures are not adequate to supply sufficient forage, the pasture may be supplemented with either hay or silage.

Hauling Pasture to Cattle. Green lot feeding of fattening cattle is practiced by some cattle feeders. The practice was described in Chapter 12. The advantages and disadvantages of green lot feeding of fattening cattle are the same as for the breeding herd.

Fattening Cattle on Grass. Cattle feeders who have a considerable amount of pastures available may wish to utilize this grass to replace roughage in the ration. When cattle are pastured, they are usually bought in the fall, wintered at the rate of one to 1½ pounds of gain daily, and turned on pasture when the grass has made sufficient growth in the spring. They are fed a concentrate ration while on grass. Some feeders finish them entirely while on grass, while others will put them in dry lots for a few weeks or months for the final finish. The kind of cattle, market conditions, and available feed largely determine the system followed.

Advantages and Disadvantages of Pasture Fattening. Some advantages of fattening cattle on grass are:

1. Pasture gains are cheaper because less grain and protein is used in the fattening process.
2. The manure is dropped on the pasture (unless green lot feeding is practiced), saving labor in hauling the manure onto the fields.
3. Little or no roughage other than grass is required, reducing labor in feeding and preserving roughages.

Some disadvantages of feeding cattle on grass are:

1. Cattle take longer to reach a desirable finish.
2. They have a lower carcass yield and usually sell for less than the same quality cattle dry-lot fed.
3. Summer heat and flies may slow up gains.

4. Cattle to be fed on grass have to be purchased in the spring, when feeders are scarce, or in the fall, when they must be wintered, thus increasing the time they must be kept.

Starting Cattle on Feed. When cattle are shipped in from a distance, they are tired and need rest. They should have plenty of water and comfortable quarters. Until the cattle become adjusted to their new home, no attempt should be made to start grain feeding. Cattle should be given all the dry hay (preferably a legume and grass mixed hay) they can eat for from ten to 15 days before starting them on grain. They may go on pasture until fully recovered from the effects of shipping. A pasture that has been allowed to grow with partially mature plants provides an excellent feed supply for newly purchased feeders from the range areas. After the cattle have become completely adjusted to their new environment, those intended to be immediately placed on a fattening ration may be started on whatever concentrates the feeding program calls for.

If grains are to be the principle concentrates, yearlings may be started on from two to three pounds of corn, or its equivalent in other grains, per head and continued on this amount until all the cattle are eating grain. Many Western cattle have never tasted grain and must learn to eat it. Placing grain over the roughage will help to get them started on the grain. Care must be exercised to prevent a few that start to eat quickly from overeating. The grain may be increased one pound per head daily until the cattle are consuming 1½ pounds per 100 pounds live weight for cattle which are intended to be finished on a high-grain ration. Further increases should be made at the rate of one pound every four days until they are receiving two pounds per 100 pounds live weight, which is generally considered a full feed. Cattle to be finished on high-roughage rations may be started on grain the same way, but only brought up to four to six pounds or the amount called for in the feeding program. Whatever protein is to be fed should be started with the grain. One-half pound of linseed, soybean, or cottonseed meal, or any other accepted cattle protein may be used at the start of the fattening ration. The rate of increase will depend upon the kind of roughage used. From one to 1½ pounds is usually sufficient when full feeding legume hay or legume silage. When low-quality roughages are used in quantity, from three to 3½ pounds may be necessary. If a high protein equivalent supplement such as one containing urea is used, the amount of the supplement will need to be limited in accordance to the protein content. The common oil seed meals will range from 32 to 47 per cent protein. If the supplement is a 55 to 60 per cent protein or protein equivalent, the amount may be reduced from a third to a half.

To start calves, feed from two to three pounds of oats per head daily until all calves are eating. When all calves are eating, add one pound of shelled corn per head. Increase the corn by one-half pound daily until the calves are consuming two pounds of grain per 100 pounds live weight. The oats may be continued at from two to three pounds or gradually cut back and discontinued. Protein supplement may be fed the same as for yearlings.

When ground ear corn is fed to fattening cattle, it should be remembered that the cob makes up about one-fourth of the total weight, so more will be needed than if shelled corn is used.

Feeding Efficiency Factors

Rate of Gain. Thin two-year-old cattle that are thrifty and healthy will make the greatest gains in the feed lot, followed by yearlings and calves. This may be explained on the basis that big cattle consume more total feed that may be turned into beef and, therefore, make more rapid gains.

Economy of Gains. Calves will produce 100 pounds of gain on less feed than older cattle of the same quality, although the time required for the same gain will be greater. The gain in body weight of older cattle is due largely to fat, while much of the gain on calves is due to growth. The time required to put market finish on calves is greater than for older cattle. Calves digest their feed more thoroughly than do older cattle.

As cattle fatten, the amount of feed required per hundred weight gain becomes greater. Experiments show that cattle weighing approximately 600 pounds when started on a fattening ration require 10 units of feed for the first 100 pounds of gain, 13 units for the second 100 pounds, 14-15 units for the third, 17-18 for the fourth and 22 or more for the fifth hundred pounds of gain. The difference in market price for highly finished cattle, as compared to medium finish, is the important consideration in deciding how long to feed cattle.

TABLE 27

Good to Choice Steers, Dry Lot, High Grain Ration, Corn Calculated at $1.10 and $1.50 per Bushel*

	400-lb. calf		640-lb. yearling		840-lb. 2-year-old	
	Corn		Corn		Corn	
Grain	$1.10	$1.50	$1.10	$1.50	$1.10	$1.50
1st 100 lbs.	9.57	13.05	11.55	15.75	11.77	16.05
2nd 100 lbs.	10.67	14.55	13.53	18.45	14.41	·19.65
3rd 100 lbs.	11.99	16.35	15.73	21.45	18.48	25.20
4th 100 lbs.	13.64	18.60	19.25	26.25	25.74	35.10
5th 100 lbs.	17.16	23.40	24.64	33.60	(17.93)	(24.45)
6th 100 lbs.	19.14	26.10				
7th 100 lbs.	24.09	32.85				

Iowa State College Extension. EC Inf. 70.

* For 50 lbs. gain.

Self-Feeding Fattening Cattle. Cattle that have been brought up to a full feed of grain may be successfully put on self-feeders. Self-feeders are especially valuable when full feeding cattle on pasture. Self-feeders reduce labor, but they require that proteins and grains be thoroughly mixed.

Purdue researchers successfully self-fed cattle using a ratio of eight pounds of ground ear corn to one pound of Purdue Supplement A (see page 255). No hay was available after the first 28 days. The only roughage the cattle received after that period was the cobs contained in the ear corn. A complete pelleted ration, consisting of 65 per cent ground ear corn, 5 per cent blackstrap molasses, 10 per cent soybean meal, 20 per cent ground hay self-fed, plus 12 pounds of corn silage, produced an average of 2.75 pound gain per head daily and produced 100 pounds of gain on 729 pounds of pellets and 442 pounds of corn silage in an Illinois experiment. The rate of gain could have been increased, and the amount of feed per hundred pounds of gain reduced, by implanting the cattle or adding stilbestrol to the pelleted ration in the recommended amount.

Summary

Cattle feeding involves a considerable capital outlay and risk. Only those who carefully plan their feeding operations and thoroughly understand cattle feeding can expect to make a profit. Direct cattle feeding profits must come from margin on original weight, profit on gain, or both. Manure value and increased fertility of the land are important sources of indirect profits.

Roughages should make up a large part of the cattle ration. Preserved dried roughages may be divided into two major classes: (1) dry roughages and (2) silage. There may be further classification as high-quality and low-quality roughages. Good legume and grass hay or silage, corn or sorghum silage are recognized as high-quality roughages, while corn cobs, dry corn stalks, or corn stalk silage, straw, and coarse stemy hay are considered low-quality roughages.

All of the grains may be successfully fed to cattle; however, corn, sorghum, and barley are the more common feed grains used. Molasses may be substituted for part of the grain. Animal fats have also been successfully substituted for part of the grain in cattle fattening rations.

The oil seed meals are the most common sources of protein supplements used in cattle feeding. Urea, a nitrogen product, may be successfully substituted for a part of the protein in the ration. The amount that can be safely fed depends upon the age of the animal and the kind of ration fed.

Several complete supplements have been developed for feeding cattle, especially when low-quality roughage is used. These supplements include vitamins, minerals, and some high energy feeds, such as molasses or corn, in addition to 30 to 50 per cent protein.

Minerals and vitamins A and D need to be provided in the ration for beef cattle. When legume hay or a good quality silage is fed, vitamin A will usually be supplied. Sunshine will supply vitamin D if cattle are exposed to direct sunlight.

Antibiotics, especially aureomycin and terramycin, have increased gains on young cattle, especially those receiving a high-roughage ration.

Stilbestrol, a hormone-like substance, produced faster gains when included in the ration of fattening cattle or implanted as pellets at the base of the ear.

Pelleting rations has shown some advantage in gain and efficiency over ground feeds.

Cattle will make substantial gains on pasture. Big, thin cattle will make the greatest gain. Cattle turned on pasture without grain should not be in too high a condition if they are expected to gain in weight.

Grass may be substituted for dry roughage or silage in the fattening ration. The concentrates fed to cattle on good pasture will not need to be as high in protein as those added in dry lot feeding. Grass usually cheapens gains but grass fat cattle will usually not sell for quite as high a price.

Cattle should be started on feed slowly and gradually brought up to full feed. Caution must be exercised to prevent overeating during the start of a fattening ration. Self-feeding is practical if done according to recommendations.

Calves will gain on less feed per 100 pounds than will older cattle. As the weight increases, more feed is required for each 100 pounds of gain.

• *Questions*

1. Where are most of the cattle that go into the feed yards produced?
2. What are the sources of profit from feeding beef cattle? Explain.
3. Discuss the comparative value of the various kinds of dry roughages.
4. Why is it essential to include some high energy feeds in the ration when low-quality roughage is fed?
5. What kind of materials make good preservatives?
6. Compare the feeding value of the grains for fattening cattle.
7. What advantages are there in feeding molasses?
8. How do the various oil seed meals and dehydrated alfalfa meal compare as cattle supplements?
9. Under what conditions is it advisable to feed a complete supplement?
10. How may urea be used as a protein replacement?
11. What are the limitations of feeding urea?
12. Discuss the need for minerals and vitamins in the rations for stockers and fattening cattle.
13. What is stilbestrol? What are current limitations on its use?

14. What advantages are there in feeding stilbestrol?
15. What is the recommended level for feeding stilbestrol?
16. How may stilbestrol be purchased?
17. What advantages are there in feeding antibiotics to cattle?
18. Make up several suggested rations for cattle intended to make choice or prime slaughter grades.
19. Give several rations using low grade roughages.
20. Give some good rations for wintering feeders to make only a growth gain.
21. How do pelleted rations compare to ground feeds?
22. What kind of cattle gain best on grass? Discuss.
23. What are the factors that affect the feed efficiency when cattle are fattened?
24. What advantages are there in fattening cattle on grass?
25. Discuss the various ways one could successfully start cattle on feed.

• *References*

Baker, Guy N. and Marvel L. Baker, *The Use of Various Pastures in Producing Finished Yearling Steers,* North Platte Substation Bulletin 47, University of Nebraska, Lincoln, Nebraska, 1952.

Beef Cattle Investigations in Texas, 1888-1950, Bulletin 724, Texas Agricultural Experiment Station, College Station, Texas.

Beef Cattle Feeding and Breeding Investigations, Kansas State College of Agricultural Experiment Station, Circulars 272, 278, 298, Hays, Kansas, 1951 to 1956.

Beesen, W. M. and T. W. Perry, *Supplementing Growing and Fattening Rations for Cattle,* Agricultural Experiment Station, Mimeo A. H. 123, Purdue University, Lafayette, Indiana, 1953.

Beesen, W. M., and T. W. Perry, *Chopped Forage vs. Pasture for Feeding Cattle,* Agricultural Experiment Station Mimeo A. H. 122, Purdue University, Lafayette, Indiana, 1953.

Beesen, W. M., and T. W. Perry, *Antibiotics for Suckling Calves and Yearlings,* Agricultural Experiment Station, Mimeo A. H. 130, Purdue University, Lafayette, Indiana, 1954.

Beesen, W. M., T. W. Perry and M. T. Mohler, *Fattening Cattle on Corn Silage and Grass Silage,* Agricultural Experiment Station, Mimeo A. H. 105-106, Purdue University, Lafayette, Indiana, 1953.

Burroughs, Wise, C. W. McDonald, J. M. Scholl and Bob Zimmerman, *Grass Silage, Chopped Cornstalks and Various Supplemental Feeds for Wintering Yearling Steers,* Agricultural Experiment Station FSR-54, Iowa State College, Ames, Iowa, 1951-52.

Burroughs, Wise, and C. C. Culbertson, *Adding Stilbestrol to Feeds for Growing and Fattening Beef Cattle*, Agricultural Experiment Station and Extension Service Pamphlet 215, Iowa State College, Ames, Iowa, 1954.

Cattle Feeding Experiments, Cattle Feeders Report, Iowa State College, Ames, Iowa, 1954, 1955, 1956, 1957, 1958.

Cattle Feeders Day Report, Purdue University, Lafayette, Indiana, 1957, 1958.

Cattle Feeders Day Report, University of Illinois, Urbana, Illinois, 1954, 1955, 1956, 1957, 1958.

Corn and Sorghum Silage, E. C. 131, University of Nebraska, Lincoln, Nebraska, 1954.

Feeding and Breeding Test with Beef Cattle, Feeders Day Report, No. MP-34, 1954, Oklahoma A & M College, Stillwater, Oklahoma.

Mayo, Henry, *Pastures for Growing and Fattening Cattle*, Agricultural Experiment Station Mimeo, A. H. 128, Purdue University, Lafayette, Indiana, 1954.

Recommended Nutrient Allowances for Beef Cattle, A Report of the Committee on Animal Nutrition, No. IV, Revised, National Research Council, Washington, D. C., 1950.

Webb, R. J., G. F. Cmarik, *Comparison of Feeding a Ration as Pellets and as Meal to Yearling Steers*, Agricultural Experiment Station PS-27, University of Illinois, Urbana, Illinois.

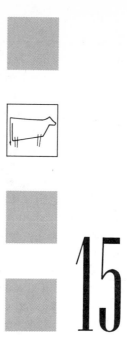

Buying and Selling
Beef Cattle

The farmer, rancher, or feeder who has produced or fattened cattle for the market is very much concerned over the price received for his product. The market price, at the time of sale, is largely responsible in determining whether the enterprise is profitable.

Marketing Feeder Cattle

The producer of feeder cattle depends largely upon the farmers in the grain producing areas for his market. It is equally true that farmers who make a business of fattening cattle are dependent upon producers for the cattle to fill their feed yards. The methods whereby the producer and feeder get together are important to both.

Direct Buying and Selling. In recent years there has been an increase in the number of sales made by ranchers directly to the feeder. Such sales are generally made on the ranch. Feeders make the purchases either by contract in advance of delivery date or take the cattle immediately after sale. Approximately 20 per cent of cattle sales are made directly to farmers and ranchers.

Contract Sales. When cattle are contracted for, an agreement is made between the buyer and seller. The important provisions in contract sales are: (1) *Price*, which involves the amount paid down to seal the bargain and the final amount at the time the cattle are removed from the farm or the ranch. (2) *Time and place of delivery*. If the ranch is equipped with scales and loading facilities, the cattle may be taken directly from the range by the buyer; otherwise the seller usually agrees to deliver the cattle to a certain weighing and loading point. (3) *The percentage of shrinkage to be allowed*. When cattle are moved for any distance or handled extensively, a certain amount of body weight is lost, resulting largely from the feed and water the animal eliminates that is not being replaced by regular feeding and watering. The amount of shrinkage depends upon the time in transit, weather conditions, the length of time cattle are allowed to rest, feed and drink before weighing, and the age and weight of the cattle. No figure can be used that will be accurate enough to determine shrinkage in all cases, but 3 per cent is commonly used for feeder cattle.

If it is agreed to pay a certain price per hundred at the ranch, but is necessary to transport the cattle several miles before weighing, a shrinkage percentage ranging from 1 to 5 per cent (depending upon the distance moved and time in transit) may be agreed upon. The practice of adding to or deducting from actual weight is referred to as *pencil shrinkage*.

Direct Selling with Immediate Delivery. Immediate delivery or acceptance of the cattle involves no type of contract other than the price per hundred and allowable shrinkage. Ownership of the cattle is transferred from seller to buyer within a short time.

The chief advantage of direct dealing is that it eliminates the middleman and the profit he would necessarily have to make for handling the cattle. Contract sales are usually made for the following reasons: they insure the buyer the cattle he wants when he wants them; usually, both buyer and seller feel they have made a good price bargain; and both know in advance what the price will be and when delivery will be made.

Figure 15-1. (above) The auction sale is one of the principal methods for selling feeder cattle.

Figure 15-2. (left) Choice feeder cattle ready for shipment into the Corn Belt for fattening. (Courtesy American Hereford Association)

Selling Through a Dealer. Cattle dealers are individuals or companies that make a business of buying cattle for the feeders. The dealers either buy on a commission basis or depend on reselling the cattle at a higher figure than the cost for their profit. Many times small operators can get their cattle more cheaply through a dealer than if they spent the time and money necessary to inspect and buy their own cattle.

Order Buyers. An order buyer is a cattle dealer who specializes in buying cattle to meet the needs of his customers. Since the order buyer makes it his business to know where the cattle are and the market conditions, he can very quickly inform the feeder of the prospects he has of filling his order.

Auction Sales. Auction sales are a common method of transferring cattle from producer to feeder. Most auctions are private or company owned. The selling service is paid for by a commission (which is usually paid by the seller) charged on a percentage of the selling price.

Terminal Markets. Large terminal feeder cattle markets are located in many Western and Midwestern cities. Producers who sell through these markets consign their cattle to a commission firm that will sell on a commission basis. A terminal market usually consists of a stockyard company which furnishes yards, scales, loading and unloading facilities, and feed and water for the stock. For this service, the stockyards company charges a fee. The amount will vary, but it usually ranges from 75 to 90 cents per head for yardage.

If the cattle are shipped to a commission firm, selling experts will handle and dispose of the cattle for the owner. They sort mixed grades into uniform lots and see that the cattle bring the best possible price obtainable at the time. The costs of yardage, feed, insurance, and selling charges are deducted, and the balance is paid to the owner. Cattle shipped to a central market must be consigned to a commission firm.

Selecting a Method of Marketing. The important factor in selecting the method of marketing is determining which method will bring the greatest net income. The wise operator, in attempting to determine what his cattle will bring at home, will get market information from prospective markets and estimate shrinkage and other costs before finally deciding upon the method of marketing he will use.

Information That Is Helpful in Determining When to Sell. No one can consistently predict the time when the market will be highest. However, a knowledge of certain facts will be helpful.

The Total Number of Cattle. Numbers of cattle, as compared to normal, will affect the markets. When cattle numbers are high, increased marketings will result, and downward pressure on the market can be expected.

Conditions in the Grain Area. The Corn Belt farmer is the principal buyer of feeder cattle. The number he buys will depend upon his feed supply. If crop conditions are good, the producer can

Figure 15-3. These cattle are in the stock yards at a large terminal market where they will be sold by a commission company. (Courtesy Fred Fredrich)

276

expect a heavy demand for feeders. The reverse is true if the crop outlook is unfavorable.

Slaughter Cattle Prices. When slaughter cattle prices are high in proportion to feed costs, it indirectly affects the price of feeder cattle. Cattle feeders are inclined to buy more cattle and pay higher prices, if the outlook for fat cattle is good. Also the packers will furnish more competition for range cattle that are in good flesh.

Grass Condition on the Range. When the range areas are well supplied with moisture, there will be lots of feed. Ranchers are inclined to keep their cattle until late, putting on as much weight as possible before selling. Under good grazing conditions, early fall feeder markets are usually high, followed by an exceptional slump with the first general snowfall, at which time feeders pour into the market.

If a severe drought should occur over a large area of the range country, it will usually force large numbers of cattle to market unseasonally. Such a condition will usually cause a rather sharp drop in feeder cattle prices.

Employment Conditions. Farmers and ranchers are dependent upon the consumer for his final market. What, and how much, the average American eats are the factors that determine prices of farm products. Since the largest group of people are the laboring class, their wages and the number employed are important. When the number of unemployed increases, beef and all farm products can be expected to move downward in price.

Sources of Market Information. Current market information based on the previously mentioned conditions may be obtained from agricultural colleges, state and federal market information services, newspapers, magazines, radio and television reports, and private outlook information services.

While no one can always be sure when the market conditions will be best, a careful study of the available information should enable the cattle producer to judge the market with reasonable accuracy, resulting in a more profitable beef business.

Marketing Slaughter Cattle

Classes and Grades. The successful marketing of slaughter cattle is determined by feeding for the proper grade, methods of marketing, and the time the producer sells. Slaughter cattle are classified and graded according to sex, age, weight, and grade. The following table shows the commonly used system of classifying and grading.

TABLE 28

CLASSIFICATION AND GRADES OF SLAUGHTER CATTLE

	Sex	Age	Weight	Grade
Vealers	Bulls Heifers	Less than 3 months	Light Medium Heavy	Prime, choice, good, standard, utility, cull
Calves	Bulls Heifers Steers	3 to 8 months	Light Medium Heavy	Prime, choice, good, standard, utility, cull
	Steers	Yearlings 2-year-olds	Light Medium Heavy Light Medium Heavy	Prime, choice, good, standard, commercial, utility, cutter, canner Prime, choice, good, standard, commercial, utility, cutter, canner
	Heifers	Yearlings 2-year-olds	Light Medium Heavy Light Medium Heavy	Prime, choice, good, standard, commercial, utility, cutter, canner Prime, choice, good, standard, commercial, utility, cutter, canner
	Cows	All ages	All weights	Choice, good, standard, commercial, utility, cutter, canner
	Bulls	Yearlings 2-year-olds and older	All weights Light Medium Heavy	Choice, good, commercial, utility, cutter, canner Choice, good, commercial, utility, cutter, canner
	Stags	All ages	All weights	Choice, good, commercial, utility, cutter, canner

The higher grades consist of cattle well-developed in the areas of valuable cuts (back, loin, and hind quarters) and uniformly covered with a high degree of finish. Choice and prime cattle usually are long-time grain-fed cattle. They not only cut a high yielding carcass, but also one with a clear, white, firm fat that is well distributed around and through the muscle or lean meat. Calves, yearlings, and two-year-olds produce the more popular-sized cuts

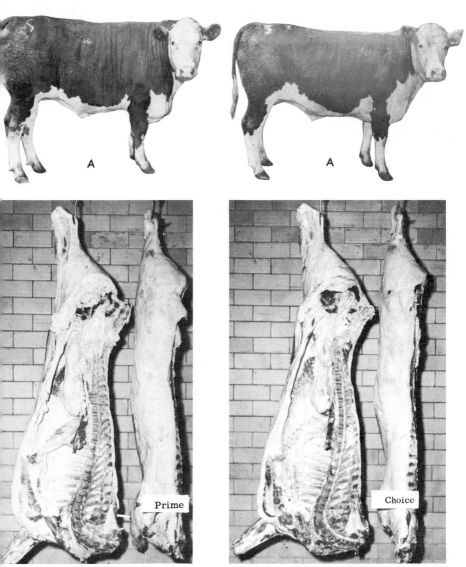

B

B

Figure 15-4. (left) (A) A prime slaughter steer and (B) the carcass from the same steer. Note the uniform covering of fat, the plump well-developed round, the width of loin, and general uniformity. (Courtesy Rath Packing Company)

Figure 15-5. (right) (A) This choice slaughter steer made a desirable carcass. (B) However, as compared to the prime carcass, it shows less finish, lacks the width and uniformity, and is not as well developed in the round as the prime carcass. (Courtesy Rath Packing Company)

Buying and Selling Beef Cattle • 279

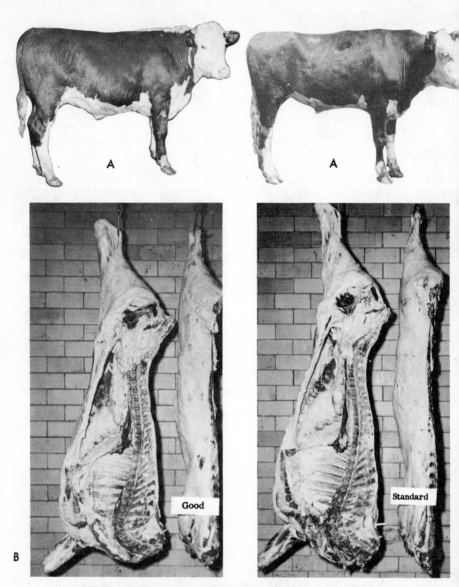

Figure 15-6. (left) (A) This steer graded "good." Although the carcass (B) is quite desirable, it definitely lacks finish and proper development in the back, loin, and round. (Courtesy Rath Packing Company)

Figure 15-7. (right) (A & B) This commercial slaughter steer is too low in finish and too poorly developed in the regions of the valuable cuts for high quality beef. (Courtesy Rath Packing Company)

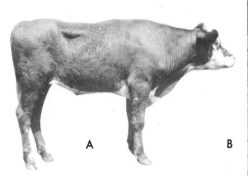

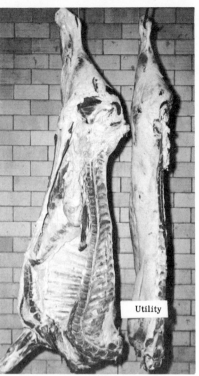

Utility

Figure 15-8. (A & B) This utility grade slaughter steer would not provide tender, highly palatable steaks. A few fair quality roasts may be provided from the loin and round. The rest of the carcass could best be utilized as boiling beef, hamburger, or processed meats. (Courtesy Rath Packing Company)

and are more tender and flavorful than older cattle. In contrast to older and lower grade animals, young prime cattle usually are sold at premium prices. The carcass yield is important in determining grades. Young prime cattle will dress from 62 to 67 per cent; choice, from 60 to 64 per cent; good, from 58 to 60 per cent; and standard, from 52 to 58 per cent, while cutters and canners will average around 42 per cent. Vealers have a different flavor then calves, yearlings, and two-year-olds. Their meat is classed as veal rather than beef.

Types of Market Procedure. The cattle feeder may (1) sell cattle directly to the packer or a packer-buyer, who generally works on a salary paid by the packer he represents, (2) ship to a central market and consign to a commission firm or (3) sell to a private buyer, who buys from the feeder and either sells directly to the packer or ships to a central market.

Selling to the Packer or Packer Buyer. Many cattle are trucked or shipped directly to the packer. Usually on the day they arrive they are weighed and paid for at the price being paid for their grade. Most packing companies have buyers in the field who will bid on the cattle at the farm; such bids may be qualified by adding a shrinkage stipulation.

Selling on Grade and Yield. During recent years there has been some interest on the part of farmers in selling their cattle to the packers on what has become known as the *grade and yield*. Under this method of sale, the live weight of the cattle has nothing to do with the price that is paid. After the cattle are slaughtered, the pounds of meat, the grade, and the yield are the determining factors in establishing the price. For example, suppose a farmer sells a 1,000 pound steer and the steer hangs up a 560 pound carcass of good beef. If the value given to this grade of beef is $.50 per pound, then 560 pounds times $.50 equals $280 or the amount the farmer received. This is equivalent to $.28 per pound of live weight. Should the animal grade higher or lower than good, the price is adjusted upward or downward, depending upon the grade. If the dressing percentage is higher or lower than that given in the example (56 per cent), then there will be more or less weight in the dressed carcass, and the farmer will be paid accordingly.

Selling Through a Commission Firm. When slaughter cattle are shipped to a central market, either by rail or truck, they are billed to a commission firm. The process of yarding and marketing of fat cattle is essentially the same as that described for the marketing of feeder cattle through a central market. The chief difference lies primarily in who buys the cattle. In the large, central markets that deal essentially with slaughter cattle, the packer is the chief purchaser. There are several packing plants located near the stockyards at the central markets. They rely principally on the cattle shipped to that market for their supply. In addition to the packing plants located at the market, other plants may send buyers to pur-

Figure 15-9. This photo shows the location of the wholesale cuts of beef and the average percentage of each. (Abernathy photo. Courtesy American Aberdeen-Angus Breeders' Assn.)

RUMP 4%
SIRLOIN 9%
SHORT LOIN 8%
RIB 9%
CHUCK 26%
ROUND 20%
FLANK 4%
SHORT PLATE 7%
FORE SHANK 4%
BRISKET 5%
SUET 4%

282

chase animals of a certain weight and grade for which they have a demand. These buyers are known as *order buyers*.

Selling to Private Buyers. Many communities have private stock buyers who buy cattle and other livestock and send them on to the packers. Such buyers offer an outlet for small lots of animals, because they generally have yard facilities where they can bunch animals according to age, sex, and grade before shipping or trucking them on to market.

Cooperative Marketing. Various types of cooperative marketing facilities have developed during recent years. Cooperative commission companies have been the principal type of cooperative that has affected beef cattle marketing. The commission companies operate much like private concerns except the profits are paid to the members in the form of patronage dividends.

Seasonal Price Trends. The marketing of slaughter cattle follows a rather definite seasonal pattern, if a period of years is used to determine that pattern. However, so many factors may affect the marketing for any one year that the long-time trends cannot always be relied upon as a means of hitting the top market in any one given year. However, for the cattleman who continues in the feeding business over a period of years, a study of these long-time trends may prove profitable.

Losses Due to Damaged Carcasses

Losses running into millions of dollars are sustained by the livestock industry as a result of damaged carcasses. Most of this damage could be prevented. Producers are not aware of the personal losses caused by bruises, because such injuries can only be determined after slaughter. Usually the producer has his check by the time the animal is slaughtered and thinks this loss is the packers'. However, packers have learned through experience the percentage of such losses, and these losses are reflected in the prices bid for live animals. Most bruised carcasses result from horn damage, careless handling, overcrowding, prodding with clubs, and feed lot obstacles. Bruised areas in the carcass must be trimmed out. The areas of the carcass removed cannot be sold for human consumption. They usually go into the manufacture of livestock feed where they are worth less money. Most of the bruises occurring on beef animals are in the regions of the most valuable cuts, loins, rumps, rounds, and ribs.

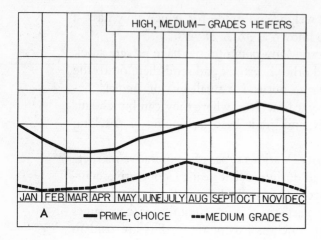

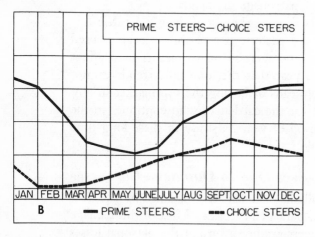

Figure 15-10. (A) This chart shows the average seasonal price trends for the high and medium grades of heifers, while (B) shows the price trend for prime and choice steers. (Courtesy U.S.D.A.)

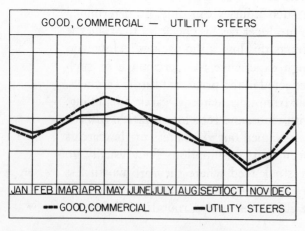

Figure 15-11. This chart shows the price trend for the lower grades of steers. (Courtesy U.S.D.A.)

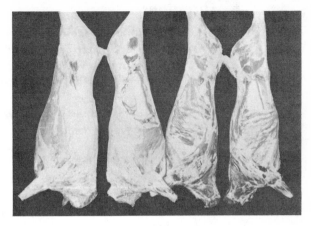

Figure 15-12. Losses such as these cost the livestock industry millions of dollars each year. Most of this loss could be prevented by dehorning and more careful handling of livestock. (Courtesy Livestock Conservation, Inc.)

Summary

Feeder cattle may be marketed by direct selling either on contract for future delivery or immediate transfer from buyer to seller. Other methods of selling feeder cattle are through auctions, dealers, and central markets.

The shipping cost, shrinkage, and prices are important considerations in determining the methods of marketing.

Information that is helpful in deciding when to market feeder cattle consists of numbers of cattle, feed conditions, prices of slaughter cattle, and the employment situation. This information may be obtained from agricultural colleges, state and federal market information services, newspapers, magazines, radio and television reports, and private outlook information services.

Slaughter cattle are classified according to sex, age, weight, and grade. They may be sold directly to a packer or a packer buyer on a liveweight basis or grade and yield. Other methods are through a commission company at a central market or to a private buyer.

Seasonal price trends for the various grades, national income and employment conditions, supply of cattle, and the feed situation constitute information helpful to the successful marketing of slaughter cattle.

Damage to valuable parts of the carcass resulting from unwise handling of the live animals costs the cattle industry thousands of dollars each year. Most of this loss could be averted.

● Questions

1. List the different methods by which feeder cattle may be marketed and describe each method.
2. What is meant by contract sales?
3. What is shrinkage? How does the shrinkage affect the prices received?
4. What are the important factors in selecting a method of marketing feeder cattle?
5. What information is helpful in determining when to sell and how may it be secured?
6. What are the classes and grades of slaughter cattle?
7. How may slaughter cattle be marketed? Explain.
8. What information is needed to market slaughter cattle successfully?
9. Explain the price trends for different grades of cattle.
10. Discuss the losses due to damaged carcasses and how they may be averted.

● References

Hamilton, Eugene, *Seasonal Market Variations and Their Importance to the Iowa Farmer*, Agricultural Experiment Station and Extension Service, Bulletin P 5, Iowa State College, Ames, Iowa.

Malone, Carl C., *Making Your Farm Pay*, Iowa State College Press, Ames, Iowa, 1951.

Marketing Feeder Cattle and Sheep in the North Central Region, Agricultural Experiment Station, Bulletin 410, University of Nebraska, Lincoln, Nebraska.

Potter, E. L., *The Marketing of Oregon Livestock*, Agricultural Experiment Station, Bulletin 514, Oregon State College, Corvallis, Oregon.

Stevens, I. M., R. T. Burdick, H. G. Mason and H. P. Gazaway, *Marketing Western Feeder Cattle*, Agricultural Experiment Station, Bulletin 317, University of Wyoming, Laramie, Wyoming.

DAIRY PRODUCTION

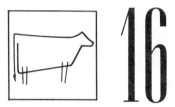

16

The Dairy Production Industry

The production of dairy products in this nation is big business. Dairy cattle are kept on about 51 per cent of the farms, and in 1955 provided 15.1 per cent of our nation's cash farm income. The income from the sale of dairy products was larger than the income from hog sales, or from poultry and sheep sales combined.

Milk has an important place in the American diet. It is palatable and nutritious. It contains most of the food nutrients needed by humans and by young animals.

Consumption of Dairy Products

When our grandfathers were boys, cows were used to supply the family with milk and butter. Occasionally, the milk and cream

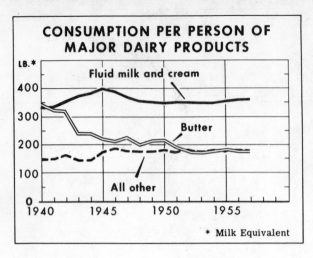

CONSUMPTION PER PERSON OF MAJOR DAIRY PRODUCTS

Figure 16-1. Consumption per person of major dairy products, 1940-1957. (Courtesy U.S.D.A. Agricultural Marketing Service)

were used in making ice cream and cheese. The development of refrigeration, pasteurization, homogenization, and scientific methods of producing and processing milk and milk products have made it possible for us to make more effective use of these products.

In 1924 the average person consumed 17.8 pounds of butter, 4.5 pounds of cheese, and 6.8 quarts of ice cream. The average consumption per person in 1957 was 8.5 pounds of butter, 7.8 pounds of cheese, and 14 quarts of ice cream.

TABLE 29

U.S. PER CAPITA CONSUMPTION OF DAIRY PRODUCTS

Year	Butter	Cheese	Ice Cream	Fresh Whole Milk
	pounds	pounds	pounds	pounds
1924	17.8	4.6	8.8	269
1930	17.6	4.7	9.8	270
1936	16.8	5.4	9.5	264
1942	15.9	6.4	15.8	290
1948	10.0	6.9	18.5	295
1954	8.9	7.9	17.4	301
1957	8.5	7.8	17.9	308

Dairy Statistics, U.S.D.A., 1957

The average consumption of butter has decreased yearly since 1924, and the consumption of cheese and ice cream has nearly doubled.

Fluid Milk and Cream. In 1925 the per capita consumption of fluid milk and cream was 353.5 pounds, whereas the consumption at the close of World War II in 1945 was 425.0 pounds. Milk and cream consumption has increased about 20 per cent since 1940.

Evaporated and Condensed Milk and Dry Milk Solids. The consumption of these products has not been large, but there has been some increase during recent years. Some processors are now marketing a concentrated liquid milk which may greatly influence the methods used in processing and transporting fluid milk. During the 1935-1939 period, each person in this country consumed an average of 15.2 pounds of evaporated milk, 1.6 pounds of condensed milk, and 1.9 pounds of nonfat milk solids. The 1957 consumption was 13.2 pounds, 1.8 pounds and 5.7 pounds of these milk products per person.

Butter Versus Margarine. We consume about one-half as much butter today as we consumed before World War II. We use less fats in our diets, and margarine is replacing part of the butter consumption. During 1935-1939, the per capita margarine consumption was 2.9 pounds, but the average in 1957 was 8.6 pounds. In 1957, we consumed more margarine than butter.

Oleomargarine production has increased from 614 million pounds produced in 1945 to 1,369 million pounds produced in 1956. Margarine sold in 1957 for about two-fifths the price of butter.

TABLE 30

USE OF MILK SOLD BY FARMERS

(Expressed in Percentages of Total)

Year	Fluid milk	Butter	Cheese	Evaporated milk	Condensed whole milk	Dry whole milk	Frozen dairy products
	%	%	%	%	%	%	%
1925	36.4	46.3	7.9	4.1	1.2	.1	4.3
1930	36.5	43.4	6.9	4.1	.9	.2	4.0
1935	35.5	44.5	8.4	5.2	.6	.2	3.4
1940	34.3	42.6	9.1	6.1	.7	.3	4.4
1945	41.2	27.8	11.3	8.3	.8	1.7	5.3
1950	43.1	28.3	12.0	6.3	.8	1.0	7.0
1955	46.0	25.4	12.5	5.1	.7	.8	7.5
1956	46.3	25.1	12.4	4.9	.8	.7	7.6

Agricultural Marketing Service, U.S.D.A.

Utilization of Milk

The changes in consumption of dairy products have been influential in the methods used in processing milk and in the emphasis placed upon the butterfat content of milk. The butterfat content is becoming less important in milk production.

Shown in Table 30 are the changes that have come about in the use of the milk produced in this country since 1925.

Production of Dairy Products

With the exception of a few years during the drought, cow numbers increased in this country until 1944. Since that time, the number of cows has decreased from nearly 26 million in 1944 to 20.5 million by January, 1958. Production of dairy products has increased even more rapidly than cow numbers, because of increased production per cow. Shown in Figure 16-3 are the changes that have come about in cow numbers and in production per cow from 1940 to 1957.

Leading States in Dairy Cow Numbers. The states with the most dairy cows by January, 1957 were:

1	Wisconsin	2,279,000	6	California	868,000
2	Minnesota	1,390,000	7	Ohio	830,000
3	New York	1,315,000	8	Missouri	813,000
4	Iowa	992,000	9	Michigan	781,000
5	Pennsylvania	942,000	10	Illinois	758,000

Nearly 50 per cent of the dairy cows in the nation on January, 1957 were in the North Central states. Eighteen per cent were in the South Central states, 15 per cent in the North Atlantic states, 9 per cent in the South Atlantic states, and 10 per cent were in the Western states.

In 1924, there was roughly one cow per every five persons in this nation. There was one cow to nine persons in 1958.

We had only 87 per cent as many cows in 1957 as we had in 1940, but they produced 134 per cent more than the 1940 milk production.

The demand for milk and milk products in the future is bright. Our national population is increasing at the rate of about three million persons per year. We will need 132 to 133 million gallons of milk each year just to feed the increase in population.

Figure 16-2. A highly specialized dairy farm. Note the large barns and silos. (Courtesy The Holstein-Friesian Assn. of America)

Average Milk Production Per Cow. According to the Bureau of Agricultural Economics, the average cow in the United States in 1957 produced 6,162 pounds of milk. The high states in average production of milk per cow in 1957 were: California, 8,880 pounds; Rhode Island, 7,970 pounds; New Jersey, 7,950 pounds; Arizona, 7,850 pounds; Wisconsin, 7,640 pounds; and Massachusetts, 7,400 pounds.

Production of Cows in Dairy Herd Improvement Association Herds. By January, 1958; there were 1,548,884 cows on test in the 1,544 dairy herd improvement associations in the United States. These cows represented 39,985 herds and about 7.6 per cent of all dairy cows in the nation.

TABLE 31

AVERAGE PRODUCTION OF COWS

IN DAIRY HERD IMPROVEMENT ASSOCIATIONS, 1906-1956

Year	Cows on Test (Number)	Average Milk (Pounds)	Production Butterfat (Pounds)
1906	239	5,430	215
1910	25,000*	5,730*	227*
1920	203,472	6,241	247
1930	507,549	7,642	303
1940	676,141	8,133	331
1950	1,088,872	9,172	370
1956	1,406,306	9,713	383

U.S.D.A., Bureau of Dairy Industry
* Estimated.

In 1906, there were 239 cows on test, which produced an average of 5,430 pounds of milk and 215 pounds of butterfat. In 1956, there were 1,406,306 cows on test, which produced an average of 9,713 pounds of milk and 383 pounds of butterfat.

Creamery Butter Production. Although only about 25 per cent of the milk produced in this country is used in making butter, the industry is very important in some states. Minnesota produced, in 1956, 305 million pounds of butter; Wisconsin produced 243 million pounds; and Iowa produced 196 million pounds. These three states produced 53 per cent of the 1,409 million pounds of butter produced in 1956.

Cheese Production. About 12 per cent of the milk produced in 1956 was used in the production of American cheese. Wisconsin was responsible for nearly 50 per cent of the 1956 cheese production. Wisconsin produced 451 million pounds; Missouri, 92 million pounds; Minnesota, 49 million pounds; and Illinois, 43 million pounds. The nation's production in 1956 was 852 million pounds.

Ice Cream Production. The consumption of ice cream has nearly doubled since 1935. Approximately 7.6 per cent of the milk produced in this country in 1957 was used in ice cream production. Pennsylvania led all states in ice cream production in 1957 with 75 million gallons. New York ranked second with 66 million; California, third with 51 million; Ohio, fourth with 42 million; and Illinois ranked fifth with 33 million gallons produced.

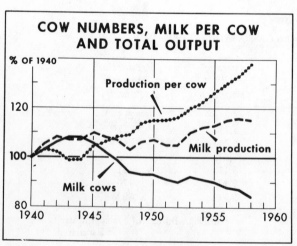

COW NUMBERS, MILK PER COW AND TOTAL OUTPUT

Figure 16-3. Cow numbers, milk per cow, and total output. Cow numbers in 1958 were about 84 per cent of the 1940 figure but production per cow had increased to 137 per cent. (Courtesy U.S.D.A. Agricultural Marketing Service)

Figure 16-4. This 10-cow Ayrshire herd had in 1958 a lifetime production of over 1,000,000 pounds of milk. (Strohmeyer and Carpenter photo. Courtesy Ayrshire Breeders' Assn.)

Advantages and Disadvantages of Dairying

The fact that dairy cattle are maintained on approximately 51 per cent of our farms indicates that the enterprise has certain advantages. The fact that the enterprise is not popular on about the same number of farms, and that the number of farms on which dairy cattle are kept is decreasing, indicates certain disadvantages.

Advantages of Dairying. 1. *Dairying fits in well in diversified farming programs.* Diversification is highly recommended on many farms to permit efficient use of farm labor and economical use of buildings and equipment, and to reduce the risk involved in having but one or two sources of income.

2. *Cows are efficient consumers of roughages.* Cows make effective use of large quantities of roughages which on some farms may be wasted.

3. *Dairying provides a stable income.* Beef and sheep prices are less stable than the prices of dairy products.

4. *Income is distributed throughout the year.* Most of such farm income, such as that from beef, lamb, corn, wheat, and other crops, is seasonal. Dairy production and income may be distributed throughout the year.

5. *Dairy production improves the family diet and reduces food costs.* Milk is a basic food, and an important item in the family food budget. A small dairy enterprise can be justified on many farms, if

The Dairy Production Industry • 293

only for the production of milk products for family consumption. This is especially true where large families are involved. Farmers in the South Central states in 1956 used more milk for home consumption than was marketed.

6. *Skim milk is of high value as poultry and swine feed.* Farmers who sell butterfat make effective use of skim milk in feeding pigs and poultry. Skim milk is an excellent source of protein, minerals, and vitamins.

7. *Dairying aids in maintaining soil fertility.* Dairy farming fits in well with grassland farming. Legumes and grasses are grown for hay and pasture. These crops are soil-conserving or -building crops. The manure produced is distributed on the land, and returns plant food nutrients to the soil.

Disadvantages of Dairying. 1. *Dairying has a high labor requirement.* Dairying is a full-time job. Cows must be fed and milked at least twice each day, and time is consumed in managing the enterprise and in marketing the products, whereas other types of livestock require less labor.

2. *Considerable capital is required.* The production of high-quality dairy products requires that certain sanitary housing and equipment standards be met. These standards have increased the investment in the dairy enterprise. According to U.S.D.A. data, the average dairy cow in the nation by January, 1958, was valued at $176. The cows in New Jersey were valued at $260, those in Wisconsin at $200, and those in California at $215. A herd of 20 good cows involves an investment of from $4,000 to $6,000.

The investment in feed for a herd of 20 cows is quite large. The average cost of feeding a cow in 1957, according to national dairy herd improvement association records, was about $151. A herd of 20 cows will cost about $3,000 to feed.

3. *There are many hazards in dairy production.* Dairy cows may become infected with brucellosis, tuberculosis, and other diseases. Disease losses are serious when valuable animals are involved.

Breeding, nutritional, housing, and market problems also may cause losses, but these losses are usually no more serious with dairy cattle than with other types of livestock.

4. *Substitutes for dairy products are materially affecting the dairy enterprise.* The change in status of butter due to butter substitutes has affected the profitableness of the dairy enterprise. The

quality of butter needs to be improved, and better marketing practices are needed. The cost of producing butter must be reduced if it is to compete with butter substitutes.

Factors in Profitable Production

Dairying usually can be expected to produce a rather high return on investment in feed, when labor costs are ignored. Where family labor can be used, dairying is quite profitable. It may be another matter, if hired labor must be used. Labor and feed costs are the major factors in dairy production. Building and equipment costs are secondary in most cases.

Data shown in Table 32 indicate the returns per $100 feed fed to dairy cattle and to other classes of livestock.

TABLE 32

RETURNS PER $100 WORTH OF FEED

FED TO DIFFERENT CLASSES OF LIVESTOCK

Classes of Livestock	Returns per $100 feed fed	
	5 yr. ave. 1952-1956	24 yr. ave. 1933-1956
Beef cow herds	$ 92	$115
Dairy cow herds	162	171
Dual purpose herds	103	133
Feeder cattle bought	103	123
Native sheep raised	98	122
Feeder sheep bought	97	121
Hogs	140	146
Poultry	129	161

Illinois Farm Bureau, Farm Management Service Report, Northern Ill., 1956

Effect of Quantity of Production upon Cost. According to DHIA records, the best way to increase the profit from the dairy herd is to increase production. Records show that the income over feed costs increases as the level of milk production is increased. It costs about $16.50 more per year to feed a cow which produced 9,000 pounds of milk than it costs to feed a cow which produced 7,000 pounds. The income over feed cost was $188 for the cow which produced 7,000 pounds, and $218 for the 9,000 pound cow.

A herd of twenty cows, producing an average of 9,000 pounds of milk, will net the owner $600 more per year than will the same number of cows which produce an average of only 7,000 pounds, even though the feed bill was higher for the former.

TABLE 33

HIGH-PRODUCING COWS PRODUCE MILK
AT LOWER FEED COST PER 100 POUNDS

Level of Milk Production	Value of Product	Feed Cost	Income over Feed Cost	Feed cost per 100 lbs. of milk
Pounds	Dollars	Dollars	Dollars	Dollars
5,124	255	134	128	2.62
7,035	345	156	189	2.22
9,122	396	174	222	1.91
10,974	452	194	258	1.77
12,928	523	211	311	1.63
14,880	590	231	352	1.55

Dairy Statistics, U.S.D.A., 1957

Methods of Increasing Dairy Profits

The average production of the cows in the dairy herd improvement associations of this nation, in 1957, was about one and one-half times as much milk and butterfat as the average cow in the nation. Production can be increased on most farms by carefully analyzing methods, and making the changes necessary to bring the herd up to the most profitable level of production.

The following are the essentials in developing a profitable dairy enterprise:

1. Select carefully production and breeding stock.
2. Follow a constructive breeding program.
3. Provide adequate but economical housing.
4. Feed cows a balanced ration according to their maintenance and production needs.
5. Make efficient and economical use of high quality hay, pasture, and silage crops.
6. Provide an adequate water supply.
7. Use good management practices in growing out herd replacement stock.

8. Follow production practices conducive to the production of high quality milk.
9. Safeguard the herd from diseases and parasites.
10. Keep production records of individual cows, and cull animals as the need arises.
11. Select the best method of marketing and the best outlet.
12. Adjust the scope of the dairy enterprise to the capital, feed, and labor available, and to the market outlook.

Summary

Dairy cattle provided 15.1 per cent of our nation's cash farm income in 1955. The number of dairy cows in this nation by January, 1958 was 20.5 million, a reduction of 5.5 million from the number in 1944. Wisconsin, Minnesota, and New York lead the states in number of milk cows.

The average production per cow in 1956 was 9,713 pounds of milk and 383 pounds of butterfat.

Minnesota, Wisconsin, and Iowa produced 53 per cent of the nation's butter in 1956. Only about 25 per cent of the nation's milk production is used in making butter. Twelve per cent of our total milk production is used to make cheese. Wisconsin was responsible in 1956 for nearly 50 per cent of the nation's cheese production. About 7.6 per cent of the milk produced in this country is used in the manufacture of ice cream. Pennsylvania, New York, and California are the largest ice cream producing states.

Each person in the United States consumed, in 1957, 8.5 pounds of butter, 7.8 pounds of cheese, and 17.9 quarts of ice cream. Butter consumption is declining and margarine consumption is increasing.

Dairying fits well in diversified farming programs. The income from dairying is quite stable and well distributed throughout the year. Dairy production is less risky than beef production, encourages soil conservation, and aids in reducing family living costs.

The income per hour of labor is not great in dairy production because of the high labor requirement. Labor and feed are the two major factors in milk production.

Dairy income may be increased by careful selection of production and breeding animals, by feeding better rations, by making efficient use of hay and pasture crops, by controlling diseases, by improving the quality of product marketed, and by adjusting the scope of the enterprise to the market outlook and to the capital, housing, feed, and labor available.

● Questions

1. How does the income from the dairy enterprise in your community compare with the income from the other livestock enterprises?
2. What changes have come about in the consumption of dairy products in this country during the past 25 years?
3. Which states lead in milk production, and how do you account for their large production?
4. What changes have come about in average production of milk and butterfat per cow during the past 20 years?
5. How does the production of the average cow in your herd, or in the herd with which you are most familiar, compare with the average for all cows (a) in the nation? (b) in Dairy Herd Improvement Associations?
6. Which provides the best market for milk in your community: fluid milk distributors, the cheese factory, the creamery, or the condensed milk plant? Explain.
7. Explain the chief advantages and disadvantages of dairy production.
8. How much milk and butterfat do the cows on your farm need to produce to net a profit?
9. What factors do you need to consider in improving dairy production on your farm?

● References

Knodt, C. B., Successful Dairying, McGraw-Hill Book Company, Inc., New York, 1954.

National Milk Producers Federation, Dairy Producer Highlights, Washington, D. C., 1957.

U. S. Department of Agriculture, Dairy Statistics, Statistical Bulletin No. 218, Washington, D. C., 1957.

U. S. Department of Agriculture, The Dairy Situation, Agricultural Marketing Service, Washington, D. C., August, 1957, December, 1957.

Yapp, Wm. W., and Wm. D. Nevens, Dairy Cattle, Selection, Feeding and Management, John Wiley & Sons Inc., New York, 1955.

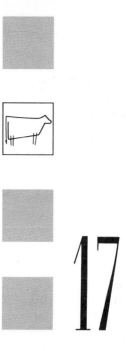

Selection of Breeding Stock

Good seed stock is essential for profitable production in both crops and livestock. Fertilizer applications made to high-yielding hybrid strains of corn net more profit than when applied to low-yielding strains. Heavy feeding of concentrates to choice feeder cattle may be very profitable, while the same feeding program applied to common steers usually is unprofitable. The same principle may be applied to dairy production.

Dairy cows are maintained for their production of milk and offspring, and they vary in their capacity to produce. In 1956-1957, the 25 high-producing herds in the Dairy Herd Improvement Association in Iowa produced an average of 13,863 pounds of milk and 547 pounds of butterfat. The 13 low-producing herds produced an average of 4,968 pounds of.milk and 196 pounds of butterfat. The differences in production were due to several factors, but most important were the type and inherent productiveness of the cows, and the feeding programs which were followed.

It is not unusual to discover cows in individual herds which produce 1½ to two times as much milk and butterfat as other cows in the same herd which were fed the same rations. In one state nearly 9 per cent of all cows in DHIA herds were sold in 1956-1957 because of low production. It pays to use good judgment in selecting the cows to be used in starting a dairy enterprise, and it pays to cull out the unprofitable cows in established herds.

Factors in Selecting Dairy Animals

Four factors or criteria may be involved in selecting dairy animals: (1) breed, (2) pedigree, (3) production records, and (4) physical appearance.

Most dairymen who maintain breeding herds maintain but one breed. With the use of artificial insemination, however, it is possible to keep cows of more than one breed and provide satisfactory bull service. Pedigree information is available for purebred dairy animals but is not always available for grades.

Production records are available for animals in DHIA herds and in many other herds which have been tested by vocational agriculture students, 4-H members, or by the individual breeders. More than 7.6 per cent of the milk cows of the nation by January, 1958, were on test in dairy herd improvement associations.

Quite often the selection of dairy animals is based largely upon the general physical appearance and type of the individual. When pedigree and production record information is not available, selection must be based upon the characteristics of the individual animals.

The ideal method in selecting dairy animals is to have available and consider carefully all four criteria—breed, pedigree, production record, and physical appearance.

Parts of a Cow

It is important that we know the parts of a cow, and understand the terminology applied to those parts, to be able to follow the discussion related to the selection of dairy animals. Shown in Figure 17-1 is a picture of a dairy cow with the various parts indicated.

Breeds of Dairy Cattle

There is no one best breed of dairy cattle, but there may be a best breed for an individual farmer. The type and quality of breeding stock available in the community, the climatic conditions,

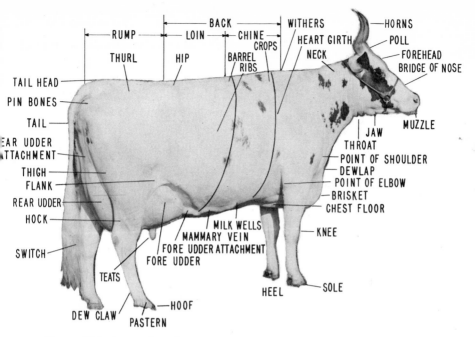

Figure 17-1. Parts of a dairy cow. (Strohmeyer and Carpenter photo.
Courtesy Ayrshire Breeders' Association)

the availability of markets for milk and butterfat, the types of
pasture and forage crops available, and the personal preference of
the individual dairyman are the determining factors in selecting a
breed.

Some breeds are more rugged than others and, as a result, are
better grazers and can stand colder climates. Some breeds consume
larger amounts of roughages and concentrates. The breeds differ
somewhat in the butterfat content of the milk.

There are good individuals in every breed, and the differences
between breeds are of less importance than the differences within
the individual breeds. The breed best suited to a production program should be carefully selected, and major emphasis should be
placed upon the breeding or selecting of individuals which will be
most productive under your management.

The five common breeds of dairy cattle are the Holstein-Frie-
sian, the Guernsey, the Jersey, the Ayrshire, and the Brown Swiss.
Two other dairy breeds are grown in smaller numbers—the Red
Danish and the Dutch Belted.

Holstein-Friesian. *Origin.* Holstein cattle had their origin in Holland, and were imported to this country beginning about 1625. In Holland, they were called Friesians and were bred to produce large quantities of milk for use in making cheese. Most of the importations of Holsteins were made between 1875 and 1905.

Color. To be eligible for registration, a Holstein must be black and white, and the amounts of black and white may vary from white with a few black spots to almost black. The switch must always be white. Animals that are all white, all black, or have black on their legs below the knees or hocks are not recorded.

Size. The standard weight for Holstein cows is 1250 pounds, and bulls should weigh at least 1800 pounds. Many cows weigh 1300 to 1600 pounds, and some bulls weigh over a ton. Holsteins are larger than most of the animals of other breeds.

Conformation. Animals of this breed are ruggedly built, and possess large feeding capacities and udders. The head is long, narrow, and straight. Straight thighs and slightly rounded withers are desired.

Disposition. The cows are quiet and docile, but the bulls may be vicious.

Grazing Ability. Holstein cows are excellent grazers, especially on good pastures. They have large middles and can consume large amounts of forage. They do not thrive as well as some of the smaller breeds on poor pastures.

Production. Holstein milk is lower in fat than is milk from any of the other dairy breeds. It averages about 3.5 per cent butterfat but varies from about 2.5 to 4.3. Holsteins produce large quantities of milk and rate high in total butterfat production.

The all-time top butterfat producer of the breed is Haven Hill Crescent Gewina Count 2891773 (Ex.). She is owned by Rock River Farms, of Byron, Illinois. Her official 365 day record made on three milkings a day and completed in 1956 totalled 38,878 pounds of milk and 1,523 pounds of butterfat.

The milk champion of the Holstein breed is Green Meadow Lily Pabst 2802406 (GP) owned by Merle H. Green of Elsie, Michigan. This cow completed, in December, 1951, a record production of 42,805 pounds of milk containing 1,246 pounds of butterfat in 365 days. She also was milked three times a day.

Holstein cows on official test are classified according to their production as Advanced Registry cows. Cows two years old must produce 318 pounds of fat in 365 days: three-year-olds, 372 pounds; four-year-olds, 426 pounds; and five-year-olds must produce 480 pounds of butterfat in 365 days.

Holstein calves are large and vigorous, weighing an average of about 90 pounds. Steers of this breed feed out well and produce lighter colored fat than steers of the other dairy breeds.

Availability of Breeding Stock. More Holsteins were recorded in 1957 than cows of any other dairy breed. A total of 212,445 animals were recorded with the Holstein-Friesian Association of America, Brattleboro, Vermont. Of the 1,074 proved dairy sires used by the artificial insemination associations in this country in 1957, 485 were Holsteins. According to DHIA records, more Holsteins were reported in some states than cows of all other dairy breeds combined.

Guernsey. *Origin.* This breed has been imported from the small Island of Guernsey, which is located off the coast of France. Approximately 113,000 head of Guernseys have been imported.

Color. The color of the Guernsey varies from a light fawn to almost red, with white markings on the face, legs, switch, and flank. Some white may appear on the body. The nose should be cream or buff-colored; however, smoky color is permitted. The skin is yellow.

Size. Guernsey cows average about 1,100 pounds but vary from 800 to 1,300 pounds. The bulls average about 1,700 pounds.

Conformation. The Guernsey is less rugged than the Holstein, but more rugged than the Jersey. The cows may be inclined to be rough over the rump and weak in the loin. The udders are less symmetrical than those of the Jersey. The face of the Guernsey is double-dished but longer than that of the Jersey.

Disposition. Cows of this breed are alert and active but are not nervous. They are easily managed.

Grazing Ability. The Guernsey is a good grazer but not equal to the Holstein on good pasture or to the Jersey on poor pasture.

Production. Guernsey milk has a golden color and is popular on the consumer market. It contains nearly 5 per cent fat. "Golden Guernsey" milk quite often sells at a premium. Guernseys usually produce less milk than the Holstein, but that is higher in fat content.

To June, 1948, a total of 29,302 cows on official test carried calves 200 days or more and produced an average of 10,716 pounds of milk and 532 pounds of butterfat. The average test was 4.9.

Figure 17-2. The ideal type Holstein bull. (Courtesy The Holstein - Friesian Assn. of America)

Figure 17-3. The ideal type Holstein cow. (Courtesy The Holstein - Friesian Assn. of America)

Figure 17-4. Green Meadow Lily Pabst 2802406 (GP), the champion Holstein milk producer. She produced 42,805 pounds of milk containing 1,246 pounds of butterfat in 1951. (Strohmeyer and Carpenter photo. Courtesy The Holstein - Friesian Assn. of America)

Figure 17-5. The ideal type Guernsey bull. (Courtesy The American Guernsey Cattle Club)

Figure 17-6. The ideal type Guernsey cow. (Courtesy The American Guernsey Cattle Club)

Figure 17-7. Longmeadow Minnie 1104226, the champion butterfat producer of the Guernsey breed. She produced, in 1957, 1,461 pounds of butterfat. (Courtesy The American Guernsey Cattle Club)

Figure 17-8. Chief's Son of Etta, Grand Champion Jersey bull at the 1957 International Dairy Show. (Strohmeyer and Carpenter photo. Courtesy The American Jersey Cattle Club)

Figure 17-9. Masteraim Sleeper Dora, Grand Champion Jersey Cow at the 1957 National Jersey Show. (Strohmeyer and Carpenter photo. Courtesy The American Jersey Cattle Club)

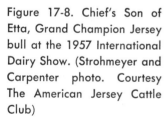

The champion butterfat producer of the Guernsey breed is Langmeadow Minnie 1104226. She produced, in 1957, in 365 days, 1,461 pounds of butterfat and 26,695 pounds of milk. She is owned by Howard H. Colley of Romeo, Michigan.

Haddon's M. Ida 1245489 is the top Guernsey milk producer. In 1957, she produced 28,787 pounds of milk and 1,235 pounds of butterfat on three times a day milking in 365 days. She is owned by Grace and Robert Moffat of Dayton, Pennsylvania.

Availability of Breeding Stock. Guernseys are grown in all areas of the nation and, in 1957, ranked second to the Holstein breed in number of purebred animal recordings. A total of 75,899 animals were recorded by the American Guernsey Cattle Club of Peterborough, N.H. Of the 1,074 proved sires used by artificial insemination associations in the nation in 1957, 229 were Guernseys.

Jersey. *Origin.* This breed was developed on the Island of Jersey in the English Channel. Importations of Jerseys to this country began around 1850. About 37,000 animals have been imported, of which 4,800 head were brought in since 1935.

Color. Jerseys vary in color from light fawn to black and from white-spotted to solid in marking. The tongue and switch may be black or white. The muzzle is black with a light encircling ring.

Size. The Jersey is the smallest of the dairy breeds. The cows range in weight from 800 to 1,100 pounds and the bulls from 1,200 to 1,600 pounds. The imported animals are usually smaller than the Jerseys produced in this country.

Conformation. The Jersey approaches the true dairy type. The cows have straight top lines, level rumps, and sharp withers. Their heads have a double dish, and they show dairy temperament in eyes and neck. Jerseys have excellent udders, both in shape and in fore and rear attachment.

Disposition. Jerseys are inclined to be nervous and sensitive. They can be pets under good management or mean under poor management. The bulls of this breed are often quite vicious.

Grazing Ability. No dairy animal excels the Jersey in grazing ability on medium to poor pastures. They are small and active, so their maintenance requirements are lower than for cows of the larger breeds.

Production. Jersey calves are small at birth and more difficult to raise than calves of some of the larger breeds. Calves usually weigh from 50 to 60 pounds. Jerseys mature, however, in 24 to 26 months.

Jersey milk averages about 5.3 per cent fat and contains almost 15 per cent solids. It sells at a premium because of its superior quality. It is yellow in color and is often sold as "Jersey Cream Line" milk.

Jerseys do not produce large quantities of milk, but they produce it economically on little feed.

The Register of Merit and Herd Test records are kept of the production of Jersey cows by the American Jersey Cattle Club of Columbus, Ohio. To March 1948, 76,862 production records had been accepted. They averaged 9,037 pounds of milk and 485.3 pounds of butterfat. The average butterfat test was 5.37 per cent.

The top butterfat producer of the Jersey breed is June Volunteer Fantasy owned by John Lindow of Independence, Oregon. She produced 1,319 pounds of fat and 20,097 pounds of milk in 365 days on three times a day milking. The milk tested 6.6 per cent fat.

Marlu Milady owned by Marlu Farm of Lincroft, New Jersey is the highest milk producer of the breed. She produced 25,293 pounds of milk and 1,210 pounds of fat in 365 days. She also was milked three times a day. The average milk tested 4.8 per cent fat.

Availability of Breeding Stock. Jerseys are more numerous in the South, East, and Pacific Coast areas. In 1957, 68,403 animals were recorded. The breed ranks third in number of animals recorded, in the number of bulls used in artificial insemination associations, and in the number of cows in DHIA herds.

Ayrshire. *Origin.* This breed was developed in Scotland and was first imported to this country in 1822. Since 1920 Ayrshire importations have been largely from Canada.

Color. Ayrshires are red with white markings or white with red markings. The red may be very light or almost black.

Size. The size of the Ayrshire is in between that of the Guernsey and the Holstein. Cows average about 1,250 pounds, and the bulls weigh from 1,600 to 2,300 pounds.

Conformation. The Ayrshire is considered by many as the most beautiful dairy breed. The animals have straight top lines, level rumps, and good udders. Ayrshires have long horns which are trained upward. Ayrshires may be shorter and thicker in the neck than some of the other dairy breeds.

Disposition. Ayrshires are very active and may be nervous and hard to manage. They are good rustlers.

Grazing Ability. Ayrshires are excellent grazers because of their ruggedness, stamina, and activity.

Production. Ayrshires do not produce as much milk or butterfat as some of the other breeds. The milk usually averages 4.0 per cent butterfat and about 12.75 per cent total solids.

The Ayrshire Herd Test plan is followed in production testing. All cows in the herd must be tested, being milked twice daily for 305 days. Neshaminy Miss Phett 269618 completed in 1951 an all-breed record of 20,946 pounds of 4.9 per cent milk and 1,036 pounds of actual fat in 305 days.

The average production of cows, tested on the Ayrshire Herd Test plan up to 1948, was 9,016 pounds of milk and 367.8 pounds of butterfat. The average butterfat test was 4.08 per cent.

Ayrshire calves weigh 70 to 80 pounds and make good vealers. The meat from Ayrshire cattle has better color than that from Jerseys or Guernseys. Ayrshires mature in 26 to 28 months.

Availability of Breeding Stock. Ayrshires are more prevalent in the New England states, Pennsylvania, and New York. Only 19,238 animals were recorded by the Ayrshire Breeders Association of Brandon, Vermont, in 1957, and only 56 of the 1,074 proved bulls used by the artificial insemination associations in 1957 were of this breed. Only 1.4 per cent of the cows tested in Dairy Herd Improvement Associations in Iowa in 1956-1957 were Ayrshires.

Brown Swiss. *Origin.* Brown Swiss cattle were developed in the mountainous areas of Switzerland and the first importation to this country took place in 1869. A total of about 185 animals have been imported.

Color. The color varies from a light fawn to almost black. The muzzle and a stripe along the backbone are light in color. The nose, tongue, switch, and horn tips are black.

Size. The Brown Swiss breed is the largest, most rugged, and meatiest breed of dairy cattle. Mature cows weigh from 1,200 to 1,400 pounds, and bulls weigh from 1,600 to 2,400 pounds.

Conformation. This breed is used in Switzerland for power as well as for milk and beef, and as a result is not as refined as the other dairy breeds. The type and conformation of Brown Swiss cattle has been greatly improved during the last 20 years. Cows of this breed have large bones, large heads which are usually dished, and thick, loose skin. Animals of this breed are not as angular as those of the other dairy breeds.

Disposition. This breed is quiet, docile, and easily managed.

Grazing Ability. Brown Swiss cattle are good grazers, because they are rugged and active.

Figure 17-10. Vista Grande King, ideal type Ayrshire bull. (Strohmeyer and Carpenter photo. Courtesy Ayrshire Breeders' Assn.)

Figure 17-11. Sandy Springs Better Cheer, ideal type Ayrshire cow. Grand Champion at 1957 Dairy Cattle Congress and International Dairy Show. (Strohmeyer and Carpenter photo. Courtesy Ayrshire Breeders' Assn.)

Figure 17-12. Hy Crest Diamond Jubilee, Grand Champion Brown Swiss Bull 1958 National Dairy Cattle Congress. and 1958 International Dairy Show. (Strohmeyer and Carpenter photo. Courtesy Brown Swiss Cattle Breeders' Assn.)

Production. Calves of this breed will weigh from 90 to 100 pounds at birth. The fat is white, and they make good vealers. Steers and cows put on gains rapidly, producing good beef.

Brown Swiss milk is white in color and contains about 4 per cent fat. Registry of Production and Herd Improvement Tests are supervised by the Brown Swiss Breeders Associations of Beloit, Wisconsin. To October, 1947, 11,171 cows had completed 305 day records, averaging 9,446 pounds of milk and 365 pounds of butterfat on two-times-a-day milking.

Active Acres Bessie owned by Fred Schluter of Titusville, New Jersey holds the all-time, all-breed butterfat record. She produced, in 1957, 1,544 pounds of fat and 31,166 pounds of milk in 365 days on three times a day milking. The Brown Swiss milk champion is Royal's Rapture of Lee's Hill. She is owned by Lee's Hill Farm of New London, New Jersey.

Availability of Breeding Stock. Brown Swiss cattle are most numerous in Wisconsin, Illinois, New York, and Michigan. Only 6.6 per cent of DHIA cows in Iowa in 1956-1957 were of this breed. Seventy-nine of the 1,074 proven bulls used in artificial insemination associations in the nation in 1957 were Brown Swiss. In 1956-1957, 20,861 animals were registered.

Red Danish. This breed was imported from Denmark by the U. S. Department of Agriculture, and animals were placed with some state colleges for experimental purposes. There were two males and 20 females in the original shipment.

The Michigan State College and a group of Michigan farmers have been proving sires for the U. S. Department of Agriculture, and as a result the American Red Danish Cattle Association has been formed with headquarters at Fairview, Michigan.

The American Red Danish Cattle Association News listed nine herds with 400 or more pounds of butterfat produced per cow in 1952. The butterfat test averages slightly over 4 per cent. Mature cows in average condition weigh from 1,300 to 1,500 pounds.

Dutch Belted. Dutch Belted cattle are native of Holland, and were imported in 1840 by P. T. Barnum of the Barnum and Bailey Circus. A number of herds were developed in the New York and Pennsylvania area.

According to R. F. Litsey, of Nashville, Tennessee, Secretary of the Dutch Belted Cattle Association of America, no animals are now on test. Herds are located in the New England states, Georgia, Florida, and Tennessee.

Mature cows weigh from 900 to 1,500 pounds, and bulls average about 2,000 pounds. The milk tests about 4 per cent butterfat. The highest producing Dutch Belted cow, Loraine No. 3020, produced 18,211 pounds of milk and 816 pounds of fat.

Pedigree

A pedigree describing the ancestors of an animal may be very helpful in selecting dairy cattle. Only a small percentage of all dairy cattle are purebreds, and the pedigrees of grade animals are not usually available. Following is a partial pedigree for a former butterfat producer owned by Carnation Farms, Seattle, Washington:

CARNATION HOMESTEAD DAISY MADCAP

H. B. No. 2337079-Ear Tag 5083
Born July 20, 1942
Advanced Registry Records

At 9 years, 5 months: milk 36,414.1 lbs.; fat 1,511.8 lbs.; 4.1%; 365 days.
At 7 years, 6 months: milk 34,533 lbs.; fat 1,413.6 lbs.; 4.1%; 365 days.
At 6 years, 3 months: milk 30,942 lbs.; fat 1,173.1 lbs.; 4.1%; 365 days.
At 2 years, 8 months: milk 17,971 lbs.; fat 696.2 lbs.; (Class B) 365 days.

Sire: Governor of Carnation
629472
Sire, All-American Get of
Sire, 1939 and 1940

35 Daughters over 1,000 lbs.
of fat.

Grandsire: North Star Joe Homestead
291065
All-American Aged Bull, 1924
57 A. R. Daughters
12 from 837 to 1,027 lbs. fat.

Grandam: Carnation Inka Walker
Hazelwood 1281792
Fat, 365 days   1,149.4 lbs.
Milk, (4.7%)   24,481.2 lbs.

Dam: Carnation Daisy Madcap
2023545
Fat, 365 days (9y)   1,018 lbs.
Milk, 365 days   29,188 lbs.
Fat, 365 days (2y)   944 lbs.
Milk, 365 days   29,185 lbs.

Grandsire: Carnation Butter King
739005
Sired by Sir Inka May, All-American
Junior Yearling, 1924.
Sired two daughters with 1,000 lbs. fat
records.

Grandam: Carnation Orms by Madcap
1554602
6-3 A-milk, 36, 851 lbs.; fat 1,313 lbs.
5-2 A-milk, 31,644 lbs.; fat 1,061 lbs.

The production records of a purebred animal and of its ancestors appear on the pedigree, as shown in the previous paragraphs. Increasingly large numbers of our dairy herds are being tested in dairy herd improvement association programs. During 1957, more than 565,360 lactation records were reported by the dairy herd improvement association supervisors in the United States. A large number of purebred cows were on official tests that were supervised by the various breed associations. It is not difficult to find breeding stock with production records, or from sires and dams with production records. This information takes much of the guesswork out of dairy cattle selection.

Proven Sires. The Bureau of Dairy Industry began, in 1936, a sire-proving program and in 1956-1957, 5,265 dairy sires were proved. New York, Pennsylvania, Wisconsin, Iowa, and Minnesota lead the states in number of bulls proven. More than 390 sires were proven in each of these states.

To prove a bull, the production of at least five daughters is compared with the production of their dams. This information is very helpful in buying both male and female breeding stock.

Testing the Home Herd. Only a small percentage of our dairy cows are in DHIA herds because of the cost of the program, and because of shortages of DHIA supervisors. Some dairymen, too, have not been sold on the testing program. What methods can the small dairyman use in making his own tests? In the main, there are two methods: (1) he can cooperate with the local DHIA in an owner-sampler testing program, or (2) he can take his own samples and do his own testing, using equipment owned privately, cooperatively, or by the local school or extension service.

On January 1, 1958, there were 39,985 herds participating in the 2,293 dairy herd improvement associations in the United States. Owner-sampler dairy records were being kept in 1958 by 21,269 owners. Records were being kept on 3,629 additional herds whose owners were participating in the weigh-a-day-a-month plan.

Owner-Sampler Testing. County-wide dairy herd improvement cooperatives with central laboratories for testing milk and keeping records are the answer to the need for more record keeping at lower costs. The owner-sampler records are based on a one-day test each month. The supervisor leaves sample bottles, barn sheets, and scales at several farms each day. Each dairyman records the weight and takes a composite sample of the evening and morning milk from each cow. The association supervisor picks up the samples and weight records and takes them to the laboratory, where the samples are tested and the records are computed for each cow. The completed records are mailed to the dairyman and are discussed with him by the supervisor on the next trip to the farm. This system provides accurate testing and record keeping at a low cost, since one supervisor can handle several herds in one day.

The Babcock Test. An individual dairyman can weigh the milk from each cow, each milking, during one day of each month, take a composite sample and make his own tests, if equipment is available. Facilities are usually available in the vocational agriculture department of the school or in the office of the agricultural extension director. The following suggestions are in order in making home tests by use of the Babcock test:

1. Weigh the milk from each cow for each milking during one day.
2. Take from each milking a small sample of milk. The same amount of milk should be taken from each milking.
3. Mix the samples to make a composite test.
4. Warm the thoroughly mixed sample to 65° or 70° F.
5. Draw milk into the pipette until it is level with the 17.6 cc. mark.
6. Discharge the milk from the pipette to the test bottle, being careful that every drop of milk is transferred to the bottle.
7. Add slowly, as the test bottle is being tilted and rotated, 17.5 cc. of cold commercial sulphuric acid. Adding about 50 per cent of the acid and mixing it with the milk before adding the other half is recommended.
8. Mix the acid with the milk by rotating the bottle. Do not shake bottle or hold finger over the opening.
9. Place the mixed samples in the centrifuge tester. Space them properly to balance the centrifuge.
10. Whirl the centrifuge for five minutes at the speed indicated on the machine.
11. Add warm, soft water to bring the contents of each bottle up to the base of the bottle neck.
12. Centrifuge for two minutes.

13. Add water carefully, using a pipette, to bring the fat column up into the graduated scale of the bottle neck. Centrifuge for one minute.
14. Place the bottles in a water bath at 130° to 140° F. for five minutes.
15. Read the test by using dividers to get the height of the fat column, then lower them, placing one divider at 0; the other divider will indicate the butterfat test.
16. The reading is made from the extreme top of the top meniscus to the extreme bottom of the lower meniscus.
17. The weight of milk multiplied by the butterfat test, times the number of days in the month, will indicate the monthly butterfat production of the cow.

The BDI Detergent Test. Numerous attempts have been made to replace the Babcock butterfat test, which involves the use of concentrated sulfuric acid. The Bureau of Dairy Industry, Agricultural Research Administration, U. S. Department of Agriculture developed a test which involves the use of detergents and methyl alcohol. The test is easy to make, and the results check closely with those obtained with the Babcock method.

Schain Detergent Test. A large number of vocational agriculture students are using the Schain test. It is considered by some to be as accurate as the Babcock test, and eliminates the need for a centrifuge, water bath, and acid-proof facilities. The test reagent and directions for making the test are available from Merck & Company, Rahway, New Jersey.

Figure 17-13. Lee's Hill Keeper's Raven, high butterfat producer of all breeds. At nine years of age, she produced 34,850 pounds of milk and 1,579 pounds of butterfat. (Strohmeyer and Carpenter photo. Courtesy Brown Swiss Cattle Breeders' Assn.)

314

Physical Appearance

It has been found that certain physical characteristics in cattle are associated with high production. An understanding of these characteristics makes it possible for us to judge the productive capacity of an individual for which production records are not available.

Dairy Cow Score Card. The five dairy breeds of this nation through the medium of the Purebred Dairy Cattle Association have prepared score cards for dairy cows and bulls. The score cards have been approved and made official by the five dairy breeds.

DAIRY COW SCORE CARD
(Based on Order of Observation)

1. General Appearance   (30 Points)
   Attractive individuality, revealing vigor, femininity with a harmonious blending and correlation of parts; impressive style and attractive carriage with a graceful walk.
   Breed Characteristics—Color, size, and horns characteristic of the breed.
   Head—medium in length, clean cut; broad muzzle with large open nostrils; lean, strong jaw; full, bright eyes; forehead broad between the eyes and moderately dished; bridge of nose straight; ears of medium size and alertly carried.
   Shoulder Blades—set smoothly against chest wall and withers, forming neat junction with the body.
   Back—strong and appearing straight with well-defined vertebrae.
   Loin—broad, strong, and nearly level.

Figure 17-14. Lush Acres Hermes Quest, Grand Champion Guernsey cow at the National Guernsey Show in 1956. She sold for $15,500 in 1957. (Strohmeyer and Carpenter photo. Courtesy The American Guernsey Cattle Club)

315

Figure 17-15. Da-Co-Ton Crescent Fannie 3398005, Grand Champion Holstein Cow 1957 National Dairy Cattle Congress. Note the excellent dairy character in head, neck, and withers. (Strohmeyer and Carpenter photo. Courtesy The Holstein-Friesian Assn. of America)

Figure 17-16. Par's Red Sheila. This Ayrshire cow completed a lifetime production record in 1952 of 175,-065 pounds of milk and 7,570 pounds of butterfat in 3,887 days. Note her long and deep body. (Strohmeyer and Carpenter photo. Courtesy Ayrshire Breeders' Assn.)

Figure 17-17. Jane of Vernon, Queen Mother of the Brown Swiss breed. Note the excellent mammary development. (Strohmeyer and Carpenter photo. Courtesy Brown Swiss Cattle Breeders' Assn.)

Figure 17-18. Caumsett Tore, Grand Champion Guernsey Bull 1957 National Dairy Cattle Congress. (Strohmeyer and Carpenter photo. Courtesy The American Guernsey Cattle Club)

Rump—long, wide; top line level from loin to, and including, tail head.

Hips—wide, approximately level laterally with back, free from excess tissue.

Thurls—wide apart.

Pin Bones—wide apart and slightly lower than hips, well-defined.

Tail Head—slightly above and neatly set between pin bones.

Tail—long and tapering, with nicely balanced switch.

Legs—wide apart, squarely set, clean cut, and strong with forelegs straight.

Hind Legs—nearly perpendicular from hock to pastern. When viewed from behind, legs wide apart and nearly straight. Bone flat and flinty, well-defined tendons. Pasterns of medium length, strong and springy. Hocks cleanly molded.

Feet—short and well-rounded, with deep heel and level sole.

2. Dairy Character   (20 Points)

Animation, angularity, general openness, and freedom from excess tissue, giving due regard to period of lactation.

Neck—long and lean, blending smoothly into shoulders and brisket; clean-cut throat and dewlap.

Withers—well-defined and wedge-shaped, with the dorsal process of the vertebrae rising slightly above the shoulder blades.

Ribs—wide apart; rib bone wide, flat, and long.

Flank—deep, arched, and refined.

Thighs—incurving to flat from the side, wide apart when viewed from the rear, providing sufficient room for the udder and its attachment.

Skin—of medium thickness; loose and pliable; fine hair.

3. Body Capacity   (20 Points)

Relatively large in proportion to size of animal, providing ample digestive capacity, strength, and vigor.

Barrel—deep, strongly supported, ribs wide apart and well-sprung; depth and width tending to increase toward rear of band.

Heart Girth—large, resulting from long, well-sprung fore ribs, wide chest floor between front legs, and fullness at the point of elbow.

4. Mammary System   (30 Points)

A capacious, strongly attached, well-carried udder of good quality, indicating heavy production and a long period of usefulness.

Udder-Capacity and Shape—long, wide, and of moderate depth; extending well forward, strongly attached, reasonably level floor; rear attachment high and wide; quarters evenly balanced and symmetrical.

Texture—soft, pliable, and elastic; well-collapsed after milking.
Teats—uniform, of convenient length and size, cylindrical in shape, free from obstructions, well-apart, and squarely placed; plumb.
Mammary Veins—long, tortuous, prominent, and branching, with numerous large wells; veins on udder numerous and clearly defined.

Selecting Dairy Bulls. The same general characteristics desired in dairy cows, are wanted in dairy bulls but greater emphasis is placed upon the production records and pedigrees of their ancestors. A bull is half the herd. He must be selected very carefully.

General Appearance. A dairy bull should be large for its age and attractive, show masculinity, and have balance in type and conformation. He should have a long, clean-cut, masculine head with bright prominent eyes and a large muzzle.

He should have a straight top line, be long in body, and long and level in the rump. The tail setting should be smooth. Width of body at the fore rib, loin, hips, and pin bones is desired. In addition, the bull should possess the characteristics of the breed.

Dairy Character. Dairy bulls are angular in conformation rather than rectangular. They should be fairly sharp over the withers and smooth in the thighs. The neck should be long, lean, and masculine. There should be no tendency toward beefiness.

The skin should be mellow, loose, and pliable, and the animal should have a fine hair coat.

The rudimentary teats should be well-spaced and wide apart. The testicles should be normal in size.

Body Capacity. A long, wide, deep barrel is desired. Width between the front legs and spring of fore rib is necessary. Dairy animals must be able to consume large quantities of roughages.

Feet and Legs. Sound feet and legs are very necessary in dairy animals and especially so in the case of bulls. Bulls need straight legs, set out on the corners. The pasterns should be strong and springy.

Disposition. A bull that is active is desired, but nervous and mean animals ought to be avoided. The disposition of the bull determines the methods which may be used in handling him, and may determine the use which may be made of him in the herd.

Pedigree and Record. Methods of artificial insemination have made it possible to make more effective use of proven bulls. Most bulls in use in artificial breeding are proven sires or trace back to proven sires and high-producing dams.

It is not always possible for the average dairyman to use a proven sire. In areas where artificial insemination facilities are not available, it may be necessary to select outstanding sons of proven sires with desirable ancestors in the pedigree.

Health

Sterility, udder troubles, mastitis, Bang's disease, leptospirosis, and tuberculosis are the most serious causes of health problems. It is a good idea to check carefully the health history of a herd before making final selection of animals. An inspection of the entire herd and a visit with the owner or herdsman will provide much of the needed information. The reliability of the owner is very important.

The general health of the herd and of individuals, the number of calves produced by the cows during the past year, the number of cows in production and the stages of production, and the milk production of the herd will give a good indication of the herd's health.

It is a good idea to buy animals only from herds that have been tested for Bang's disease, leptospirosis, and tuberculosis. Animals vaccinated for Bang's disease and leptospirosis are preferred. Insist upon a retest if the last test was made more than 30 days prior to the purchase. Sometimes it is necessary to have a veterinarian examine the animal.

The physical factors discussed in connection with the selection of dairy stock will provide a fairly good indication of the general health of the animal.

Summary

Breed, physical appearance, pedigree, production records, and health are the important factors in selecting dairy animals. Efficiency in selection is determined by how well we consider each of these factors.

There is a close relationship between type and production. It is possible to select dairy animals on the basis of type and predict to some extent their productive capacity.

The five most common breeds of dairy cattle ranked according to numbers available in the United States are (1) Holstein-Friesian, (2) Guernsey, (3) Jersey, (4) Ayrshire, and (5) Brown Swiss.

Holstein cows lead all breeds in milk production, but the milk is low in butterfat content. The milk of the Jersey and Guernsey leads in quality, color, and butterfat content. Ayrshires are more rugged than Jerseys and Guernseys, and are noted for their style and conformation.

Brown Swiss and Holstein are the most rugged of the breeds, and Jersey and Guernsey cattle are the most refined. Brown Swiss cattle have been greatly improved during recent years.

There is no best breed of dairy cattle, but an individual dairyman may select a best breed for his farm and market conditions.

The pedigree, production record, and physical appearance are the determining factors in selecting dairy animals. Dairy animals should be angular and have sharp withers, smooth thighs, sharp hip and pin bones, and long-dished faces. Body capacity is important in selecting both cows and bulls. Width, depth, and length of body are essential. Dairy temperament is shown by angularity, leanness of neck, absence of beefiness, and quality of skin and hair.

A good mammary system includes a large udder with good fore and rear attachment. The teats are normal in size and properly spaced, and the udder is mellow, possessing no meaty tissue. The milk veins are large and crooked and lead to large milk wells.

Masculinity, breed character, dairy temperament, and a strong constitution are essential in selecting dairy bulls.

Production records and pedigrees of the individual and of the ancestors should be evaluated in selecting dairy animals. A comparison is made of the production of five daughters with that of their dams in proving a bull.

Health factors should be considered in the selection of dairy animals. It is best to bring into the herd only animals free from Bang's disease, tuberculosis, mastitis, udder difficulties, and sterility. It is a good practice to inspect the herd and check upon the production of calves and milk.

• Questions

1. Which of the following factors should be given most consideration in selecting dairy animals; breed, pedigree, production record, or physical appearance? Why?
2. List the most common dairy breeds, and outline the advantages and disadvantages of each.

3. What factors should be considered in selecting dairy cows by their physical appearance?
4. Which is most important in a dairy cow—the general appearance, the body capacity, the dairy temperament, or the mammary system? Why?
5. Describe the ideal mammary system on a Guernsey cow.
6. Survey your home county, and determine the number of herds of dairy cattle for which production records are available.
7. Of what value is a pedigree in selecting foundation animals?
8. What is the place of the Dairy Herd Improvement Association in your community?
9. Outline the plan which you will use on your home farm in improving your herd through selection.
10. In selecting a bull, what factors will you consider which are not considered in selecting dairy cows?

• References

Diggins, R. V. and C. E. Bundy, *Dairy Production*, Prentice-Hall, Inc., Englewood Cliffs, New Jersey, 1955.

Harrison, E. S., H. A. Strohmeyer, and J. T. Carpenter, Jr., *Judging Dairy Cattle*, John Wiley & Sons, Inc., New York, 1940.

Knodt, C. B., *Successful Dairying*, McGraw-Hill Book Company, Inc., New York, 1954.

The American Jersey Cattle Club, *Jersey Judging Made Easy*, Columbus, Ohio, 1953.

The Holstein-Friesian Association of America, *The Judging Manual*, Brattleboro, Vermont, 1952.

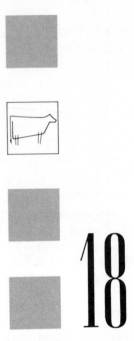

Feeding and Management of the Producing Herd

Profitable dairying may be achieved by: (1) selecting foundation animals with inherent producing ability; (2) feeding and managing the herd in such a way as to enable the cows to reach maximum economical production. It makes little difference how well bred your herd is, if the cows are not given the proper kind and amount of nutrients for the manufacturing of milk.

Feed for the Dairy Cow

Roughages. Dairy cattle are efficient users of roughages. When the ration is properly balanced, dairy cows will convert into milk large quantities of relatively inexpensive roughages.

Legumes. Legumes lead the field as roughages for dairy cattle, with alfalfa ranking number one. Alfalfa is unexcelled as a dry roughage, being high in protein and total digestible nutrients. Red clover, if cut before the blossoms turn brown, ranks only slightly

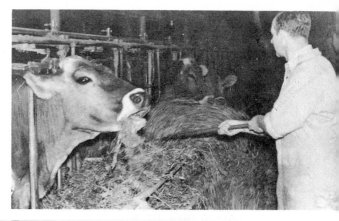

Figure 18-1. Legumes rank high as a roughage for dairy cattle. (Courtesy Cornell University) →

Figure 18-2. Silage made from legumes, grasses, corn, or sorghums makes good roughages for dairy cattle. (Courtesy Wallaces' Farmer and Iowa Homestead) ↓

below alfalfa as a dry roughage for dairy cows. Other clovers, lespedeza, soybeans, and many other legumes are highly regarded as roughages for dairy cattle. When legumes furnish the bulk of the roughages fed, a considerable savings in protein concentrates will result. Legumes will minimize the risk of vitamin and mineral deficiencies because they are high in these nutrients.

Nonlegume Hays. Native grasses, brome, timothy, fescue, millet, orchard grass, and many others will provide forage. However, the grasses are considerably lower than legumes in protein and in some of the minerals and vitamins. When nonlegume hays are used extensively, greater care must be exercised if the ration is to be balanced.

Feeding and Management of the Producing Herd • 323

Fodder, Corncobs, Cornstalks, and Straw. All these roughages are low in proteins, minerals, vitamins, and total digestible nutrients. Although they may be used under certain conditions for cattle feeding, their value is doubtful as a feed for dairy cattle. The good milk cow must consume large amounts of highly digestible feed if she is to maintain production. Most dairymen agree that high quality forage, such as legumes and good silage, are the cheapest feeds.

Corn or Sorghum Silage. Corn or sorghum silage makes very good roughage for dairy cattle. If well-eared corn or grain sorghum silage is fed, less other grain will be required because a considerable amount will be contained in the silage. However, the protein content of these silage crops is low, requiring additional amounts of protein concentrates to balance the ration.

Legume and Grass Silage. More dairymen are using legume, grass, or a mixture of the two as a silage feed for dairy cattle. Very little protein is lost when these crops are made into silage. When the silage is made from legumes, or a mixture with a high percentage of legumes, the feed is very nutritious.

Citrus Pulp. In the citrus fruit growing areas of the United States, dried citrus pulp is becoming increasingly popular as a dairy cattle feed. The pulp is largely a by-product of the canneries. The bulk of the dried pulp comes from grapefruit and oranges; however, lemons, limes, and tangerines are entering into the dried pulp industry. The feeding value varies to some extent, depending upon methods of manufacturing and content of the pulp. It is fairly high in carbohydrates, but low in protein and vitamin A. It contains from 70 to 76 per cent digestible nutrients. Since calcium carbonate is added in the processing, it is fairly high in calcium but low in phosphorus. Owing to its bulky nature, it is used more as a roughage than as a concentrate, but as a nutrient it is more like the grains.

Beet Pulp. Beet pulp is the residue of the sugar beets after the sugar has been removed. Beet pulp is often referred to as a roughage, but in nutrient composition it is more nearly like the grain concentrates. Beet pulp carries about 88 per cent as many total digestible nutrients as corn but is lower in protein. Its value should be figured on the cost per pound of digestible nutrients.

Pastures. The natural feed for dairy cattle is pasture. The pasture season should be made as long as possible. Fall-seeded rye provides early spring pasture, in areas where it is adapted, and may be followed by native grasses, or a legume and grass mixture. Sudan grass, or a sudan grass and soybean combination, makes an excellent summer and early fall pasture. In general, a legume and grass combination provides more grazing per acre of highly nutritious forage than any other common pasture crop. Pastures recommended for beef cattle are suitable for dairy cattle.

Concentrates. The feeds making up the group commonly referred to as concentrates, which are used extensively in dairy cattle rations, consist primarily of the grains and by-products of grain or oil seed.

Corn. Corn is palatable and very nutritious as a feed for dairy cattle. Throughout the Corn Belt, it is considered the most important grain for dairy cattle production. Corn, like most other grains, is fed primarily for its energy value but does supply some protein, minerals, and vitamins.

Grain Sorghums. Grain sorghums may be substituted for corn, pound for pound, in the dairy ration, if the price per pound is equal to or less than that of corn. The nutrient value of sorghum grains is very similar to that of corn.

Wheat. Wheat is equal to corn in food value, but because of its gluten content, it becomes pasty when eaten unless mixed with other feeds. Wheat should not make up more than half of the grain ration. Wheat is 3 to 5 per cent higher in protein than is corn.

Ground Ear Corn. Ground ear corn has only about 90 per cent of the feed value of ground shelled corn, but many dairymen prefer it. Probably the chief advantage lies in labor saving, as it does not have to be shelled.

Oats. Oats, an excellent feed for dairy cows, are somewhat less digestible than corn, but they have a higher protein content. Pound for pound, quality oats have about 90 per cent of the value of ground shelled corn, or about the same value as ground ear corn, for dairy cattle. Oats vary probably more than most other grains in feed value. Light oats, containing a high proportion of hulls to berry, may not have more than 50 to 60 per cent of the value of corn.

Barley. Barley, which may be used to replace corn, is the chief grain fed in many dairy herds. Good quality barley has about 95 per cent of the value of corn on a pound-for-pound basis for dairy cows.

Rye. Rye is unpalatable to dairy cows. In food value it is about equal to barley. It should not be used to make up more than one-fourth of the grain ration.

Wheat Bran. Wheat bran is a by-product resulting from the processing of wheat into flour. It is composed primarily of wheat hulls and is a very common dairy feed. It is higher in protein than the common grains and is somewhat laxative. Bran compares favorably with oats in total digestible nutrients.

Molasses. Both cane and beet molasses are fed to dairy cattle. Molasses is low in protein and has about 60 to 70 per cent as much total digestible nutrients as does corn. Molasses is very palatable and some authorities believe it speeds up the fermentation process in the digestive system. Under most conditions, it does not pay to buy molasses unless it is as cheap as or cheaper than corn per pound of digestible nutrient.

Soybean Oil Meal. Soybean oil meal ranges from 40 to 47 per cent protein and is an excellent source of protein for dairy cattle. It is palatable, and in the soybean growing areas it is often the cheapest protein concentrate.

Linseed Oil Meal. Linseed oil meal is an old standby and is well liked by dairymen as a protein supplement. It is an excellent feed and may well be used when its price per pound of digestible protein is in line with that of other high-protein feeds.

Cottonseed Meal. Cottonseed meal is a common high-protein feed used for dairy cattle. Experiments show that it is a very good source of protein. The price per pound of protein, compared to that of other feeds, should be the principal consideration in its use.

Soybeans. Ground soybeans provide an excellent source of protein. Generally, the price is too high to make them an economical feed. However, when soybeans are a cheap source of protein, they provide a good home-grown protein supplement.

Other Protein Feeds. Corn gluten meal, corn gluten, and distiller's grains are good sources of protein for cattle, but are lower in percentage of protein than meals made from the oil seed crops.

Urea. Urea is a nitrogen compound. Dairy cattle can convert a certain amount of urea into protein. Except for high producing animals, urea could replace the protein concentrates in a ration that provides a full feed of good legume hay or silage, plus sufficient grains to meet the production requirements of the cow.

Urea has no advantage, except as an economy measure, over the oil seed meals and other common protein supplements. Its value should be determined in terms of replacing the protein value of other feeds.

Commercial protein supplements containing urea have no advantage over feeds similar in protein equivalent, unless they can be purchased more cheaply.

The rules for feeding urea are the same for both beef and dairy cattle (see Chapter 14 for the rules).

Vitamins. When dairy cows have access to good pasture during the summer and are fed liberally on good roughage during the winter, there is seldom any need for vitamin supplements. The group of vitamins known as the B-complex or water-soluble vitamins are manufactured in the cow's digestive system. Vitamin A is found in yellow corn, good-quality cured roughage, pasture, and many other feeds. Vitamin D is supplied to animals coming into contact with sunshine and is contained in sun-cured forages.

Very inferior rations could cause a deficiency in vitamins A and D. Fish-liver oils are high in vitamins A and D, but they may reduce the fat content of the milk and cause other injurious effects when fed to cows. If a need for these vitamins exists, a prepared vitamin concentrate for dairy cattle should be used.

Minerals. The mineral requirements of dairy cattle vary considerably, depending upon the soil that produces the feed they are eating and the amount and kind of ration provided. Soils vary greatly in content of the various minerals. Cattle are known to require more than a dozen mineral elements for growth and production. If the plants they are eating are high in any one or several of these minerals, it may not be necessary to provide a supplement that contains all the required minerals.

With the exception of very few areas in the United States, it will be necessary to provide salt, calcium, and phosphorus in larger amounts than would ordinarily be provided in the ration. If mineralized salt is used, the trace minerals will likely be provided. Many dairymen feed a pound of mineralized salt and a pound of steamed bone meal for every hundred pounds of concentrate mixture. Bone meal is high in calcium and phosphorus, and the mineralized salt provides the salt and trace minerals. The recommendations of the agricultural college in your area should be followed regarding mineral supplements. The mineral mixtures recommended for beef cattle (see Chapter 13) may be used for dairy cattle.

Feeding the Dairy Cow

The dairy cow uses feed for maintenance, for developing her unborn calf, and for milk production. About one-half of the daily ration consumed by the cow is used for maintaining her body and nourishing her unborn calf. No matter what their milk flow may be, the maintenance costs will be the same for cows of equal weight. That is why high-producing cows are so important for profitable production. The cow that produces only 200 pounds of butterfat in a year will consume about two-thirds as much feed as the cow that produces 400 pounds of butterfat. It will take the entire milk check, under average conditions, to pay the feed bill for the 200-pound-producing cow. The 400-pound-producing cow will pay her feed bill and leave the owner from 100 to 150 pounds of butterfat as profit.

TABLE 34

DAILY MAINTENANCE REQUIREMENTS OF DAIRY COWS

Weight of Cow (Pounds)	Digestible Crude Protein (Pounds)	Total Digestible Nutrients (Pounds)	Calcium (Grams)*	Phosphorus (Grams)*
800	0.504	5.60	16.0	8.00
850	0.536	5.95	17.0	8.50
900	0.567	6.30	18.0	9.00
950	0.599	6.65	19.0	9.50
1,000	0.630	7.00	20.0	10.00
1,050	0.662	7.35	21.0	10.50
1,100	0.693	7.70	22.0	11.00
1,150	0.725	8.05	23.0	11.50
1,200	0.756	8.40	24.0	12.00
1,250	0.788	8.75	25.0	12.50
1,300	0.819	9.10	26.0	13.00
1,350	0.851	9.45	27.0	13.50
1,400	0.882	9.80	28.0	14.00
1,450	0.914	10.15	29.0	14.50
1,500	0.945	10.50	30.0	15.00

* 28.35 grams equal one ounce.

Source: Extension Bulletin 218 (Revised), University of Minnesota, St. Paul, 1952.

TABLE 35

DIGESTIBLE NUTRIENTS REQUIRED FOR PRODUCING ONE POUND OF MILK

Per Cent of Fat in Milk	Digestible Protein	Total Digestible Nutrients
3.0	.0402	.2773
3.5	.0422	.3059
4.0	.0462	.3353
4.5	.0491	.3638
5.0	.0518	.3904
5.5	.0548	.4159
6.0	.0573	.4415
6.5	.0618	.4697

Source: *Extension Bulletin 218* (Revised), University of Minnesota, St. Paul, 1952.

Computing Rations for Dairy Cows

Before the proteins and total digestible nutrients required for any given cow can be determined, it is necessary to know the weight, daily milk production, and butterfat percentage of the milk.

Computing T. D. N. and Protein Requirements. Suppose we have a cow weighing 950 pounds and producing 40 pounds of 4.5 per cent milk. If we look at Table 34, we note that she requires about 0.6 pound of protein and 6.65 pounds of total digestible nutrients per day for maintenance. Table 35 tells us we will need to add approximately 0.05 pound of protein and 0.36 pound of total digestible nutrients for each pound of milk produced daily.

Example	Digestible Protein	Total Digestible Nutrients
For Maintenance	0.6	6.65
For Milk Production	40 × 0.05 = 2.0	40 × 0.36 = 14.40
Total Requirements	2.6	21.05

After determining the protein and total digestible nutrients required for any given cow, our next problem is to plan a ration that will provide these requirements. Many different feeds and combinations of feeds may be used. It is important that we use those feeds that will provide necessary amounts of protein and total digestible nutrients at the lowest possible price. By using the tables in Chapter 2 that show the average composition of common feeds, we can select the kind and amount of feeds best suited to our conditions and prepare a ration for the cow just described.

Example 1

	Digestible Proteins	Total Digestible Nutrients
20 pounds corn silage	0.26	4.00
17 pounds average alfalfa hay	1.78	8.55
8 pounds ground ear corn	0.42	5.85
4 pounds oats	0.38	2.80
Total	2.84	21.20

Example 2

	Digestible Proteins	Total Digestible Nutrients
20 pounds corn silage	0.26	4.00
17 pounds good timothy hay	0.61	8.64
8 pounds ground ear corn	0.42	5.85
4 pounds oats	0.38	2.80
2 pounds soybean oil meal	0.91	1.52
Total	2.58	22.81

In Example 2, when timothy hay, which is low in protein, was substituted for alfalfa, which is a high-protein roughage, it was necessary to add a protein concentrate in order to bring the protein content up to the desirable level. This increased the total digestible nutrients slightly above the required level. However, the cow should receive sufficient protein, if her production is to be maintained.

Under average conditions the dairyman would not need to compute a ration for each individual cow, as shown in the example, but could select a typical cow in the herd and plan a concentrate mixture that would fit the roughage available. Then he should follow one of the practical rules described later in this chapter.

Roughages Are the Basis of Dairy Rations. Cows can maintain themselves and produce a calf and a limited amount of milk on a full ration of good-quality roughage, mineral mixture, and water. Roughages vary greatly in feeding value. A high-quality roughage is one that has approximately the same total digestible nutrients and digestible protein as the second or third cutting of alfalfa harvested in the early bloom stage. Grain and protein supplement are added to the ration in proportion to the amount of milk a cow produces, over and above what can be produced from the roughage part of the ration.

Amount of Roughages Consumed by Cows. When dairy cows are fed all the dry roughages they will consume, they will eat approximately 2 ½ pounds per 100 pounds of live weight. When fed high-moisture roughages, such as silage, they will consume about 2½ to three times as much by weight as when dry roughages are used, the difference being in the water that is taken in with the feed.

Concentrates for Milk Production. The larger breeds of dairy cattle (Holsteins, Brown Swiss, Ayrshires) can be expected to maintain their body weight and produce from 15 to 20 pounds of milk daily from roughages. The smaller breeds (Jerseys, Guernseys) can be expected to produce only ten to 15 pounds of milk daily from roughages alone. Concentrates will need to be provided for all milk over these amounts that the cow is capable of producing.

Feeding Concentrates According to Profits. Except for cows on test for the purpose of making a high production record, it is seldom profitable to feed for maximum production. When the dairyman reaches the point where the value of the increased production is less than the cost of the feed, he is not getting economical production. The concentrates should be increased only until the cow has reached the maximum point of profitable production.

Rules for Feeding Producing Cows Not on Pasture. Several rules have been worked out to govern the amount and kind of concentrates for cows in production. A concentrate mixture to fit the protein content of the roughage should be selected for a herd that is not on pasture but is getting all the roughage it will consume. When cows are receiving all the high-quality legume hay or legume silage they will consume, a concentrate mixture containing from 9 to 10 per cent protein will be sufficient except for very high-producing cows. If the roughage is average-quality legumes, the protein level of the concentrate mixture should be about 13 per cent. When the roughage is half grass hay, fodder, corn or sorghum silage, or any other similar feed, the concentrate mixture should contain 15 per cent protein. If the roughage contains no legumes and is entirely of a low-protein nature, a concentrate ration of 17 to 20 per cent should be fed.

How Much Concentrates to Feed. When a concentrate ration has been selected that will fit the roughage, one of the following rules may be used to govern the daily allowance of each cow.

1. A pound of concentrate mixture for each 3½ pounds of milk testing below 4 per cent, and a pound for each three pounds of milk testing above 4 per cent.

2. The pounds of butterfat produced monthly divided by four equals the pounds of grain mixture to feed daily.
3. When legume roughages are fed, a pound of grain for each two pounds of milk a Holstein, Brown Swiss, Ayrshire, or Shorthorn produces over 20 pounds daily; a Guernsey, over 15 pounds daily; and a Jersey, over 12 pounds daily.

Table 36 may serve as a guide in planning rations when high quality roughages are used.

TABLE 36

AMOUNT OF CONCENTRATE MIXTURE REQUIRED FOR DAIRY
COWS THAT ARE FULL-FED HIGH-QUALITY ROUGHAGE

Breed	Amount of Milk Cows Can Produce on Roughage Alone (Pounds)	Pounds of Concentrates for Each Extra Pound of Milk
Holsteins	20	.40
Brown Swiss	18	.45
Milking Shorthorns	16	.45
Ayrshires	16	.45
Guernseys	12	.55
Jerseys	10	.60

Following are some suggested rations of various protein levels that may be used in areas where they are economical:

(9 to 10 per cent digestible protein)	
No. 1	
Ground Ear Corn	550 pounds
Ground Oats	400 pounds
Soybean or Linseed Oil Meal	50 pounds
	1,000 pounds
No. 2	
Ground Grain Sorghum	550 pounds
Ground Barley	425 pounds
Cottonseed Meal	25 pounds
	1,000 pounds
No. 3	
Ground Shelled Corn	450 pounds
Ground Barley	200 pounds
Ground Oats	325 pounds
40 per cent Protein Meal	25 pounds
	1,000 pounds

	No. 4
Ground Shelled Corn or	
Grain Sorghum	700 pounds
Wheat Bran	300 pounds
	1,000 pounds

(12 to 14 per cent digestible protein)

	No. 5
Ground Ear Corn	600 pounds
Ground Oats	200 pounds
Soybean, Linseed, or	
Cottonseed Meal	200 pounds
	1,000 pounds

	No. 6
Ground Barley	300 pounds
Ground Soybean Grain	300 pounds
Wheat Bran	200 pounds
Soybean Meal	200 pounds
	1,000 pounds

	No. 7
Ground Ear Corn	500 pounds
Ground Oats	100 pounds
Wheat Bran	200 pounds
Corn Gluten Meal	200 pounds
	1,000 pounds

	No. 8
Ground Shelled Corn	500 pounds
Ground Oats	300 pounds
Soybean Meal	100 pounds
Cottonseed Meal	100 pounds
	1,000 pounds

(17 to 20 per cent digestible protein)

	No. 9
Ground Shelled Corn	200 pounds
Wheat Bran	200 pounds
Ground Oats	200 pounds
Cottonseed Meal	200 pounds
Soybean Meal	100 pounds
Dried Brewer's Grains	100 pounds
	1,000 pounds

	No. 10
Ground Ear Corn	500 pounds
Soybean Meal	200 pounds
Ground Oats	200 pounds
Linseed Meal	100 pounds
	1,000 pounds

Urea may be used to replace part or all of the proteins, if fed according to directions.

From ten to 15 pounds of a mineral mixture recommended for the area should be added to each of the suggested rations. Cattle should have free access to salt.

Preparing Feeds for Dairy Cows. The digestibility of grains is usually increased by grinding them. However, too finely ground grains become pasty in the mouths of cattle and are not palatable. Coarsely ground feed is better.

Feeding Producing Cows That Are on Pasture. Pasture is the most nearly perfect dairy feed available. The dairyman who has given careful attention to the amount and quality of pasture crops is able to maintain high production at relatively low cost. Feed specialists have sometimes likened pastures to concentrates. Young pasture grasses and legumes are high in protein, low in fiber, and high in moisture. The fiber content is the chief factor that determines whether a feed is a roughage or a concentrate. Young pasture grasses contain about 18 per cent fiber, whereas good alfalfa hay contains from 23 to 28 per cent and grains from 2 to 12 per cent.

Pasture crops are usually high in minerals, although the mineral content varies with the fertility of the soil. Phosphorus is most likely to be lacking in pastures. Occasionally, however, other essential minerals may be insufficient to meet the needs of animals. When soils deficient in minerals are properly fertilized, the forage they produce will generally provide adequate minerals. Vitamins are seldom a problem for cattle on good pasture. Vitamin A is found abundantly in green forage, and the sun will provide vitamin D.

Limitations of Pasture. Although good pastures are important in the·economical production of dairy products, they have certain limitations. The limitations of pasture must be understood by the dairyman, if he is to make the best use of pasture crops.

In the more humid areas, pasture grasses may run about 80 per cent water, especially in the spring. Since the cow's capacity is limited, she may not be able to consume enough to provide the nutrients needed for milk production. Successful dairymen usually provide some good dry forage and grain for high-producing cows on pasture.

Nutrient Value of Pasture Varies. The nutrient value of pasture crops does not remain the same during the season. As plants become more mature, the fiber content increases and the protein and vitamin content decreases. The same is true when the growth of plants is retarded because of dry weather.

Not only does young pasture grass contain more protein, but it is of a highly digestible nature. Any experienced dairyman knows that when cows are turned on fresh young pasture they usually respond with an increased production commonly referred to as a spring flush. This spring flush is the result of the high nutrient content and palatability of the young pasture grasses. For the best results, pastures should be kept young.

Feeding Concentrates to Cows on Pasture. When pastures are good and cows can get their fill in two to four hours of grazing daily, very little grain is necessary for cows of average production. Jerseys and Guernseys will produce up to 30 pounds of milk; Holsteins, Brown Swiss, Ayrshires, Milking Shorthorns, and other breeds of nearly equal size will produce 40 pounds of milk daily on pasture alone. There are several rules followed by different dairymen for feeding concentrates to cows on pasture.

A common rule followed by many dairymen is to feed one pound of concentrate for each five to seven pounds of milk to cows producing one pound or more of fat daily. Kind and quality of pasture determine the protein percentage of the concentrate.

Feeding the Dry Cow. The dairy cow needs from 45 to 60 days of rest between lactation periods. While she is dry, the cow should replace the body weight lost during the previous lactation period. Unless she has at least six weeks of rest and a proper ration during the dry period, she will not be in condition for best production during the next lactation.

When the drying-off process (which will be discussed later) has been accomplished, the conditioning ration should be started. The stored fat, which the cow puts on during the dry period, serves as a reserve supply to be drawn upon for milk production. Protein cannot be stored, so a ration with a protein content in excess of what the cow needs to put on flesh is not necessary. The ration should contain minerals to put back into her bones the calcium and phosphorus that have been utilized in the milk production. Experiments show that cattle can store vitamins A and D. Cows that are dry during the summer will probably not need any special attention to the vitamins contained in the ration if they are on good pasture.

During the winter, greater care needs to be exercised to insure ample supplies of these important vitamins.

Feeds for the Dry Cow. The amount and kind of feed necessary for the dry cow depends upon her ability to produce and upon her condition when she is dried up. High-producing cows are usually thin and need to be full-fed grain during the rest period. Average to low producers will not lose a great deal of weight, and pasture or cured roughages are sufficient to recondition them.

TABLE 37

RATIONS FOR CONDITIONING DRY COWS

Kind of Roughage	*Concentrate Mixture in Pounds*
Good quality legume forage or good pasture	1. 100 ground oats 400 ground ear corn
	2. 200 ground barley 200 ground shelled corn 100 ground oats
	3. 300 ground grain sorghum 200 ground oats
Mature grass pasture or low protein forage	1. 300 ground shelled corn or sorghum grain 100 ground oats 50 wheat bran 50 linseed, soybean, or cottonseed meal
	2. 200 ground barley 200 ground shelled corn 75 wheat bran 25 soybean meal

Five to seven pounds of a mineral mixture used for cows in production should be added to each of these rations.

Feeding the Cow Just Before Calving. A week before calving, the grain may be partially replaced with more bulky feeds. Do not reduce the feed too much before and after calving, for ketosis may develop in high-producing cows from insufficient carbohydrate foods. The ration should be mildly laxative. Beet pulp is used by many dairymen as part of the ration during the last week of the rest period. Two examples of rations that may be used two days before calving follow on the next page.

RATION 1	RATION 2
175 pounds ground oats	200 pounds ground oats
100 pounds wheat bran	100 pounds beet pulp
25 pounds linseed oil meal	25 pounds soybean oil meal
25 pounds molasses	

Feeding the Cow Just After Calving. The cow should be given all the fresh, reasonably warm water she will drink after calving. For the next three days, she may be continued on the same ration fed the last week before calving. Some dairymen add two to three pounds of molasses to the ration to keep the energy value high as a precaution against ketosis. Concentrates may be moistened with water and sprinkled with a pinch of salt. The regular dairy ration may be started on the fourth day. The concentrates should be increased as rapidly as the cow's appetite will permit.

Managing the Cow Herd

The successful management of the dairy herd depends upon an intimate knowledge and understanding of the animals.

Exercise. Contrary to popular belief, dairy cows need but limited exercise. Too much movement will result in food nutrients being used for body maintenance that would otherwise go into milk production. However, it seems advisable, during cold weather when the cows are confined, to take advantage of any warm days to turn the cows out for an hour or so. When the loose housing system is used, cows have room for sufficient free movement to provide the needed exercise.

Cleaning and Grooming. Cows in the milking herd should be kept clean, not only for the production of clean milk but for the health of the animal as well. Daily brushing will remove dirt and loose hair. Regular grooming will help to keep the hide pliable and the hair will develop a sheen that aids the appearance of the cows. The clipping of the long hair from the udder, hind legs, and rear flanks will help to prevent accumulation of filth.

Milking a Cow. Research studies have provided us with much information concerning successful milking practices. Cows will respond favorably to certain stimuli and conditions, and unfavorably to others. Individual dairymen vary in the routine they follow during the milking period. It is important that the same procedure be carried out in the same order at each milking period.

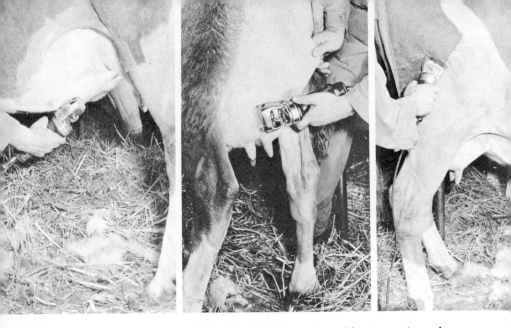

Figure 18-3. Clipping the underline (left), udder (center), and rear flank (right) is important in keeping the cows clean. (Courtesy Sunbeam Corporation)

Preparing the Milking Area and Equipment. The milking area should be clean and free of odors before the cows enter. Milking equipment should be set up and made ready for milking. The operator must be prepared to give his undivided attention to the job at hand.

Washing the Udder and Preparing the Cow for Milking. Washing the udder has two chief advantages: it stimulates the cow to let down her milk and decreases the danger of contaminating the product. When the cow is stimulated by her udder's being washed with warm water and massaged, a hormone is released into the bloodstream and reaches the udder in about one minute. This hormone causes a contraction of the muscles surrounding the milk-cistern. If the cow is frightened or made nervous by any change in routine, another hormone is secreted, causing a constriction of the blood vessels that prevents the milk-secreting hormone from entering the blood stream. Even though the cow is not disturbed in any way, the milk let-down hormone is effective for only about seven minutes after it enters the udder. Milking should be accomplished within this period.

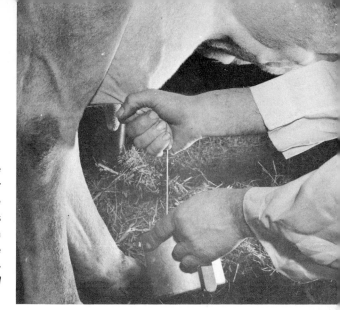

Figure 18-4. The use of the strip cup will help to detect udder infection and clean the teat canal. A few streams should be milked from each quarter before applying the milker. (Gordon photo. Courtesy *Wallaces' Farmer and Iowa Homestead*)

Strip Cup. Use a strip cup and draw two or three streams of milk from each quarter before attaching the milking machine or hand milking. This removes any dirt from the teat canal and gives the operator a chance to see if the milk is normal. If any abnormality appears, the cow should be milked last and that milk kept separately.

Drying Off Cows. Frequently dairymen have considerable difficulty in drying off high-producing cows. Three methods are used to dry up cows: (1) intermittent milking, (2) incomplete milking, and (3) abrupt cessation of milking.

Intermittent Milking. Under this procedure, the cow that is to be dried off will be milked once a day for a while, then once every other day, and finally milking will be stopped altogether.

Incomplete Milking. Dairymen who follow this system start by not extracting all the milk from the udder at milking time for the first few days after the drying-off period has begun. Later they milk intermittently but never completely. After the production decreases to only a few pounds daily, milking is stopped.

Abrupt Cessation of Milking. Of the various systems, experiments have proven that for cows producing 25 pounds of milk or less abrupt cessation of milking is the best, if the udder is sound and there has been no mastitis infection. Three days before milking is stopped, all concentrates should be removed from the ration. The hay should be reduced to about one-half to two-thirds of the normal ration. The reduction in feed will reduce the milk flow. It has been shown that milk will build up to a certain pressure, secretion will stop, and reabsorption of the milk into the blood stream will begin. It is recommended that after the last milking, the teats be washed and dipped in collodion, which will seal the ends and prevent infectious organisms from entering the udder.

Care of the Cow at Calving Time. A few days before the cow is expected to calve, she should be placed in a well-bedded box stall with ample room for calving. The stall should be isolated insofar as possible from any disturbances. Occasionally, in high-producing cows, the udder may become swollen to such extent that milking before calving will be necessary. If such is the case, the milk should be frozen and saved for the newborn calf. The practice of milking before calving is not recommended except in extreme cases.

Provide the cow with plenty of water to drink. In cold weather, many dairymen prefer the water to be warm. Remove the afterbirth as soon as the cow has cleaned to prevent her from eating it. Cows will eat the afterbirth, probably owing to instinct developed by their wild ancestors to prevent the odor from attracting marauding animals. If the cow does not expel the afterbirth completely within 48 hours, call your veterinarian. Cows should be observed closely for signs of milk fever or ketosis. (See Chapter 22.) Should either of these ailments develop, treatment should start immediately. As soon as the cow shows a desire to eat, she should be given feed according to the recommendations for feeding the fresh cow. If the cow has not been milked before calving, allow the calf to nurse or save the colostrum and hand-feed it. Start regular milking to relieve the pressure on any quarter not nursed by the calf. The mature cow should not be milked dry for at least four milkings; this practice should be followed especially on those cows known to be subject to milk fever.

Heat Periods. For cows, the average time from one heat period to the next, known as the estrus cycle, is 21 days, but it varies from 17 to 26 days. The heat period lasts from six to 36 hours, with an average duration of 18 hours for cows and 15 for heifers.

Breeding the Cows. Cows may be bred naturally (direct service by a bull) or artificially. The best method depends upon the size of the herd, production level of the herd, whether or not the sale of bulls is part of the dairy program, and whether artificial insemination service is available in your community.

Natural Breeding. Natural breeding consists of direct service of the cow during her heat period by a bull. In some localities, this is the only means by which a cow may be bred. Artificial insemination service is not available in all localities. The natural breeding method has the following advantages: (1) It is easy to detect when the cows are in heat. Many cows have rather feeble or silent heat periods, making it extremely difficult to know when they should be bred. When the time for their heat period approaches, they may be turned in with the bull daily until they have been bred. (2) Dairymen who have developed very high-producing herds may not be able to get the services of a well-proven bull for all their cows unless they own or have a share in a proven bull. (3) Breeders who sell breeding stock as a major part of their dairy business will often want blood lines not available through artificial insemination. (4) Cows may be bred more than once during the heat period. There is some evidence that breeding the cow twice six to eight hours apart has some advantage in getting hard-to-settle cows with calf.

Artificial Breeding. Artificial breeding or insemination is a practice in which the semen of the bull is transferred to the cows by a person generally known as an inseminator or technician. The semen is often produced at bull studs or semen-producing centers, and it is shipped to local associations as needed. In many localities dairymen have formed cooperative breeding associations. The usual practice is to charge a membership fee, plus a service charge for each cow serviced. The money is used to purchase bulls and equipment, and for the hiring of technicians.

Advantages of Artificial Insemination. Artificial insemination, when properly administered, will give conception rates as high as those with the natural breeding method. Dairymen can secure the service of proven sires or those from a high-producing line at a moderate cost. The bother and danger of keeping a bull on the place is eliminated. The services of outstanding sires are greatly extended. The necessity of locating and purchasing a new herd sire every two years is eliminated.

How to Insure Good Results When Breeding Artificially. As previously stated, it is possible to obtain conception rates from artificial insemination equal to those from natural breeding if the proper procedure is followed. Probably the greatest disadvantage of artificial breeding is the inability of some operators to detect when the cows are in heat. To insure good results, the following rules should

Figure 18-5. Artificial insemination of a cow. (Courtesy Eastern Iowa Artificial Breeding Assn.)

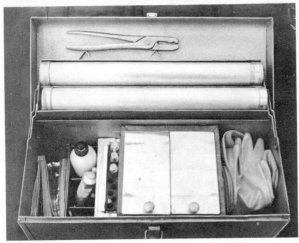

Figure 18-6. Technician's kit showing tools used which includes pliers and tags for identification; aluminum carrying cases for plastic tubes for breeding the cow; rubber glove and sleeve; ice chest for holding semen; syringes and disinfectant. (Courtesy Eastern Iowa Breeders' Assn.)

be observed: (1) Don't breed cows before 60 days following calving. It usually takes a cow approximately 60 days to become normal after calving and in proper condition for breeding. Although many cows will conceive during the first heat period following calving, the conception rate is generally higher if they are bred during the second or third heat period. (2) Know when the cow first appeared in heat and tell the technician. Ovulation does not take place until about 14 hours after the end of the heat period. A study made at the Nebraska Experiment Station showed that best conception rates were obtained when cows were bred more than six hours but less than 24 hours before ovulation. Cows first noticed to be in heat during the early morning should be bred in the afternoon of the same day. Cows noticed to be in heat between nine in the morning and noon should be bred early the next day; those that come in heat during the afternoon should be bred about noon the next day. (3) Put the cow in the barn and leave her for four hours after breeding. (4) Keep accurate records of heat periods, breeding, and calving dates for all cows. (5) Have hard-to-settle cows examined by a veterinarian. (6) Have all cows examined by a veterinarian for pregnancy 12 weeks following breeding. Many cows will not come in heat owing to retained corpus luteum (yellow body) or some other organic trouble. Such conditions can often be corrected by a veterinarian. If cows are not examined for pregnancy and no heat period is evident, the operator may not notice that they are not with calf for several months.

Time to Breed. Dairymen who are retailing milk and must produce about the same amount each month find it necessary to have cows freshening throughout the year to prevent a serious drop in production during any one period. However, those who wholesale milk or butterfat usually prefer to have their cows freshen in the fall months (September, October, and November). Fall freshening has the following advantages: (1) Milk production is greater. Cows freshening in the fall will hold up on milk production longer than will cows freshening when it is spring or summer. The cow that was freshened in the fall will have a spring flush almost equal to a second freshening when she goes on grass. (2) Butterfat and milk prices are usually higher during the winter. (3) The farmer has more time during the winter, when he does not have to give so much attention to crop production. (4) Fall calves are often stronger, owing to the excellent ration provided the cow by good pasture, and thus there is less danger of a nutritional deficiency.

Gestation Periods. The period from the time a cow conceives until she gives birth to a calf is known as the gestation period. It varies with individual cows and with breeds. First-calf heifers will average approximately two days less than older cows of the same breed. Ayrshires, Holsteins, and Jerseys have an average gestation period of about 278 to 279 days; Brown Swiss, 288 to 290 days; and Guernseys, 283 to 284 days.

Housing and Equipment for Dairy Cows

The dairy cow requires about 150 man-hours of labor per year. Labor cost is second only to feed cost in dairy cattle expenses. Every effort should be made to reduce labor cost. Housing and equipment should be planned with a view to reducing the time required in caring for the cow. There are two common systems for housing dairy cattle: (1) stanchion barn, and (2) loose housing.

Stanchion Barn. There are two general types of stanchion barns: (1) the two-story barn, commonly used in the northern regions, and (2) the single-story barn, frequently found in the southern regions and becoming more popular in the North.

The Two-Story Barn. In the two-story barn, feed, especially roughage, is stored on the second story. The lower story is used for housing cattle. The advantages of the two-story barn are: (1) it is convenient to work in because all feed may be stored on the second story and moved down by gravity; (2) it provides more cubic feet of storage space in relation to ground area covered by the building.

The Single-Story Barn. With the increased use of baled or chopped hay and silage, the one-story barn has gained in popularity. Less storage room per ton of feed is required when hay is baled or chopped. Silage is not commonly stored in the barn. The weight per cubic foot of baled or chopped hay is so great that considerable bracing and heavy timbers are required in the barn when the roughage is stored in the second story. The advantages of the single-story barn are: (1) less windstorm hazard, (2) reduced fire risk, (3) easier building, and (4) easier repairs.

The Stanchion-Barn Plan. Space will not permit a detailed discussion of the many types of stanchion barns one may decide to build. The agricultural colleges of each state will furnish plans, free

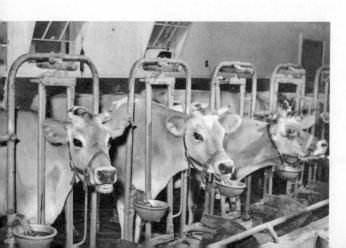

Figure 18-7. A modern stanchion barn. (Courtesy *Wallaces' Farmer and Iowa Homestead*)

344

or for a small charge, from which one may select a type that will best fit individual conditions. Cows spend a great deal of time in the stanchion when this type of barn is used. They generally feed and, in the more modern type, drink from the stanchion area. It is important that the stanchion area be of a size that will be comfortable for the cattle and easy to clean. Gutters should be constructed to provide for the installation of barn cleaners.

TABLE 38

RECOMMENDED DIMENSIONS OF COW STALLS

Weight of Cow	Width of Stall	Length of Stall
800	3' 4"	4' 6"
1000	3' 8"	4' 8"
1200	4' 0"	5' 0"
1400	4' 4"	5' 4"
1600	4' 8"	5' 8"

Insulation and Ventilation. Since cows spend much time in the stanchion of the stanchion-type barn, especially in the northern areas, it is important that the building be well-insulated and ventilated. Floors must be easy to clean because the cows are milked, housed, and fed in the same area. The floors should be made of cement or some other easy-to-clean material which is likely to be cold unless the barn is properly insulated. When the cow's udder is subjected to cold floors and drafty conditions, there is more danger of udder diseases developing.

Successful insulation depends upon two principles: (1) a double wall filled with a recommended insulating material, and (2) a vapor barrier applied to the inner wall. The purpose of the insulating material is to break up the air circulation between the walls, which prevents the transfer of heat or cold through them. The vapor barrier prevents moisture from penetrating the inner wall where it would condense. There are a number of good commercial insulating products from which to choose. The vapor barrier may consist of two coats of aluminum paint applied to the inner wall. Waterproof glazed surface paper or other waterproof material that will prevent moisture from penetrating the inside wall may be used. Warm air will hold more moisture than will cold air. When a barn is full of livestock, considerable moisture is picked up by the air as it is warmed from the heat given off by the animals. When the air is cooled, it can no longer hold as much water, and condensation oc-

Figure 18-8. An electrically operated automatic barn cleaner for use in stanchion-type barns. (Courtesy Great Lakes Steel Corporation, Unit of National Steel Corporation)

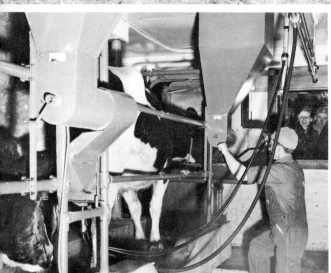

Figure 18-9. A well-bedded loafing area. (Courtesy Great Lakes Steel Corporation, Unit of National Steel Corporation)

Figure 18-10. An elevated milking parlor showing automatic feed measuring device. (Courtesy De Laval Separator Company)

curs. When the air that circulates inside a building strikes the cold walls and ceiling, the moisture condenses and the walls or ceiling becomes wet. If the walls and ceiling are properly insulated, they remain at about the same temperature as the interior of the building and no condensation takes place.

Ventilation is the controlling of the air movements by the proper installation of intakes and outlets. Cool, dry air from the outside is brought in. As the air warms, it picks up moisture given off by the livestock. The outlets afford a place for the warm, moist air to escape, and the process is repeated. Tight walls and ceiling that permit the control of air circulation are necessary for good ventilation.

Temperature. Cows do not need especially warm barns in order to produce well. A stanchion barn maintained at a temperature of about 50 degrees is sufficiently warm. Sudden changes of temperature will cause a drop in milk production. A well-insulated barn is one where ventilation may be controlled; the dairyman can prevent the radical changes in temperature that will occur in a poorly constructed building.

The Loose Housing System

The loose housing system provides for a flexible housing arrangement that may be enlarged easily as the herd increases in size. The cows are free and have access to fresh air and sunlight. Ventilating problems are held to a minimum. The loose housing system provides for low-cost housing that may be arranged so as to reduce labor to a minimum.

The loose housing system consists of four units: (1) a feeding and feed storage area, (2) a paved lot, (3) the loafing and bedding storage area, and (4) the milking parlor. The four units may be under the same roof or in separate buildings.

Feeding and Feed Storage Area. The feeding area is where the feed is stored and where the cows are fed their daily ration of hay. The feed may be stored in the rear of the shed and a movable feed rack constructed. As the cows eat into the hay, the rack is moved, thereby saving the labor of handling the hay. The feeding area should be paved and the manger constructed so as to prevent the cows from pulling out the hay and lying on it.

The Loafing Area. This is the area where the cows rest. The manure pack is allowed to accumulate. The fermentation of the manure creates heat which keeps the cows warm and comfortable. The area needs to be bedded heavily if the cows are to be kept clean. About 12 pounds of bedding will be required per cow per day. At least 60 square feet of space per cow should be provided. The area does not have to be kept especially warm, but drafts should be avoided. The calf pens and calving stalls may be constructed in this area. In building the loafing shed, the need for cleaning with a power loader should be kept in mind. By spring, the manure may be from two to four feet deep and trampled solid.

The Paved Area. Cows make good use of sunshine every day, even in very cold weather, if a windbreak is provided. The building may be constructed so as to give protection on the north and west. The paved lot should extend east and south of the buildings. Silage may be fed in bunks on the paved lot.

The Milking Parlor. The milking parlor is where the cows stand in either stanchions or elevated stalls for milking.

The Floor Level System. This system consists of stanchions for confining a few cows at a time for milking. The operator stands on the same level as the cows. They are usually fed their grain ration while in the stanchion. The cost is low and construction is easy with this type of milking parlor. Usually four stanchions are required for from eight to ten cows.

The Elevated Stall System. Under this system the cow is 30 inches above the level of the floor on which the operator stands. The self-closing doors may be opened by rope and pulley. One cow is changed at a time because turnover is easy. The operator can do his work with a minimum of stooping, which lessens fatigue.

Feeding and Management
of the Herd Sire

It is desirable that outstanding dairy sires be kept in active service for a number of years. The service of bulls that have proven their ability to transmit high-production qualities to their offspring is sought by all progressive dairymen. A bull is usually six to seven years of age or older by the time he has sired a sufficient number of daughters with records to establish his transmitting ability. Many bulls become sterile by the time they have proven themselves unless they have had careful feeding and management.

The herd sire should be fed in such a way as to insure his development in size to the fullest extent of his inheritance. Although a small or stunted bull may be as good a breeder as a larger one, dairymen who wish to buy breeding stock usually look upon such a sire with disfavor. Therefore, a bull of at least average size for the breed is desirable. The mature bull should be fed according to his size and to the extent he is being used for breeding.

Feeding the Mature Bull. It is commonly believed that excessively fat bulls may lack a desire to breed and become impotent. However, a bull should not become too thin. During the season of heavy breeding, the bull should have an increase in the daily concentrate ration. During periods when the sire is not in heavy service, feed may be reduced. The roughage ration should be controlled to keep the paunch to minimum size. The paunch must be kept down to medium size or bulls will have difficulty performing the act of breeding.

Management of the Bull. The management of the bull calf is similar to that of heifer calves until he is about five months of age. By that time, the bull may have become sexually mature enough to breed and, therefore, should be removed from the heifers.

The bull should be taught to lead while young. At first, a halter made of rope or some other inexpensive material is all that is needed. Later, a ring should be placed in his nose, and a staff should be used for leading. The bull is more easily controlled when led by a staff and ring, and there is less danger to the operator.

Ringing the Bull. When the bull calf is about six months of age, he should have a small ring placed in his nose. This may be accomplished by tying him up in such a way as to hold his head firmly. Find the soft part in the nose, force the ring through, and clamp or fasten it together with a screw, depending upon the type of ring used. A trocar may be used to puncture the nose before inserting the ring. On young bull calves, the trocar is not essential if a self-piercing ring is used. As the bull grows older, the cartilage between the nostrils become tougher, and a trocar is essential for ringing. The first ring should be of light-weight, nonrusting material about 1.5 inches in diameter. When the bull is ten to 12 months old, replace the ring with a strong three-inch brass or cannon metal ring.

Exercise. Plenty of exercise is essential if the bull is to be kept in good breeding condition and in active service over a long period of time. One of the best methods of providing exercise is to construct a pen adjacent to the shed or housing quarters. The bull should not be tied up for long periods at a time or he will become sore and stiff.

Housing. The dairy bull should have his own shelter. The shed should be located on a well-drained area so that it will stay dry. It should be tight enough to provide protection from cold weather, and shade during warm weather. A feed alley, from which the bull may be fed without endangering the operator, may be located along one side of the shed. An overhead storage area for roughage and bedding will decrease the amount of labor necessary in the caring for the bull.

Exercise Lot. The safest and easiest way to provide exercise is to have a yard adjoining the bull shed. The yard need not be wide, but it should be at least 80 feet long. The bull will have a tendency to walk from one end of the yard to the other. A block of wood that is suspended to hang about four feet from the ground and that will swing back and forth as the bull plays with it will encourage him to exercise.

The pen should be constructed of heavy plank or pipe fastened to substantial posts. A breeding chute located on one side of the pen is essential for the safety of the operator. The cow is placed in the chute, and the bull is allowed to reach the cow by means of a swinging gate. This eliminates the necessity of the operator's entering the bull yard. It is desirable to have the bull pen located where the cows pass frequently. The bull will be inclined to exercise more if the cows come near his pen, and cows may be more easily placed in the chute for breeding.

Service Age. A young, well-grown bull may be used occasionally for breeding when ten months of age. He should not be used regularly before he is a year to 15 months old. Until the bull is 18 months old, the number of services should be limited to two per week. Mature bulls may be used for four services per week for short periods. Such heavy service should not extend for more than two weeks for any one period. One bull for 50 to 60 cows is sufficient if the breeding is spread out over the year. One bull to 30 cows is necessary if the cows are bred to freshen largely during one season of the year—that is, if the entire herd must be bred during a two-to-three-month period.

Summary

Profitable dairying is achieved when cattle with high inherent producing ability are fed according to their productive ability.

Roughages are the basis of dairy cattle rations. Legumes are recognized as being the best source of roughage, for they are high in minerals, protein, and vitamins.

Many native grasses, brome, timothy, fescue, millet, and orchard grass are some of the more common grasses used as forage. The grasses make very acceptable roughage when properly balanced with protein, mineral, and vitamin supplements.

Low quality roughages have little value in rations for producing cows. Fodders from corn and sorghums may be used successfully if properly supplemented, but they are not considered ideal forages for milking cows.

Silage made from legumes, grasses, corn, and sorghums makes excellent roughage. However, it is low in protein unless half or more of it consists of legumes.

In certain areas of the United States, citrus pulp is used as a roughage. Beet pulp has a rather wide usage among dairymen. These two feeds are low in protein, but they are higher in digestible nutrients than are most roughages.

Pastures are the natural feed for dairy cows and should be extended over the longest possible time.

Corn is generally considered the number one grain for dairy cattle, but a combination of other grains makes very good rations.

Soybean oil meal, linseed oil meal, soybeans, cottonseed meal, corn gluten feed, corn gluten meal, distiller's grains, and dried brewer's grains are common dairy feeds that are high in protein.

Urea may be used to replace part or all of the protein in the ration, but it should never exceed 0.3 pound per cow per day. Urea should be used only in conjunction with high energy feeds, such as the grains or molasses.

Vitamins are seldom a problem when cows have access to good pasture or any high quality forage. Under some conditions, it is advisable to feed a supplement containing vitamins A and D.

Mineral mixtures containing salt, calcium, and phosphorus are essential in most areas. Mineral mixtures recommended for the area should be followed.

The proper feeding of the dairy cow requires that her weight, her milk production, and the butterfat percentage of her milk be known. One of the acceptable rules governing the amount of concentrates to feed should be followed.

Grinding grains reduces waste and facilitates mixing. Grains should be coarsely ground; fine grinding reduces palatability.

Good pastures minimize feeding problems. However, some forage and grain should be fed to high-producing cows that are on pasture. The amount and kind of forage and grain to feed will depend upon the quality and quantity of pasture available.

The cow needs a dry or rest period of from six to eight weeks for replacing body weight lost during the last lactation period. She should be fed a ration in the amount and kind that will put her in top condition for the next milking period.

Just before freshening, the concentrate part of the ration may be replaced in part with more bulky feeds. The first three days following calving, a mildly laxative ration that is bulky in nature is advisable. Feed should not be reduced severely following calving, for ketosis may develop. The cow should be brought up to full feed as quickly as her appetite will permit following calving.

The paunch size of breeding bulls should be held at a minimum size to facilitate breeding. The size of the paunch may be controlled by the amount of roughage.

Ringing the bull and using a staff when leading him minimize dangers to the operator.

The bull needs plenty of exercise, which can best be provided by constructing an exercise lot adjoining the bull shed. A bull shed that will provide shelter from the cold and shade during warm weather is essential. A breeding chute should be constructed along one side of the exercise pen.

Bulls may be used for limited service when 10 to 15 months of age. Mature bulls can service 50 to 60 cows if the breeding is spread out evenly over the year.

There are two systems of housing—the loose housing system and the stanchion type system. Both systems have advantages and disadvantages.

A moderate amount of exercise should be provided for cows but excessive exercise may reduce milk production. Cleaning and grooming the animals is essential to health and a clean product.

Managed milking is recommended. A milking system should be planned and followed. Barns and equipment should be kept clean and free from offensive odors.

The drying-off process may be accomplished by intermittent milking, incomplete milking, or abrupt cessation of milking. Cows with sound udders will generally respond best to abrupt cessation of milking.

At calving time, the cow should be placed in a well-bedded, well-ventilated, clean stall with adequate room for calving. Occasionally, high-producing cows may require milking before calving. The practice is not generally recommended.

Cows may be bred naturally or artificially. Artificial breeding is common, with a conception rate equal to that of natural breeding. Artificial insemination provides the dairyman with the service of good bulls at low cost and eliminates the problems of securing and maintaining a bull.

Fall freshening is generally more profitable except when the dairyman is retailing milk and must maintain a constant supply.

• *Questions*

1. List the common grain concentrates fed to dairy cows.
2. Compare the other common grains with corn as a feed for dairy cattle.
3. List some common protein concentrates used for dairy cow feed.
4. Explain how urea may be used as a protein substitute.
5. What are the precautions that should be taken when feeding urea?
6. Why are roughages considered the basis of dairy cow rations?
7. What are the advantages of legume roughages over other kinds of forage crops?
8. How much milk can a dairy cow produce on good roughages alone?
9. What information is necessary to balance a dairy cow's ration?
10. Show by example how you would determine the amount of protein and total digestible nutrients for any given cow.
11. Show by example how you would determine the protein percentage of a ration.

Feeding and Management of the Producing Herd • 353

12. List some concentrate mixtures to be fed with various kinds of roughages.
13. What rule would you follow to determine the amount of concentrate mixture to feed a cow on pasture?
14. Why is pasture so important to the dairyman?
15. Give a good concentrate mixture to fit various kinds of pasture.
16. Why is it usually necessary to provide additional forage to high producing cows that are on pasture?
17. What are some of the pasture limitations?
18. Give a good rule for feeding concentrates to cows that are on pasture.
19. Why is it usually necessary to feed concentrates to the dry cow?
20. What and how much would you feed the dry cow four or five days before freshening?
21. What and how much would you feed the cow one to four days after freshening?
22. Why should the same procedure be followed for each milking?
23. Discuss the three common methods of drying off cows.
24. Explain how you would care for the cow at calving time.
25. What is the advantage of natural breeding? Of artificial breeding?
26. When should cows calf? Why?
27. What is the average gestation period for different breeds?
28. Why is it unwise to milk a cow dry shortly after freshening?
29. At what time of year is it generally best to have cows freshen? Why?
30. How can you help to insure good results from artificial insemination?
31. How should cows be prepared for milking?
32. Explain the two common systems of housing dairy cows.
33. What are the advantages of each housing system?
34. Give a good ration for the dairy bull.
35. Why should a ring be placed in the nose of the bull?
36. Explain how to ring a bull.
37. How would you feed the mature bull?
38. Why is it important to control the paunch size?
39. Describe a good bull shed and exercise lot.
40. List ways and means by which you would reduce the dangers in handling a dairy bull.

• References

Feeding and Management of Dairy Cattle, Extension Service, Pamphlets 244 to 249, Iowa State College, Ames, Iowa, 1957-1958.

Henderson, H. O., and Paul M. Reaves, *Dairy Cattle Feeding and Management* (Revised), John Wiley and Sons, Inc., New York, 1954.

Johnson, Floyd, Arthur R. Porter, and Lyle W. Jackson, *Feeding Dairy Cows,* Agricultural Experiment and Extension Bulletin (Reprint), Iowa State College, Ames, Iowa, 1950.

Nevens, W. B., *Feeding the Dairy Herd,* Agricultural Extension Circular 677, University of Illinois, Urbana, Illinois, 1951.

Nibler, C. W., *Dairy Herd Management,* Agricultural Extension Bulletin EC 631, University of Nebraska, Lincoln, Nebraska, 1953.

Nibler, C. W., *Feeding Milk Cows,* Agriculture Extension Circular EC 627 (Revised), University of Nebraska, Lincoln, Nebraska, 1951.

Petersen, W. E., *Dairy Science,* J. B. Lippincott Company, Philadelphia, 1950.

Searles, H. R., R. W. Wayne, T. W. Gullickson, and R. D. Leighton, *Feeding the Dairy Herd,* Extension Bulletin 218 (Revised), University of Minnesota, St. Paul, Minnesota, 1952.

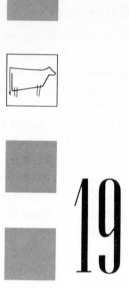

Feeding and Management
of Young Dairy Stock

The first step in the production of dairy calves is to have strong calves at birth. To insure strong calves, the cows should have at least six weeks of rest between lactation, and they should receive a well-balanced ration.

Feeding the Calf from Birth to Six Months of Age

The rumen of the calf does not develop and begin to function for several days after birth. Until rumination has started, the young calf is unable to manufacture the vitamins and protein amino acids that older ruminants are capable of manufacturing. Therefore, young calves are dependent upon the ration provided for them to obtain all the essential food nutrients. The problems involved in the feeding of newborn calves are very similar to those of swine and other simple-stomach animals. In addition to vitamins A and D, the B-complex vitamins will need to be contained in the ration. Animal proteins are necessary to insure a complete protein balance.

Figure 19-1. Strong, healthy calves are the result of good feeding and management. (Courtesy *Wallaces' Farmer and Iowa Homestead*)

Antibiotics in Dairy Calf Rations. Recent experiments indicate that aureomycin and terramycin will increase the growth rate of dairy heifers without any apparent effect upon reproduction or milk production. Aureomycin fed in the milk at the rate of 80 milligrams of aureomycin hydrochloride per calf per day from four to 116 days of age produced the following results:

1. Increased the growth gain from 10 to 30 per cent.
2. Improved the appetite.
3. Decreased the number of cases of calf scours.
4. Produced smoother hair coats.

Feeding the Calf for the First Three Days. The first milk produced by the cow is known as colostrum. The colostrum is nature's especially prepared formula for starting the young calf. It is rich in protein, vitamins, and minerals, and contains these food nutrients in the proper balance necessary to meet the needs of the calf. Colostrum contains antibodies that help to protect the calf from diseases. Science has been unable, up to the present time, to duplicate the colostrum or first milk. Calves that fail to get the colostrum are difficult to raise, and losses are generally heavy.

Dairymen are not all agreed as to the best way to provide the colostrum to the calves, but most seem to favor leaving the calf with the cow for the first three days. This practice insures the calf of getting the colostrum at body temperature and free from contamination.

Any additional colostrum produced by the cow in excess of what the calf needs may be fed to older calves. It is a waste of a highly nutritious feed to throw it away.

Systems of Feeding Dairy Calves. There are four common systems of feeding calves from the third day until they are nine weeks of age. The systems are: (1) liberal milk feeding, (2) using milk replacers, (3) limited milk feeding plus a dry calf starter, and (4) the nurse cow method.

Liberal Milk Feeding. Maximum growth can be obtained when the calf is fed liberally on milk. The common procedure, when this system is followed, is to feed whole milk at the rate of one pound to each eight to ten pounds of body weight for the first three to four weeks, then gradually to switch to skim milk (the same amount in proportion to body weight) until the calf is getting from 14 to 18 pounds of milk daily. No more than this amount should be fed. It is important for calves not to be overfed on milk. The milk should be fed at from 90° to 100° F. Clean pails should be used. If scouring is observed, the amount of milk should be reduced. Fifty milligrams of aureomycin may be added to the daily milk feed. When calves are kept inside and are not exposed to direct sunlight, there is some danger that a vitamin D deficiency will develop. Whole milk will generally provide adequate amounts of vitamin A. Since the vitamin A content of milk is contained in the butterfat, additions of a vitamin A supplement when skim milk feeding is started will provide insurance against vitamin A deficiencies. Many dairymen follow the practice of adding a few drops of fish liver oil or some other vitamin A and D concentrate to the daily milk ration to prevent vitamin A and D deficiencies.

Using Milk Replacers. On dairy farms, where production costs are high and the product is sold as whole milk, many dairymen are turning to milk replacers as a means of lowering the cost of raising young stock. Milk replacers usually consist of a dry feed mixture that is reconstituted with warm water and fed as a replacement for milk. The successful raising of calves on milk replacers depends very largely how complete nutritionally the product is. Many dairymen are reporting excellent success with milk replacers:

Formula No. 1

Dried Skim Milk	50.0 lbs.
Dried Whey	10.0 lbs.
Distiller's Dried Solubles	15.0 lbs.
Oat Flour	5.0 lbs.
Dried Buttermilk	10.5 lbs.
Dextrose	7.0 lbs.
Dicalcium Phosphate	2.0 lbs.
Trace Minerals	0.5 lbs.
Aureomycin	2.0 grams
Vitamin D	300,000 I. U.*
Vitamin A	1,000,000 I. U.*

Formula No. 2

Dried Skim Milk	50.0 lbs.
Dried Whey	9.5 lbs.
Red Dog Flour	15.0 lbs.
Distiller's Dried Solubles	15.0 lbs.
Soluble Blood Flour	10.0 lbs.
Trace Minerals	0.5 lbs.
Aureomycin	2.0 grams
Vitamin D	300,000 I. U.*
Vitamin A	1,000,000 I. U.*

* I. U. = International Units.

When a milk replacement similar to those listed is to be used, the calves should be fed the cow's milk for the first five days.

Calves should be fed twice daily. After the calves are 50 days old, the milk replacer may be gradually reduced, and it may be discontinued when the calves are two months of age. Several feed companies manufacture milk replacement mixtures. If a commercial replacement is used, the manufacturer's directions should be followed.

TABLE 39

DAILY FEEDING RATE OF MILK REPLACEMENT

Age (Days)	Milk (Pounds Daily)		Water Added to Milk (90° to 100°) (Pounds Daily)		Milk Replacement (Pounds Daily)	
	Large Breeds	Small Breeds	Large Breeds	Small Breeds	Large Breeds	Small Breeds
6–8	5	4	4	2	0.6	0.4
8–10	3	2	7	6	0.8	0.6
11–20	0	0	9	8	1.0	0.8
21–40	0	0	12	10	1.2	1.0
40–50	0	0	14	12	1.4	1.2

Dried skim milk mixed with water at the rate of a pound of powder to nine pounds of water will give good results, if the change from whole to powdered skim milk is made gradually over a ten-day period. Dried buttermilk may be used instead of skim milk. When they are fed either of these products, calves should not receive more than a pound of reconstituted milk for each ten pounds of body weight daily. Antibiotic and vitamin supplements recommended for skim milk feeding will also apply when dried skim milk or dried buttermilk is fed.

Limited Milk Feeding Plus a Dry Calf Starter. When calves are approximately ten days old, they will start to eat dry feeds. On many dairy farms where whole milk is sold, calves will be started on whole milk and gradually shifted to a calf starter. Good calf starters are nutritionally adequate and will supply a sufficient amount of the various nutrients for the growth and development of the calf. When this system is followed, as little as 250 to 350 pounds of whole milk fed over a period of six to seven weeks is used. The calves should be fed whole milk at the rate of a pound for each ten pounds of body weight for the first three weeks following the colostrum feeding period. The dry calf starter should be made available to the calf at ten days of age. The calf can be induced to eat at an earlier age if some of the starter is rubbed on its nose and mouth after each milk feeding.

When the calf is four weeks old, it should be eating from 0.5 to one pound of starter daily, and no additional increase in the milk feeding is necessary. During the fifth week, the milk should be reduced by two pounds and the calf given free access to the starter. A reduction of the milk by another two pounds may be made during the sixth week, and the milk may be discontinued when the calf is seven weeks old. The calf should be given free access to the starter up to five pounds daily. When the five-pound level has been reached, a less expensive feed may be substituted for the starter. Following are two suggested calf starters:

Mixture No. 1	
Corn (cracked or coarse ground)	27.00 lbs.
Oats (rolled)	15.00 lbs.
Wheat Bran	10.00 lbs.
Wheat Middlings	10.50 lbs.
Dried Skim Milk or Dried Buttermilk	7.00 lbs.

Soybean Oil Meal	18.00 lbs.
Molasses	3.50 lbs.
Alfalfa Meal (dehydrated)	5.00 lbs.
Irradiated Yeast	0.05 lbs.
Steamed Bone Meal	1.50 lbs.
Salt	0.75 lbs.
Trace Mineral Mixture	0.20 lbs.
*Aureomycin	1.00 gram
Vitamin A Feed (2,000,000 I. U. per Pound)	1.50 lbs.

Mixture No. 2

Corn (cracked or coarse ground)	20.00 lbs.
Oats (ground)	30.00 lbs.
Distiller's Dried Corn Solubles	25.00 lbs.
Linseed Oil Meal	12.00 lbs.
Wheat Bran	11.00 lbs.
Steamed Bone Meal	1.00 lbs.
Salt	1.00 lbs.
Trace Minerals	0.20 lbs.
*Aureomycin	1.00 gram
Dry Vitamin A & D Concentrate to provide 1,000,000 I. U. of A and 300,000 I. U. of D	

* Any recommended antibiotic supplement for calves. The amount should be sufficient to furnish approximately 1 gram of antibiotic per 100 pounds of feed mixture.

Nurse Cow Method. Calves that are to be grown out rapidly, such as veal calves or purebred animals intended for early sale, may be put on a nurse cow. This method is more expensive but reduces calves' danger of digestive disturbances. Sometimes two, or even three, calves are placed on one cow. The usual practice is to turn the cow and calves together morning and evening so the calves may nurse.

Purebred breeders often retain old foundation cows in the herd long after their usefulness as milk producers is over. These cows are retained to produce calves. Many times one or more quarters of the udder no longer function. Such cows often make good nurse cows.

Grain Feeding. When a calf starter is used, no other grain is necessary for the first six to seven weeks. It is generally recommended that calves on nurse cows, and on methods featuring a liberal supply of milk or milk replacers, be fed a grain mixture starting when they are ten days old. Some recommended mixtures with good legume forage and lower quality of roughage that may be fed to growing calves follow:

When Good Legume Roughage Is Fed

A. 40 pounds ground shelled corn or ground sorghum grain
   40 pounds ground oats
   18 pounds wheat bran
   1 pound iodized salt
   1 pound steamed bone meal
   * 1 gram aureomycin

B. 25 pounds ground shelled corn
   25 pounds ground barley
   25 pounds ground sorghum grain
   23 pounds ground oats
   1 pound iodized salt
   1 pound steamed bone meal
   * 1 gram aureomycin

When Low-Quality Roughage Is Fed

A. 30 pounds ground shelled corn or ground sorghum grain
   20 pounds ground oats
   10 pounds dehydrated alfalfa meal
   20 pounds wheat bran
   17 pounds linseed or soybean oil meal
   1 pound salt
   1.5 pounds steamed bone meal
   0.5 pound trace minerals
   2 ounces irradiated yeast
   * 1 gram aureomycin

B. 30 pounds ground barley
   20 pounds ground sorghum grain
   20 pounds wheat bran
   15 pounds dehydrated alfalfa meal
   12 pounds soybean or linseed oil meal
   1.5 pounds steamed bone meal
   0.5 pound trace minerals
   1 pound salt
   2 ounces irradiated yeast
   * 1 gram aureomycin

* May be any recommended antibiotic supplement for calves, fed to provide 1 gram of antibiotic per 100 pounds of total feed.

After the fifth week, the concentrate mixture should be fed according to the weight of the growing calf.

TABLE 40

GUIDE FOR FEEDING CONCENTRATES TO DAIRY CALVES

Weight of Animals (lbs.)	Concentrates Daily (lbs.) with Good Legume Roughage	Concentrates Daily (lbs.) with Fair Quality Roughage
100	Free Choice	Free Choice
150	2	3
200	3	4
250	3.5	4.5
300	4	5
350	4	5.5
400	4	6

Feeding Roughages to Calves. Calves will start to eat hay at about ten days of age. Choice green, leafy legume, or legume grass mixed hay is best. Remove any leftovers from the rack and replace with new hay each day. Silage is good feed for calves after they reach the age of four months. Calves like silage, but it should be limited to two pounds daily per 100 pounds body weight.

Pasture. Calves under six months of age will generally do better on dry lot than on pasture. Young calves do not have the capacity to secure the needed nutrients from pasture alone. If the calves are turned on pasture, they should receive some good quality dry forage and the recommended amount of concentrate for their body weight.

Water. Calves should have free access to clean, fresh water after they are three weeks of age. Water is especially important when calves are fed on a dry starter as the milk is reduced. Young, growing animals have high water requirements.

Minerals. If the growing calf is fed on legume hays and a complete concentrate mixture, it will seldom suffer from a shortage of minerals. As a precaution, equal parts of salt and steamed bone meal should be kept before the calves.

Feeding Heifers from Six Months of Age to Freshening Age

Although it is important to feed heifers sufficiently to produce normal growth, it is not economical, nor is it in the best interests of producing good cows, to overfeed them.

TABLE 41

AGE, WEIGHT, HEIGHT, AND CHEST GIRTH STANDARDS FOR GROWING DAIRY HEIFERS

Age	Holstein Females Weight (Lbs.)	Height at Withers (In.)	Chest Girth (In.)	Ayrshire Females Weight (Lbs.)	Height at Withers (In.)	Chest Girth (In.)	Guernsey Females Weight (Lbs.)	Height at Withers (In.)	Chest Girth (In.)	Jersey Females Weight (Lbs.)	Height at Withers (In.)	Chest Girth (In.)
Birth	92	29.5	30.0	72	27.5	29.0	67	27.5	29.0	54	25.5	26.0
1st month	102	30.0	32.0	82	28.0	31.0	76	28.5	30.0	66	26.5	28.0
2nd month	138	32.0	35.0	114	30.5	35.0	98	30.0	33.0	92	29.0	31.0
3rd month	186	34.0	38.0	157	32.5	38.0	138	32.0	37.0	130	31.0	35.0
4th month	251	36.5	43.0	218	35.0	42.0	182	34.0	40.0	181	33.5	39.0
5th month	307	38.5	46.0	280	37.0	46.0	234	35.5	43.0	230	35.5	42.0
6th month	369	40.5	49.0	328	38.5	48.0	289	37.5	46.0	274	36.5	44.0
7th month	429	41.5	52.0	389	40.0	51.0	338	39.0	49.0	324	38.0	47.0
8th month	492	43.0	54.0	441	41.0	53.0	390	40.0	51.0	365	39.0	49.0
9th month	553	44.5	57.0	486	42.0	55.0	437	41.0	53.0	407	40.5	51.0
10th month	613	45.5	59.0	512	42.5	56.0	468	42.0	54.0	447	41.5	53.0
11th month	645	46.0	60.0	556	43.5	58.0	513	43.0	56.0	491	42.5	55.0
12th month	701	47.0	62.0	587	44.0	59.0	566	44.0	58.0	515	43.0	56.0
13th month / 14th month	762	48.0	64.0	643	45.0	61.0	592	44.5	59.0	560	43.5	58.0
15th month / 16th month	829	49.0	66.0	700	46.0	63.0	667	46.0	62.0	613	44.5	60.0
17th month / 18th month	898	50.0	68.0	754	47.0	65.0	727	46.5	64.0	667	45.5	62.0
19th month / 20th month	968	51.0	70.0	824	48.0	67.0	761	47.0	65.0	703	46.5	63.0
21st month / 22nd month	1,044	52.0	72.0	871	48.5	68.0	827	48.0	67.0	763	48.0	65.0
23rd month / 24th month	1,122	53.0	74.0	930	49.5	70.0	901	49.0	69.0	801	48.5	66.0

Extension Circular E.C. 622, University of Nebraska, Lincoln, Nebraska.

Feeding Dairy Heifers on Pasture. Dairy heifers six months of age or older may be turned on pasture. The shift from dry feeds to pasture should be made gradually, and some good dry forages as well as grain should be provided during the first two weeks. Dry forage may be discontinued after two weeks if the pasture is good, but some grain should be provided. The amount of grain need not exceed 0.5 pound per 100 pounds of body weight with a maximum of four pounds. Any of the common grains or grain mixtures used for dairy cattle feeding are sufficient. When the pasture contains legumes, it is not necessary to feed protein concentrates, unless the pasture plants become dry and mature. Following are examples of concentrate mixtures that may be fed successfully to dairy heifers on pasture:

With Good Legume Pasture

1. Oats (ground)	300 lbs.
Corn (cracked)	200 lbs.
2. Barley (ground)	250 lbs.
Grain Sorghum (ground)	250 lbs.
3. Oats (ground)	200 lbs.
Wheat Bran	50 lbs.
Corn (cracked)	250 lbs.

With Dry Matured Pasture

1. Oats (ground)	275 lbs.
Corn (cracked)	200 lbs.
Soybean, Linseed, Cotton-	
seed, or Peanut Oil Meal	25 lbs.
2. Oats (ground)	200 lbs.
Corn (cracked)	200 lbs.
Wheat Bran	100 lbs.
3. Barley (ground)	250 lbs.
Grain Sorghum (ground)	225 lbs.
Cottonseed, Soybean, Lin-	
seed, or Peanut Oil Meal	25 lbs.

Feeding Dairy Heifers in Dry Lot. Dairy heifers that are receiving all the high quality legume hay they will consume, or legume hay plus good silage, need very little grains for normal growth. Concentrate mixtures recommended for heifers on pasture may be used for those in dry lot. When high-protein forage is fed, protein concentrates are not necessary. If the forage is low in protein content, the concentrate should contain from 12 to 15 per cent protein. Citrus or beet pulp may replace all or part of the oats and barley. Citrus or beet pulp is lower in protein than oats, so some additional protein concentrate should be added to the mixture.

Management of Dairy Calves

Losses range from 13 to 17 per cent of live calves during the first four months after birth. Most losses of young dairy calves are the result of pneumonia, calf .scours, and navel infections. Proper management will eliminate a large percentage of calf deaths due to these ailments.

Care of the Newborn Calf. When the calf is born, the mucus and phlegm should be cleaned from the nose and mouth. If the calf does not start to breathe, it should be held by the rear legs and lifted from the floor with the head down. This procedure is to form a type of artificial respiration and will often produce results if repeated several times. Alternate compression and relaxation of the chest will often start the calf breathing when other methods fail.

As soon as the calf is breathing properly, the navel should be disinfected. Squeezing out the navel cord and painting the navel with iodine will help to avoid infection. If the cow does not lick her calf dry, or if the weather is cold, the dairyman should wipe the calf to hasten drying.

Figure 19-2. Disinfecting the navel of a new born calf. (Courtesy Michigan State University)

Figure 19-3. An individual calf pen equipped with feed box and hay rack. (Courtesy Cornell University)

The next step is to remove all cleanings and wet bedding from the pen and to wash the cow's udder with a chlorine solution to prevent any infectious organisms from being taken in through the calf's mouth during the first feeding. If the calf is normal, it will stand and suck within 30 minutes. If it fails to do so, it should be given assistance in getting a feeding of the first or colostrum milk.

Within two hours after the calf has had its first feed, its bowels should move to eliminate the material accumulated in the digestive tract before it was born. If this does not pass in due time, an enema consisting of one-half teaspoonful of soda in a quart of warm water should be given.

Calf Pens. Well-lighted, well-ventilated, clean, dry pens, adequately bedded and free from drafts, are essential to successful calf raising.

If adequate room is available, individual solid-wall pens for calves up to eight to ten weeks of age have many advantages. The solid wall helps to prevent pneumonia, for it decreases drafts. Calves in individual pens cannot suck each other, a habit common among calves raised in groups. A recommended size is 24 square feet per pen with removable feed boxes eight by ten by six inches deep.

When it is not possible to provide individual pens for calves, they may be raised in groups in pens equipped with stanchions for each calf. The calves may be fed milk in the stanchion and left tied up for 15 to 20 minutes after each feeding. This period immediately after milk feeding is the time when sucking of each other is common. By keeping them tied up for a few minutes, the sucking will be prevented and there will be less danger of accumulating hair balls in their stomachs. Feedboxes should be ten inches wide and six inches deep. They should be long enough to provide two feet of space per calf. Boxes that may be removed for cleaning are desirable. Place boxes 20 inches from the floor and away from the waterer.

Dehorning. Calves that are from three to ten days old can be dehorned more easily and with less danger of loss than can older cattle. The horn button does not become attached to the skull until the calf is past ten days of age. Several methods may be used to remove the horn; those recommended for beef cattle are suitable for dairy cattle. (See page 228.)

Marking Calves. The marking of calves for identification is an important management procedure. For registration of purebreds, calves must be positively identified. See Beef Cattle, page 233.

Figure 19-4. Determining the teats to be clipped, and clipping the extra teats. (Courtesy University of Wisconsin)

A

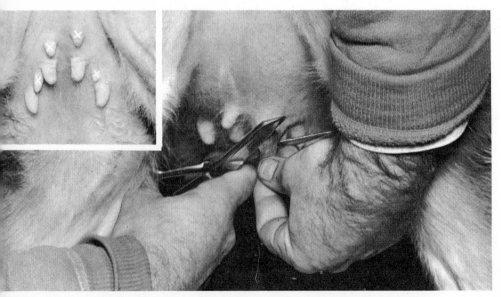

Removing Extra Teats. Dairy heifers often have extra teats in addition to the four normal ones. These extra teats should be removed when the calf is between one and two months old. The best method for removing an extra teat is to disinfect the area around the teat and clip it off with a pair of scissors. Usually it will bleed very little. If bleeding is considerable, holding a cotton pack over the wound for a few minutes will stop it.

Breeding and Calving Records. Breeding and calving records are essential to good dairy management. The dairyman should be able at any time to determine the sire and dam of a calf. He should also know when the calf was born. Breeding dates of heifers and cows and expected calving dates are important. There are many different types of forms one may use for this purpose. The following form is an example of a simple record adequate for many herds.

BREEDING AND CALVING RECORD

Name or Number of Cow	Sire	Date Bred	Date Due	Date Born	Sex	Identification of Calf	Disposition
Molly No. 27	Chief 41683	Oct. 1, 1955	July 11, 1956	July 12, 1956	F	MA 42	Sold April 1, 1958 to John Smith

Age to Breed. The size rather than the age of a dairy heifer at breeding time is important. Breeding undersized animals is never a profitable practice. They may be stunted or slow to reach maximum size. Small heifers are more apt to have difficulty in calving.

TABLE 42

AGE AND SIZE TO BREED DAIRY HEIFERS

Breed	Age	Weight	Heart Girth in Inches
Holsteins	18 months	850-900	67
Brown Swiss	18 months	800-850	65
Ayrshires	18 months	750-800	64
Guernseys	17 months	700-750	62
Jerseys	16 months	600-650	59

Summary

Since the rumen of the calf does not develop and begin to function for several days after birth, the problems of feeding the calf are similar to those of feeding simple-stomach animals. Most of the vitamins and proteins have to be provided in the ration.

Antibiotics have proven beneficial in reducing calf scours and increasing growth rates when fed in small amounts daily.

The calf should receive the colostrum milk for the first three days. After this, any one of several systems may be successfully followed. They are: (1) the liberal milk system, (2) using milk replacements, (3) limited milk feeding plus a calf starter, and (4) the nurse cow method.

When a calf starter is used, no additional grain is necessary for the first six to seven weeks. Calves being raised on the liberal milk, milk replacement, or nurse cow methods are generally started on a concentrate mixture and fed according to body weight until they are five to six months old.

It is important to provide good roughage for young calves. Until calves are six months old, they do better in dry lot.

Water is very important to calf growth and development.

Dairy heifers six months old or older need very little grain if plenty of good pasture or other high quality roughage is available.

The newborn calf should have the phlegm and mucus cleaned from its mouth and nose, be dried off, have its navel disinfected, and be allowed to nurse. The pen should be clean, warm, well lighted, and well ventilated.

Dehorning should be done at an early age. Caustic, hot iron, or spoons may be used successfully if calves are dehorned early. Clippers or saws, especially prepared for that purpose, are commonly used to dehorn older cattle.

Normal healthy calves should gain from one to 1.5 pounds daily up to six months of age. The rate of gain will vary with the breed.

Calves should be marked for identification.

Extra teats should be clipped off with a pair of scissors when heifers are between one and two weeks of age.

Complete breeding, calving, and disposal records should be kept for the entire herd.

The size rather than the age should be considered when breeding dairy heifers.

• Questions

1. What are the principal differences in the digestive system of calves and older cattle?
2. Why are animal proteins and most of the vitamins necessary in the ration of young calves?
3. What effect do antibiotics have on the growth and development of calves?
4. What is the recommended level for feeding antibiotics?
5. How should the calf be fed the first three days?
6. Describe the common systems of feeding dairy calves until they are five to six months old.
7. What are the advantages of each system listed in Question 6?
8. Give a good formula for a milk replacer, a milk substitute, and a regular concentrate ration for calves getting liberal amounts of milk.
9. At what age will calves start to eat grain and hay?
10. What kind of hays would you recommend for calves?
11. At what age would you recommend turning calves on pasture?
12. Give a concentrate mixture for calves on good pasture and one for calves on fair pasture.
13. What quantity of concentrates should growing heifers receive daily?
14. What percentage of calves die during the first four months after birth?
15. How can calf losses be reduced?
16. What advantages do individual pens for calves have over group pens?
17. When group pens are used for calves, how can sucking of each other be prevented?
18. Give the methods of dehorning calves.
19. Why is sanitation important in calf raising?
20. Give a sanitation program that you would recommend.
21. What are the normal growth rates for heifer calves?
22. Explain the different systems of marking calves for identification.
23. Why should breeding and calving records be kept?
24. What information would breeding and calving records Give ?

Feeding and Management of Young Dairy Stock • 371

• References

Murley, Ray, Norman L. Jacobson, and John B. Herrick, *Raising Dairy Calves,* Agricultural Extension Service Bulletin P. 106, Iowa State College, Ames, Iowa, 1950.

Nibler, C. W., *Dairy Herd Management,* Agricultural Extension Bulletin 631, University of Nebraska, Lincoln, Nebraska, 1953.

Rupel, I. W., and George Werner, *Better Dairy Calves,* Extension Bulletin 359, University of Wisconsin, Madison, Wisconsin, 1945.

Turk, K. L., and J. D. Burke, *Raising Dairy Calves and Heifers,* Agricultural Extension Bulletin 761, Cornell University, Ithaca, New York, 1949.

Weaver, Earl, L. A. Johnson, and E. S. Smiley, *Raising Dairy Calves,* Extension Bulletin 105, Michigan State College, East Lansing, Michigan, 1950.

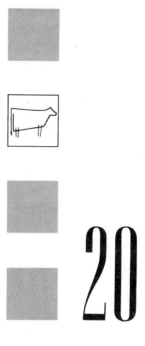

Marketing Dairy Products

The profit from dairy production is determined by the economy of production and by the selling price. Feed makes up about 50 per cent of the cost of production; labor makes up about 33 per cent. Efficient production practices alone, however, will not insure a profitable enterprise. The dairy products must be of such quality and produced at such a time that the consumer market will absorb the products at a reasonably high price. The form in which the products are sold also may affect the net income from the enterprise. Milk may be sold as Grade A, Grade B, or Grade C, or as ungraded milk. The milk may be separated on the farm, the butter-fat being sold and the skim milk being used on the farm as feed.

A farmer can increase the income from the dairy enterprise through improved marketing practices by: (1) planning production so that large quantities of milk or butterfat can be marketed during the seasons of high prices; (2) selecting the form in which to sell the products that will yield the largest net return; and (3) improving the quality of the products he has to sell.

Seasonal Price Trends

Milk Prices. A common practice on many farms is to have the cows freshen in the spring so that they make maximum use of pastures. This system minimizes the need for feed, labor, and housing during the winter months, but it encourages heavy production of milk and butterfat in the spring and early summer. Since a large share of the dairy cows in this nation are kept by farmers with small herds, we have heavy production of milk in the spring and light production during the winter months. As a result, the price of milk is low in April, May, and June, and high in September, October, and November.

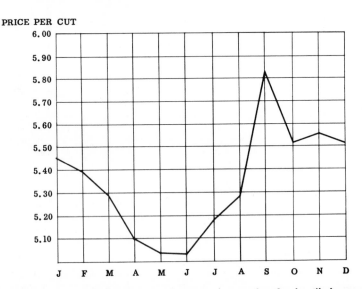

Figure 20-1. Dealers' average buying prices for fluid milk by months, U. S. 1953-1957. (Courtesy U.S.D.A. Agricultural Marketing Service)

Usually about 40 per cent of a cow's production takes place in the first four months after calving. It is a good idea to breed the cows so that 40 per cent of the total production can be sold during the months of high prices. As shown in Figure 20-1, milk sold in May during the 1953-1957 period sold for an average of $5.03 per hundredweight, whereas milk sold in September for an average of $5.82. The difference in the selling price of the milk produced in

374 • *Marketing Dairy Products*

one month by a herd of ten cows producing an average of 40 pounds per day would amount to $94.80. The difference in selling price was $.79 per hundredweight.

Butterfat Prices. A number of factors have affected the price of butter since 1940. The competition of oleomargarine has lowered the demand for, and the price of, butter; the governmental price stabilization programs have also influenced butter prices.

Figure 20-2 shows butterfat prices in January and February during the 1952-1956 period to be about 3.5 cents higher than in October and November, and about 5.2 cents higher than the prices in June and July.

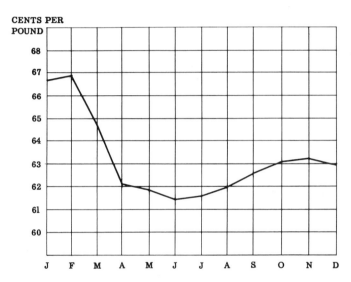

Figure 20-2. Average price received by farmers for butterfat in cream, U. S. by months, 1952-1956. *Dairy Statistics, 1957.* (Courtesy U.S.D.A.)

Milk-Feed Price Ratios. Another method of determining the best time to produce and sell milk is to compare the milk-feed price ratios (milk-feed price ratios refer to the pounds of feed equivalent in value to one pound of wholesale milk).

According to information in Table 43, the highest ratios during the 1952-1956 period were during October, November, and December. The lowest ratios were during the months of April, May,

TABLE 43

Month	Ratio	Month	Ratio
January	1.32	July	1.19
February	1.28	August	1.24
March	1.23	September	1.32
April	1.16	October	1.41
May	1.13	November	1.46
June	1.13	December	1.40

Dairy Statistics, U.S.D.A., 1957

and June. This information indicates the advisability of planning heaviest milk production for the fall and early winter months.

Form in Which Milk Should Be Sold

The method of disposing of milk varies with the area of the country and from community to community. In 1957, 78 per cent of the milk produced in the nation was sold as whole milk, 9.7 per cent was sold as farm skimmed cream, and 1.9 per cent was retailed by farmers as milk or cream. The remaining 10.4 per cent of the nation's total milk production was used on the farms where produced.

Only 5 per cent of the milk produced in the Atlantic States in 1956 was used in the manufacture of butter; more than 71 per cent was utilized as fluid milk.

In the West North Central States, more than 55 per cent of the 1956 milk production was utilized in the production of butter and an additional 13 per cent was used in the manufacture of cheese, ice cream, and other dairy foods.

Each dairyman must make a careful analysis of the market available in his community and calculate the probable income from the use of various marketing programs. At one time, skim milk was indispensable as a feed for calves, chickens, and pigs. We now have feeds which will take its place, and farmers are more willing to sell whole milk than they were 20 years ago.

Here are the calculations made by one dairyman to determine the best method of disposing of the milk produced by his herd.

Example

The herd consisted of 18 cows, which produced, during the previous year, an average of 341 pounds of butterfat and 9,220 pounds of milk. The milk could be sold as Grade A milk for $4.40 per hundredweight. It had an average butterfat test of 3.7 per cent. The milk could be separated and sold as butterfat for $.74 per pound. A truck would pick up the milk or cream at the farm.

Plan 1 Income from the Sale of Milk:

165,960 pounds of milk (9,220 × 18) at $4.40 per cwt.	$7,302.24

Plan 2 Income from the Sale of Butterfat and Use of Skim Milk as Feed:

6,138 pounds of butterfat @ $.74 per pound	$4,542.12
159,822 pounds of skim milk @ $.40 per cwt. (to be used as feed)	639.29
Total income	$5,181.41
Difference in income in favor of Plan 1	$2,120.83

Under Plan 1, it would be necessary for the dairyman to provide the sanitary quarters, milk room, and milk-cooling facilities required in producing Grade A milk.

These conditions are desired under Plan 2 but are not required. A separator and cooling tank for cream must be provided. Pigs, calves, or chickens must be available to consume the skim milk.

The example presented points out the following important considerations which must be made in deciding the form in which milk should be sold:

1. The value of the butterfat produced must be compared with the value of the Grade A milk.
2. The use and value of the skim milk must be determined.
3. An estimate must be made of the increase in cost necessary to produce Grade A milk.
4. A study must be made of the availability, cost, and dependability of transportation to market.

In the case presented, the butterfat price was low in comparison to the price of Grade A milk, and the skim milk value for feed purposes was under its value on the commercial market for drying or condensing purposes.

Markets Available

The number and types of markets available in a given area are determined by the density of population in the area, the quantity of milk produced, and the cost of transporting the dairy products to market. Table 44 shows a summary of the milk-processing plants in the United States in 1950.

TABLE 44

MILK PROCESSING PLANTS IN THE UNITED STATES—1950

(*Number of Plants*)

Region	Butter	Ice Cream	Cheese	Evaporated Milk
New England and Middle Atlantic	244	783	214	5
North Central	2,172	1,250	1,676	71
South Atlantic and South Central	264	741	123	21
Mountain and Pacific	379	497	146	25
Total	4,059	3,271	2,159	122

U.S.D.A.

Improving the Quality of Dairy Products

The quality of milk and cream to be used for pasteurization and bottling, and for butter production, has been given considerable attention by city health authorities and by milk processors. Most cities have ordinances that stipulate the quality of milk which may be sold, and the conditions under which it must be produced. Most ordinances are based upon Grade A milk standards recommended by the U. S. Department of Health, Education, and Welfare.

Milk retailers have found that increased quality stimulates consumption, and that consumers are willing to pay higher prices for milk of high quality. As a result, the demand for milk of superior quality is such that milk processors and dairies are paying the producers premium prices for high-quality milk. In some cases the premium amounts to as much as $1.00 per hundredweight. The added income from the sale of high-quality milk from a herd of ten cows producing an average of 9,000 pounds of milk may range from $200 to $300 to nearly $1,000 per year.

Most creameries pay several cents more per pound for butterfat in sweet cream of superior quality than for butterfat in sour cream of poor quality. Sweet cream butter sells better on the consumer market and can compete with butter substitutes.

Grade A Milk

Definition. According to the U. S. Public Health Service Ordinance, Grade A raw milk for pasteurization is raw milk from producer dairies conforming to certain standards of sanitation. The bacterial plate count, or the microscopic clump count of the milk, as it is delivered from the farm, shall not exceed 200,000 bacteria per milliliter. (A milliliter is approximately one-thousandth of a gallon.) The ordinance provides for the inspection of the cow herd, the milking barn, the milk house, the utensils and equipment, and the milking of the cows, by an authorized public health officer.

Requirements. *Healthy Cows.* Since disease may spread through the cows to humans and to other animals, the herd must be accredited or tested for tuberculosis at least once every six years, according to the modified accredited area plan of the U.S.D.A. The herd must also be certified as free from Bang's disease, according to procedures approved by the U.S.D.A. Bloody, stringy, and other abnormal milk produced by cows with mastitis must be excluded.

Sanitation. The presence of bacteria in milk will reduce the length of time it may be kept and may even make it unfit for human consumption.

The cows, especially their udders and flanks, should be cleaned at milking time. The yards should be well drained and clean. The barn floor should be made of concrete and kept clean.

The utensils and milking equipment should be made of tinned iron or stainless steel that is in good condition.

The milk house should have a concrete floor, sloped for drainage. It should be separated from the barn and have wash and rinse vats, hot water, storage racks for utensils, and a tank for cooling and storing milk. The milk house should be screened and well ventilated.

The water supply for washing utensils and cooling the milk should be free from pollution. Wells should be protected from pollution from outdoor toilets, sewer lines, and from surface water.

Cooling Facilities. Bacteria multiply very slowly in cold milk. Milk should be cooled to 50° F. or lower immediately after milking.

Figure 20-3. Milking parlor in Dairy Cattle Housing Demonstration and Research Project, Michigan State College. Milk flows from cow's teats into glass tank suspended from scale, which permits measurement of each cow's production. Milk is carried through pipes to cooling and bulk storage tank in adjoining milkroom, from which it is pumped into a dairy-bound milk truck. (Courtesy Great Lakes Steel Corp., Stran Steel Division)

Producing Grade A Milk

The methods recommended in this section are just as applicable to the production of quality cream as to the production of Grade A milk.

Maintaining a Healthy Herd. The herd should be tested regularly, according to the ordinance requirements for tuberculosis and Bang's disease. A veterinarian's statement certifying that the herd is free from both diseases is necessary. Cows that have swollen or sore udders, or those that produce abnormal milk, should be removed from the herd. The herd also should be free of leptospirosis.

Housing Facilities. If a stanchion-type barn is used, it should be clean, adequately lighted, and well ventilated, and have a concrete floor. From 400 to 500 cubic feet of air space is needed for each cow in this kind of barn.

Figure 20-4. Well-bedded loose-housing quarters. (Courtesy The Holstein-Friesian Assn. of America)

Figure 20-5. A healthy herd of cows in a stanchion-type barn. (Courtesy The Holstein-Friesian Assn. of America)

The interior of the barns should be kept free from dust and cobwebs. It should be whitewashed once each year or painted each two years. Manure should be removed from the barn daily. Lime should be used in gutters and on the passageways.

Under the loose-type housing system, from 50 to 75 square feet of floor space should be provided for each cow. Adequate bedding is essential. A milking parlor with a cement floor and proper drainage should be provided.

Figure 20-6. An inexpensive milkhouse attached to the barn. (Courtesy Iowa State College)

Milk House. The milk house should be located near the milking parlor or barn but should not open directly into the barn. The doors and windows should be screened, and the doors should be self-closing. The floors should be of concrete and well drained. The window area should be at least 10 per cent of the floor area. The walls and ceiling should be finished and painted. A house 10 x 12 or 12 x 16 feet is recommended, depending upon the size of the herd.

Cooling Facilities. Bacteria that cause souring and undesirable flavors in milk grow ten times as quickly at 90° F. as at 50° F. The milk should be cooled as soon as possible after milking. A cooling tank, adequate in size to take care of the volume of milk produced, should be provided. A mechanical cooler is preferred.

The cooler should lower the temperature of the milk to 50° or 55° within an hour.

Figure 20-7. Milk coming to a mechanical cooler from the milking parlor. (Courtesy The Creamery Package Mfg. Company)

382

Bulk Tanks. A rapidly increasing number of farmers have installed bulk milk tanks during the past few years. On January 1, 1957, 16 per cent of all producers in 65 of our larger market areas were using bulk tanks. With bulk equipment, milk is cooled immediately and is held under refrigeration until it is picked up and transported by bulk-tank trucks to the processing plant.

In some western states, 90 per cent of the market milk is now bulk-handled. On January 1, 1957, more than 7,700 bulk tanks were in use in Wisconsin.

Capacity. In a study of the tanks in use in 39 market milk areas, it was found that the majority ranged from 200 to 400 gallons in size. Most dairymen prefer tanks which will hold two to four peak milkings.

Cost. Bulk coolers vary in cost according to size and quality of materials and workmanship. Prices of tanks, not including housing, range from $1,200 to $4,000. The minimum size of herd that will pay for a bulk tank ranges from ten to 12 cows.

Utensils. Seamless or electric-welded pails made of noncorrodible metals should be used. Milk strainers of an approved type with single-service filtering pads are recommended.

When utensils are not in use, they should be stored on racks in an inverted position in the milk house.

Cleaning Utensils and Milking Machines. The milking-machine teat cups, tubes, pails, and strainer should be rinsed thoroughly immediately after each milking to remove milk film. Fol-

Figure 20-8. Milk room interior with equipment stored on racks. (Courtesy Iowa State College)

lowing the rinsing, the utensils should be washed with warm water containing a suitable washing compound or wetting agent. Soap should not be used because it leaves a greasy film. The surfaces of the utensils should be brushed with a stiff brush. After washing, rinse the utensils with hot or boiling water. Steam or chemical sterilizers may also be used.

Cleaning the Milking Machine. Be certain that all milking machine parts are accessible for cleaning and are in a good state of repair. Taking the machine apart and brushing all parts during washing is the best way to get them clean. After the teat-cup assembly and tubes have been washed, they may be rinsed with very hot water and hung up to dry, or they may be immersed in a 0.4 to 0.5 per cent lye solution All parts treated with lye solution should be thoroughly rinsed with clean water before they are used again.

The lye solution should be made up in an earthenware jar by adding one 13-ounce can of lye to one gallon of water. One cup of this solution should be used with each gallon of water to make up the 0.4 or 0.5 per cent solution.

Cleaning the Bulk Tank. Stainless steel bulk tanks will last indefinitely if housed in a good, well-ventilated milk house and if given proper care. Adequate warm water facilities for cleaning are a necessity.

The bulk tank should be rinsed with tap water immediately after use, to remove all milk before it dries on the surface. The rinsing should be followed by cleaning with hot water and a commercial dairy cleaner. The cleaner should be used according to the manufacturer's recommendations, with the cleaning solution brushed over all of the surface.

Solid deposits or milkstones should be removed, when they appear, by use of a brush and acid cleaner or a commercial milk stone remover. After cleaning, the tank and equipment should be rinsed with warm water to remove the detergent. A hot water rinse should follow.

A chlorine solution may be used just before the equipment is to be used again. It should be used according to directions and the equipment rinsed thoroughly before beginning milking.

Cleaning the Cows. The udders of the cows should be washed and wiped with a chlorine sterilizer solution just before milking. A dirty udder provides a source of sediment and bacteria. Some dairy-

Figure 20-9. (left and right) Cleaning the milking machine. (Courtesy Iowa State College)

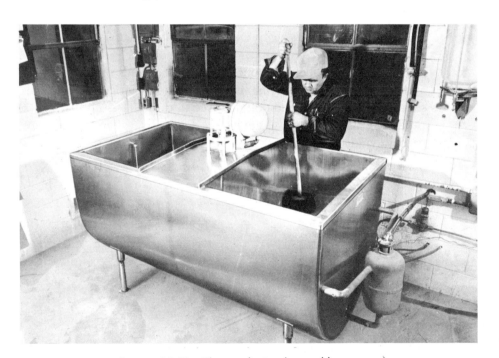

Figure 20-10. The tank is thoroughly washed, disinfected, and rinsed after the milk has been removed. (Courtesy United States Steel Corporation)

Figure 20-11. Cleaning the cow's udder before milking. (Gordon photo. Courtesy *Wallaces' Farmer and Iowa Homestead*)

men brush their cows daily and clip the long hair from the legs, flank, and udder.

Milking. If milking is done by hand, the hands should be clean and dry. Wet-hand milking is not a good practice. A teat cup should be used before milking, to see if the milk is normal. Milk produced during the first four to six days after calving should not be marketed.

TABLE 45

MAJOR COSTS TO CONVERT TO GRADE A MILK*

(*Omaha*)

Items	Average cost
Mechanical cooler	$ 408
Barn construction and/or alteration	331
Milk house construction and/or alteration	242
New milk utensils	172
Cleaning utensils (Water, heater, water vat, water rack)	132
Other costs (Installation of water system and drainage system)	88
Total	$1,373

* Henry A. Homme, Eddie Easley, and John Shaul, "If You Are Thinking of Going Grade A," *Iowa Farm Science*, November 1952.

Cost in Changing to Grade A Milk Production

A survey in the Omaha-Council Bluffs milkshed indicated that about 70 per cent of nearly 2,000 milk producers had changed production methods so that they could produce Grade A milk. Table 45 shows a summary of the average cost of the changes made by dairymen who were already producing market milk.

Improving the Quality of Cream

In general, the methods recommended in the production of Grade A milk are applicable to the production of cream. The milk should be separated as soon as possible after milking, and the cream should be cooled immediately in the cooling tank or refrigerator. Dust and any undesirable aroma should be kept out of the cream can, but a tight lid should not be used. Cream should be sold as sweet cream.

The cream separator should be housed in the milk house and given the same treatment in cleaning and sterilization that was recommended for the milking machine.

Summary

Dairy income can be increased by: (1) planning production so that milk and butterfat can be marketed during the seasons of high prices; (2) selling the products in the form that will yield the largest net return; and (3) improving the quality of the products to be sold.

About 40 per cent of a cow's production is in the first four months after calving. Milk and butterfat prices are highest in September, October, and November and lowest in April, May, and June.

Each dairyman must analyze his production and marketing system to determine whether to sell milk or cream. Most dairymen report greater profits from the sale of Grade A milk.

Considerable differences may exist in the prices offered by various milk processors in the same community for milk of the same quality. The local market must be analyzed carefully.

To improve the quality of dairy products, the herd should be free from disease and the barn should be sanitary, ventilated, and adequate in size. The milkhouse should be sanitary and separate from the barn, and should provide an abundant supply of water. The separator, milking machine, and utensils should be thoroughly washed and disinfected after each milking. The cows' udders should be washed and disinfected and strip cups used before milking.

A milk and cream cooler or cooling tank should be provided. Dairy products should be cooled to 50° or 55° within one hour after milking.

The bulk cooling and storage of milk is recommended. The cold-wall bulk cooler should be of sufficient size to allow for the expansion of the herd and to hold two to four peak milkings, depending upon whether truck pickups are made daily or every other day. The cooler should be conveniently located and kept clean. Bulk coolers vary in cost from about $1,200 to $4,000, depending on size.

The production of Grade A milk requires an additional investment in housing and equipment amounting to $1,000 or $2,000 or more. The added income from the sale of Grade A milk usually justifies the added investment.

• Questions

1. When should you have your cows freshen to be able to market milk and butterfat at the highest prices?
2. What is meant by the milk-feed price ratio?
3. What changes should you make in the seasonal production and marketing of dairy products on your farm?
4. Which is the best way for you to market milk on your farm, as milk or as butterfat? Why?
5. Outline the requirements for Grade A milk production.
6. What changes would you need to make in your production and marketing program to be able to market Grade A milk? What would these changes cost?
7. Outline a program for properly cleaning the milking machine, milking utensils, and cream separator on your farm
8. Describe a desirable milk house.
9. Outline the requirements of a good bulk cooling tank installation.
10. Outline a program for improving the marketing of dairy products on your home farm.

• *References*

Baker, M. P., *Producing Grade A Milk for Pasteurization*, S-685, Iowa State College, Ames, Iowa, 1951.

Knodt, C. B., *Successful Dairying*, McGraw-Hill Book Company, Inc., New York, 1954.

Morris, W. H. M., R. P. March, J. C. White, and C. N. Turner, *Bulk Cooling and Storage of Milk on the Farm*, Cornell Extension Bulletin 899, Cornell University, Ithaca, New York.

U. S. Department of Agriculture, *Dairy Statistics*, Statistical Bulletin No. 218, Washington, D. C., 1957.

U. S. Department of Health, Education, and Welfare, *Milk Ordinance and Code*, Washington, D. C., 1953.

DUAL-PURPOSE
CATTLE

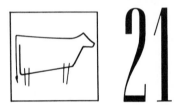

21

Breeding and Management
of Dual-Purpose Cattle

Dual-purpose cattle have been bred and developed as intermediate breeds between the strictly dairy and beef breeds. The breeds of dual-purpose cattle will not equal the dairy breeds as economical producers of milk. They are not equal to the beef breeds as producers of beef. They are, however, better producers of milk than are the beef breeds, and they will produce a better carcass than will the dairy breeds.

Adaptability of Dual-Purpose Cattle. Dual-purpose cattle are well suited to the small farms where a monthly milk or cream check is desired and there is surplus grain for fattening a few cattle. Many large-scale farm operators, who are not equipped for specialized dairying and whose cattle cannot be given the care required for high-producing dairy cows, have turned to dual-purpose cattle.

Dual-purpose cattle provide an opportunity to make a quick shift from dairy to beef or vice versa. Animals that are to be disposed of will do very well in the fattening lot. Experiments show that dual-purpose cattle will finish into good to choice slaughter animals. The dual-purpose cattle breeder of grade animals need not veal his bull calves, as many dairymen do, but may grow them out and fatten them for the market.

Cows that have completed their usefulness as milk animals and those culled from the milking herd will fatten up and bring a good price for cow beef.

Selecting a Breed

The same general principles of breed selection apply for dual-purpose cattle as for other breeds of livestock. They are: (1) personal likes, (2) availability of breeding stock, (3) outlet for surplus animals, and (4) environmental conditions under which the cattle will be raised.

Breeds of Dual-Purpose Cattle

Three breeds of dual-purpose cattle are relatively common in the United States—Milking Shorthorns, Red Poll, and Devon.

Milking Shorthorns. Milking Shorthorn cattle were first developed in England and came from much the same parent stock as did the beef Shorthorns. As a result of a different emphasis by the breeders in developing the strains, the chief dissimilarity between

Figure 21-1. Model type Milking Shorthorn bull. (Abernathy photo. Courtesy American Milking Shorthorn Society)

391

Figure 21-2. Model type Milking Shorthorn cow. (Abernathy photo. Courtesy
American Milking Shorthorn Society)

the beef and Milking Shorthorns came about. In the case of the milking strain, the emphasis was divided more evenly between beef and milk. The result was a shorthorn cow possessing good milking qualities but lacking some of the excellent qualities of the beef strain.

Figure 21-3. A champion Red Poll bull.
(Strohmeyer and Carpenter photo. Courtesy Red Poll Cattle Club of America)

The Milking Shorthorn is red, white, or any combination of these colors. There are two strains of Milking Shorthorns, polled and horned. The polled animals were developed from "mutants" or animals that were naturally polled even though they were born of parents having horns. The polled strain has the same characteristics as the horned cattle except for the poll.

Red Poll. Red Poll cattle were developed in England by merging the Norfolk and Suffolk strains of cattle. They are solid red in color, hornless, and quite compact in body form. They are good milkers, and will do well in the fattening lot. The Red Poll is popular among dual-purpose cattlemen.

Devon or Ruby Reds. Devon cattle were developed in England, and are one of the oldest of the English breeds. The Devon is probably the first of the dual-purpose breeds introduced into America. Records show that several importations of Devon cattle were made into this country during its early history. The Devon cattle are red in color. The skin is yellow and the head supports medium-sized, upward-curving horns that are creamy white with black tips.

Figure 21-4. Champion Red Poll cow. (Strohmeyer and Carpenter photo. Courtesy Red Poll Cattle Club of America)

Breeding and Management of Dual-Purpose Cattle • 393

Figure 21-5. Devon cow. (Courtesy American Devon Cattle Club)

The cows are good milkers, producing milk testing about 4.5 per cent butterfat. Cattle placed in the fattening lot have produced good to choice beef.

Selection of Breeding Stock. It has been explained that the objective of the breeder of dual-purpose cattle is to combine good milking and beef qualities into the same animal. In the selection of breeding or foundation stock both the beef and dairy qualities must be considered.

Using Production Records in Selection of Breeding Stock. The most reliable method of determining a cow's ability to produce is her production record or the records of her ancestors.

In selecting dual-purpose cattle, both their records of milk production and ability to produce beef should be taken into consideration. Many herds of dual-purpose cattle have been on test in dairy herd improvement associations. It is not difficult to find animals with good milk production records back of them.

Other Factors to Consider in Selection. Since the dual-purpose animal should economically produce both beef and milk, this ability should be apparent in the animals selected for breeding purposes. The mammary system should be well-developed. The body form is intermediate between the beef and dairy types. The legs should be medium short, the body compact, the top and underline straight. The covering of flesh should be uniform, less than that of beef animals but more than that generally found in the dairy breeds.

Summary

Dual-purpose cattle are adapted to both milk and beef production. The breeds do not equal dairy cattle in milk production nor beef cattle in beef production. Many farmers, not wishing to specialize in either dairy or beef cattle, have found the dual-purpose breeds satisfactory.

There are three common dual-purpose breeds in the United States: Milking Shorthorns, Red Poll, and Devon.

In body form, dual-purpose cattle are intermediate between the dairy and beef types.

• Questions

1. Under what conditions would dual-purpose cattle be a wise choice?
2. Describe the general type of the dual-purpose cattle.
3. What would you consider in making a selection of foundation stock for starting a dual-purpose herd?
4. What are the common breeds of dual-purpose cattle?

• References

Baker, Marvel L., V. H. Arthaud, and C. H. Adams, *Feeding Milking Shorthorn Steers,* Agricultural Experiment Station, Circular 91, University of Nebraska, Lincoln, Nebraska, 1951.

Peters, W. H., J. B. Fitch, H. R. Searles, and W. E. Morris, *Dual-Purpose Cattle,* University of Minnesota, Extension Bulletin 203, Minneapolis, Minnesota, 1943.

CATTLE
DISEASES
AND PARASITES

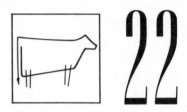

Keeping Cattle Healthy

Cattle diseases, parasites, and other ailments may be divided into four groups: (1) external parasites, (2) internal parasites, (3) infectious diseases, and (4) noninfectious ailments. The average cattleman is not a veterinarian; therefore, his chief duties in maintaining a healthy herd are good sanitation, the proper use of sprays and disinfectants, and the vaccination of his herd against those diseases for which vaccines have been perfected, when recommended by a reliable veterinarian.

Most infections and diseases to which cattle are subject are brought into the herd as a result of poor management practices.

A Program of Disease
and Parasite Prevention

The following steps are important if a disease- and parasite-free herd is to be maintained.

1. Bring only clean animals into the herd. Many serious diseases, such as brucellosis, can be detected through a test for the disease.

A veterinarian may prevent serious losses if called to examine animals before they go into the herd.

2. Drain lots so that they will remain dry and free of stagnant water. Paved lots will aid in keeping cattle out of the mud and filth.

3. Isolate all animals that are known to have contagious infections. Newly acquired animals should be isolated until it is reasonably certain that they are free of disease.

4. Have the breeding herd tested regularly for brucellosis, tuberculosis, and other diseases for which tests have been developed.

5. Vaccinate for diseases common in the community, if a successful vaccine exists.

6. Disinfect housing and equipment regularly.

7. Treat open wounds and the navel of newborn calves with a reliable disinfectant.

8. Provide plenty of exercise for the breeding herd.

9. Use spray or dust for external parasites, such as flies, and eliminate manure piles and other filth accumulations where flies breed.

10. If cows calve in places other than clean pastures, be sure the area is well bedded and disinfected.

11. Avoid cold floors and drafty housing quarters for young calves dropped during cold weather.

External Parasites

The Screw Worm. Screw worms are more prevalent in the Southern and Southwestern states. In these areas, they are one of the most important causes of cattle losses.

Life History. The screw worm fly is bluish green in color, with orange shading below the eyes. The three prominent dark stripes along its back distinguish it from similar insects. The flies lay their eggs in masses along the edges of open wounds. The eggs hatch into tiny maggots that burrow into the flesh, where they feed from four to seven days.

When the worms have reached their full growth, they drop to the ground and burrow into the soil. A few days later they emerge from the pupa or dormant stage as adult flies. The entire life cycle may be completed within 21 days under favorable conditions.

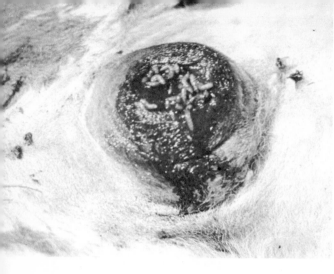

Figure 22-1. Screw worm infestation of a calf. (Courtesy U.S.D.A.)

Prevention and Control. The U. S. Department of Agriculture has developed several smears that will kill the worms or prevent their infecting wounds. The newest of these smears is known as "Smear EQ 335."

Dehorning, castrating, and other operations should be performed during the winter season, when the screw worm is less active.

Grubs. Cattle grubs, or heel flies, seldom cause death in cattle, but the loss resulting from the uncomfortable effect they produce upon the animals is greater than is generally realized by herd owners. Milk production may be severely reduced and the growth rate of young animals slowed down.

Life History. The heel fly lays its eggs on the lower parts of the animal during the spring and early summer. The eggs hatch, and the tiny grubs bore through the skin and migrate through the animal's body, feeding on the tissues for about nine months. They appear as lumps along the back from early winter until spring. The mature grubs perforate the skin and come out through the openings in the hide, drop to the ground, and soon develop into adult flies. These flies seldom travel more than a mile, so if a cooperative effort is made they can be controlled in any area.

There are two species of cattle grubs, one known as the *common cattle grub* and the other as the *Northern cattle grub.* The life cycles of the two are similar except that the duration is longer for the Northern grub.

Prevention and Control. Very good control has been given by a new product known by the trade name of Trolene. Properly

398 • *Keeping Cattle Healthy*

administered, this will destroy the grub soon after it enters the body. This product should be given as a bolus six weeks before the grubs appear in the back. The time to give the treatment will vary from October to December, depending upon the area. The treatment consists of five grams active ingredient per 100 pounds of body weight. *Lactating dairy cows should not be treated with Trolene nor should beef cattle be treated within 60 days of slaughter.* A balling gun is used to give the capsule.

Cattle Lice. Cattle lice are most abundant during the winter. Cattle infested with lice rub along fences and feed bunks in an effort to relieve the irritation. The hair appears dry and dead. There will be bare places on the shoulders, neck, top line, and flanks where the hair has been rubbed off. Milk production may decline and young animals may slow up in their development.

Prevention and Control. Spraying with *rotenone* over the entire body is effective in lice control. Only two sprays, from 16 to 18 days apart, are generally required to free the cattle from lice. Two pounds of 25 per cent wettable lindane powder plus two pounds of detergent to 100 gallons of water, or eight pounds of 50 per cent methoxychlor plus two pounds of detergent in 100 gallons of water will give effective control of lice on cattle in one application. Malathion (57 per cent) applied at the rate of one gallon plus two pounds of detergent to 100 gallons of water is the newest treatment, and very effective. *Lindane, malathion, and methoxychlor spray should not be used on lactating dairy animals* nor beef animals within 30 days of slaughter. Pyrethrin spray or rotenone is recommended for these animals.

Figure 22-2. A little treatment at the right time would have prevented this animal from being infested with lice and resulted in a much healthier condition. (Courtesy Livestock Conservation, Inc.)

Horn Flies. Horn flies are the first flies to appear in the spring and continue as cattle pests the entire summer. They are small black flies, often seen resting in large numbers around the base of the horns. They suck the blood from around the back, shoulders, and withers, causing considerable loss of gain and reduction of milk.

Prevention and Control. Horn flies may be controlled by spraying with malathion, methoxychlor, or pyrethrin. The spray is prepared the same as for lice. The cattle should be sprayed every two weeks. Do not use malathion or methoxychlor spray on lactating dairy cows or on beef animals within 30 days of slaughter.

Lactating dairy cows may be treated by rubbing one tablespoon of 50 per cent methoxychlor dry wettable powder into the hair *only*. This will be effective for about three weeks.

All-Purpose Spray. A product known by the trade name of Co-Ral has recently been approved for use on *beef cattle only*. Co-Ral, when properly applied, will control grubs, horn flies, lice, ticks, and screw worms. The spray is made by adding 25 gallons of water and one half pound of household detergent to four pounds of 25 per cent Co-Ral wettable powder. For grub control, apply one gallon of spray per animal in a single application soon after heel fly activity has ceased. The time will vary with the area.

Stable Flies. Stable flies remain on the cattle only while feeding on the blood of the animal. When not feeding, they will be found resting on fences and other objects outside the barn. They are more commonly found around the barn lots than in the pastures. This is because they depend upon manure, rotting straw, and other similar materials in which to breed.

Prevention and Control. Clean surroundings are essential to good control of stable flies. Spraying the animals (see the preceding section on horn flies) will help to keep them off the cattle. Sprays containing pyrethrum, which can be purchased commercially, are among the most effective that may be applied directly on the animals. Malathion applied to the walls of barns, fences, manure piles, straw stack bottoms, ground around water tanks, and other places where stable flies breed is an effective control measure.

Horse Flies, Deer Flies, and Mosquitoes. Although these species of insects differ considerably in their life cycle and habits, the control measures are essentially the same. They breed around swampy

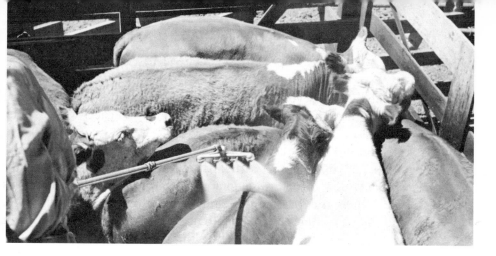

Figure 22-3. Spraying cattle for fly control. (Bailey photo. Reprinted from *Successful Farming*)

areas and water holes, and rest in trees, bushes, or other tall growing plants when not feeding.

Prevention and Control. Spraying trees and shrubs near swampy areas with spray recommended for other flies will help to control them.

Ticks. There are several species of ticks that affect cattle, one of which may carry the disease known as Texas fever, which in the past resulted in heavy losses in the South. However, as a result of the work of the U. S. Department of Agriculture and the state experiment stations, Texas fever has all but been eliminated from the United States.

Prevention and Control. A lindane spray consisting of eight pounds of 25 per cent lindane wettable powder and two pounds of a wetting agent per 100 gallons of water is an effective control measure for ticks. Do not use on lactating dairy cows or beef cattle within 30 days of slaughter.

Mites. Cattle mites produce what is known as sarcoptic mange or cattle scab. The mite spends its entire life cycle on the body of the animal, piercing the skin and feeding on the lymph, producing a thickened, tough, wrinkled skin.

Prevention and Control. The same lindane spray as that recommended for ticks sprayed at 300 to 400 pounds of pressure is very effective in the control of mites. Dairy cattle in lactation must be removed from the milk line at least four days after treatment.

Keeping Cattle Healthy • 401

There are several different types of stomach and intestinal worms that affect cattle, but the common stomach worm is the greatest menace.

Common Stomach Worm. Worms, similar to those found in sheep, may infest young cattle, particularly calves under six months of age. Adult cattle are seldom affected. Heavily infected animals lose weight and become thin and weak. The hair becomes rough, and the membranes of the mouth are pale. A soft swelling, known as *bottle jaw*, may develop under the jaw.

Prevention and Control. Sanitation is the most important means of prevention. Worm eggs pass in the droppings and hatch into tiny worms, which are picked up by other animals. Placing water and feed where it will not be contaminated by droppings is a helpful precaution and rotating pastures is also an effective control.

Infested animals may be given a fluid drench, containing 20 grams of phenothiazine powder per 100 pounds of body weight. The maximum dose should not exceed 60 grams, regardless of the animal's weight.

Doses should be repeated every 20 days where heavy infestation occurs. The drench may be given with a syringe placed in the side of the mouth and discharged near the base of the tongue. Usually after the first dose, low-level feeding of two grams per animal of phenothiazine powder will keep it free of worms. To accomplish this, the drug may be mixed with the mineral or supplement. A mixture of one part phenothiazine powder to nine parts salt and mineral mixture may be fed.

Coccidiosis. This disease is the result of poor management and unsanitary conditions. It is caused by the entrance of protoza into the digestive systems of young calves through contaminated feed and water.

Symptoms. Common symptoms are loss of appetite, bloody diarrhea, and weakness.

Prevention and Control. Sanitation, the drainage of pastures and yards, rotation of pastures, and general good management are the best preventive measures. Veterinarians may successfully treat infected animals in the early stages of the disease with sulfa and other drugs.

Infectious Diseases

There are many infectious diseases of cattle, but only those that cause the greatest economic losses will be discussed.

Brucellosis. Brucellosis, or Bang's disease, is number one in importance, not only because of the economic losses resulting from the disease, but also because a disease known as undulant fever, which affects human beings, may be contracted from animals affected with it.

Symptoms. Infected animals may abort or give birth to a dead or weak calf; this is the most commonly observed symptom of brucellosis. On the other hand, the birth may be normal, but the cow may fail to clean or expel the afterbirth. Animals that are infected often have higher than normal temperatures at calving time. Milk production is reduced. Heavily infected herds may have 50 per cent or more aborted or dead calves among heifers. Great care must be taken by persons coming in contact with animals infected with brucellosis to avoid contracting undulant fever. The disease may be contracted from the consumption of non-pasteurized milk produced by infected animals, and great danger exists in handling newborn calves or aborted fetuses from infected herds.

Prevention and Control. Brucellosis finds its way into a herd through any of the following: (1) the purchase of infected or exposed animals; (2) contact with a neighbor's herd over a line fence; (3) exposure at livestock shows where an infected animal may be on exhibit; (4) livestock trucks that go from farm to farm handling animals and that have not been properly cleaned and disinfected; (5) public livestock auctions where proper sanitation is not practiced; (6) aborted calves that are dragged on the place by carnivorous animals.

Brucellosis may be detected by having a veterinarian blood test the herd. If the disease is found to exist, the recommended plans for eradication are:

1. Test all the cows and heifers, removing any reactors from the herd and vaccinating all calves between the ages of six and eight months that are not infected. This is the only recommended plan for dairy cattle.

2. Test and keep all reactors separate from the herd and vaccinate the calves. Since cows will generally produce normal calves

Figure 22-4. Cow and aborted calf, the result of Bang's disease. (Courtesy U.S.D.A.)

after the second calving, reactors may be kept, but should not be in the same area with heifers since they are carriers of the disease. The plan should be to eliminate the reactors as quickly as it is economically possible. This plan may be used for beef herds.

Since brucellosis may crop up in any herd at any time, it is advisable for any cow herd owner to start a program of calfhood vaccination as a preventive measure.

Tuberculosis. Tuberculosis is a serious disease of cattle, but, because of the state and federal eradication programs, it is steadily declining in the United States.

Symptoms. Many times animals will show no outward sign of the disease. There may be a gradual loss of weight, swelling of the joints, and labored breathing. The part of the animal affected has much to do with the outward symptoms.

Prevention and Control. Tests have been perfected for determining the presence of tuberculosis in the herd. Periodic testing and elimination of reactors constitutes a reliable control program.

Blackleg. Blackleg is one of the most infectious diseases of young cattle and generally proves fatal.

Symptoms. Blackleg is usually accompanied by high fever, loss of appetite, and labored breathing. Rapidly developing tumors under the skin that make a crackling sound when subjected to pressure (because of gas) are one of the best indications of the disease.

Prevention and Control. If blackleg infection is found in the area or in the herd, vaccination of animals not affected is the only prevention. Affected animals will not generally respond to vaccination, but if the disease is diagnosed during its early stages, penicillin treatment by a veterinarian may cure some animals. Carcasses of animals killed by blackleg should be burned.

Anthrax. Anthrax is caused by an organism that may live in the soil for many years. For this reason, some areas have more outbreaks of the disease than others. Outbreaks usually occur during dry spells, when pastures are short and cattle tend to pick up soil while grazing. They may also occur following a flood, when the pastures are overflowed.

Symptoms. Sudden death without apparent cause is the most striking symptom. High temperatures and bloody discharges from natural body openings are other symptoms.

Prevention and Control. The prevention of anthrax lies mainly in the following of a vaccination program, especially in areas where outbreaks of the disease occur quite regularly. Vaccination provides immunity for the season but will not permanently immunize the animals. Infected animals may be cured by penicillin treatment, if it is given during the early stages of the disease. If the cattleman suspects that anthrax infection is present, he should immediately call a veterinarian.

Shipping Fever. Shipping fever is a blood disease chiefly affecting young cattle. A weakening of resistance, because of exposure when being shipped from one point to another, often leads to infection by the germs that cause shipping fever.

Symptoms. High temperature, coughing, and watery discharges from the nostrils and eyes are common symptoms.

Figure 22-5. Calf with shipping fever. (Courtesy U.S.D.A.)

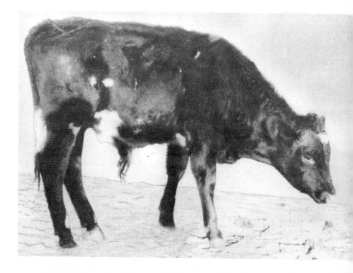

405

Prevention and Control. Overexposure and drafty means of transportation should be avoided. The cattle should have plenty of water and should not be overcrowded. Infected animals should be separated from the rest of the herd. The cattle should be kept dry and in protected places for a few days after shipping. Vaccines are used, but should be given ten days before shipping. Serum should be used if animals are to be shipped immediately or are exposed by coming in contact with animals suffering from the disease. Antibiotics, especially penicillin, are effective in the treatment and prevention of shipping fever.

Foot Rot. Foot rot is an infection of the feet of cattle and is a serious disease in many beef herds. It usually occurs when cattle are confined for long periods in muddy lots. It is caused by a germ that invades the tissues of the foot from the soil. An injury resulting in a break in the skin of the foot provides a means by which the germs may enter.

Symptoms. Affected animals become sorefooted, and the infected foot swells and is foul-smelling. There may not be any visible sore at the start. Later, the skin cracks open and a dirty yellowish material is present.

Prevention and Control. Keeping lots clean and well drained, and barns free from manure or well bedded are good preventive measures. A box four inches deep filled with hydrated lime and placed where the cattle will be forced to walk through it will aid in preventing the disease. Infected animals may be treated by scraping away all dead tissue and saturating the foot with 2 per cent formalin solution or a solution of copper sulphate. Veterinarians have successfully treated foot rot with sulfa and other drugs.

Pink Eye. Pink eye attacks animals of any age, but seldom occurs during the cool season.

Symptoms. The first indication of pink eye is a flow of tears and a tendency to keep the eyes closed. There will be a swelling of the eyelids and a general inflammation of the eye.

Prevention and Control. Affected animals should be segregated Blowing sulfa powders into the eyes is helpful in many cases. If left alone, most animals will recover.

Mastitis. Mastitis is one of the worst diseases of dairy cattle but is less common in beef cattle. It is caused by types of germs that find their way into the udder, often as a result of an injury.

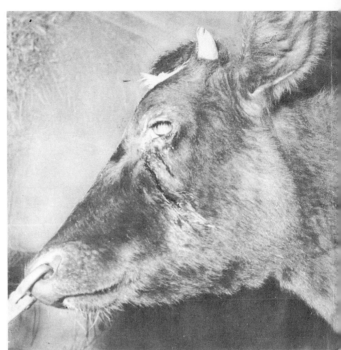

Figure 22-6. Calf with pink eye. Note the watery condition of the eye. (Bailey photo. Reprinted from *Successful Farming*)

Symptoms. There are two forms of mastitis, one known as the acute and the other as the chronic form. In the acute form, the teat and quarter are swollen and painful. This form is often accompanied by fever and loss of appetite. The milk will be stringy and sometimes bloody. The chronic form is more mild and may go unnoticed by the operator until it flares up in the acute form. In chronic mastitis, there may be no swelling. The milk, however, will generally show clots and watery consistency under close inspection. Usually only one quarter is involved at a time. Milk production drops and the udder may be ruined, unless treatment is started during the early stages of the disease.

Prevention and Control. Eliminating sources of udder injury, such as obstacles that may cause bruises or cuts, is important in mastitis prevention. Poorly bedded cement floors are invitations for udder injuries. Milking a few streams from each quarter will give the operator an opportunity to observe any stringiness or clots in the milk. The Brome-Thymol-Blue test, although not 100 per cent accurate, will give a good indication of the presence or absence of mastitis. To conduct the test, place a drop of Brome-Thymol-Blue

Keeping Cattle Healthy • 407

on a blotter with an eyedropper, using one drop in a separate spot for each quarter of the udder. Place a few drops of milk on the same spot. If the color changes to a bluish green, mastitis infection may be suspected. In mild cases, successful treatment may result by administering antibiotic ointment that comes in a small tube fitted with a spout. The ointment is injected into the affected quarter through the teat canal. In the most serious cases, or in cases where there is no response to this treatment, the cows should be placed under the care of a veterinarian.

Foot-and-Mouth Disease. Foot-and-mouth disease is highly infectious. The few outbreaks that have occurred in the United States have been quickly brought under control.

Symptoms. The disease is characterized by blisters that form on the tongue, the lips, the cheeks, and the skin around the claws of the feet, and on the teats and udder. The blisters cause a heavy flow of saliva that hangs from the lips in strings. Infected animals smack their lips and, owing to tenderness of the feet, sway from one hind foot to the other.

Prevention and Control. To control the disease, infected animals should be destroyed and the premises disinfected with a lye solution. A vaccine has been developed that is used in areas outside the United States. Authorities in the United States have not recommended vaccination, for it is not considered to be conducive to complete eradication. The policy followed in the United States has been to destroy infected animals, and disinfect and quarantine the area where the outbreak occurred until the disease has been eradicated. If foot-and-mouth disease is suspected, federal authorities should be notified, because quick control is essential.

Warts. Warts on calves are caused by a tiny germ known as a *virus.* The condition spreads from one animal to another by contact.

Symptoms. The warts appear around the neck and head, often near the eyes.

Prevention and Control. Wart-infected calves should be placed away from other calves. Painting the warts with iodine once or twice during a two-day period, followed by application of castor oil, will often eliminate them. A vaccine has been developed that is very effective in controlling warts.

Calf Scours. Calf scours is one of the worst diseases of young calves. It has been reported that from 10 to 15 per cent of deaths in calves are the result of calf scours.

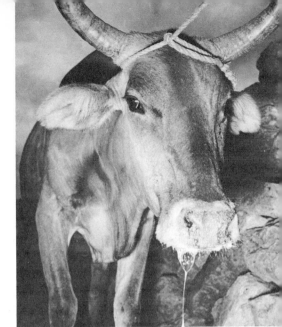

Figure 22-7. (right) Foot and mouth disease.

Figure 22-8. (below) Calf with warts. (Courtesy U.S.D.A.)

Symptoms. Calf scours is characterized by a pasty white scour that usually affects calves under three weeks of age. The animals become weak and lose their appetite.

Prevention and Control. The first step in prevention is good management. Calves should be kept in clean, well-bedded stalls when they are dropped during cold weather.

Antibiotics fed in small daily amounts, particularly aureomycin or terramycin, have been effective in the prevention of calf scours. A dose of three milligrams of aureomycin per pound of body weight for the first three or four weeks and 1½ milligrams per pound of body weight from three weeks to three to six months of age is recommended as a prevention. Calves that have the disease should have concentrated doses administered under the direction of a veterinarian.

Ringworm. Ringworm is a contagious skin disease of cattle. Young stock are more susceptible to the disease than older cattle.

Symptoms. Oval, scaly areas around the sides, neck, eyes, and back are signs of ringworm.

Prevention and Control. Infected animals should be separated from the rest of the herd and treated by applying phemerol to the areas affected. Washing with soap and water and painting the infected area with a tincture of iodine will often control ring worms.

Figure 22-9. Typical ringworm infestation. (Reprinted from *Successful Farming*)

Leptospirosis. Leptospirosis is a disease threat to cattle that was first discovered in the United States in 1944. The disease is one of the most serious of those affecting cattle. The death rate will average about 5 per cent for those animals infected with the disease, but it may run up to 25 per cent for young stock. About 25 per cent of the cows infected will abort.

410 • *Keeping Cattle Healthy*

Symptoms. Fever, depression, loss of appetite, and loss of production are common symptoms. The milk may take on a yellow color and become thickened in consistency. Sometimes it will be bloody. There may be blood in the urine.

Prevention and Control. Great care should be taken to eliminate the possibility of bringing infected animals into the herd. Animals that are questionable should be given a blood test by a veterinarian. Antibiotics, especially penicillin, are effective in treating animals when treatment is started during the early stage of the disease. Vaccines have been perfected that are effective up to a year or more. In areas where the disease is common, the vaccination of the herd is recommended.

Pneumonia. Pneumonia is a serious threat to young calves. The disease often occurs in calves weakened by scours. The highly infectious type may invade healthy calves and result in death unless treated in the early stage.

Symptoms. Labored, rapid breathing, coughing, high body temperature, nasal discharge, weakness, and loss of appetite are common symptoms.

Prevention and Control. Clean, well-bedded pens, free from drafts and maintained at even temperatures, will help to prevent the disease. Infected calves may be successfully treated with the sulfa drugs and antibiotics administered under the supervision of a veterinarian.

Noninfectious Ailments

Milk Fever. Milk Fever affects many high-producing cows. Cows are usually affected shortly after calving, but sometimes the condition will develop just prior to calving. The condition is caused by a rapid change in the balance of the blood calcium be-

Figure 22-10. Cow with milk fever. Note the head drawn back toward the udder. (Reprinted from *Successful Farming*)

411

cause of the inability of the blood calcium regulatory mechanism to meet the sudden demand made by milk production. Milk fever seldom affects cows later than five days after freshening.

Symptoms. Cows become dull and difficult to move, stagger, and lose their appetite during the first stages of milk fever. Constipation is very common as an early symptom. Later, the animal goes into a coma. When a complete coma has taken place, the head will be drawn back against the chest.

Prevention and Control. Cows should have a mineral mixture including calcium, phosphorus, and salt available at all times. Massive doses of vitamin D (30 million units per day) for from five to seven days before the calf is born will help to ward off milk fever without apparent injury to the cow. Irradiated ergosterol, or type 142 F irradiated dry yeast, may be used as a source of vitamin D.

Cows subject to milk fever should not be milked completely dry for the first few milkings after they have freshened. If milk fever does attack the cow, intravenous injections of calcium borogluconate will generally check the difficulty. Unless the dairyman has had considerable experience in giving the injections, a veterinarian should be called.

Ketosis. Ketosis is thought to be caused by a shortage or faulty utilization of sugar in the body. It usually affects either cattle fed for long periods on poor roughage without sufficient concentrates to balance the rations, or high-producing cows during the first month of lactation.

Symptoms. Animals affected by ketosis are nervous, lose their appetite, and drop in milk production. High-producing cows are the most susceptible.

Prevention and Control. Good rations with plenty of high-quality hay and silage are the best preventive measures. Some dairymen increase the carbohydrates for fresh cows by adding sugar or molasses to the ration. Several treatments have been administered by veterinarians to cows affected by the disease, with varying results. Excellent results have been reported in the treatment of ketosis by a single injection of 1.5 grams of cortisone. Giving affected animals 0.25 pound of sodium propionate daily in two doses for three to ten days is another method of treatment that some dairymen have reported to be effective. Other ketosis control drugs made available to veterinarians include a combination of ACTH and penicillin, and a combination of ACTH and glucose.

X Disease. X disease, which is usually fatal, has appeared in many areas. The cause of the disease, according to most authorities, is chlorinated naphthalene, which is present in some types of grease used on farm and feed-mixing machinery.

Symptoms. The disease has a rather slow course, often as long as three months, before death occurs. It generally begins with a loss of weight and watery discharges from the nose and eyes. Animals slobber at the mouth, and sores are often found in the mouth.

Prevention and Control. No known treatment exists. Close inspection of animals for running eyes, slobbering, and sore mouths should be made before purchasing them. Keep the cattle away from any grease that may contain chlorinated naphthalene.

Bloat. Bloat is a condition in which the rumen becomes filled with gas that the animal is unable to expel. The condition may be caused by a growth or other obstruction in the esophagus, but is more often caused by feeds that ferment rapidly in the rumen, causing large amounts of gas to form. Feeding on legume pastures is one of the most common causes of bloat. Saponins (plant materials that produce a soapy lather) are thought to be the principal ingredient in legumes responsible for bloat.

Symptoms. The chief symptom is a great distention of the upper left side of the abdomen. Rapid breathing and uneasiness occur. If the animal is not relieved, it will stagger and fall. The pressure becomes great enough to prevent lung action, and suffocation is the final cause of death.

Prevention and Control. If the gas pressure is not too great, walking the animal will induce belching and provide relief. Tying a rope or a stick in the mouth will often help. If immediate relief is required, a puncture of the rumen becomes necessary. The puncture should be made in the center of a triangle formed by the last rib, the hip bone, and the transverse processes of the backbone on the left side.

Pastures should not contain more than 50 per cent legumes. Giving the cattle a fill of dry hay before they go on pasture or making dry hay available to cattle on legume pastures will help to prevent bloat. Cattle that have water easily accessible are less apt to bloat than are those that drink only in the morning and in the evening when they come from the pasture. Research work to find an effective method of controlling bloat is in progress. The most promising, at this time, is the administration of water-dispersible oil by adding it to the drinking water, and the sprinkling of crude soybean oil over fresh cut alfalfa at the rate of ¼ pound per animal daily. Antibiotics, especially penicillin, administered at rather short intervals have given some promise of bloat control.

Poisonous Plants. Many plants are poisonous to cattle. A large group of plants will develop what is known as *prussic acid*, especially under conditions that retard growth, such as extreme dry weather or frost. This group of plants includes sudan grass and other plants belonging to the sorghum family, Johnson grass, chokecherry, black cherry, arrow grass, velvet grass, and Christmas berry. Prussic acid is very poisonous and often proves fatal within a few minutes after consumption of the plant containing it.

Sweet clover hay or silage not properly preserved often proves toxic to cattle. Certain weeds, such as snakeroot, larkspur, loco weed, water hemlock, milkweed, and cocklebur, will poison cattle if consumed in large enough quantities.

Summary

The first steps in the prevention of disease and parasite infestation of the herd are sanitation, clean and well-drained lots, clean and regularly disinfected buildings, and precautions against the purchase of sick animals or animals that have been exposed to infections. Many diseases can be prevented with vaccines.

The most effective control measure for external parasites is the use of proper sprays and dusts, except for screw worms. Applying Smear EQ 335 on all wounds will prevent screw worm and blow fly infestation. The common stomach worm may be controlled with phenothiazine.

Brucellosis is best eradicated by a testing and vaccinating program, whereas tuberculosis is controlled by testing and eliminating reactors. Blackleg and anthrax can be prevented by vaccination.

Foot rot may be successfully treated by using disinfectants. If the case is advanced, a veterinarian should be called.

Mastitis can often be detected by the Brome-Thymol-Blue test. Antibiotics injected into the udder through the teat canal will help in many cases.

Warts may be treated with iodine followed by applications of castor oil. A special vaccine is also effective. Ringworms are best treated by applying phemerol or iodine to the affected area.

Prevention of milk fever consists of supplying animals with adequate minerals and massive doses of vitamin D for from five to seven days before calving. Treatment consists of intravenous injections of calcium borogluconate.

Ketosis prevention consists of maintaining adequate carbohydrates in the ration. Cortisone, sodium propionate, and other drugs have been successfully used in treating affected animals.

Bloat is caused by the formation of gas that the animal is unable to expel. It is often caused by certain feeds, such as young legume pasture. Treatment that will induce belching should be used. If such methods fail, making a slit through the animal's side into the rumen will allow the gas to escape.

Poisonous plants cause death losses among cattle. Knowing the poisonous plants and preventing their consumption is the only means of prevention.

• Questions

1. List the steps of a good disease- and parasite-prevention program.
2. Give the control program for brucellosis and explain the circumstances under which you would recommend each method.
3. Name the common external parasites of cattle and give the methods of control of each.
4. How would you control the common stomach worm?
5. What diseases can be successfully controlled by vaccines?
6. Give the home treatments for warts and ringworms.
7. How would you control calf scours?

• References

Animal Diseases, The Yearbook of Agriculture, United States Department of Agriculture, Washington, D. C., 1956.

Controlling Livestock Pests, Agricultural Extension Service, IC-228 Rev., Ames, Iowa, 1958.

Prier, J. C., Disease Prevention in Young Livestock, Agriculture Experiment Station, Circular 47, University of Wyoming, Laramie, Wyoming, 1954.

Snapp, Roscoe R., Beef Cattle, John Wiley & Sons, Inc., New York, Fourth Edition, 1952.

SHEEP PRODUCTION

The Sheep Production Industry

Many opportunities exist in one or more of the several different phases of the sheep producing industry for those who like livestock and are willing to put forth sufficient effort to gain the knowledge required for success.

Advantages of Sheep. Sheep have many advantages over some other classes of livestock and are particularly well adapted to many areas. Sheep will produce two different kinds of crops each year, wool and lambs, bringing in an income to the flock owner twice a year. Since the crops are entirely different, the price of one will not necessarily have a bearing on the other. Wool may be stored and held for higher prices or sold at shearing time, whichever seems advisable. A crop of lambs may be marketed from three to six months after they are born, bringing in rather quick returns.

Sheep will eat more different kinds of plants than any other kind of livestock. This makes them excellent weed destroyers, a class of livestock that can turn waste into profit and, at the same time, improve the appearance of many farms.

416

Since roughage is usually cheaper than grain and sheep have the ability to produce prime carcasses on roughage alone, they are especially well adapted to many areas unable to produce grain profitably. Studies show that sheep utilize an average of 13.6 acres of pasture and forages to each acre of grain to provide choice to prime carcasses; whereas beef cattle use 4.8 acres of pasture and forage to each acre of grain, and hogs only 0.2 acre of pasture and forage to an acre of grain.

Sheep do not require expensive buildings and equipment. Lambs, if born during cold weather, require warm housing at lambing time, but after that only protection from wind, storms, and a dry place to lie down are needed. Natural protection furnished by hills or trees is all that many range flocks have.

Since sheep prefer to graze on hilltops and high land, the droppings are left where they are usually most needed. Farms that are low in fertility may be improved considerably with sheep.

Figure 23-1. The western range is characterized by large bands of sheep. This scene shows such a band being moved to fresh feeding grounds. (Courtesy of American Rambouillet Sheep Breeders' Assn.)

Classes of Sheep Producers

Sheep producers may be divided into four general classes: (1) the rancher, (2) the farm flock owner, (3) the lamb feeder, and (4) the producer of purebreds. Some individuals combine two or more of the above classes of production.

Sheep Production on the Range. In the northern plains region, where the amount and quality of feed are usually good, most of the lambs are sold for slaughter at weaning time as milk fat lambs. Where grazing conditions are less favorable, many lambs are sold into the grain-producing areas for fattening. There are also many commercial feed yards located in the sheep-producing areas, where the operators make a business out of buying feed and finishing lambs purchased from the ranchers.

The Farm Flock. Farm flock owners usually have enough feed to produce fat lambs. Very few lambs are sold from farm flocks before they are ready for slaughter. Some produce fall and winter lambs for the off-season markets, while others follow much the same procedures common on the northern range. Markets, labor, available feed, and the breed of sheep the flock owner raises are to be considered in planning his program.

The Lamb Feeder. Lamb feeders are generally located in the grain-producing areas. They buy feeder lambs, usually from the range, in the late summer or fall. Lamb feeders depend upon their profits from the increase in value per 100 pounds as a result of fattening, known as *margin*, and from the value of the gain over the feed and other costs.

Figure 23-2. A typical farm flock which is characteristic of the Midwest and Eastern states.

Figure 23-3. A large lamb-feeding establishment. (Courtesy Rath Packing Company)

The Purebred Breeder. The breeder usually produces purebred animals. His principal markets are other breeders, ranchers, and farm flock owners who buy rams or ewes for breeding purposes. The purebred breeder requires more skill than do other types of producers because he needs to know the demands of consumers and flock owners, in addition to understanding feeding and management. The sheep industry depends largely upon the breeders for improvement in type, growing ability, and qualities of fleece. Purebred sheep breeders are located wherever sheep are produced. The feeding of large quantities of grain is not essential in the purebred industry, except where the breeder is fitting animals for show. The size of the flock should be based on average feed conditions on the farm.

Combination Enterprise. Many sheepmen prefer to combine two or more forms of sheep enterprises. Often purebred breeders start with a small flock of registered animals, depending upon their commercial flock to provide the profits until they can establish the purebred enterprise on sufficient scale to provide the expected income. The size of the flock should be based on average feed conditions on the farm.

Summary

Many opportunities exist in one or more of the several different phases of sheep production.

Sheep provide two different crops per year, wool and lambs. These crops usually come at different seasons, which makes for a good distribution of income. Sheep are excellent gleaners, making use of much waste feed and improving the appearance of the farmstead. They consume large quantities of roughage, converting a relatively cheap feed into a good cash product. Sheep help to maintain soil fertility.

Equipment for sheep need not be elaborate or expensive, unless lambing is done during cold weather.

Sheep production in the range sections is characterized by large flocks and migratory enterprise, and usually represents the principal, if not the only, farm income to the owner. The farm flock producers usually have smaller flocks. Sheep constitute only a part of the income, and the livestock program is usually diversified.

Sheep producers may be divided into four distinct classes: rancher, farm flock owner, lamb feeder, and purebred breeder.

- ## Questions

    1. What are the classes of sheep producers? Explain.
    2. What type of sheep production best fits your farm? Your community?
    3. What are the advantages of sheep production?
    4. What are the two sheep producing areas and how do they differ in methods of production?

- ## References

Gray, James R., and Chester B. Baker, *Sheep Ranching in the Northern Great Plains,* Agricultural Experiment Station Circular 196, Montana State College, Boseman, Montana, 1951.

Horlacker, Levi Jackson, *Sheep,* The Interstate Printers and Publishers, Danville, Illinois, 1950.

Peterson, J. C., *Sheep and Wool Production,* The Peterson Sheep Company, Spencer, Iowa, 1953.

24

Selection of Breeding and Feeding Stock

When entering the sheep business, the prospective shepherd must not only decide which phase of the industry to enter, but also determine which class and breed of sheep to produce.

Classes of Sheep

How sheep are classified depends upon the factors one wishes to emphasize. Sheepmen may talk about wool classification, western or native, wool or mutton type, white face or black face, horned or polled. Sometimes classifications are designated according to the area from which they originate, such as mountains, uplands, lowlands, southern, or northern.

Wool Classification. The most common classification of sheep is that which is based upon the type of wool they produce. These classes are: (1) fine-wool type, (2) medium-wool type, (3) long-wool type, (4) crossbred-wool type, (5) carpet-wool type, and (6) fur sheep.

Fine-wool type. The fine-wool breeds consist of those that produce a fine, wavy fiber of wool. The fleece is dense and contains a large amount of yolk or oil. The fine-wool breeds produce a heavy fleece of good quality. These breeds were originally developed primarily for their wool production, but modern breeders have been improving their mutton qualities so that lambs from the fine-wool class produce very acceptable carcasses when fed out and slaughtered. The fine-wool breeds possess a strong banding instinct and the ability to graze on poor quality range, which makes them especially adaptable for many Western range areas.

Medium-wool type. The medium-wool breeds were developed primarily for meat production, but increasing emphasis has been placed on wool production during the last few years. They are called medium-wool breeds because their fleece is medium in fineness and length. The medium-wool breeds are low-set, blocky, and compact in type. With the exception of the Tunis and Montadale, they were developed in England, with the major emphasis placed on mutton or meat qualities, and until quite recently little attention was given to wool production. Medium-wool breeds are considered the best when judged from a strictly meat animal standpoint.

Long-wool type. The long-wool sheep, as a class, are larger than the other classes and are so-called because of the long wool fibers they produce. Fibers twelve inches long are not uncommon for these breeds. The wool is coarser than that of either the medium- or fine-wool sheep. They were developed when large, fat, and rugged sheep were popular in England; however, at the present time, they are too slow in maturing for profitable lamb production and the carcasses are of relatively poor quality overlaid with a layer of fat which makes them unpopular to both consumers and packers. Commercial purebred or straight bred flocks of the long-wool breeds are seldom found. However, they have been used extensively and successfully for crossing purposes.

Crossbred-wool type. The crossbred-wool breeds resulted from an infusion of long-wool and fine-wool breeds. As a result of selection, many recent breeds have been established from these crosses. The general objectives in developing the breeds comprising the crossbred-wool class were to improve the meat quality and length of wool fiber or staple, but to retain the banding instinct and general hardiness of the fine-wool breeds.

Breeds resulting from these crosses have become popular in many areas, especially in parts of the Western range country and among many Midwestern flock owners. The cross-bred breeds are often classified as medium-wool rather than placed in a separate class.

Carpet-wool type. Most of the wool used in the manufacture of carpets and rugs has been imported from other countries. Argentina, Pakistan, India, New Zealand, Syria, Iraq, and other countries have furnished carpet wool to the United States. Carpet wool requires a coarse, wiry, tough fleece which is not produced by the breeds of sheep that are popular in this country.

Fur sheep type. New developments in processing wool for fur have made it possible to use the pelts from several breeds for fur purposes. However, the Karakul is the only breed raised primarily for fur purposes in this country.

The production of fur sheep is a comparatively new sheep industry in the United States. The value of the mature animals for mutton or wool is very low. Profits, other than the sale of breeding stock, result from the selling of the lamb pelts. The pelts are classified as follows: (1) Broadtail is produced from stillborn or premature lambs or lambs killed shortly after birth. The hair is undeveloped and reflects light in such a way as to give the fur a watery appearance. Broadtails are the most valuable pelts. (2) Persian Lamb is produced by killing the lamb when from three to ten days old, after the hair has formed a tight, lustrous curl. It is important to take the pelt when the curl is tight; therefore carefully watching for the right time to take the pelt is essential if the highest quality is to be ob-

TABLE 46

CLASSES AND COMMON BREEDS OF SHEEP

Fine-Wool Type	Medium-Wool Type	Long-Wool Type	Crossbred-Wool Type	Carpet Wool Type	Fur Type
American Merino	Cheviot	Cotswold	Columbia	Blackfaced Highland	Karakul
Delaine Merino	Dorset	Leicester	Corriedale		
Rambouillet	Hampshire	Lincoln	Panama		
	Montadale	Romney	Romeldale		
	Oxford		Targhee		
	Shropshire				
	Southdown				
	Suffolk				
	Tunis				

Selection of Breeding and Feeding Stock • 423

tained. Persian Lamb ranks next to Broadtail in value. (3) Karakul is the third type of pelt and is taken from the lambs after the curls have opened, which is usually when the lambs are two weeks or more of age. The Karakul is the least valuable of these three classes.

There are several grades of pelts within each class, depending upon color, luster, quality, and general appearance.

Breed and Breed Characteristics

Fine-wool Breeds. Two fine-wool breeds are popular in the United States. They are the Merinos and the Rambouillets.

Merinos. There are three types of Merino sheep, all originating from the same parent stock. The types are known as the A, B, and C or Delaine Merinos. The A-type sheep are extremely wrinkled from the head to the dock, making them hard to shear. The A-type Merino has lost its popularity in the United States and is almost extinct in this country.

The B-type have less wrinkles. The wrinkles are confined mostly to the neck, whereas the C-type, or Delaine Merinos, are comparatively smooth. The Delaines are the largest of the breed, with mature rams weighing from 160 to 190 pounds and ewes ranging from 110 to 150 pounds. The Delaines have the best mutton qualities of the Merino breed. The highest quality of fine-wool fleeces are produced by Delaine Merinos.

In the trade, the smooth-bodied Merinos are designated as Delaines, and the wrinkled type as American Merinos. All are purebred Merinos and may be registered in the same breed association because they are similar in type and ancestry.

The Merinos originated in Spain, the first importation into the United States being made in 1793. Because of their banding instinct (desire to remain at all times in close contact with each other) they are easy to herd, enabling one shepherd to control large numbers of sheep. They are good grazers, foraging over large areas of poor grasslands which enables them to survive where many less-hardy breeds would fail. Where grazing conditions are not favorable for the production of grass-fat lambs, the wool-producing ability of Merinos has made them a favorite.

The Merino is a white-faced sheep with white feet. Most rams have horns, whereas the ewes are hornless. Most of the head and legs are covered by wool. Merinos have long been bred for wool production and do not carry the straight lines and compactness of the mutton breeds; they produce an average lamb crop of about 110 per cent, which means that only one ewe in ten will have more than a single lamb. Merinos are extremely hardy, being able to survive under adverse weather as well as poor grazing conditions. The ewes live and produce longer than most any other breed.

Rambouillet. The Rambouillet is a descendant of the old Spanish Merino, and was developed as a breed in France. Although Rambouillets are close relatives of the Merino, they have been bred to produce a better carcass. Rambouillets cannot be favorably compared with the best mutton breeds from the standpoint of carcass quality, but they do make a fair market lamb and produce an excellent fine-wool fleece. The rams may have horns or be polled (hornless). The ewes are polled. Rambouillets have large heads with white hair around the nose and ears. The body is not as smooth as that of the mutton types, but the lines are fairly straight, and they carry considerable depth. The breed is large, with mature rams averaging about 250 pounds and some weighing as much as 275 pounds. The ewes will weigh 150 pounds on the average with the larger ewes weighing up to 200 pounds. The fleece is heavy, close, compact, covering most of the body, including face and legs.

Rambouillets are good mothers, quite prolific, and unequalled for range qualities. A very large percentage of the range sheep carry some Rambouillet blood. When Rambouillets are crossed on medium- or long-wool breeds, the resulting lambs are good feeders and will produce top-quality fat lambs.

There are two types of Rambouillets, determined by the skin folds. The B-type is the more wrinkled variety, whereas the C-type is comparatively smooth. The B-type has lost much of its popularity in the United States and has largely disappeared. The C-type has consistently been improved, from both a carcass and a fleece standpoint, until today it is enjoying its greatest popularity.

Rambouillets were first introduced into the United States in 1840 by Mr. D. C. Collins, of Hartford, Connecticut.

Medium-wool Breeds. Among the medium-wool breeds are: Cheviot, Dorset, Hampshire, Montadale, Oxford, Shropshire, Southdown, Suffolk, and Tunis.

Cheviot. The Cheviot was developed primarily in Scotland. It is a beautiful breed with erect ears, a clean white face, and white legs.

Figure 24-1. A "C" type or Delaine Merino ewe. This is the comparatively smooth type with the skin folds confined to the neck. (Abernathy photo)

Figure 24-2. A Rambouillet ram. (Courtesy American Rambouillet Sheep Breeders' Assn.)

Figure 24-3. Cheviot ram lamb. (Courtesy American Cheviot Sheep Society Inc.)

Figure 24-4. A Dorset ram lamb. (Courtesy Continental Dorset Club)

426

The face and legs are covered with short white hair. The nose, lips, and feet are black.

The breed is small, with rams weighing on an average of 175 pounds when mature and ewes averaging 125 pounds. They are blocky, compact, and well-muscled over the back, loin, and leg of mutton. The fleece is light, averaging from six to eight pounds, but contains a small amount of yolk and is light-shrinking. The Cheviot ewes are good mothers and quite prolific, averaging about a 125 per cent lamb crop.

The first importation of Cheviot sheep into the United States was in 1838.

Dorset. Both ewes and rams of the Dorset breed have horns. The ewes will breed during most of the year, which is uncommon among sheep breeds. This characteristic makes them popular when late fall lambs are desired.

The Dorsets are medium-sized, with rams weighing from 200 to 250 pounds and ewes from 150 to 175 pounds. The ewes are prolific, averaging nearly a 150 per cent lamb crop. Dorsets will shear from eight to ten pounds of fleece.

Dorsets were developed in England. The first importation to this country was in 1885.

Hampshire. The Hampshires have most of the qualities desired in mutton sheep. They are large and grow rapidly. Mature rams will average 250 pounds in weight and ewes will average about 180 pounds. The ewes are prolific and good mothers.

Figure 24-5. A Hampshire ram. (Courtesy American Hampshire Sheep Assn.)

The face, ears, and legs of Hampshires are dark brown or black. They are among the largest of the medium-wool breeds being exceeded by the Suffolk and Oxford. The fleece is not especially heavy, averaging from seven to eight pounds and is of medium quality. Hampshires have been used extensively in crossbreeding with excellent results.

Hampshire sheep originated in England. Several importations were made into the United States prior to 1860. They grew rapidly in popularity and are one of the more popular breeds in the United States today.

Montadale. The Montadale breed was developed by Mr. E. H. Mattingly, of St. Louis, Missouri; Columbia and Cheviots were used in the foundation breeding. The original cross was a Columbia ram on Cheviot ewes, but later the cross was reversed, using a Cheviot ram on Columbia ewes. After fourteen years of selection the breed has been well established and appears to be breeding true to type. The Montadale is of good mutton conformation and the wool clip will average from 10 to 12 pounds.

Oxford. The Oxford is the largest of the medium-wool breeds. Mature rams will weigh up to 350 pounds, with an average weight of 300 pounds, and the ewes will range from 175 to 250 pounds. The head and ears are small compared to the body size. The face, ears, and legs will vary from gray to brown in color. The breed is polled.

Oxfords originated in England.

Clayton Reynold, of Delaware City, Delaware, imported the first Oxfords into the United States in 1846.

Shropshires. The Shropshire is one of the smallest of the medium-wool breeds. Mature rams weigh from 175 to 200 pounds and ewes from 135 to 150 pounds. They are a good dual-purpose type, producing a very desirable carcass and a wool clip that averages around nine pounds.

The face, ears, and legs are a deep brown color. The face and legs are covered with wool. Because of this latter characteristic, the Shropshire has lost much of its popularity. A heavy face covering of wool is conducive to wool blindness, objected to by ranchers and many other flock owners.

The Shropshire breed was developed in England and first brought to the United States in 1885.

Southdown. The Southdown is a small sheep. Rams weigh about 175 pounds and ewes 125 pounds at maturity. The head is broad,

Figure 24-6. A Montadale ram. (Courtesy Iowa Sheep Breeders' Assn.)

Figure 24-7. An Oxford ram. (Courtesy American Oxford Down Sheep Record Assn.)

Figure 24-8. A Shropshire ram. (Courtesy American Shropshire Registry Assn.)

Figure 24-9. A Southdown ram. (Courtesy Crathelvic Farms)

with a wool cap that comes just below the eyes. The face is mouse-colored or light brown. The Southdowns are unexcelled from a mutton conformation standpoint. They are low-set, compact, wide, and deep, with legs set wide apart. The breed is early maturing and has been used extensively in the production of hothouse lambs (see Chapter 26). Southdowns will produce a fleece weighing from five to seven pounds. Because of the small size of Southdowns, they have never been popular in the West or Midwest. They are quite popular in the Eastern and Southeastern states.

The Southdowns are one of the oldest of the English breeds and have contributed to the development of many other breeds of sheep.

Suffolk. The Suffolk has enjoyed a recent popularity in the United States that is unequalled by any other breed. They are being used in many Western flocks for crossbreeding and have increased considerably in the Midwest. Their sudden increase in popularity is probably due to the open faces, preventing wool blindness, and excellent conformation along with their comparatively large size. The head is small, resulting in less lambing difficulty.

The Suffolk is distinguished by its black face, legs, and ears. Rams average about 250 pounds and ewes 180 pounds when mature. The ewes are very prolific, producing 150 per cent or more lamb crop. The breed will shear a fleece ranging from eight to ten pounds in weight.

The Suffolk, like most of the medium-wool breeds, was developed in England.

Figure 24-10. A Suffolk ewe. (Courtesy American Suffolk Sheep Society)

430 • *Selection of Breeding and Feeding Stock*

Tunis. The Tunis is one of the oldest breeds of sheep known, but it has never been popular in the United States. The breed is polled and open-faced, with a tan or red face. They are among the smaller breeds. Rams average about 150 pounds and ewes 110 to 125 pounds when mature.

The breed is of Asiatic origin.

Long-wool Breeds. Among the long-wool breeds which have found favor in the United States are: Cotswold, Leicester, Lincoln, and Romney.

Cotswold. The most distinguishing characteristic of the Cotswold breed is the way the wool hangs in curls, with a tuft of wool hanging from the forehead down to the eyes. The wool is coarse and the fibers are long. Cotswold are large sheep, with rams weighing 300 pounds and ewes up to 225 pounds.

The breed has never been popular in the United States.

Figure 24-11. A Cotswold ram. (Courtesy Kansas State College)

Leicester. There are two types of Leicester sheep, the English and the Border. While they are regarded as two separate breeds in England, in the United States they are considered two types of the same breed and are registered in the same flock books.

Leicesters are medium in size, with clean faces and legs. The ewes are not very prolific. Leicesters have been used mainly for crossing purposes in the United States. The body form and wool are typical of the long-wool breeds.

Leicesters were developed in England.

Selection of Breeding and Feeding Stock • 431

Lincoln. The Lincoln is a large sheep with a broad head and large thick ears. It is very rugged and heavily fleshed. The wool is long and of good weight and quality. The ewes will produce from 12 to 16 pounds of wool annually. The ewes are fairly prolific, but are not recognized for their milking ability. While few purebred flocks exist in this country, Lincolns have been very successfully used in cross-breeding and in developing new breeds.

The Lincoln breed is native to England.

Romney. The Romney, sometimes called Romney Marsh or Kent sheep, seems to be better adapted to wet, swampy areas than most other breeds. Breeders of these sheep also claim they are less susceptible to foot rot and liver flukes (both common to wet areas) which probably gives them their reputation for being better adapted to countries of heavy rainfall.

Like the other long-wool breeds, they are slow-maturing and coarse-wooled.

Romney sheep were developed in the Romney Marsh region of England.

Crossbred-wool Breeds. The crossbred-wool breeds were developed by using crosses of long- and fine-wool sheep and by selection until the breeds were developed to the extent that they would breed true to form. As a class they are similar to the medium-wool class, but they are more hardy and better adapted to the Western range than are the medium-wool breeds. They produce a heavier fleece and superior carcass than do the fine-wool breeds, without losing too much of the banding instinct and hardiness of this class.

The Columbia, Corriedale, Panama, Romeldale, and Targhee constitute these breeds.

Columbia. This breed resulted from first crossing Lincoln rams on Rambouillet ewes. Selection was based on utility value without consideration to breed points which have little or no productive value.

The Columbia is the first of the strictly American breeds to be developed. It was started by the Bureau of Animal Industry in 1917.

The breed is the largest of the crossbred-wool class and well adapted to the bitter range conditions. The mature rams will weigh from 225 to 275 pounds and ewes will weigh from 125 to 190 pounds in breeding condition. They will produce from ten to 13 pounds of wool yearly. The lambs are of good market type, but they

Figure 24-12. (left) A Columbia ewe. (Courtesy Columbia Sheep Breeders Assn. of America)
Figure 24-13. (right) A Corriedale ram. (Courtesy American Corriedale Assn., Inc.)

are not equal to that of the medium-wool breeds. The breed is somewhat on the rangy side. This is necessary under most range conditions where large areas must be covered for feed and water. The breed is open-faced and not susceptible to wool blindness. Columbias represent a very successful breeding experiment since they produce a good market lamb and a good wool clip, are adapted to range conditions, and retain much of the herding instinct of their Rambouillet ancestors.

Corriedale. The Corriedale is blockier and smaller than the Columbia. Mature rams range from 185 to 250 pounds and ewes range from 125 to 185 pounds. The annual wool clip will average from nine to 12 pounds. The quality of the wool is good, as is the carcass value of the lambs. Corriedales have less appeal to many range sheepmen than Columbias because of their smaller size and finer bone.

The Corriedale resulted from a combination of the Merino, Lincoln, and Leicester breeds. They were developed in New Zealand in about 1880. The Bureau of Animal Industry imported the first Corriedales into the United States in 1914. They were tested under Western range conditions and were reported to be well adapted to the bitter range areas.

Panama. The Panama and Columbia originated from the same cross. The difference being that the cross was reversed. That is, Rambouillet rams were mated to Lincoln ewes. The breed is an

Figure 24-14. (left) A Panama ram. (Courtesy Kansas State College)
Figure 24-15. (right) A Targhee ram. (Courtesy U.S.D.A.)

American breed originated by Laidlaw and Brockie, of Mildoon, Idaho. The Panama closely resembles the Columbia. They are a little smaller and show somewhat more mutton qualities.

Romeldale. The Romeldale is a new breed developed by A. T. Spencer, Woodland, California. New Zealand Romney Marsh rams were used on Rambouillet ewes and, as a result of inbreeding and rigid selection, the Romeldale is producing a fleece ranging from ten to 13 pounds and is a compact, good-quality meat animal.

Targhee. Starting in 1926, the United States Department of Agriculture Sheep Experiment Station at Dubois, Idaho, has been working with a combination of Rambouillets, Corriedales, and Lincolns blending this breeding into a strain which they have called Targhee. They are white-faced, hornless, and of medium size. Rams weigh about 200 pounds and ewes about 130. They are open-faced, produce a good-quality wool clip weighing from ten to 12 pounds, and are a good mutton-type lamb. The breed gives promise of being well adapted to much of the range area.

Carpet-wool Breeds. Carpet-wool sheep are of minor importance in the United States. Only the Black-Faced Highland exists in any quantity in this country and there are only a small number of them.

Black-Faced Highland. Both sexes of this breed have horns. It is a typical carpet-wool type with a long coarse outer wool coat which resembles hair more than wool. They have a finer undercoat which helps to give protection against the inclement weather of their native home in the Scottish highlands. The breed is small, rugged, and able to graze on areas sparse in vegetation and rough in terrain.

Fur Sheep Breeds. The fur sheep industry is new in the United States and many problems must be overcome before success may be obtained with these sheep. Since the primary purpose for raising these sheep is the production of pelts, a good market for pelts is essential. Coats and other garments require matching pelts. To be able to market, at one time, a sufficient number of matching pelts for a coat has been difficult for the producer. Single pelts command much less in price than several matching pelts.

The feeding value of the lambs is very poor, as is the wool clip of mature animals. It is questionable whether it would be wise for the beginner to enter into the fur sheep business.

Figure 24-16. (A) A mature Karakul ewe. (Abernathy Photo) (B) This Karakul lamb shows the fur locks at the open-type wavy pattern stage. (Courtesy Don Collinson)

Karakul. The characteristics of the various types of pelts were discussed earlier in the chapter. The rams have horns, but the ewes are polled. Rams weigh about 200 pounds and ewes weigh about 145 pounds at full maturity.

Selecting and Establishing the Breeding Stock

Whether a small farm flock or a large range operation is to be established, success will depend upon the economical production of lambs and wool. Each individual breeding animal in the flock should be selected on the basis of efficiency in producing these two products.

Selecting a Breed

In selecting a breed of sheep the more important considerations are: (1) environmental conditions under which the animals will be produced; (2) market price and demand for the principal product to be produced; (3) cost and availability of breeding stock; and (4) personal likes.

Environmental Conditions. Certain breeds have the ability to forage and survive over range areas that have sparse vegetation, producing a wool clip and a lamb where other breeds would fail. Also some breeds have what is known as a banding instinct or the tendency to graze in close, compact groups. When large bands of sheep are grazed over unfenced areas and where predatory animals are prevalent, it is important that the sheep maintain a close formation. One shepherd is usually charged with the care of the flock. He has the help of well-trained sheep dogs, but his task would be impossible under many conditions with breeds that tend to spread out as they graze. Certain breeds have a wool-covering over the face. Some individuals of these breeds are subject to wool blindness, especially where snow, ice, and the awns of certain grasses may get into the fleece. Unless individual attention is given each animal, such breeds may not be a wise choice.

In areas where feed is plentiful and where the flock may graze on fenced pastures, mutton or fat lamb production will probably be the best source of income. The medium-wool or crossbred-wool breeds generally produce a better quality of lamb than either the fine-wool or long-wool breeds.

Some breeders of fur sheep have found the enterprise to be profitable. The fur sheep numbers are not large in the United States and most breeders of this type have been selling surplus animals for breeding rather than for fur purposes. The problem of having enough matching pelts at one time to produce a coat has made marketing of lamb skins a problem for the breeders.

Market Price and Demand. Market outlets and the price paid for wool and lambs are a consideration in selecting a breed. The purebred breeder must rely upon commercial producers and other breeders for his sales. The number of breeding animals in proportion to the demand for such animals determines to a large extent the demand and price a breeder will receive for his stock.

Cost and Availability of Breeding Stock. Commercial producers must depend upon the purebred breeders for improved breeding animals, especially rams. How far will he have to go to get these animals and what will they cost him on the farm and ranch are two questions he must answer before choosing a breed. It is usually cheaper and easier to find breeding animals if the breed is common to the community. However, if a new breed has been developed, or if the establishment of another breed in a community will be a decided improvement, the first producers to get a start in the breed will probably harvest some handsome profits. Such breeders will have a good demand for breeding stock until a general change-over of breeds has been accomplished in the community.

Personal Likes. Success depends largely upon one's interest in his work. To choose a breed that does not appeal to the producer makes it difficult to develop the interest necessary for success.

Selecting Foundation Stock

Having decided upon the breed of sheep to raise, the breeder is next confronted with the problem of selecting foundation stock. While some breeds are considered superior for the amount and quality of their wool and other breeds for mutton qualities, the general type desired is very much the same, regardless of the breed.

The breeder of fine-wool sheep may be especially concerned about the quantity and quality of wool they produce, but he also depends upon the sale of lambs for a good share of his income. The meat qualities of the lambs largely determine the price they will bring, as either feeder or slaughter lambs. It is also true that the breeder of mutton sheep depends on the wool clip as a secondary source of income. His chief concern is the mutton qualities of the animals, but if a heavy fleece of good quality is produced, his chances of a profit from the enterprise are considerably better.

Each breed has its own characteristics which are desirable and in many cases essential for registration, but are not important from a production standpoint. Color, wooled or clean legs, and horns or hornless are examples of breed characteristics. Purebred breeders are more concerned about individual breed characteristics than are commercial producers. The breed associations will furnish the needed information on the breeds.

Selection Based on Health, Soundness, and Uniformity.

Health. Health of the stock is of first importance when selecting animals for breeding purposes. Animals that are listless or show dark skins or paleness in the lining of the nose and eyelids are not a good choice. Such animals may not live to produce a lamb and even if they do are not likely to produce enough milk for the rapid growth of the lamb.

Soundness. Old ewes with broken mouths are a poor choice, as they will have difficulty in eating and therefore will not be in condition for lamb production.

Udders on breeding ewes should be carefully checked for soundness. Abscesses, ruptures, blind teats, or missing teats make ewes useless for breeding purposes. Some ewes have hard meaty udders or abnormally large teats. These should be rejected.

A

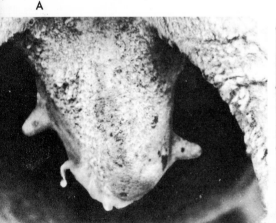 

Figure 24-17. (A) An example of an abscessed udder caused by mastitis. (B) Overshot and undershot jaws are inherited. All such animals and their offspring should be culled from the breeding flock. (Courtesy Kansas State College)

The upper and lower jaws should be even in length, with the incisors of the lower jaw fitting against the hard pad or cartilage of the upper jaw. A sheep with either jaw protruding beyond the other will have difficulty grazing and will be a poor forager.

Any ewe that is exceptionally heavy or enlarged directly below the rear flank undoubtedly has a weak abdominal wall or a breach and should not be kept as a lamb producer.

Uniformity. If one expects to produce a lamb crop uniform as to size and type, he should start with a uniform ewe flock of the same breed or cross. Breeds of sheep range considerably in size and type. Keeping the small, fast-maturing breeds in conjunction with the larger breeds would result in a lamb crop lacking in uniformity and market value.

Selection Based on Body Conformation. Sheep, unlike other livestock, must be judged largely with the hands rather than the eye, because of the wool covering. Wool many times covers up defects that cannot be seen. Going over the animal from the neck to the leg of mutton with the hands enables the trained judge to uncover any possible defects.

If the animals are shorn, more may be seen by the eye than when they are in the fleece. While one must use both the eye and the hand to judge, a general idea of the conformation may be gained by sight alone. As in judging other livestock, the first step is to survey the animal from a distance of about ten to 15 feet. From a side view the animal should appear compact, blocky, low-set, with a straight top and underlines. The legs should be strong, with short, reasonably straight pasterns. From a front view the muzzle should be broad and square, the nostrils large and wide, and the eyes alert. The head should show masculinity in the ram and femininity in the ewe, but be free of coarseness. The chest should be deep, with good width between the front legs. The shoulders should blend smoothly with the body.

From the rear of the animal observe the width and uniformity of width from shoulders to dock. Remember the back and loin are where the lamb chops and choice roasts come from. They should be wide and uniform. The twist should be deep, the dock wide, and the legs full and plump. The entire animal should move with ease.

After gaining a general idea by looking over the animal from at least three positions, stop immediately behind the sheep, placing

Figure 24-18. (A) (Top left) A shorn ram. This ram is of good type. When the fleece is off, more can be seen with the eye. (Top right) Using the hands to determine the smoothness of the shoulders. (Bottom left) Determining the depth of the fore quarters. (Bottom right) Measuring the width of the loin. (B) (Top left) Finding the width of the dock. (Top right) Determining the depth of the twist. (Bottom left) Determining the amount of muscling in the leg. (Bottom right) Examining the fleece for staple length, cleanness, quality, and health condition of the skin. (Courtesy University of Minnesota)

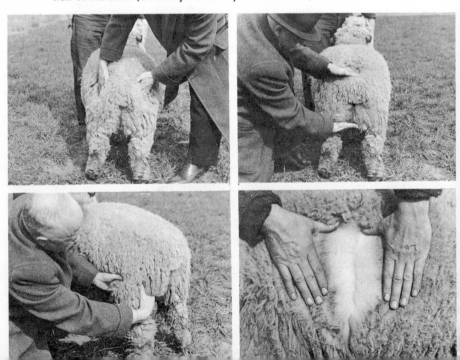

both hands around the neck. Observe whether the neck is short and thick, well-blended into the shoulder. Bring the hands back on either side at the shoulders. Is the heart girth full, or do you find a depression behind the shoulder down along the side? Next bring the hands up just below the top line on either side and work back to the dock. The animal should be wide, uniform, and firm.

Selection Based on Age. The lamb has eight milk teeth in the lower jaw. Between the ages of 12 and 18 months, the center pair is replaced by permanent teeth which are much longer and wider. At two years of age, the second pair of permanent teeth appear, and at three years of age the third set is present. When the sheep reaches its fourth year, the last or fourth pair of permanent teeth has replaced the milk teeth. The animal is then said to have a full mouth.

After four years the teeth begin to slant forward or, in the case of range sheep, they may wear down short. As the sheep ages, the teeth either spread and eventually break off or wear completely away. This condition is referred to as *broken mouth*, and when all teeth have disappeared the sheep are called *gummers*.

Selection Based on Production Records. The surest way of selecting animals for breeding purposes is on a production test. Production testing includes: (1) the type and finish at weaning time, (2) prolificacy, (3) the rate of gain based on weight of lambs at weaning time, and (4) the weight and quality of fleece. A ram whose offspring has shown up well in production test is known as a desirably proven sire. Proven sires are not plentiful and breeding stock sired by a proven ram would be less difficult to find and purchase than the proven sire himself. Animals sired by a ram with a number of offspring that have shown up well under production testing are usually quite certain to give satisfaction.

Selecting Feeder Lambs

Feeder sheep are sheep that are to be fattened for slaughter purposes. Most of the feeders consist of lambs, but a few ewes and some yearlings go into the feed yards.

Feeder Lambs. Feeder lambs are young animals, wethers or ewes, under one year of age that are not carrying sufficient finish for slaughter. The grade classification indicates the probable length of the feeding period to produce a slaughter lamb, and the health,

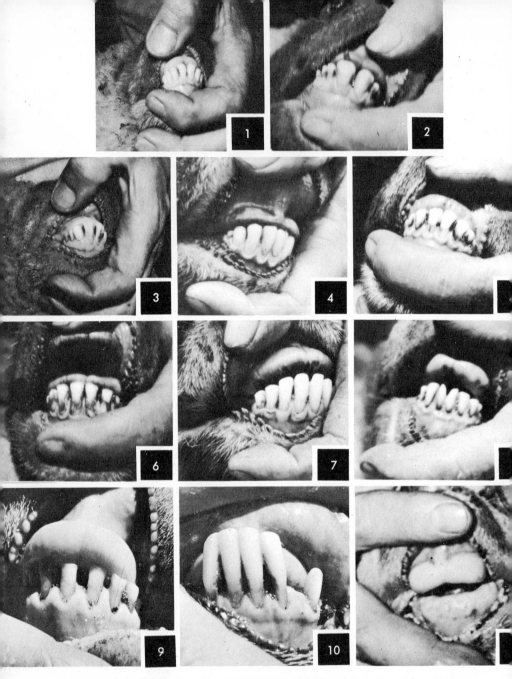

Figure 24-19. (1) Lamb mouth. (2) Yearling, first pair of permanent teeth. (3) Two-year-old. (4) Three-year-old. (5) Four-year-old. (6) Five-year-old. (7) Six-year-old. (8) Seven-year-old. (9) A spreader, sign of advanced age. (10) A broken mouth. (11) A gummer, all teeth are gone. (Courtesy Michigan State University and Kansas State College)

TABLE 47

CLASSES AND GRADES OF FEEDER SHEEP

Sheep or Lambs	Sex	Age	Weight	Grades
Feeder Sheep	Ewes and Wethers	Yearlings	All Weights	Fancy Choice Good Medium Common
	Ewes	2-Year or Older	All Weights	Choice Good Medium Common Inferior
Lambs	Feeder Lambs Ewes or Wethers	All Ages	All Weights	Fancy Choice Good Medium Common Inferior
	Shearer Lambs Ewes or Wethers	All Ages	All Weights	Choice Good Medium

vigor, quality, and type of lamb. Fancy is the highest grade. They represent excellent mutton type and freedom from diseases and parasites, and are usually carrying enough finish so that only a short feeding period of from 40 to 90 days will be required to finish them into prime slaughter lambs. Very few fancy grade feeder lambs are available, as the qualifications for this grade are very high and most of them are bought for exhibition purposes. Choice is recognized as the top commercial grade. The lower grades are usually thin lambs, may show a predominance of fine-wool breeding, and, in the case of common or inferior grades, may lack the health and vigor of the higher grades. They usually are shallow-bodied and upstanding, and show indications of being heavily infested with parasites.

Wethers. Wethers are male lambs castrated at an early age before they reached sexual maturity and before they developed the characteristics of a ram.

Feeder Sheep. Sheep that are over a year old, but are best fattened before marketing, are known as feeder sheep. A few ewes that have been culled are fed out and some Texas ranchers, when the price is too low, may carry lambs over, take a wool clip, and market them as yearlings. Some of these yearlings are fed out on grass in the Corn Belt before going to slaughter.

Shearer Lambs. Shearer lambs carry nearly a full year's growth of wool. Such lambs are usually shorn before going into the fattening yard, especially during warm weather. Shearer lambs bring less money on the slaughter market per pound than lambs with fleeces. However, the value of the fleece plus the better gains during hot weather usually more than offset the lower market value.

Selecting the Weight and Grade of Feeder Lambs

The weight at which to buy lambs depends considerably upon the length of time they are to be fed. Lamb feeders usually plan a feeding period of from 30 to 120 days. Expected daily gains will range from one-fourth to one-half pound, depending upon the kind of feed used and the method of feeding. The slaughter market prices are usually best for the finished lambs that weigh less than 110 pounds. Heavier lambs are subject to a large price discount.

Lambs on a heavy grain ration may be expected to gain about .4 pound per day. Those fed primarily on pasture or cured forage will average less daily gain.

The lamb feeder should calculate the gain his lambs will make, after considering the ration to be fed and the length of the anticipated feeding period. Ninety- to 105-pound finished lambs are usually bought by packers at top slaughter lamb prices. Therefore, 50 to 60 pounders will best fit a long feeding period of 120 days, while heavier lambs will be better suited for short feeding periods.

It should be pointed out that lambs of the small breeds such as the Southdowns, Cheviots, and Shropshires will finish at weights of from 45 to 65 pounds. However, nearly all the feeder lambs available for sale are westerns. Most westerns are either of the larger cross-bred type such as the Columbia or Corriedale or fine-wool and the larger medium-wool crossbreds. These lambs are large and will not usually finish out at less than 90 pounds.

Grade. Generally speaking, choice feeder lambs are the best buy. Lambs grading lower than choice will require a longer feeding period and will have a heavier death loss. Most lamb feeders expect from 2 to 3 per cent death loss during the feeding period. However, less thrifty lambs will run considerably above expected loss.

Price is an important consideration, but the lower-grade lambs will necessarily have to be bought at a figure considerably under the price of choice lambs if they are to be a good buy.

Summary

Sheep are classified several different ways. However, wool-type classification is most common. Under the wool-type classification there exists six usual classifications. They are: fine-wool, medium-wool, long-wool, crossbred-wool, carpet wool, and fur sheep type.

The fine-wool breeds produce a fine fiber, but heavy fleece containing a large amount of yolk. The American and Delaine Merinos and Rambouillets are the breeds of the fine-wool class most commonly found in the United States.

The medium-wool class consists of those breeds that have a fleece of medium fineness and length. They are unexcelled in mutton type conformation. The breeds of this class commonly found in the United States are: Cheviots, Dorsets, Hampshires, Montadale, Oxford, Shropshire, Southdown, Suffolk, and Tunis.

The long-wool class consists of those sheep with exceptionally long fibers of coarse wool. They are large and rugged and have been popular for crossbreeding purposes, especially on fine-wool breeds. The most common breeds of this class found in this country are the Cotswold, Leicester, Lincoln, and Romney.

The crossbred-wool type consists of a number of breeds developed by first crossing long-wool and fine-wool types. The main purpose for these breeds was to develop animals with a good fleece, good carcass qualities, and the herding instinct and hardiness essential for rugged range conditions.

The common crossbred-wool breeds are: Columbia, Corriedale, Panama, Romeldale, and Targhee.

Carpet-wool sheep produce a long, coarse, tough wool suitable for carpet manufacture. The Black-Faced Highland is the most common breed, but very few are found in the United States.

Fur sheep, of which the Karakul is the chief breed, are produced for their lamb pelts. They are of very poor mutton qualities and the fleece from the mature animals is of little value.

Environmental conditions, market price and demand, cost of available breeding stock, and personal likes are important factors in selecting a breed.

Foundation stock should be selected on the basis of body conformation, production records, age, mouth condition, and soundness of udders.

Feeder sheep and lambs are animals that need more finish before they are ready for the slaughter market. Sheep and lamb feeding is carried out by farmers and big commercial feeders. Profit may result from one or more of the following sources: margin, gain, or wool clip.

Feeder lambs and sheep are classified and graded according to sex, age, weight, and grade.

The weight and grade of lambs to buy will depend upon how long they are to be fed, the kind of ration to be used, and the prices of feeder and slaughter lambs.

Choice grade lambs usually prove to be the best buy, as they are of high quality, healthy, and vigorous.

● *Questions*

1. List the classes of sheep and the important breeds in each class.
2. What are the distinguishing characteristics of each class of sheep?
3. Which class is recognized chiefly for wool production?
4. Which class produces the best-quality slaughter lambs?
5. For what purposes were the crossbred-wool types produced?
6. What breeds of sheep were used in the development of the crossbred-wool type?
7. What are carpet-wool sheep?
8. What are fur sheep?
9. What breeds of sheep best fit the conditions of your community? Why?
10. Explain what you would look for in selecting breeding stock.
11. How can you tell the age of sheep by looking in their mouths? Explain.
12. What factors would you consider in selecting a breed?
13. What information do production records furnish?
14. Under what conditions would you advise going into the purebred sheep business?

15. What is a feeder lamb?
16. What is the purpose of buying and feeding lambs?
17. Explain how lamb feeders may profit from their operations.
18. How are feeder lambs classified?
19. How are feeder lambs graded?
20. Explain the following terms: wether lamb, sheep, shearer lamb.
21. What are the factors to consider in determining the weight of feeder lambs to buy? Explain.

● *References*

Alexander, M. A., W. W. Dorrick, Fouts, K. C., *Farm Sheep Facts,* Agricultural Extension Service, Bulletin E. C. 255, University of Nebraska, Lincoln, Nebraska.

Brown, George, *Selection and Care of the Farm Sheep Flock,* Agricultural Extension Service, Bulletin 242, Michigan State College, East Lansing, Michigan.

Cadmus, W. G., *Sheep Records for Greater Profits,* Agricultural Experiment Station, Circular 182, Oregon State College, Corvallis, Oregon.

Cox, R. F., Donald T. Bell, H. G. Reed, *Sheep Production in Kansas,* Agricultural Experiment Station, Bulletin 348, Kansas State College, Manhattan, Kansas.

Francis, Eugene, *Buying and Feeding Lambs,* Pamphlet 220, Iowa State College Extension Service, Ames, Iowa, 1955.

Improvement of Sheep through the Selection of Performance-Tested and Progeny-Tested Breeding Animals, Texas Agricultural Experiment Station, Miscellaneous Publication 125.

25

Feeding and Management of the Breeding Flock

If a healthy productive flock of sheep is to be maintained, the shepherd should give special attention to his feeding and management practices.

Flushing. About two weeks before the rams are turned in with the ewes, the good sheepman will put ewes on a grain ration, or move them to fresh pasture areas where feed is more abundant. This process is known as "flushing." Flushing the ewes will start the heat periods earlier, which is an advantage when early lambs are desired. It also has the effect of bringing all of the ewes into heat at more nearly the same time than otherwise would be the case, resulting in more uniformity as to the time ewes are bred.

When the ewe is gaining flesh, her reproductive organs usually begin functioning normally. The ovaries will produce more healthy female germ cells or eggs, fertility is increased, and a higher conception rate and more twin lambs result. Twins under rugged range conditions are sometimes a disadvantage. Twins are smaller at birth

Figure 25-1. These ewes are being turned on fresh pasture for flushing prior to breeding. (Courtesy Cornell University)

than a single, and ewes milk less under scanty feed conditions. A strong single is more apt to survive. Generally speaking, however, twins are an advantage.

Rations for Flushing. Ewes that have been on pastures sufficient only to maintain them in a healthy condition without abnormally increasing their body flesh are in the best condition for flushing. These ewes may be moved to an area with abundant pasture. Immediately, the breeding flock will considerably increase their weight gains and be ready for breeding from ten days to two weeks later. The same results may be obtained by giving the ewes a full feed of good quality legume hay or from one-half to three-fourths pounds of corn, barley, oats, or sorghum grain daily.

Overfat Ewes. If ewes are overfat at breeding time, many unbred ewes will result. If it is apparent that ewes are going to be too fat, they should be placed on a sparse pasture or in a dry lot where feed will be limited, at least six weeks before the breeding season. Ordinarily, the feeding of ewes to lose body weight when not suckling lambs is not recommended. However, overfat ewes should be thinned down so that they may be placed on a flushing ration prior to breeding.

Feeding the Ewes during Gestation

One cannot overemphasize the need for proper nourishment of the ewe during gestation. Unless the ewes receive a proper ration, weak and dead lambs will be the harvest for the owner.

Proper feeding of the ewes during pregnancy will: (1) increase the number of live lambs born; (2) decrease the number of weak or crippled lambs; (3) lessen the danger of lambing paralysis; (4) prolong the productive lifetime of the ewes; (5) increase the ewe's milk flow; (6) improve the quality and quantity of the wool clip;

and (7) decrease the danger of ewes not owning their lambs as a result of their weakened condition.

Feeds for the Pregnant Ewe. As the unborn lamb, or fetus, develops within the ewe, the greater are her needs for nourishment. During the first half of the pregnant period the fetus grows rather slowly. For this reason, the demands on the ewe for nourishing her unborn offspring are not too great. If only a limited amount of good forage is available, it should be saved until the latter part of the gestation period when the nutritional requirements of the ewe becomes greater.

A large combination of roughages and pastures may be successfully used during the gestation period. Small-grains stubble field and the grasses growing in them, either those that have been seeded or the wild weedy plants, will furnish a large part of the nutrient needs of the ewes. Corn fields that have been harvested (and gleaned by other livestock to remove excess corn left by the harvesting machinery) will provide forage, some grain, and often much weedy green material for the ewe flock.

It is a good practice to make use of as much crop residue, fall pasture, and waste feed as possible during the early gestation period of the ewes. When this feed consists mostly of dry, nonlegume weeds and grasses, it should be supplemented with feeds high in protein and vitamin A.

Legume hay or good quality legume grass, corn, or sorghum silage will supply the necessary amount of vitamin A when used to supplement the dry feeds of low quality. When fresh, growing pastures are available, little additional feed is necessary.

Under most circumstances, ewes will get sufficient mineral, except for salt, from the natural feed that is provided. However, phosphorus and many of the trace minerals may be lacking in feeds grown in some sections of the country. Because we cannot always be sure whether the natural feeds are providing the necessary minerals, it is a good plan to furnish a mineral mixture free choice. Salt should be available at all times. This may be provided separately or as part of the mineral mixture. Minerals recommended for cattle may be used for sheep. (See Chapter 13.)

The use of a two compartment mineral feeder with salt in one compartment and the salt mineral mixture in the other is recommended for pregnant ewes.

Many feeds, rich in protein, are available for sheep feeding. Among the more common protein concentrates are cotton seed oil meal, cotton seed cake, linseed oil meal, and soybean oil meal.

Rations for the First Ten Weeks of the Gestation Period. The gestation period of ewes will range from 143 to 151 days. The first half of the gestation period is less critical from a nutritional standpoint than the last half. While it is important that the ewes be properly nourished during the entire pregnancy period, the early part of gestation possesses less nutritional problems than the latter part.

Some suggested rations for the first half of the gestation period are:

1. Legume hay, free choice
2. 2 to 4 pounds corn or sorghum silage
   1 to 2 pounds legume hay
3. Chopped corn or sorghum fodder, free choice
   $\frac{1}{8}$ pound of soybean, linseed, or cotton seed oil meal
4. Grass hay, free choice
   $\frac{1}{10}$ pound of protein supplement containing five pounds of urea and 95 pounds of soybean or linseed oil meal

These are only suggested rations and may be altered using other available feeds. Ewes may find adequate roughages by grazing winter range or gleaning harvested grain fields, and need only to have added to these feeds a protein supplement.

Feeding Ewes During the Last Half of the Gestation Period. During the last half of the gestation period, the best forages available should be fed. The ration given for ewes during the first part of the gestation period may be continued, but starting with the eleventh week, one fourth of a pound of grain should be added to the rations. Beginning with the sixteenth week, the grain ration should be increased one-half to three-fourths of a pound. Unless the roughage is entirely legume hay, an additional amount of protein supplement should be added.

Ewes, especially those carrying twin lambs, are frequently affected with lambing paralysis shortly before lambing, usually resulting in a dead ewe and loss of her lambs. The cause is thought to be due to the inability of the liver to transform body fats into food. While ewes that have had one-half pound of grain in the daily ration and plenty of exercise during the last six weeks of pregnancy are seldom affected, some sheepmen feed one pint of liquid molasses per head daily during this time or supply the equivalent of from one-fourth to one-half pound of sugar, either as dry molasses or in some other form. The molasses or sugar product may replace most of the grain, but since these products have little or no protein, a slight increase in the protein supplement would be advisable when they are used to replace the grain. Molasses is quickly digested and highly regarded by many sheepmen as a precaution against lambing paralysis.

Following are some suggested rations for ewes between the eleventh and sixteenth week of pregnancy.

1. Legume hay free choice
   ¼ to ½ pound corn, sorghum grain, barley, or ½ to ¾ pound of oats

2. 2 to 4 pounds legume and grass silage
   1 to 2 pounds legume hay
   ¼ to ½ pound corn, sorghum grain, barley, wheat or ½ to ¾ pound of oats

3. 2 to 4 pounds corn silage
   1 to 2 pounds legume hay
   ¼ to ½ pound of oats

4. 2 to 4 pounds grass hay
   ¼ to ½ pound corn-oats mixture
   ⅒ to ⅛ pound 35% protein supplement

Note: Salt and mineral mixture fed free choice with the above rations.

The fetus or unborn lamb is developing rapidly during the last few weeks of gestation. This is a critical time in the gestation period. Some suggested rations for the last five weeks of gestation are:

RATIONS	*POUNDS DAILY*
1. Oats—5 parts	
Shelled corn, or grain sorghums—3 parts	
Bran—1 part	½ to 1 pound
Soybean or linseed meal—1 part	
Dry molasses—1 part	
Corn silage	2 to 3
Legume hay	2

2. Barley, sorghum grain, or shelled corn $\frac{1}{2}$ to $\frac{3}{4}$
      Corn silage   2 to 3
      Legume hay   2 to 3

3. Oats and shelled corn $\frac{1}{4}$ to $\frac{1}{2}$
      Liquid molasses $\frac{1}{2}$
      Legume hay   2 to 3

4. Wheat and oats $\frac{1}{2}$ to $\frac{3}{4}$
      Cotton seed meal $\frac{1}{10}$ to $\frac{1}{8}$
      Sorghum silage   6 to 8

Note: Salt and mineral mixture fed free choice with above rations.

Feeding Ewes that Are Suckling Lambs

Ewes should be fed liberally while suckling lambs. The lambs make their most economical gains while nursing the ewes. Therefore it is important that the ewe supply a liberal amount of milk.

Feeding Ewes for the First Ten Days after Lambing. Immediately after lambing, most successful sheepmen reduce the concentrates in the ration. Ewes are less likely to have swollen udders or other udder trouble if the concentrates are reduced for the first ten days. The amount of grain given the ewes may be increased as the lambs grow and are able to take all the milk. The amount to reduce the concentrates depends upon the condition of the ewe, whether she has a single lamb or twins, and the amount of milk she is producing. When large flocks are involved, individual attention given to each ewe's ration may not be practical. Therefore, it is recommended that ewes be given all the legume hay they will consume but little concentrates for the first ten days after lambing.

Ewes that lamb after the start of the pasture season will not need any supplementary feeding, if the pasture is of good quality and plentiful.

Feeding Ewes Ten Days after Lambing until Weaning of the Lambs. Ewes that lamb on the pasture will not require supplemental feeding, other than salt and a mineral mixture, as long as they have an adequate amount of good quality pasture. When pastures are short or dry, they may not supply enough total digestible nutrients or enough protein to maintain milk flow at a high level. Under these conditions additional feed in the form of high quality hay, silage, or grain will need to be provided. If the lambs are creep fed, less feed will be required for the ewes. When supplementary feeding on pasture is necessary, the amount of additional feed may be calculated on the basis of one pound of good hay, plus three pounds of silage or three-fourths of a pound of grain, to replace about one-half of the average ewe's daily pasture requirements.

Ewes that lamb during seasons when pasture is not available present a more complicated feeding problem. Since milk is high in protein, ewes suckling lambs need slightly more protein than pregnant ewes. Ewes suckling lambs will usually increase their consumption of hay or silage by one to two pounds daily over the amount eaten during gestation. Roots and silage are excellent feeds to stimulate the flow of milk.

Following are some suggestions for dry lot rations for ewes suckling lambs:

RATIONS	POUNDS DAILY
1. Good legume hay	2 to 4
Oats—60 pounds	
Corn or sorghum grain—25 pounds	¾ to 1
Wheat bran—15 pounds	
2. Corn, or sorghum silage, or root crops	3 to 5
Barley or oats—46 pounds	
Corn or sorghum—34 pounds	½ to 1
Soybean, cotton seed or linseed meal—20 pounds	
3. Grass hay	2 to 4
Oats—30 pounds	
Corn—30 pounds	
Bran—20 pounds	½ to 1
Linseed meal—20 pounds	

Feeding the Breeding Rams. Well-developed rams should be selected in advance of the breeding season. If the ram is overfat, he should be thinned down by gradual reduction in feed and plenty of exercise. If the ram is in normal condition at breeding time, he will need some extra grain unless the pasture is excellent during breeding season. The amount of grain to feed will vary with the size of the ram. A ration consisting of three parts oats, one part corn, and one part bran, fed at the rate of one pound per day is usually sufficient for the ram during breeding season. Barley or sorghum grain may be substituted for corn or oats.

Usually, the feeds available to the ewes will provide adequately for the ram. Unless the ram is penned up separately part of the day he cannot be given a special ration. Under small flock conditions, some sheepmen pen the ram away from the ewes during the day and then turn him out at night. If this procedure is practiced, the ram may be given a special ration.

Management of the Breeding Flock

Successful management practices must necessarily vary depending upon the conditions and type of sheep enterprise with which one is associated. Management of the farm flock, where numbers average considerably less than range flock, involves many practices that would not be practical under range conditions. It is also true that many recommended range management practices would have little practical value under farm flock conditions.

The conditions under which the various practices are recommended will be described so that the student, beginner, or the established sheepman may select those that will be of value to him.

Heat Periods, Gestation, and Breeding Season

Heat Periods. The heat period, or oestrus, is the period in which the ewes will permit the ram to make contact. The duration of the heat period will range from 3 to 73 hours. Three-fourths of the ewes will remain in heat from 21 to 39 hours. The heat periods will occur every 13 to 19 days, averaging 16½ days from one heat period to the next, during the season when the ewe will mate. Unlike other farm animals, ewes in general do not come in heat at the regular intervals throughout the year but are seasonal in this respect.

Mating Seasons. Most breeds come in heat during the periods of shorter daylight hours and cooler nights. Dorsets and Tunis come in heat quite regularly throughout the year, while the out-of-season months tend to vary from May to September for the other breeds. The reason for this difference in the seasonal mating pattern of sheep is much disputed. Some authorities believe the length of daylight may be a factor, as the mating season changes with areas. Regardless of the reasons, it is well known that mating is seasonal except with the Dorset and Tunis, and the seasonal pattern varies with breeds. Therefore, it is not wise to have a ewe flock of mixed breeds, if a short term drop of fall or early winter lambs is desired.

Gestation Periods. The gestation period will vary from 144 to 152 days.

Figure 25-2. Clipping the wool from around the eye to prevent wool blindness. (Courtesy *Successful Farming*)

Preparing the Ewe and Ram for Breeding

Tagging. Before the breeding season starts the wool should be removed from around the dock; this is referred to as "tagging." Ewes sometimes are not bred because wool or tags prevent the ram from making satisfactory connection. Tagging also prevents the ewes from befouling themselves, especially important when they are first turned on green pasture which has a loosening effect on the bowels.

Eyeing. Wool blindness may result from sharp grass seed awns and other materials collecting in the wool around the eyes. Open-faced breeds of sheep (those that do not have wool growing around the eyes) will not be troubled. However, to prevent wool blindness in those breeds with covered faces, the wool should be clipped away from around the eyes. This process is referred to as "eyeing."

Shearing and Ringing the Ram. *Shearing*. When the breeding season starts during warm weather, shearing the ram just prior to turning him with the ewes will make him more active and, in many cases, will improve his fertility. Many rams that are fertile and good breeders during cool weather will become impotent during the heat of summer. Higher body temperature, particularly that of the testicles, is probably the cause of this infertility. Many sheepmen shear the breeding rams twice a year and this practice is highly recommended when ewes are to be bred during the warm weather.

Ringing. If the ram is not completely shorn, he should at least be clipped from the neck and from the belly in the region of the penis (ringing). This will make it easier for the ram to make proper contact with the ewes during the act of mating.

Care of the Feet. Both ewes and rams should have their feet well trimmed so they can walk naturally. Sheep raised under range conditions usually keep their feet worn down smooth. Sheep under average farm conditions, where less walking for feed is necessary and when they are kept confined in small lots, do not wear down the hoof. Filth accumulates under the overgrown hoof, causing the feet to become sore. This filth may also harbor organisms responsible for infection—foot rot—which is difficult to control once it has become established. A sharp knife or pruning shears may be used to trim the feet.

A   B

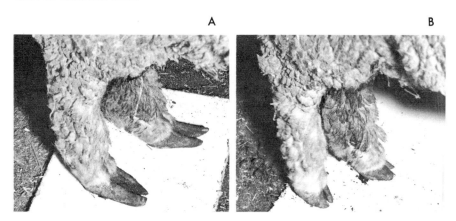

Figure 25-3. (A) Long grown-out hooves accumulate filth and increase the danger of foot infection. This animal's foot needs trimming. (B) The same sheep after the feet were trimmed. (Courtesy *Successful Farming*)

Marking the Ram. It is very difficult to tell when a ram is breeding, whether or not he is sterile, and when ewes are bred unless the ram is properly marked, and notes as to the breeding date of the ewes are kept. Marking the ram may be done either by breast painting the ram or using a marking harness.

A good breast paint may be made by mixing lamp black or venetian red with raw linseed oil into a thick paste. One of these mixtures should be applied to the brisket with a paddle at least once a week. When the ram mounts the ewe in the act of breeding, she

Fig. 25-4. (above) Side view of a ram with a marking harness properly attached. (Courtesy Gilman Brothers)

Figure 25-5. (left) Breast-painting the ram for the purpose of marking ewes that are bred. (Courtesy Gilman Brothers)

will be marked on the rump. It is important to identify the ewe by ear tag number and make a note of her identity and the date she was bred. The owner will now have a record as to the date the ewe may be expected to lamb. If several ewes return in heat, the ram is probably sterile and a replacement may be made before it is too late. If the color of the paint is changed every 16 to 18 days, detection of unbred ewes and breeding dates will be easier.

A device consisting of an apron-like pad with straps for attaching it to the breast of the ram is available on the market. Some are fitted with a metal slot fastened to the portion between the ram's front legs, where a special type of crayon may be placed for marking the ewes. In some types, a colored chalk is used. This device is known as a marking harness.

Ewe Ram Ratio and Age of Ram

While a nine to ten month old well-developed ram lamb may be used to breed ten or 12 ewes, his use is not recommended unless the supply of good yearling or older rams has been used. Good rams over five years of age may be used successfully, but they should be checked carefully as they should be regarded with suspicion as to fertility. They may also lack the vigor and ability to get around under range conditions.

Yearlings and rams up to five years old may be relied upon to breed up to 45 ewes during the breeding season. Under rough range conditions the rates should be one ram to 30 ewes.

Many farm flock owners have too many ewes for one ram and not enough for two. These owners can increase the breeding capacity of their rams by removing them during the day and feeding them from two to three pounds of grain. The rams will soon learn to come out of the flock for their feed. Since most of the breeding takes place at night, no breeding time is likely to be lost.

Age to Breed and Average Productive Life of Ewes. The recommended age to breed ewes has been the first breeding season after they are one year of age, or to produce their first lamb at about 24 months of age. However, many experiment stations and flock owners have reported success in breeding ewe lambs.

The productive life of ewes will vary considerably depending upon both the breed and environment. Under average range conditions, ewes may be expected to produce about five crops of lambs if bred for the first time as yearlings. This calls for eliminating them from the flock when they are about seven years of age. Under farm flock conditions which are less vigorous, the life span will average a little longer.

Should Ewe Lambs Be Bred? A summary of the experimental results and the experience of practical sheepmen seem to indicate the following: (1) ewe lambs must be well grown out if they are to be bred; (2) they should not be bred until they are nine months of age; (3) ewe lambs bred at nine months of age gain faster than those not bred, but they weigh less when the lambs are weaned; (4) lambs will be born later than the average for the rest of the flock; therefore, they must be weaned earlier if the ewes are to conform with the rest of the flock for the next season lamb crop; (5) first lambs will be smaller at birth than those from older ewes, but subsequent lambs will be equal in size; (6) ewe lambs will need a better ration during pregnancy than older ewes to prevent underdevelopment; (7) more lambing difficulty (ewes needing help at lambing time) will be evident among ewe lambs; (8) ewe lambs of the larger breeds should be mated the first time to small type rams such as the Southdown; (9) under good feeding and management, ewe lambs bred at nine months of age produced a wool clip equal to those bred the first time as yearlings and averaged about three-fourths lamb per head more during their life span; (10) more broken mouths occur at six to seven years of age among ewes bred as lambs than among those bred as yearlings.

How Long the Rams Should be Allowed to Run with the Band. A uniform lamb crop requires that the rams be allowed to run with the ewes for not more than eight weeks but preferably for only six. If plenty of rams are used, the ewes have been properly conditioned for breeding, and each band or flock consists of the same breed or crossbreed, very few unbred ewes will result.

Managing the Ewes During Gestation

Exercise. Lack of exercise during pregnancy is a contributing factor to lambing difficulties, including lambing paralysis. Range sheep are much less likely to suffer from lack of exercise than are the farm flocks.

Dry winter pastures and cornfields when not covered with snow provide good exercise areas as ewes will forage over them all winter long. Loading the hay or other forage onto a wagon and scattering it out at considerable distance from the bedding area will induce ewes to exercise when snow covers the fields.

Ranchers who supplement the winter range with cottonseed cake can force the ewes to get more exercise by feeding the cake at considerable distance from the bed grounds.

Shade. Ewes, during extremely warm weather, should have protection from the hot sunshine. Under farm flock conditions this can be accomplished either by buildings, trees, or temporary shades.

Protection from Other Livestock. It is not a good practice at any time to let ewes run in the same area with cattle or hogs. This is especially true of ewes heavy with lamb. Cattle may kick or bunt ewes, injuring them and causing an abortion. Hogs, especially old sows, may grab a ewe, causing her to bleed. After getting a taste of the blood, they proceed to kill and eat her.

Management During the Lambing Season

Dividing the Flock Before Lambing. When the flock is large, much time and labor may be saved by separating the ewes that are nearest to lambing. If breeding dates have not been recorded, the next best method is by general observation and bagging. Ewes about to lamb will sink away on either side of the rump in front of the hips, the vulva will enlarge, wax will form on the ends of the teats, there will be distension of the udder, and the teats will be tight and show signs of filling.

Marking Ewes. In making the examination and marking ewes for separation into drop bands, a chute with a swinging gate at one end (dodge gate) and a recommended solvable branding paint consisting of two colors are recommended equipment. The chute may be filled and udder examinations made. Those about to lamb marked with one color, those about two weeks away marked with another color, and those more than two weeks away left unmarked.

Handling the Ewes About to Lamb. The ewes about to lamb may be successfully handled by several different methods, depending upon conditions. When flocks are large, lambing on pasture or in the open is generally more practical than to attempt to furnish lambing barns or sheds. Naturally the weather must be reasonably warm for pasture lambing. Many successful range operators will confine the heavy ewes to a corral at night. The corral may be fitted with temporary pens made from panels, where the ewes may be confined for a day or so with their lambs. Individual lambing tents may be used to give the ewe and her new-born lambs temporary protection from inclement weather.

Lambing Pens or Jails. If the flock is not too large, it will pay to provide individual lambing pens for the ewes. The use of lambing pens (often referred to as jails) helps to prevent losses of lambs. Very often, ewes producing twins will wander away with the stronger lamb and leave the weaker one to chill or starve. Ewes having twins sometimes move, after having the first lamb, to a different area where the second is born. The first lamb may not be

Figure 25-6. Temporary lambing pen made from panels wired together. (Courtesy Ken Faulkner)

recognized and owned by the mother. When several ewes are lambing at the same time, it is more difficult to identify lambs with their mothers when the flock is running together. By numbering the ewes and giving the lambs the same identification marks, poor milking ewes, or those not producing strong lambs, may be more easily identified and later removed from the breeding flocks.

Lambing pens may be temporary and made from panels 36 to 40 inches high and four feet long, hinged or wired together. Burlap sacks may be placed around and over the pens to make them warmer, or they may be of a permanent type fitted with feed and watering facilities. The ewes should be left in the pens until the lambs are at least three to four days old.

Brooders. If ewes are lambing during cold weather, brooders may be provided in the lambing pens or in the lambing barn as a means of preventing chilled lambs. These brooders are of two types; those that provide for the lambs from several ewes, known as *colony brooders*, and those which provide for only two to three lambs known as *individual brooders*, which are used in connection with lambing pens. The colony type is used when ewes lamb in a barn or shed but are not confined to lambing pens. They are enclosures heated with electric heat bulbs (usually 250 watt size) and will accommodate several lambs. They have openings that will admit the lambs but exclude the ewes. The individual type is used in the lambing pen and is built to accommodate only one ewe's lambs at a time.

Preparing the Ewe for Lambing. Just prior to lambing the good shepherd will tag his ewes. This is the process of cutting off, from the rear of the ewes the locks of wool that have accumulated dung and filth. He also clips the wool from around the teats so the lambs will be able to find them and will not suck on a lock of wool. Wool-faced breeds may also have the wool clipped away from around the eyes at the same time.

Delivering the Lamb. Ewes that are vigorous, well fed, and well managed seldom have difficulty in lambing. Do not disturb the ewe during the first stages of labor. However, if it becomes evident that the ewe will need help, wash and disinfect the hand and arm, and apply a coating of Vaseline to the hand and arm. Lay the ewe on her right side, make entrance, and determine whether the lamb is in proper position for delivering. If the lamb is in normal

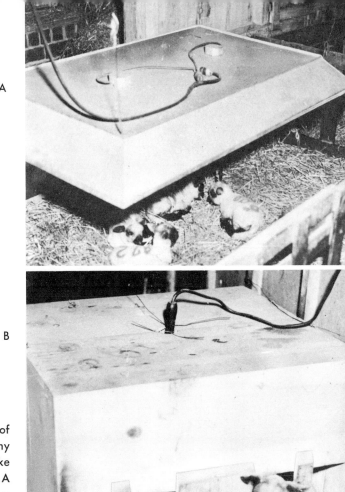

A

B

Figure 25-7. Two types of lamb brooders. (A) A colony type brooder that will take care of several lambs. (B) A small brooder designed for a lambing pen to accommodate one ewe's lambs. (Courtesy *Successful Farming*)

position, it will be right side up, back toward the back of the ewe, front feet extended with the nose on or between the front feet. In a normal delivery the nose will show first with the feet on either side.

Unfortunately the position of the lamb inside the ewe is not always normal and the ewe will be unable to expel the lamb without assistance. The most common difficulty is when one or both front feet are doubled back instead of protruding outward. If the ewe has labored long there will likely be considerable swelling of the lamb's head, adding to the difficulty. The procedure is to push the lamb back slowly and carefully. This will have to be done against the straining of the ewe. By sliding the hand down the neck and locating the front legs, they may be straightened out in a normal position. Lubricating the walls of the vagina by dipping the hand into a light mineral oil and applying it to the vaginal walls will make it easier to maneuver the lamb into position.

Occasionally, the legs will be properly presented but the head and neck are twisted back. If the head cannot be guided out with the hand, tie a heavy string around each leg leaving plenty of string protruding, and double the legs back into the womb. Next make a loop; just large enough to slip over the lamb's head, from a piece of clean unrusted wire. Slip the loop inside the uterus and over the lamb's head, then by pulling on the strings and the wire the lamb may be successfully delivered.

The position of the lamb may be backwards with the tail presented first. Usually the lamb can be delivered in this position by gently pulling on the tail and rear of the lamb.

Whenever it is necessary to go inside the ewe with the hands, it is advisable to give the ewe an injection of penicillin to help prevent infection from developing.

Care of the Ewe Immediately After Lambing. The ewe should be kept under observation for several days after lambing. The shepherd should be sure the ewe cleans and that her udder and bowels are in good condition. If the ewe is constipated, a drench consisting of one-fourth pint of raw linseed oil or three ounces of epsom salts dissolved in warm water will start bowel movements. A rectal injection of one quart of warm soapy water brings quicker results than giving a laxative. The ewe should be given plenty of water. A light feed of bran and legume hay is recommended for ewes in pens or dry lot. Careful examination of the ewe's udder may detect any abnormality or infection in time to administer treatment before the udder is damaged.

Management of the Newborn Lambs

The most critical period in the life of a lamb is during the first 48 hours. Most of the problems causing lamb losses, such as chilling, weak lambs, dry ewes, ewes with plugged teats, and ewes failing to claim their lambs occur during this period.

When the lamb is born, pinch off the umbilical cord about four inches from the body. Be sure all mucus is removed from the nose and mouth. The navel should be disinfected with a tincture of iodine to prevent infection.

The lamb should be placed near the ewe's head. She may rest and clean the lamb. If the ewe will own the lamb, it is best to leave her alone. A strong lamb will usually nurse unassisted.

Chilled Lambs. Lambs born during cold weather or during storms often become chilled. Quick action on the part of the operator will result in reviving many lambs that appear to be nearly lifeless. The best and quickest method of reviving a chilled lamb is to immerse it in water just as hot as one's elbow can bear. Place the entire body except the head in the water and hold it for a few minutes. Then after rubbing it dry, wrap it in a burlap sack or some heavy material along with another lamb that is warm. As quickly as possible, get some milk into it as nothing revives a chilled lamb more quickly than some warm milk in the stomach.

Weak Lambs Will Need Help. Weak lambs will usually not survive unless given assistance in getting something to eat. The first step in assisting a weak lamb is to milk a few drops from the ewe to make sure the milk channels are open. Place the teat in the lamb's mouth and squeeze some milk into its mouth.

Ewes that own and mother their lambs will lick the lamb under the tail while they are sucking. Weak lambs may be encouraged to suck by tickling the lamb under the base of the tail with the finger in imitation of the ewe.

How to Encourage Ewes to Own Their Lambs. Most ewes can be coaxed into owning their lambs. Ewes identify their lambs by smell. Sprinkling the ewe's milk on the lamb will often help. Tying the ewe in the lambing pen a few days so that the lamb may suck is often all that is necessary.

Yearling ewes or ewe lambs having their first lamb are most likely to disown them. For that reason, where a considerable number of ewes carrying their first lamb make up the flock, they should be penned separately and not allowed to lamb in the open with the rest of the flock. When the lambs are born, they should be placed near the ewe's head, where she will lick and clean them. They should then be placed at the teats and the ewe closely watched by the operator until he is sure she will own them.

Feeding and Management of the Breeding Flock • 465

Figure 25-8. The hide of this ewe's dead lamb has been placed over the lamb from another ewe. The job was successful as indicated by the ewe owning the lamb. (Courtesy Kansas State College)

Grafting. Many times a ewe that has lost her lamb may be induced to take one or more lambs from another ewe if the proper procedure is followed. Occasionally, sprinkling the ewe's milk over the lamb will work and should be tried first as it is the easiest. Ewes identify their lambs by smell and this system may be enough. Some ewes, if caught quickly after they have lambed, may be induced to take another lamb by rubbing kerosene or some similar agent over their nostrils. This temporarily disturbs their sense of smell and makes it difficult to detect the difference in lambs. Tying the ewe up in a pen or jail so that she cannot butt the lamb away and keeping her there for a couple of days will often work.

When a ewe has lost her lamb and it is desired to place another on her, the most successful method is to remove the hide of the dead lamb and place it over the new lamb. In removing the hide, cut the front legs off at the knees and slit the hide around the hind legs just below the hocks. Make a slit from hock to hock on the under side of the carcass and through the tailbone so the tail will stay on the hide. Start pulling the hide from rear toward the front, down over the neck and cut it off. The hide is then pulled over the new lamb so its head sticks out the neck hole in the hide, and the front legs are through the leg holes. This will hold the hide on the lamb and no further tying is necessary.

The ewe should be confined to the place where she lambed and the new lamb presented to her tail first as she will then get the odor of her own lamb from the hide.

Raising Orphans. Lambs that are left without a mother where no ewe is available for grafting, will have to be hand-fed if they are to survive. If this is necessary, the lamb should be fed two or three feeds of colostrum or first milk, either from the mother or another ewe. This may be accomplished by milking the ewe and using a bottle to feed the lamb. The milk should be warmed to 98° F. before feeding. Later, cow's milk may be substituted. The secret of using cow's milk is to feed often but only small amounts at a time. For the first day or so, one ounce fed at two-hour intervals is sufficient. Later the amount may be slowly increased and the feeding intervals spread farther apart.

Management of Growing Lambs

Pinning Passages. The first bowel passages of the lambs are sticky and often pin the tail to the bodies, preventing any further excretion. This is called pinning. The tail should be loosened and the excrement cleaned from the lamb.

Castrating. Castrating of the lambs should be done when the lambs are from seven to 14 days old. Lambs to be castrated should be placed in a clean, dry pen where they may be easily caught. Instruments used for the operation and the hands of the operator should be clean and disinfected. The ewe's pen should be clean and freshly bedded, unless they are on clean pasture, so that the lambs will be in a clean place when placed with their mothers after the operation. There are several methods of castrating. Each method has some advantages as well as disadvantages.

Proper Position to Hold the Lamb While Castrating. Holding a lamb in proper position for castrating requires that the holder place the lamb on its rump in a sitting position on the castration table. He then pulls each hind leg forward and upward to a position inside the front leg on the same side. Four fingers should be around the hind leg just above the hock, while the thumb is around the front leg at the knee. Thus he is holding a front and hind leg in each hand. This positions the lamb and renders it nearly motionless, unless the lamb is so large that he is well beyond the age recommended for castration.

Using a Knife. The most common method of castrating lambs is to cut off one-third of the lower end of the scrotum. With the thumb and forefinger of the left hand, force out the testicles by squeezing the base of the scrotum next to the abdomen. Grasp the testicles, either with the teeth or the thumb and crooked forefinger

A

Figure 25-9. (A) Removing a part of the scrotum is the first step in castrating with a knife. Lambs may be held in the position shown or placed rump down on the castrating table. (Courtesy Iowa Sheep Breeders' Assn.) (B) Castrating with a specially designed tool. (left) Cutting off one-third of the scrotum. (center) Note the testicles protruding. (right) Pulling the testicles until the cord breaks. (Courtesy University of Nebraska)

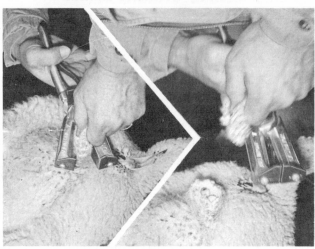

of the right hand, and pull gently outward one at a time, until the cord breaks. There is some aversion to the use of the teeth, but it is the quickest method and where large numbers are to be castrated it will save considerable time. From a sanitation standpoint it is cleaner than grasping with fingers that have become soiled.

A mild disinfectant may be used to wash the wound, but if the operation has been done under sanitary conditions this is usually not necessary. The operation should be done on a clear warm day.

Castrating by removing the testicles is sure and does not require any special equipment. It does, however, create an open wound which may become infected if precautions are not taken to prevent infection. In screw worm infested areas, considerable danger of screw worm infestation exists when animals have open wounds.

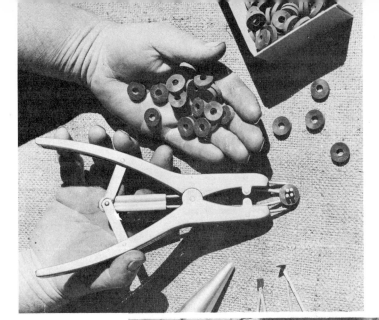

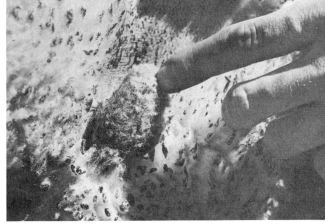

Figure 25-10. Castrating with the elastrator. (above) Rubber bands and elastrator. (below) Rubber bands placed around scrotum. (Courtesy University of Nebraska)

Castrating with Emasculator or Pincers. The emasculator is an instrument used to crush the cord leading to the testicles. The cord is destroyed, leaving the testicle to gradually dry up or wither away. This method does not leave an open wound and is bloodless. While the emasculator or "Burdizzo" gained considerable popularity for a time, careless use of the instrument resulted in so many partly castrated lambs, which become staggy as they grow older, that it has lost much of its former popularity. The operator must be skilled in its use if the operation is to be successful.

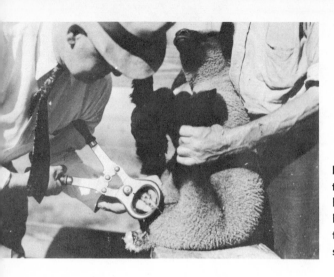

Figure 25-11. Castrating with the emasculator. The cords leading from the testicles are located and crushed. (Courtesy Michigan State University)

Elastrator. The elastrator is an instrument used to spread tight rubber bands which are slipped over the scrotum and released. The bands fit tightly around the cords at the base of the scrotum near the abdomen. The circulation is shut off and the scrotum and testicles gradually dry and drop off.

Docking. Lambs may be docked at the time they are castrated. Castrating should be the first operation followed by docking. Several methods, all of them designed to remove the tail from the body, may be employed in docking lambs. Lambs not docked accumulate a great deal of filth around the tail, which often results in fly strike and maggot infestation.

Docking with a Knife. When a knife is used to dock lambs, locate the joint to be cut by feeling on the under side of the tail, push the skin toward the body so there will be a surplus of skin to cover the stub. After cutting off the tail, pinch the end to prevent excessive bleeding. By twisting the tail a quarter of a turn before cutting, a diagonal cut across the blood vessels is obtained and increases the possibility of the blood clotting quickly.

The use of a knife should be confined to lambs that are not more than a week or ten days old as the older lambs can easily bleed to death. The knife is undesirable when lambs are confined to pens or corrals where the sanitation is not good or when docking is done during fly season. The bleeding makes it difficult to apply a disinfectant. Lambs should not be overheated just prior to docking with a knife as bleeding will be more severe.

Figure 25-12. (left) An undocked lamb. Note the accumulation of filth, a good condition for fly strike. (right) A properly docked lamb. (Courtesy Kansas State College)

Docking with a Hot Iron. While much slower than the knife method, the hot iron is much safer as it not only sterilizes but sears the wound and prevents bleeding. Docking irons may be home-made or purchased from livestock supply houses. Good home-made irons can be shaped from a piece of iron two feet long and the thickness of a heavy car or truck spring leaf. The cutting edge should

Figure 25-13. Docking with a hot iron. (Courtesy Michigan State University)

Feeding and Management of the Breeding Flock • 471

not be knife sharp, but rather blunt so that when heated it will burn through rather than cut through the tail.

Heating the Iron. The iron should not be so hot it will go through the tail so rapidly that the large blood vessel will not be seared or so cold that it slows the cut too much, causing a slow-healing sore. A black heat just turning red, rather than a red heat, is desirable. If bleeding occurs after the docking process, the operator should just touch the main blood vessel with the corner of the iron. By keeping several irons in the fire the process will not be slowed waiting for irons to heat. Electric irons thermostatically controlled are excellent when docking is done where electricity is available.

Even though the hot iron is used, it is good practice to disinfect the stub with a swab soaked in iodine.

Rubber Band Method of Docking. The use of rubber bands fitted around the tail with the elastrator is a bloodless method of docking. The principle is the same as that for castrating in that the circulation is prevented and the tail drops off. This method is objected to by many as the tail is slow in coming off. It putrifies and yet may be held by the tail bone, creating a condition favorable to fly strike.

Docking with the Emasculator. The emasculator is sometimes used for docking. The tail of very young lambs may be clamped in the emasculator and pulled off, but older lambs usually require the use of knife to sever the tail just outside the jaws of the emasculator. The pressure tends to squeeze the main artery and prevent bleeding.

The Point where the Tail Should Be Removed. Ewe lambs that are good prospects to become replacements in the breeding flock based on the breeding, quality, and records of their ancestry should have the tail removed about two inches from the body. Wethers and ewe lambs to be sold may have their tails cut longer for easier identification at market time.

Holding the Lamb for Docking. The lamb's rump should be resting on a block of wood, or bench of convenient height for the operator. The lamb should be held in much the same position as for castrating with the tail resting topside down of the board.

Marking. Marking of the lambs for identification is an important sheep management practice. Purebred lambs are marked so that proper identification as to their sires and dams might be made for pedigrees. Range sheepmen mark their lambs so that if one owner's

Figure 25-14. Paint brands will identify the ewe and her lamb. (Courtesy University of Wyoming)

sheep become mixed with another they can be sorted out and separated. Such mixing of bands happens frequently when grazing is done on an unfenced range.

If ewe lambs are marked differently from the wethers they may be more easily sorted out and separated as they are run through a dodge chute. Since ewe lambs are often held back as replacements in the breeding flock, or sold separately from the wethers, quick identification provided by a good marking system saves time and labor. Well marked lambs are a precaution against thieves, as the lambs may be more easily traced.

Marking may be done at the same time the lambs are docked and castrated.

Paint Brands. Paint brands are quickly applied and are quite reliable. However, they may wear off to the point where they are difficult to see. Ordinary lead-base paints should not be used as they will not come out with normal wool-scouring and may lower the market value of the fleece.

Commercial branding fluids that will remain on the sheep for a year, and may be removed from the fleece in the regular scouring process, are now available.

Metal Tags. Purebred sheepmen use metal ear tags as a means of identification. Metal tags with any combination of letters and numbers may be purchased. Two tags, one in each ear, may be used. One tag carries the individual number and the other the flock number. This system provides not only owner identification but identifies the lamb with its sire and dam. The metal ear tag marking system is too slow and costly for use in large commercial flocks.

Ear Notches. For commercial flock identification ear notching provides a quick means of marking and one that is easily recognized. It does disfigure the ears to some extent and, for that reason, is seldom used by purebred breeders.

Ear notching may be done with a knife or a commercial ear notcher designed to cut a V or a U notch.

Shearing. Shearing is more than just removing the wool from the sheep. A poor job lowers the quality and therefore the market value of the wool.

Shear in a Clean Place. Foreign materials such as dung, straw, water, and sand or soil should not be allowed to get mixed with the fleece. A wooden shearing floor, canvas, or old rug may be used to shear sheep on and to help keep the fleece clean. The shearing floor should not be close enough to the bedding or storage area to permit chaff to be carried by the sheep or to be blown out to the shearing floor. Straw and other vegetable materials are much more difficult to clean from the fleece than sand or other soil particles. Hard bare ground is a better place to shear than a floor where straw and chaff accumulates.

Holding pens, where sheep are crowded into compact groups to await shearing, become saturated with droppings and urine. When this material becomes mixed with the fleece the quality and value drops considerably. Providing elevated slatted floors in the holding pens will allow the manure to drop through and will keep the fleeces free of such material.

When to Shear. The schedule will vary with various operators; therefore, the shearing time will not always be the same. Whenever possible, shearing should not be done until there have been enough warm days to bring out the grease in the fleeces. Well-greased fibers are stronger. The natural oil in the fleece lubricates the shears and they cut more easily and more uniformly. Sheep shearers dislike shearing sheep with dry fleeces.

If the grease is out sufficiently, ewes should be shorn before they go on pasture. Pasture has a loosening effect on the bowels and more stained wool will result when sheep are shorn after they have been turned on the pasture. Proper tagging before the ewes are turned on the pasture will reduce the amount of damaged wool.

Figure 25-15. Shearing should be done in a clean place. (Courtesy Sunbeam Corporation)

When the wool is left on too late in the year, losses from natural shedding will reduce the weight of the fleece, and when the weather becomes warm, ewes in fleece suffer a great deal of discomfort.

Lambs not ready for market, or those intended as replacements to the breeding flock, should be shorn during July or August. Shorn lambs feed better, are more comfortable, and will gain more quickly during warm weather if the fleece is removed. Lambs intended for the early market should be left in fleece bcause of the added market value of the pelt.

Lambs that are to be marketed for slaughter and are in good condition at shearing time may grow a No. 1 fleece if shorn with handpieces with high runner combs. The fleece is not removed as close to the body and the length of time required to grow a fleece is reduced. Lambs on good ration will grow a No. 1 pelt in 60 days when shorn close.

Removing the Fleece. Three fundamental principles should be kept in mind when removing the fleece from a sheep. They are: (1) Remove it in one piece; never break or tear the fleece apart. Shear close to the animal's body except in case of fattening lambs as previously mentioned. (2) Avoid second cuts. Second cuts simply add short length fibers to the fleece which lowers the value. Never attempt to smooth up the job by going over parts of the animal a second time. (3) Remove all dung locks and grease tags first and keep the fleece free of other foreign materials.

Feeding and Management of the Breeding Flock • 475

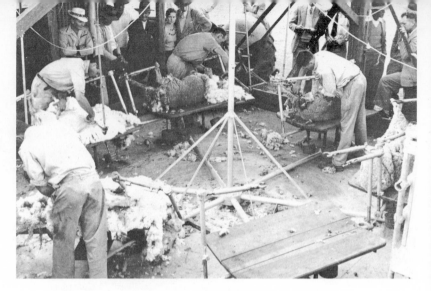

Figure 25-16. The assembly line type of shearing using the Barthwick Tables. (Courtesy Australian *Queensland Country Life*)

It is extremely difficult to describe how to shear sheep in writing or in words. Observing or working with an experienced shearer is the best way to learn.

Australian Shearing Table. An Australian invention known as the Barthwick power-driven shearing table which works on the assembly-line principle is expected to speed-up the process of shearing sheep. The sheep walk up a ramp and are held in a specially designed loading pen until the rotary table comes around for loading. The loader is tilted by pulling a string and the sheep is on its back on the table where the operator fastens its leg into specially designed holders. The process of shearing is accomplished without the operator having to hold the sheep.

Sacking the Fleece for Market. A properly prepared fleece will enchance its market value. Lamb's wool, black wool or fleeces containing black fibers, buck wool, and tags of all sorts should be packed separately.

Every fleece will contain several different kinds of wool referred to in the trade as *sorts*.

There may be 15 or more sorts in a single fleece depending upon the breeding of the sheep. Every fleece will contain the following sorts: (1) top knot, (2) head and neck wool, (3) shoulder, back and side wool, (4) leg wool, (5) belly wool, (6) breech wool, and

(7) tags. The shoulders, back, and side wool make up about three-fourths of the fleece and is the most valuable. The fleece should be tied so that the most valuable wool is on the outside.

Tying the Fleece. After the fleece is removed, spread it out flesh side down. Place the belly wool in the center. Fold in each side and roll the fleece from both the head and breech ends. The shoulder and side wool thus will be exposed.

A fleece prepared in this manner may be spread out at the mill and sorted into the portions used for different yarns.

The fleece should be tied with a paper twine. Never use a sisal or hemp twine, as the fibers from the twine become mixed with the wool fiber and are difficult to separate. Go around the fleece once with the paper twine, cross, and go around once at right angles to the first, and tie. The fleeces should not be rolled or tied too tightly as springy fleeces are preferred.

Figure 25-17. A fleece being tied properly. (Courtesy Kansas State College)

Packing the Fleece. Wool may be packed in bags ranging from six to seven feet in length. Burlap or commercial waterproof bags should be selected. The seams should be turned to the outside so the bags may be more easily opened for display at the warehouse. If tags are stuffed into the corners of the bag and tied off, it will form handles that will make handling the filled bags easier.

The sacking process is simplified if a sacking stand is used. The sacking stand holds the bag up and open so the fleeces may be properly packed.

Storage of the Packed Bags. The bag should not touch the ground after removing it from the sacking frame. Wool picks up a coating of dirt when the bags are rolled on the ground which may lower its market value. The wool must be stored in a dry, clean place. Moisture will cause staining and mildew. Truck or freight cars should be thoroughly swept and cleaned before loading the wool. Wool loaded into open trucks should be covered with a tarpaulin to protect the fleeces from dirt and moisture.

Records and Record Keeping

What the Record Should Reveal. Good records should identify the offspring with the parents. They should also give the birth date, sex, and the final disposal of the individual. Most important, in selection for breeding flock replacement, or culling from the flock, are growth rates, fleece weight, quality, and prolificacy. This information together with desirable conformation is the basis upon which selection for flock improvement should be made.

On pages 479 and 480 are examples of record forms which will give the needed information for wise selection and culling.

Catching Sheep. The proper method of catching sheep is to grab them under the chin with one hand and the rear flank with the other. Small sheep can usually be stopped by holding them under the chin and forcing the head upward. It will be necessary to hold large animals by the rear flank as well as the chin.

Under no circumstance should sheep ever be caught by the wool. Grabbing them by the wool, especially on the back, opens the fleece so that rain may penetrate down to the skin. Grabbing the wool also damages the fleece, lowering the market value.

Shelters and Equipment for Sheep

Sheep do not require elaborate or expensive equipment. Many sheep flocks both large and small are maintained with little or no shelter even in the colder regions of the United States. However, new-born lambs must be protected against inclement weather and older sheep must be protected from cold, wet weather immediately after shearing.

Sheep Shelters. The single-story buildings of pole construction, which are relatively cheap to build and maintain, and are

Lamb No.	Date of Birth	Sex (M or F)	Birth Wt. (Lb) (Optional)	Sire No.	Date and Age when Weighed	Wt.	Wt. Adj. to 120 Days of Age	Staple Length	Staple Length Adj. to 120 Days of Age	Lamb Index	Notes About Lamb: (Born Dead, Date and Reason for Disposal, etc.)

Source: University of Wisconsin, Madison, Wisconsin, Extension Service Circular 470, 1953.

OWNER _____

BREED (S) _____

Reg. P.B. _____ P.B. _____

Grade _____ XB

Ewe's Record as Lamb

Date of birth _____

Birth weight (lb) _____

Type of birth   S( )   Tw( )   Tr( )

Sire No. & Breed _____

Dam No. & Breed _____

Adj. wt. at 4 mos. (lb) _____

Adj. staple length (cm) _____

Index as lamb _____

ADDRESS _____

EWE NO. _____

COUNTY _____

Ewe's Fleece Record

Date	Wt. (lb)	Grade	Ewe Index	Notes about ewe: (Trouble at Lambing, Wouldn't Own Lambs, etc.)

Source: University of Wisconsin, Madison, Wisconsin, Extension Service Circular 470, 1953.

480

flexible in usage, are becoming popular among sheepmen. When fitted with large doors on the side opposite the prevailing cold winds (which is the south side in most of the United States) it may be either made tight for lambing or left as an open shed to give protection to breeding sheep or feeder lambs. Many such sheds are used as open shelters for breeding or feeder sheep until lambing time. The shelter is then fitted with lambing pens and the doors closed, and thus it is converted into a lambing shed.

Feeding Equipment. Feeding equipment varies with the kind of feed being fed.

Chopped hay, or stacked long hay, may be self-fed; chopped self-feeding hay feeders may be constructed, or a portable manger may be built along one end of a loose haystack. As the sheep eat into the hay the manger is moved closer to the stack.

Grain feed bunks may be of two different types, depending upon which will better fit the sheep program. Stationary feed bunks may be constructed along one side of the lot. This type of feed bunk is best adapted to a lamb feeding enterprise where the lambs are confined to a feed yard.

Plans for several types of movable feed bunks are available. The important features of good feed bunks are ease of cleaning, ease of access, and durability.

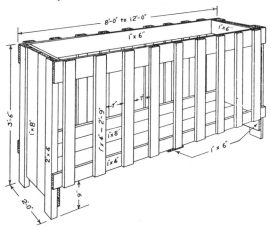

Figure 25-18A. Combination hay and grain racks are convenient equipment for small flocks. This straight-sided rack will keep fleeces fairly free from chaff, except for the head and neck wool. Chaffy necks can be easily separated at shearing time.

Feeding and Management of the Breeding Flock • 481

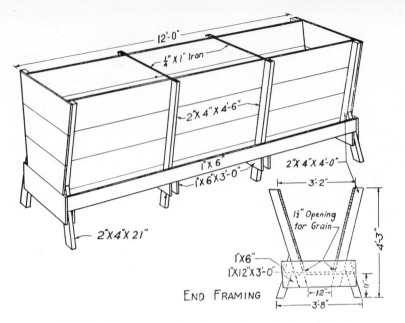

END FRAMING

Figure 25-18B. Where many lambs are being fed, self-feeding may be desirable, using ground hay and grain as the ration. An adjustable feeder permitting feeding down of the feed is necessary. This feeder is cheap and easy to construct. With hand feeding, 12 inches of space is needed for each lamb; with self-feeding, 12 inches for three lambs. Self-feeders need attention several times a day to keep the feed poked down so that it is always available.

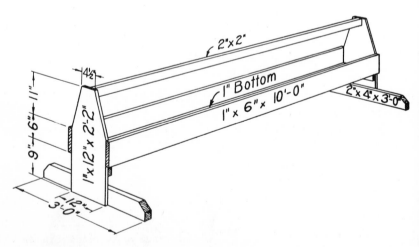

Figure 25-18C. A single nonreversible trough is shown for cheaper construction. It is not as satisfactory from a cleaning standpoint as the reversible troughs.

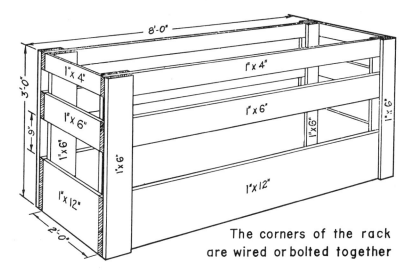

The corners of the rack
are wired or bolted together

Figure 25-18D. The knock-down or panel feed rack is an economical piece of equipment for feeding roughage to fattening lambs. These racks can be set up as bunks, as shown in the drawing, or arranged as fences with the hay fed on the far side, the sheep feeding through the fence. They can be used for a breeding flock by placing around a haystack with the hay being fed against the panels on the inside. Locating the stack away from the shed forces the ewes to exercise.

A salt and phenothiazine feeder which provides the sheep with free access to salt and phenothiazine and which will keep the material protected from the rain and snow is an important part of the feeding equipment. Phenothiazine keeps the flock worm-free.

Panels. A number of hinged panels, important for making temporary lambing jails or otherwise confining sheep that may need special attention, are handy equipment.

Loading Chutes. Loading chutes may be of a permanent or movable type. When sheep that are to be moved can easily be confined to a yard, the permanent loading chute works very well. However, if they are loaded from the pasture where they may be confined in a temporary corral, a movable type loading chute is necessary.

Cutting Chute. Every sheepman needs a sorting device as he must sort his sheep one or more times a year. A properly constructed cutting chute with a dodge gate that will swing from one side to the other permits him to make his sorts with comparative ease.

Figure 25-19. A cutting chute used for separating one or more animals from the flock, or for marking and checking. (Courtesy Kansas State College)

A good cutting chute may be constructed by using solid panel sides, 30 inches high, 12 inches apart at the bottom and slanting so they are 18 inches apart at the top. The flare top makes it possible to sort both ewes and lambs in the same chute. The length may range from 12 to 14 feet.

The dodge gate should swing from one side to the other to permit cutting into different pens.

Summary

Flushing is the term applied to the procedure of putting ewes in a rapid gaining condition just prior to breeding. Flushing helps to bring the ewes into heat and results in a more uniform lamb crop and a higher percentage of lambs.

Overfat ewes should be placed on a sparse pasture and given plenty of exercise in order to gradually reduce them in flesh prior to flushing. Breeding overfat ewes results in a smaller lamb crop.

The first half of gestation is the less critical, and little or no grain need to be provided if plenty of good to fair quality roughages are available. Starting the eleventh week of gestation, grain or molasses should be included in the ration. From one-fourth to three-fourths pound of grain or the equivalent in molasses should be added to the daily feed.

Minerals are essential and can best be supplied by using a mineral mixture recommended for the area.

Vitamins A, D, and E should be provided. Other vitamins are manufactured in the digestive system of ruminants and need not be supplied except in the case of young animals before rumination has started.

The ewe suckling lambs needs more total feed and slightly more protein than the pregnant ewe. Good pastures will meet the nutritional requirements of ewes suckling lambs. However, ewes in dry lots need good quality roughages and grain to maintain milk flow and grow out lambs economically. Ewes from weaning to flushing can make very good use of poor quality pasture and roughages. This is the least critical time in the production cycle.

The breeding ram should not be too fat at breeding time. During the breeding season he will need about one pound of grain daily plus a full feed of good forage when confined to a dry lot. Good pasture will meet the nutritional needs of the ram.

Heat periods in ewes occur every 13 to 19 days and average 16½ days during the breeding season. Ewes remain in heat from three to 73 hours. Three-fourths of the ewes will stay in heat from 21 to 39 hours. Except for a few breeds, ewes do not come in heat regularly throughout the year, but are seasonal in this respect. Breeds differ as to their mating season. Mixed breeds of sheep running in one band are not likely to have a uniform lamb-drop.

The gestation period of ewes will range from 144 to 152 days.

Ewes should be flushed, tagged, and eyed before breeding.

Ringing or shearing the ram, in addition to tagging and eyeing, is important before the start of the breeding season. Both ewes and rams should have their feet checked and trimmed if necessary.

Marking the ram either by breast paint or a marking harness helps the sheepman to determine the fertility of the rams, make up his drop-bands and determine ewe breeding dates.

Ram lambs, nine to ten months old and well grown out, may be used to breed ten to 12 ewes. Rams over five years of age should be checked carefully for fertility. Yearling and up to five-year-old rams may breed up to 45 ewes per season. Whenever it is practical supplemental feeding of the ram during the breeding season is recommended.

The generally accepted age for breeding ewes the first time is when they are yearlings. However, under proper conditions ewe lamb᷍ may be bred.

The ram should not be allowed to run with the flock for more than eight weeks during the mating season if a uniform lamb-drop is desired.

Exercise, shade, and protection from other livestock and predatory animals are the most important aspects of bred ewe management other than proper feeding.

Careful observation and management during the lambing season will save many lambs. Dividing the flock into drop-bands or separating ewes about to lamb, either by tagging or by the use of the marking system, is the first step. Placing the ewes in jails and giving them protection from inclement weather will prevent chilling of the lambs and decrease the number of disowned lambs. Under extreme cold weather conditions lamb brooders are recommended. Tagging the ewes and clipping the wool away from around the teats improves sanitation and enables the lambs to find the teats more quickly.

Ewes that cannot expel their lambs without help will be lost unless the shepherd gives them assistance.

After lambing, the shepherd should be sure the ewe cleans properly and that her bowels are in good condition. He should also check for possible udder infection.

Chilled lambs may be revived by emerging in warm water. They should get some warm milk as quickly as possible.

Weak lambs will need assistance in getting milk. Lambs from dry ewes or ewes that do not produce enough milk for their lambs will need to be put onto other ewes or be hand-fed. Succulent feeds will help to bring ewes to their milk. Lambs should be left with the ewes and given supplemental feed until the ewes have had plenty of time to come to their milk.

Ewes that disown their lambs may be encouraged to own their lambs by sprinkling the ewe's milk on the lamb or by tying the ewe in the lambing pen for a few days.

Lambs should be watched the first few days for pinning passages. If they occur loosen the tail and clean the lamb.

Ewes that have lost their lambs may be induced to take that of another by grafting the skin of the dead lamb over the lamb that is to take its place. Orphaned lambs may be raised on cow's milk. Success depends upon proper amounts, frequency of feeding, sanitation, and temperature of the milk.

Castrating may be done with a knife, emasculator, or elastrator. The knife is the most popular and is sure. Lambs should be castrated when they are from seven to 14 days of age.

Docking may be done at the time lambs are castrated. One may use a knife, heated docking iron, rubber bands or the emasculator. The heated iron is the best from a sanitation standpoint and when properly used will prevent bleeding.

Marking for identification is important to good management and the selection of breeding stock. There are several methods and combinations that may be used. Paint brands, ear tags, and ear notches are the commonly used methods.

The essentials of a good shearing job is clean wool, allowing the grease to come out before shearing, removing the fleece in one piece, and avoiding second cuts.

The Australian shearing table is new and is expected to speed up the process of shearing where large numbers are involved.

Proper sacking of the fleeces is the final step in preparing the wool for market. This requires keeping lambs' wool, black wool or fleeces containing black fibers, buck wool, and tags separate. Fleeces should be spread flesh side down, the edges turned in and rolled from both the head and tail end into a fluffy reasonably loose bundle and tied each way with a paper twine. Burlap bags or commercial waterproof bags with the corners tied off and seams to the outside should be placed on a sacking stand and the wool packed in layers. Either a round or a flat pack may be made.

Good records will reveal the following information: date of birth, sex, disposal, growth rates, fleece quality and weight, and prolificacy.

Sheep will need shelters for lambing in cold weather or for protection if shorn during inclement weather. Expensive or elaborate shelters are not necessary.

Hay racks and feed bunks are needed equipment in many sheep enterprises, especially under lamb feeding set-ups or where the breeding flock is fed hay or grain in lots.

Salt and phenothiazine feeders are essential.

Panels for making temporary jails, loading chutes, and culling chutes should be owned or available to the sheepman.

• *Questions*

1. What are the periods in the productive cycle of the ewe?
2. Discuss a feeding program for each of these periods.
3. What are the common roughages, grains, and protein supplements commonly fed to sheep?
4. What are the primary dangers of keeping ewes on too low a nutritional plain? Discuss.
5. Give some good rations using feeds common in your locality for ewes in various stages of pregnancy.
6. Discuss feeding the breeding ram.
7. Discuss the length and frequency of heat periods.
8. Discuss the mating seasons, breed differences in mating seasons, and how it affects the lamb-drop.
9. What is the average length of the gestation period in sheep?
10. Explain the steps in preparing the ewes for breeding.
11. How would you prepare the ram for breeding?
12. Explain how ram marking is done for breeding purposes.
13. Why is ram marking at breeding time essential to good management?
14. Discuss the ewe-ram ratio under various breeding conditions.
15. Discuss ram feeding and management during the breeding season.
16. At what age should ewes be bred? Discuss breeding ewe lambs.
17. How long should the rams be allowed to run with the flock?
18. What ewes would you cull from the flock? Why?
19. Discuss the essentials of good ewe management during the gestation period.
20. How would you make up your drop-bands?
21. Explain how you would handle ewes at lambing time under various weather conditions.
22. Discuss the use of lambing jails and brooders.
23. How would you prepare the ewe for lambing?
24. What are some abnormal positions of an unborn lamb that will need to be corrected before delivery is possible?
25. How would you correct these positions?
26. How would you care for the ewe immediately after lambing?
27. Discuss the methods of reviving chilled lambs.

28. How would you handle the lambs and ewes when the ewes fail to come to their milk?
29. How may ewes be encouraged to own their lambs?
30. What are pinning passages? How would you correct this condition?
31. Discuss grafting lambs on a ewe that is not their mother.
32. Give a plan for raising orphaned lambs.
33. Discuss the method of holding lambs for castration.
34. Explain the various methods of castration and give the advantages and disadvantages of each.
35. When should lambs be docked? Explain the methods used.
36. Why should a marking system be used? Discuss methods of marking.
37. Discuss the proper shearing and handling of the fleeces.
38. Why are records important to good management? What is included in a good record?
39. What type of shelters would be most practical on your farm or ranch? Why?
40. Discuss the types of feeding equipment that is most practical in your community.
41. What other kinds of equipment should sheepmen in your community have available?

● *References*

Alexander, M. A., W. W. Derrick, and D. C. Fouts, *Farm Sheep Facts,* Extension Service Bulletin E. C. 255, University of Nebraska, Lincoln, Nebraska.

Blakeslee, L. H., H. A. Henneman, R. H. Nelson, *A Comparison of Hay, Hay-Crop Silage and Corn Silage for Ewes during Gestation,* Quarterly Bulletin, Vol. 37, No. 1, Michigan Agricultural Experiment Station, Michigan State College, East Lansing, Michigan, August 1954.

Gray, James A., *Preparing Wool for Market,* Extension Service Bulletin 237, Texas A. & M. College, College Station, Texas.

Magee, W. T., W. T. Hardy, J. H. Jones, J. C. Miller, *Emergency Roughages for Breeding Ewes,* Progress Report 1725, Texas Agricultural Experiment Station, Texas A. & M. College, College Station, Texas, 1954.

Mason, R. W., P. O. Stratton, N. W. Hilston, *Utilization of Non-Protein Nitrogen by Pregnant Ewes,* Mimeograph Circular 35, University of Wyoming, Agricultural Experiment Station, Laramie, Wyoming. 1953.

Mason, R. W., P. O. Stratton, N. W. Hilston, Irene Payne, L. C. Parker, J. O. Tucker, *Animal Tallow as Part of the Wintering Ration for Pregnant Yearling Ewes,* Mimeograph Circular 52, University of Wyoming Agricultural Experiment Station, Laramie, Wyoming, 1955.

Perry, T. W., W. M. Beeson, P. J. Reynolds, Claude Harper, *Supplementing Grass Silage for Pregnant Ewes in Drylot,* Mimeo. A H 140, Purdue University, Agricultural Experiment Station, Lafayette, Indiana, 1955.

Van Horn, J. L., *Milk Production of Ewes,* Research Seminar, Animal Industry, Range Management, and Wool Laboratory, Montana Agricultural Experiment Station, Bozeman, Montana, 1954.

Van Horn, J. L., Wm. H. Burkett, Gene F. Payne, Curtis G. Hughes, Fred S. Willson, *Nutritional Requirements of Ewes Wintered under Range Conditions,* Progress Report, Animal Industry, Range Management and Wool Laboratory, Montana Agricultural Experiment Station, Bozeman, Montana, 1950.

Wool Preparation and Marketing, Agricultural Experiment Station Bulletin 316, University of Wyoming, Laramie, Wyoming.

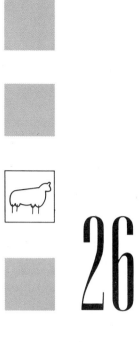

Feeding Lambs

Lamb production methods necessarily have to vary considerably to fit various feed, economic, and climatic conditions.

Producing Fat Lambs on Milk and Grass

Lands capable of producing good grass, but otherwise unfit for tillable crops, may be profitably used for grass fat lamb production. This method, producing fat lambs on grass and milk from ewes, is used throughout the United States and is the most common method in the better range areas. The milk production of the ewe largely determines how quickly the lambs will develop.

Lambs require short, tender, fresh green pasture made up of palatable plants. The grass should be abundant, allowing them to get a fill with a minimum of travel.

Creep Feeding. Creep feeding lambs is accomplished by providing an enclosure that will permit the lambs to enter but will exclude the ewes. Feed is put in the enclosure where it will be available to the lambs. Many types of creeps have been constructed and found to work successfully.

491

Figure 26-1. (above) A creep constructed with panels and rollers. (Courtesy Iowa Sheep Breeders' Assn.)

Figure 26-2. (left) An easily constructed creep. (Courtesy University of Nebraska)

Why Creep Feed? Creep feeding of lambs has several advantages. The most important are: (1) it will speed the growth and fattening rate of lambs; (2) ewes, especially those under range conditions, will not suckle down as thin and will maintain a milk flow over a longer period of time; (3) creep feeding tends to even up twin lambs and single lambs in size (Twin lambs are smaller at birth and usually get less milk per lamb than singles. Creep feeding helps to make up for this difference.); (4) lambs will be ready for an earlier market which often has a price advantage; (5) creep feeding enables many sheepmen to produce fat lambs on range that is too poor to produce anything more than feeder lambs unless extra feed is provided; (6) creep feeding prevents such close grazing as to be harmful to the range.

When to Start Lambs on the Creep. If lambs are to be creep fed on the range, they should be started when they average about three weeks of age. If there is too long a spread in the dropping period, the flock should be separated into bands according to the age of the lambs. Lambs at three weeks of age have not developed a taste for grain to the extent that an over-eating danger exists. Older lambs may over-eat, or they may have developed a taste for grass to the extent that it will be difficult to get them started on grains.

Under farm flock conditions, especially when lambs are born a month or more before the pasture season, they should be started on creeps as soon as they begin to nibble at feed. Lambs will usually start to eat when about ten days old.

How to Start Lambs on the Creep. When lambs are started on the creep, a sprinkle of grain may be placed in the troughs or feed bunks and left for the day. Each day it should be changed and fresh grain put in the creep. When the lambs have learned to eat the feed, they should be given the amount they will clean up in 20 to 30 minutes.

Lambs will eat an average of about one-fourth pound of grain per head daily during the creep feeding period. Lambs dropped in late winter or early spring prior to the grass season will need to have both hay and grain fed in the creep. Choice hay, such as high-quality legumes, should be selected for the lambs. The best hay should be held in reserve for creep fed lambs.

Some good mixed creep rations for lambs are:

(1) 300 pounds corn
    300 pounds oats
    100 pounds bran
    100 pounds linseed, soybean, or cottonseed oil meal

(2) 350 pounds sorghum grains
    300 pounds barley or wheat
    150 pounds soybean oil meal

(3) 60 pounds corn
    20 pounds oats
    20 pounds soybean oil meal

When a mixed ration is fed, grinding will be necessary for proper mixing and blending of the ration.

Production of Hothouse Lambs

Hothouse Lambs. Hothouse lambs are those that are dropped in the fall or early winter, and finished for market when from six

Figure 26-3. Hothouse lambs.
(Courtesy Cornell University)

to 12 weeks old and weighing from 30 to 60 pounds. They should be marketed during the period from Christmas to Easter to bring a premium price. Boston and New York furnish the principal markets for hothouse lambs.

Dorset, Rambouillet, Merino, or Tunis ewes are selected to produce hothouse lambs since they will breed at almost any season and are excellent milkers. Southdown rams, because of their early maturity and high quality carcasses, are used on these ewes. These crossbred lambs fatten at a very early age when properly handled.

High quality feeds for both the ewes and lambs are essential for hothouse lamb production. A large milk flow by the ewes is a must, and this requires liberal feeding of good forage, plus from one to two pounds of grain daily during the suckling period.

Feeding Replacement Ewe Lambs

Ewe lambs selected for replacement ewes in the breeding flock should be fed for maximum growth. When good pastures and high quality forages are available, grains are not essential to the growing out of ewe lambs. The best pastures and forage should be conserved for the replacement ewes. If the quality of the pasture or forage is not high, the supplemental feeding of grain is recommended.

Fattening Lambs

Lamb fattening is an enterprise usually carried out by a farmer in the grain-producing area or by large, commercial lamb feeders.

The majority of lamb feeders purchase lambs from the range. Most feeder lambs come from the range where the breeds used are of the large type. Sixty-pound lambs are generally considered a good weight. When a 60-pound lamb is fed during the average feeding period of 90 to 100 days, he should finish at 90 to 100 pounds, which is a very acceptable market weight. The lamb feeder makes his profit from the margin, gain, and wool clip. However, a fourth source of profit, manure value, should be considered.

Methods of Fattening Feeder Lambs. Feeder lambs are generally fattened in dry lot on grains and preserved forages. However, they may be finished on pasture without the use of grains.

Dry-Lot Feeding. Dry-lot feeding consists of confining the lambs in a lot devoid of green feed and using a combination of the various cured forage feeds, grains, and protein supplements to bring the lambs up to the desired weight and finish.

Pasture Fattening. When there is plenty of high-quality pasture available, lambs may be finished on pasture without grains. This method is common in the Southwest, where wheat pastures may be used. Lambs, or more generally yearlings, are brought in off the range and turned onto the wheat field. Pasture fattening may be speeded up by supplementing the pasture with grains.

Figure 26-4. These lambs are being fattened on grass. (Courtesy Rath Packing Company)

Roughages for Fattening Lambs. Lamb feeds are many and varied. The rations used depend upon cost and availability of feeds.

Roughages should make up a large part of the lamb ration. They are economical, and when properly fed, decrease the cost of gain.

High-quality legume hay is recognized as the best roughage from a nutritional standpoint. It is high in protein, minerals, and vitamins. Alfalfa, the clovers, lespedeza, soybeans, and cowpeas are all common legumes used for hay.

Many of the grasses, such as brome, fescue, orchard grass, and western native grasses, are excellent roughages but low in protein, vitamins, and minerals compared to legumes.

Chopped corn or grain sorghums stover, when properly supplemented, will produce substantial gains on fattening lambs. They must be supplemented with some high quality forage, such as alfalfa hay or a high-quality legume silage, to make up for the low-protein and vitamin content of these low-quality forages.

Alfalfa, brome grass, oats, and other legumes, or small grain crops all make good silage for lambs. These crops all vary considerably in their nutrient content. Silage made from legumes will contain more protein than that made from grasses.

Corn and the sorghums make excellent silage. The silage from these crops will be lower in protein than legume, or legume and grass mixed silage, but higher in carbohydrates.

Grains and Grain Substitutes for Fattening Lambs. The grains are the most important concentrates used for fattening lambs.

Corn is the standard fattening grain, and all other grains or grain substitutes are compared to corn in determining their value. When legume hay is fed, lambs will make very satisfactory gains on legume hay and corn as the entire ration.

Barley may be substituted for corn. Barley has about 87 per cent of the value of corn for lamb feed.

Wheat is a very satisfactory feed, equal to corn for fattening lambs, if fed in a mixture with other grains. When fed alone, it is inferior to either corn or barley, having a value of about 83 per cent that of corn.

Oats are very satisfactory for starting lambs on feed. They are more bulky than other grains and are less likely to throw lambs off feed. However, when oats are continued as the only grain in the ration, they have a value of about 80 per cent that of corn.

Rye has produced results about equal to barley in feeding tests for fattening lambs. However, a mixture of rye with corn or barley is probably better than rye alone.

Grain sorghums are about equal to corn for fattening lambs. There seems to be little difference in the feeding value of the various varieties of grain sorghums.

Recent Texas experiments show that animal fat may be used successfully up to 10 per cent of the entire ration for fattening lambs. The fats must be stabilized to prevent rancidity.

Molasses is well liked by lambs and is often used as a part of the fattening ration. It should not be used to replace grain entirely but has its highest value when fed at the rate of from one-third to three-fourths pound per head daily. Molasses is very palatable and the increased rate of gain when molasses is fed may be due to the greater feed consumption of the lambs. Molasses has very little protein and is very deficient in vitamin A and D.

Proteins and Protein Substitutes for Fattening Lambs. When a high protein roughage, such as good legume hay or legume silage, is fed as the principal roughage, protein concentrates are not essential for fattening lambs. Feeding trials have shown somewhat higher gains when protein supplements are fed to lambs receiving high-protein roughages, but the extra cost in some cases offsets the value of the increasing gains. A recent Iowa trial showed that lambs had a faster gain, a higher degree of finish, and sold higher on the market, when a protein supplement was fed with corn and alfalfa. When low-protein roughages are used, the feeding of protein supplements will be profitable. There are a large number of protein concentrates that may be successfully used in lamb feeding.

Soybean oil meal is equal to or higher in protein per cent than other protein concentrates.

Linseed oil meal has long been a favorite source of protein among lamb feeders, but it is being used less extensively now than in former years because of the greater availability of other protein supplements.

Cottonseed meal is a widely used protein supplement. It is especially popular as a cheap source of protein among sheepmen in the Cotton Belt.

Dehydrated alfalfa meal or pellets will range from 17 to 20 per cent protein and therefore closely approach what we may term a protein concentrate. Dehydrated alfalfa may be used to replace all or a part of the protein in lamb fattening rations. It is also rich in carotene (vitamin A) and several essential minerals.

Peanut oil meal is about equal to cottonseed meal, soybean and linseed oil meals for fattening lambs.

Soybeans provide a good source of protein but the price is generally too high to make them an economical feed.

Corn gluten feed and meal give fairly good results when fed as the only protein to fattening lambs.

Urea, a nitrogen compound, may be used as a partial protein replacer in the rations of fattening lambs. The rules for feeding urea to fattening lambs are the same as for cattle.

TABLE 48

COMPARATIVE FEED VALUE ON A PER-POUND BASIS OF SOME OF THE
COMMONLY USED PROTEIN CONCENTRATES FOR FATTENING LAMBS

Feed	Value Compared to Soybean Oil Meal
Soybean oil meal	100
Linseed oil meal	100
Cottonseed meal	100
Peanut oil meal	100
Dehydrated alfalfa	70
Corn gluten feed	65-70
Corn gluten meal	95
Soybeans	95

Mixed Supplements. There are a variety of mixed supplements designed for various types of feeding programs. Where good-quality forage is used as the primary roughage, any of the protein feeds that have been discussed will prove satisfactory. When low quality roughages are used, a protein supplement reinforced with additional vitamins and minerals is recommended. If urea is to be used to replace part of the protein in a ration, it is usually fed in a mixed supplement. Following are some mixed supplements that are especially designed for lamb feeding with average to poor forage.

1. 853 pounds linseed oil meal
   900 pounds soybean oil meal
   100 pounds urea
   15 pounds trace mineral mixture for ruminants

100 pounds feeding bone meal
31 pounds sodium sulphate
1 pound of irradiated yeast—9F

2. 1344 pounds linseed oil meal
500 pounds soybean oil meal
150 pounds feeding bone meal
5 pounds trace mineral mixture for ruminants
1 pound irradiated 9F yeast

Minerals. When high-quality legume roughages make up the major part of the forage fed to lambs, nothing more than salt and a mineral mixture fed free choice will be necessary to insure adequate minerals. However, when the forage contains no or only a small amount of legumes, a mixed supplement containing minerals would be advisable. Salt should also be fed free choice.

Antibiotics. Several feeding trials using antibiotics, mostly aureomycin, have been conducted. The results of these trials have varied considerably but a large number have shown a generally healthier condition of the lambs, greater gains, a reduction in the incidence of overeating disease, and some savings in feed when ten milligrams of aureomycin chlortetracycline was fed per lamb daily.

Hormones. The feeding of hormones, or implanting them in pellet form under the skin, has given increased gains ranging up to 25 per cent and reduced feed per 100 pounds of gain up to 22 per cent. However, various complications such as lower carcass quality, prolapse of the rectum, and blockage of the urinary tract have been reported from the use of hormones.

Stilbestrol, progesterone, estradial testosterone, and androgen are among the hormone or hormone-like substances that have been used in feeding trials. More research will have to be done before a recommendation as to their value can be made.

Preparation of Feed for Lambs. *Grinding.* Sheepmen are quite well agreed that grinding grain is undesirable, except when a complete mixed ration is fed and grinding is necessary for proper blending of the ration. Some of the combine types of sorghums, such as milo, are extremely hard and cracking of these sorghums is recommended, but fine grinding is discouraged.

The grinding or chopping of roughage will induce greater consumption of poor-quality feed but otherwise has little value. When lambs are fed a complete mixed ration, including roughage, it then becomes necessary to grind the roughage and grains for mixing.

Pelleted Rations. Pelleting of feeds consists of first grinding them, then running the ground material through a machine which forms the feed into pellets. These pellets vary in size but will average approximately the size of a pea. Pelleted grains, hays, and complete pelleted rations have been used in feeding trials. Lambs like the pelleted rations and labor used in feeding is reduced. Most of the trials have shown somewhat faster gains, when pelleted rations were fed.

Starting Lambs on Feed. Lambs will lose from four to seven pounds in shipment, depending upon the distance and length of time they are on the road. Upon arrival they will be tired, hungry, and thirsty. The best practice is to give the lambs access to a mixed hay (grass and legume), a grass hay, or a grass pasture for two hours before filling the water troughs to prevent water founder. Lambs that are empty and thirsty will be inclined to over-drink, creating some serious complications. Salt and mineral mixture should be made available. Block salt should be used the first few days; then a change to loose salt, kept in a protected place, should be made.

From the third day, the lambs may be fed one-fourth pound of oats per head and one-tenth to one-eighth pound of linseed oil meal pellets daily. The linseed oil meal is a good conditioner and will help to regulate the bowels and digestive system. After the lambs have been on the oats and linseed oil meal pellets for four days, a gradual shift to the fattening ration may be made.

Methods of Fattening Lambs. There are three commonly used systems of fattening lambs. Hand-feeding in a dry lot, self-feeding in a dry lot and corn field feeding with either hay or pasture.

Hand-Feeding. Hand-feeding consists of feeding the lambs concentrates usually twice a day and limiting the amount to what they will clean up in 20 to 30 minutes after they have been brought up to full feed. Hay is kept in the racks where the lambs will have access to it at the rate of one to 1½ pounds per head daily.

When the hand-feeding method is to be used, a gradual shift from the starting ration to the fattening ration should be made. Good-quality legume hay is best, but since it tends to have a loosening effect on the bowels, the shift should be made over a period of about two weeks. The concentrate ration to be fed should be started the fourth day at the rate of one-fourth pound per head daily and gradually increased over a two to three week period until the lambs are on full feed. Full feed will consist of the amount the lambs will clean up in from 20 to 30 minutes twice daily.

Following are some proven rations.

RATIONS FOR FATTENING LAMBS HAND-FED IN DRY LOT

Roughage	Concentrate Mixture	
1. Alfalfa 1¼ lbs. daily	Corn or sorghum grains	90 lbs.
	Linseed, soybean or cotton-seed meal	10 lbs.
2. Legume hay 1¼ lbs. daily	Corn or sorghum grain	40 lbs.
	Oats	30 lbs.
	Barley	30 lbs.
3. Corn or sorghum silage 1¾ lbs. daily		
Legume hay 1¾ lbs. daily	Corn or sorghum grain	85 lbs.
	30 to 40% protein concentrate	15 lbs.
4. Grass hay 1¼ lbs. daily	Barley	40 lbs.
	Corn or sorghum grain	40 lbs.
	30 to 40% protein concentrate	20 lbs.
5. Mixed hay 1¼ lbs. daily	Wheat	20 lbs..
	Corn or sorghum grain	40 lbs.
	Barley	25 lbs.
	30 to 40% protein concentrate	15 lbs.
6. Corn or sorghum silage 3 to 4 lbs. daily	Corn or sorghum grain	60 lbs.
	Barley	20 lbs.
	30 to 40% protein concentrate	20 lbs.
7. Mixed hay 1¼ lbs. daily	Molasses	30 lbs.
	Corn or sorghum grain	50 lbs.
	30 to 40% protein concentrate	20 lbs.

Salt and a mineral mixture should be provided free choice with the above rations.

Self-Feeding. Lambs may be placed on self-feeders after having become accustomed to grains, if the ration is made bulky by mixing roughages with the grains. A greater danger of overeating exists, but when large numbers are fed, the labor saving factor is important. If self-feeding is to be practiced, the roughage and grain will have to be ground and mixed into one complete ration. The self-feeding of grain and hay separately usually results in over-eating and heavier death losses.

The change from hand-feeding to self-feeding should be done slowly. The lambs are given their regular feed, and later the self-feeders are opened. The first self-feed mixture should contain not more than 30 pounds of grain and protein concentrate mixed with 70 pounds of chopped roughage. As the lambs become used to self-feeding, the mixture may be made with a larger percentage of grain to speed the fattening process. Molasses is valuable in mixed rations as a means of holding down the dust and providing a binder which holds the grain and protein in the mix.

Tests show that lambs may be fattened with as little as 30 per cent concentrates and 70 per cent good quality legume hay in the ration. They may be fattened on 80 per cent concentrates and 20 per cent legume hay. However, the most economical ration is 50 to 60 per cent concentrates and 40 to 50 per cent legume hay.

SELF-FED RATIONS FOR FATTENING LAMBS ON FULL FEED

	Pounds	*Feeds*
1.	40	Corn or sorghum grain
	15	Molasses
	9	Linseed, soybean, cottonseed meal
	36	Legume hay
2.	20	Corn or sorghum grain
	20	Barley
	10	Molasses
	10	Linseed, soybean, cottonseed meal
	40	Legume hay

Salt and mineral mixture feed should be given free choice with the above rations.

COMPLETE RATIONS INCLUDING SALT AND MINERAL

1.	60	Corn or sorghum
	4	Soybean oil meal
	34.57	Chopped legume hay
	.15	Salt
	.70	Limestone
	.50	Bone meal
	.08	Trace minerals
2.	50	Corn or sorghum grain
	3	Soybean, linseed, cottonseed meal
	45.67	Legume hay
	.15	Salt
	.50	Limestone
	.08	Trace minerals
3.	50	Corn
	10	Molasses
	5	Protein mineral supplement (see p. 498)
	35	Legume hay

Corn Field Feeding. Lambs may be successfully fattened in the corn field if properly handled. The death loss will be somewhat higher on the average than when they are fed in the lot, but labor will be considerably reduced. The lambs will harvest the corn, which not only reduces harvesting labor, but also reduces the labor required for the feeding operation.

It is very important that the roughage the lambs consume is sufficient to balance the corn and prevent over-eating. This can best be accomplished by keeping the lambs in dry lot over night and providing them with from 1¼ to 1½ pounds of hay per head before they go into the corn field the next day. The hay should be at least one-half legume to insure adequate protein. If a good pasture is available adjoining the corn field, the lambs will generally consume enough forage to prevent over-eating. Salt and a mineral mixture should be made available for corn field lambs free choice.

It is important to condition the lambs to corn before they are turned into the corn field, by starting them on corn two weeks before and bringing them up to one-half to three-fourths pound daily.

Expected Daily Gains. The rate of gain one may expect on fattening lambs will depend upon the size of lambs when started on feed, their thriftiness and the ration fed. One-third pound gain daily on 60 to 70 pound feeders is considered a good average gain, but up to one-half pound daily gain per lamb has been accomplished with good feeding and management.

Feed Requirements Per Hundred Weight Gain. Lambs on full feed will consume from one to 1½ pounds of hay and from one to 1½ pounds of concentrates daily. To fatten lambs from 90 to 100 days will require about two to 2½ bushels of corn (or the equivalent in other grains) and about 140 pounds of legume hay. The feed requirement for 100 pounds of gain will be five to six bushels of corn (280 to 340 pounds) and 420 pounds of alfalfa hay when fed a standard ration. The amount of grain and roughage will vary, if a high grain or high roughage ration is used.

Feed Lot Troubles

It takes a considerable amount of experience to feed lambs successfully. There is a greater danger of lambs having digestive troubles from over-eating than of any other kind of farm livestock.

Overeating Disease. Overeating disease causes heavy losses among fattening lambs, unless the proper precautions are taken. The disease is thought by many to be caused by an organism found in the soil that is normally present in the lower bowel. It produces a toxin or form of poisoning. Lambs on full feed of grains are more susceptible to the disease than other sheep or lambs, since the heavy feeding causes rapid growth of the organism.

Veterinarians use perfringens type D bacterin, antitoxin, and toxoid for vaccinating against the disease. Antitoxin gives quick immunity and the toxoid gives a longer lasting immunity. Many veterinarians are using, with considerable success, a combination of the latter two as a prevention for overeating disease. Mixing aureomycin in the ration to provide 10 mg. daily per animal will help to control the disease.

Coccidiosis. Coccidiosis is caused by a protozoan parasite. The disease has become more prevalent among feeder lambs in recent years, causing heavy death losses in many instances. Outbreaks occur most frequently two to three weeks after an exhausting shipment. Prevention consists of keeping feed bunks and watering facilities clean, and isolating all animals showing symptoms. Veterinarians have had some success treating the disease with the sulfa drugs.

Shipping Fever. This disease is caused by one or more bacteria. Usually the outbreak in feeder lambs occurs shortly after shipping or exposure to bad weather. Vaccinating lambs two to three weeks before shipment with a mixed bacterin has helped to prevent the disease. Veterinarians have reported good success with the sulfa drugs administered through the water upon arrival of the lambs, as a prevention, and treating those showing visible symptoms with antibiotics.

Summary

Fat lambs may be produced on grass and the milk from the ewes. This method requires plenty of good-quality, fresh, tender grasses or legumes having a high feeding value.

Supplying high-quality forage, grain, or both to suckling lambs in an area where it is not available to the ewes is known as creep feeding, and is often desirable. Creep feeding speeds the growth rate of the lambs, prevents ewes from suckling down as much, and tends to even up the size of the lambs.

Under range conditions, if lambs are to be creep fed, they should be started on a creep when they are about three weeks of age. Under farm flock conditions lambs may be placed on creeps as soon as they will eat, which is at about ten days of age.

Grains may be placed in a creep and left for the day to get lambs started on feed. After they are eating, feeding them the amount of grain they will clean up in 20 minutes once or twice daily is recommended.

Hothouse lambs are lambs finished for market when six to 12 weeks old and weighing from 30 to 60 pounds.

Lamb fattening is the feeding out of lambs to a desirable market finish. Lambs that are under finished are either put into the feed lot and fed grain or placed on a highly nutritious pasture with or without grain until they are ready for market.

The lamb feeder depends upon margin, value of gain over cost of grain, wool clip, and the fertilizing value of the manure for his profits.

Dry roughages, silage, root crops, animal fats, grains, molasses, grain by-products, and several protein supplements may be used in proper combination for fattening lambs. Minerals and salt should be provided either in mixed rations or separately. Urea may be successfully used as a partial protein substitute when properly fed in the correct combination with other feeds.

Antibiotics have shown beneficial results when fed at the rate of ten milligrams per head daily. Hormones are in the experimental stage and no recommendations are made at this time.

Except for some of the combine-type sorghums such as milo, grinding feed for lambs is not recommended, unless a complete mixed ration is fed and grinding is necessary for blending.

Lambs like pelleted feeds and experiments show some increased gains resulting from pelleted feeding.

Feeder lambs may be fattened by hand-feeding, self-feeding, or corn field fattening.

Lambs may be expected to gain from one-third to one-half pound daily and will consume from four to five bushels of corn, or its equivalent, and 420 pounds of legume hay per 100 pounds of gain.

Overeating disease, coccidiosis, and shipping fever are the most common ailments affecting feed lot lambs. Vaccination, antibiotics, sulfa drugs, and sanitation offer the best prevention and treatment methods.

● *Questions*

1. What methods are commonly used to produce fat lambs?
2. Explain the requirements for the production of grass fat lambs.
3. What are feeder lambs?
4. Explain what is meant by creep feeding lambs.
5. Discuss the advantages of creep feeding lambs.
6. When and how should lambs be started on creeps?
7. What are some recommended rations for creep feeding lambs?
8. Explain what is meant by a hothouse lamb.
9. How do lamb feeders expect to make their profits?
10. Discuss the various roughages, grains, grain substitutes fed lambs.
11. Discuss the protein feeds and protein blends that may be used in lamb feeding.
12. Have antibiotics and hormones shown any beneficial effects on fattening lambs? Discuss.
13. How should feed be prepared for lambs? Discuss.
14. Explain how you would start lambs on feed.
15. Describe the common methods of fattening lambs.
16. What advantages and disadvantages do each of the methods described in Question 15 have?
17. What are the normal weight gains fattening lambs may be expected to make?
18. How much feed will lambs consume under average conditions per hundred pounds of gain?
19. Discuss the cause and prevention of the common feed lot lamb ailments.

● *References*

Andrew, F. N., W. M. Beeson, "The Effects of Various Methods of Estrogen Administration in the Growth and Fattening of Wether Lambs," *Journal of Animal Science,* Vol. XII, No. 1, February, 1953.

Bell, Donald T., A. B. Erhart, *Lamb Feeding Experiments,* Kansas Agricultural Experiment Station, Garden City Branch, Garden City, Kansas, 1955-1956.

Botkin, M. P., Leon Paules, *Effect of Aureomycin in Various Ratios of Roughage to Concentrates for Feeder Lambs,* Agricultural Experiment Station, Mimeograph Circular No. 44, University of Wyoming, Laramie, Wyoming, 1954.

Colorado Feeders' Day Report, General Series No. 635, Colorado A & M, Fort Collins, Colorado, 1956.

Henneman, H. A., R. E. Rust, J. Meites, *The Effect of Steroid Hormones on Fattening Lambs,* Michigan Agricultural Experiment Station Report, 1956.

Illinois Sheep Day Reports, Agricultural Experiment Station, University of Illinois, Urbana, Illinois, 1953, 1954, 1955, 1956.

Iowa Sheep Day Report, Agricultural Experiment Station, A H 741, Iowa State College, Ames, Iowa, 1955.

Kansas Agricultural Experiment Station Progress Report, Circulars 320 and 335, Kansas State College, Manhattan, Kansas, 1955-1956.

Lamb Feeders' Report, Kansas Agricultural Experiment Station, Garden City Branch, Circulars GC-S-52, 1952; GC-S-53, 1953; GC-S-54, 1954; GC-S-55, 1955, Garden City, Kansas.

Lamb Feeding Experiments, "Studies Concerning the Value of Cooked Gull Beans, Stilbestrol, Progesterone and Estradiol in Rations for Fattening Lambs," Agricultural Experiment Report, Cornell University, Ithaca, New York, 1954-1955.

Means, T. M., F. N. Andrews, W. M. Beeson, "The Effect of Hormones on the Growth and Fattening of Lambs," *Journal of Animal Science,* Vol. XII, No. 1, February, 1953.

Pelleted Rations for Fattening Lambs Progress Report, Agricultural Experiment Station Report No. 19, Montana State College, Bozeman, Montana, 1954.

Rath Packing Company and Iowa State College: *Modification of a Standard Feed Mixture for Fattening Lambs,* Agricultural Experiment Station Leaflet 205, 1956; Leaflet 196, 1955: Leaflet 184, 1953; Iowa State College, Ames, Iowa.

Control of Diseases
and Parasites

Sheep diseases, parasites, and other ailments may be divided into four groups: (1) external parasites, (2) internal parasites, (3) contagious diseases, and (4) noncontagious ailments. The average sheepman is not a veterinarian; therefore, his chief preventive measures in maintaining a healthy flock are good sanitation, the proper use of sprays and disinfectants, and the vaccination of his flock against those diseases for which vaccine has been perfected, when recommended by a reliable veterinarian.

While the list of ailments that affect sheep is almost endless, few sheepmen have experienced difficulties with more than two or three diseases and parasites. Therefore, the principal sheep troubles will be discussed, but those that rarely cause losses in the United States will not be given consideration in this book.

Most infections and diseases that sheep are subject to are brought into the flock as a result of poor management practices. Parasites and diseases usually breed best under filthy conditions. Many diseases spread from infected animals to healthy ones.

A Program of Disease and Parasite Prevention

The following steps are important if a disease- and parasite-free flock is to be maintained:

(1) Bring only clean animals into the flock.

(2) Keep animals in well drained lots or pastures free of stagnant water. Paved lots will aid in keeping feeder lambs, or other sheep confined to small areas, out of the mud and filth.

(3) Isolate all animals that are known to have contagious infections. Animals that have been purchased or otherwise added to the flock should be isolated until it is reasonably certain they are free of parasites and disease.

(4) Vaccinate for those diseases for which a successful vaccine exists, when recommended by a reliable veterinarian.

(5) Disinfect housing and equipment regularly.

(6) Treat open wounds on all sheep and the navels of newborn lambs with a recommended disinfectant.

(7) Provide plenty of exercise for the breeding flock.

(8) Spray, dip, or dust for external parasites at regular intervals, and eliminate manure piles and filth accumulation.

(9) Follow a rigid program of internal parasite control using the recommended materials.

(10) Avoid overcrowding of the flock.

(11) Provide clean warm quarters for new born lambs.

(12) Rotate pastures often.

(13) Observe the animals for signs of parasites and infections.

External Parasites of Sheep

Blowfly. This group of flies include several species. The black blowfly and the bluebottle fly are the most dangerous to sheep.

Life History. After warm weather starts in the spring, the fly eggs hatch from dead and putrifying materials where they have been laid. The hatched flies mature rapidly and seek out places to deposit their eggs. Accumulations of filth attract them. Sheep with stains or dung on them provide attractive places for the blowflies to lay their eggs.

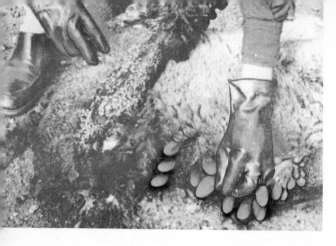

Figure 27-1. Careless management caused this lamb to be eaten alive by countless blowfly maggots. (Courtesy University of Wisconsin)

Symptoms. The first symptoms one will notice in sheep that are flyblown is twitching the dock, stamping the feet, running short distances and showing other forms of restlessness.

As the eggs hatch and the maggots enter the flesh, discolored patches of wool caused from serum-leakage will begin to show. Long-wool sheep must be checked carefully as entire maggot infested areas may be completely hidden by the wool.

Prevention and Treatment. Prevention consists of docking all lambs and tagging all sheep, keeping them clean and free from dung. All wounds should be treated with a good fly repellent. Insecticide sprays, such as lindane, sprayed on the crotch and dock help to prevent attacks by the flies.

Treatment consists of removing the wool from around the affected area. To be sure the entire area is exposed, clip the wool back to where it is clean and dry. Scrape off all the larger maggots and force the others out with a mild sheep dip. Chloroform may be applied to the area to kill those lodged deeply in the flesh.

After the maggots have been eliminated, let the area dry and apply E. Q. 335, a smear developed by the United States Department of Agriculture. The E. Q. 335 should be diluted in water at the rate of one part E. Q. 335 to seven or eight parts water.

Screw Worm. These pests are more prevalent in the Southern and Southwestern states, but may infect sheep in other areas.

Life History. The screw worm fly is bluish green in color, with orange shading below the eyes. The three prominent, dark stripes along its back distinguish it from similar insects. The flies lay their eggs in masses along the edges of open wounds. The eggs hatch into

Figure 27-2. Applying smear E-Q 335 to an area infested with screw worms. (Courtesy U.S.D.A.)

tiny maggots that burrow into the flesh, where they feed from four to seven days.

When the worms have reached their full growth, they drop to the ground and burrow into the soil. A few days later they emerge from the pupa or dormant stage as adult flies. The entire life cycle may be completed within 21 days under favorable conditions.

Symptoms. The symptoms of screw worm infestation are much the same as for the fly strike (blowfly maggots). The animals show a general restlessness due to the irritation caused by the maggots feeding on the flesh.

Prevention and Treatment. Prevention requires that operations such as castrating and docking be done during the season when screw worm flies are not active. All wounds should have a fly repellent applied to them. E. Q. 335 is both an effective repellent and will kill the screw worm maggots. When a dye is mixed in the E. Q. 335, treated animals are easily detected and can be readily separated for later inspections. When the wound is deep and the screw worms are present, the smear should be diluted (see blowflies). By diluting, the smear penetration is deeper. The worms come to the surface where they die and drop off. If the undiluted smear is applied over the deeply imbedded worms, infection may result from the putrifying forms even though they may be killed.

Lice. The louse is a flat, wingless insect. There are several species and two general types. The two types are made up of biting and sucking lice. The sucking lice are the most injurious. Lice are more prevalent on those animals that are out of condition because of improper feeding or management. They are more abundant when animals have been confined to small areas, and during the winter.

Life History. Lice spend their entire life cycle on the sheep. They attach their eggs or "nits" to the wool, where they hatch in about two weeks. The females begin laying eggs about two weeks after hatching and die after reproduction.

Symptoms. Intense irritation and itching caused by the lice make the animals scratch, rub, and gnaw at the skin. The wool may take on a dead, dry appearance. Growth is retarded, and badly infected animals will go out of condition.

Prevention and Treatment. Prevention and treatment consist of spraying, dipping, or dusting the entire flock at regular intervals. The animals should be thoroughly covered with the material and the housing area treated. Lindane is very effective in controlling lice, when used either as a spray, dip, or dust. Two pounds of 25 per cent wettable powder or one pint 20 per cent emulsifiable concentrate in 100 gallons of water makes an effective spray. If two pounds of wetting agent such as Dreft, Vel, Tide, etc. is used per 100 gallons of water, the material will stick on the animals better, especially when sprayed. Spraying should be done at 400 pounds of pressure. A 1 per cent lindane powder may be used to dust the animals when it is too cold for spraying or dipping. Lindane should not be applied during the last thirty days before an animal is marketed for slaughter.

Except in heavily infected flocks, one or two treatments per year will control lice. Best results are obtained, if the animals are treated when the wool is short.

Ticks or Keds. The sheep tick is not a true tick but a blood-sucking fly without wings. They are dark brown in color, have hairy bodies with six legs, and average about one-fourth inch in length when mature. Ticks may infest all sheep. However, the medium and long-wool breeds are more susceptible to infestation than are the fine-wool breeds.

Life History. Ticks, like lice, spend their entire life on the sheep. The eggs develop into the larvae while still in the body of the female. Females will deposit 12 or more larvae, which develop into the pupa or dormant stage, and remain attached to the wool fibers. The pupa stage lasts from 20 to 25 days, when the pupa shell is broken open and the young tick emerges. The young tick will start to deposit larvae 14 to 16 days later.

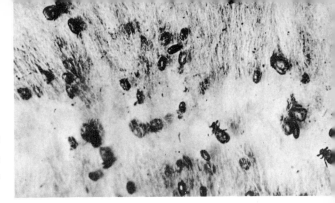

Figure 27-3. Close view of tick-infested sheep showing ticks and pupa in the wool. (Courtesy U.S.D.A.)

Symptoms. Because ticks feed by sucking blood from the skin, an intense irritation is set up causing the sheep to bite and scratch itself in an attempt to gain relief from the itching. The wool will be damaged and in cases of heavy infestation, the animal will become anemic.

Prevention and Treatment. The recommendations for control of lice (previously given) will also control ticks. When sheep are treated for either ticks or lice both will be eliminated.

Sheep Scab. Sheep scab, a serious disease of sheep, has all but been eliminated from the United States. However, it is always a threat. The disease is caused by a small insect-like parasite so small it is nearly invisible to the naked eye.

Life History. The scab mite spends its entire life on the body of the sheep. It lays from ten to 30 eggs over a two-week period.

Figure 27-4. This sheep is heavily infested with scab mite. (Courtesy U.S.D.A.)

Control of Diseases and Parasites • 513

These hatch and the mites reach maturity in another two weeks. Thus a new generation of mites is produced every 15 to 20 days.

Symptoms. The mites live on the blood serum that oozes from the skin punctures which the mites make. The serum becomes mixed with dirt which soon dries forming a crust or scab. The skin thickens and becomes hardened. The infected sheep become restless, and rub, scratch, and bite at their wool.

Prevention and Treatment. Spraying with lindane (four pounds of 25 per cent wettable powder to 100 gallons of water) or dipping with lindane (two pounds per 100 gallons of water) will give effective control. Spraying should be done at 400 pounds pressure.

General Recommendations in Using Sprays

Sprays and dips may be harmful to both men and animals when improperly used.

The authors have suggested lindane because of its all-around effectiveness against external parasites. All insecticides, especially those used on livestock, are undergoing severe scrutiny by the Food and Drug Administration. Some have been, and others may be, prohibited. The stockman should follow the recommendations of reliable agricultural teachers and veterinarians.

Read Labels and Directions. Manufacturers put the same products out under different concentrations. So it is important to follow directions when mixing a dip or spray. Precautions for safe use of the product are also included and should be observed.

Internal Parasites

Internal parasites are more numerous and heavy infestation is more likely to occur, when sheep are confined to the same area year after year, without benefit of lot or pasture rotation. Low, wet land and humid conditions are favorable to the development of internal parasites.

Common Stomach Worms. The common stomach or twisted stomach worm is one of the most common forms of internal parasites to cause losses in sheep.

Life History. The female lays eggs which pass out of the body with the feces. The eggs hatch in a few days, when temperature and moisture conditions are favorable, into tiny larvae. The larvae crawl up on the blades of grass where they are swallowed by sheep during grazing. The worms travel to the abomasum, where they grow and the cycle is repeated.

Symptoms. Infected sheep become listless, thin, weak, and unthrifty. When infestation is heavy, a swelling, known as bottle jaw, may develop under the jaw.

Prevention and Treatment. Since the tiny worms that appear on the blades of grass are dependent upon a host for survival, the rotation of pastures every two weeks will help to control the common stomach worm.

The most effective material for the removal of the common stomach worm from sheep is phenothiazine. The drug may be given as a drench or in capsules or boluses. The recommended dosage

Figure 27-5. Here is where most internal parasites live. Examine these parts in dead lambs; if worms are found, immediate steps should be taken to prevent further losses. (Courtesy University of Wisconsin)

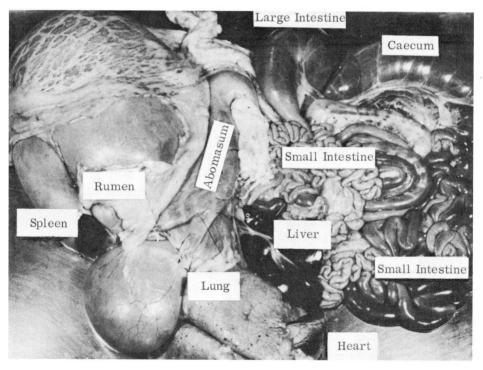

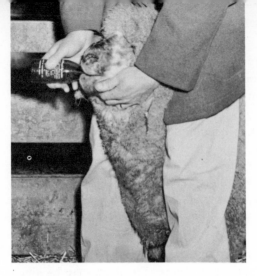

Figure 27-6. The proper way to hold a bottle when drenching a sheep. (Courtesy George A. Hormel Company)

is one ounce for each mature animal and one-half ounce for lambs under 60 pounds in weight. A mixture of one part phenothiazine by weight and ten parts salt by weight should be provided free choice for the flock. When the flock has been properly dosed, the salt phenothiazine mixture will help to keep them free of the worms.

Drenches may be given with either a bottle or a syringe. Care should be exercised not to get any of the mixture into the lungs. The head should be held in a natural position (not too high) and the drench given slowly, allowing time for the sheep to swallow.

A complete control program should include fall and spring treatment, pasture rotation, and free access to the salt phenothiazine mixture.

Other Species of Stomach and Intestinal Worms. There are several other types of stomach and intestinal worms that attack sheep, in addition to the common stomach worm that has been described. The more important ones are: brown stomach worm, small stomach worm, cooperias (four species), nodular worm, and hookworm. Except for the hookworm, the life cycle of these parasites is similar to that of the common stomach worm. The hookworm differs in that it may enter the body through the mouth or skin. The treatment is the same as that recommended for the common stomach worm.

Broad Tapeworm. The broad tapeworm in the sheep has a head which might be likened to an anchor. To the head are attached the segments of the tapeworm.

Life History. Each segment is much like an individual worm, as it is capable of producing eggs. The segments at the end break off, and may be seen in the manure as white flecks. The segments contain eggs which are ingested by soil mites in which they develop into the secondary stage. The mites crawl up on the blades of grass where the sheep swallow them while grazing, and thus become infested with tapeworm larvae which live on the partially digested food in the sheep's intestines.

Symptoms. Tapeworms seldom do damage that is particularly noticeable to sheep, but since they do use some of the food eaten by the sheep, some slowing down in growth rate is bound to result. Heavily infested sheep will show symptoms similar to those infested with stomach worms.

Prevention and Treatment. Prevention of broad tapeworm infestation is accomplished primarily by rotating pastures and generally good sanitation. A drug known as "teniatol" is very effective in removing them from the digestive track. The dosage is 15 cc. for the first 25 pounds of body weight and five cc. for each additional 15 pounds of body weight. For complete eradication the treatment will have to be repeated two or three times at two to three weeks intervals.

Gid Tapeworm. In the droppings of dogs, wolves, coyotes, and other carnivorous animals are found the eggs of gid tapeworms.

Life History. Dogs and similar animals harbor the adult tapeworms after eating the cysts in dead animals. After the dogs,

Figure 27-7. An example of a sheep infested with gid tapeworm or grub in the head. (Courtesy U.S.D.A.)

Control of Diseases and Parasites • 517

wolves, or coyotes swallow the worms, the tapeworms' heads push out from the bladder and attach themselves to the intestinal lining, where they develop to maturity. The mature worm produces many eggs which leave the host in the feces. Sheep grazing on the area, where these droppings have been distributed, pick up the eggs and become infected with the worms.

Symptoms. As the blood distributes the parasites in various parts of the body, some reach the brain where they complete their development. The affected brain produces an incoordination in the sheep, causing it to circle or stumble—the animal is said to be giddy.

Prevention and Treatment. Prevention lies in disposing of all dead carcasses by burning or deep burying. Properly disposing of the internal organs of slaughtered animals so that dogs and other carnivorous animals may not eat them is advised. Human beings should also take precautions, as the tape worm may infect man. Meats should be properly cooked before being eaten. There is no satisfactory treatment.

Grub in the Head (Sheep Bots). The sheep bot deposits larvae in the nostrils of the sheep, causing irritation and catarrh.

Life History. The larvae, not eggs, are deposited around the sheep's nostrils. The larvae crawl up into the nasal passages to the frontal sinuses. The mature larvae return by way of the nasal passages, drop to the ground, and pupate after burrowing into the soil. The flies emerge from the pupa shell in about three to five weeks. The entire life cycle lasts from three to five months.

Symptoms. The common term used by sheepmen for the condition produced by the bot is "snotty nose." The nose runs, and the sheep keeps up a continuous snuffing. Infested sheep stand with their noses near the ground or lie down, sneeze, and seem very excited.

Prevention and Treatment. Tar the noses of the sheep, or apply some noninjurious repellent to the nose during the hot season, as a preventative. Provide a shade or darkened place where bots are less likely to be found. A 3 per cent saponified cresol solution sprayed under a 38-pound pressure into the nasal cavity has proved quite effective in killing young larvae.

Coccidiosis. Coccidiosis is a parasitic disease caused by tiny organisms that live in the intestinal lining. Infested animals pass hundreds of the organisms in the feces, which are picked up by other animals spreading the infection from one to another.

Life History. There are two main phases in the life cycle of the coccidia. One is the free-living phase outside the body where they spread from one animal to the·other. The second is the parasitic phase in the intestines. The oöcysts (free living phase) have thick shells and are not easily destroyed by disinfectants. When the oöcysts are swallowed by the animal, they reach the upper part of the small intestine. The digestive juices destroy the outer membrane of the oöcysts, releasing the eight sporozoites contained in each. The sporozoites attack certain cells of the body which they destroy while at the same time growing to maturity and forming new oöcysts.

Symptoms. Lambs are more likely to be affected than older sheep. Severe diarrhea that is often bloody is the most common symptom. Animals become weak, lose their appetite, and often die. The stained, dirty wool resulting from the diarrhea is an invitation for fly strike.

Prevention and Treatment. Sanitation, keeping the quarters clean, clean feeding and watering facilities free from contamination, and avoiding low, wet places for grazing are preventative measures. All infected animals must be isolated. The treatment consists of using the sulfonamides under the directions of a veterinarian. Some veterinarians have reported good success with teniatol as a treatment.

Figure 27-8. Lamb showing stains typical in coccidiosis cases. (Courtesy of *Successful Farming*)

Contagious Diseases of Sheep

While the list of contagious diseases that may affect sheep is long, the number that has caused considerable loss in any one area is comparatively small.

Foot Rot. Foot rot is caused by specific organisms that enter the feet through a break in the skin or horn of the foot. The break is usually caused by gravel, grit, or dirt lodged between the claws. The germs are carried by infected animals and are spread from one to another. A lame ewe may infect her lamb within a few days after birth. Wet, muddy lots provide receptive places for infected sheep to plant the germs, where they can easily be picked up by other animals. While wet, muddy lots are conducive to the spread of the disease, the germ must first be planted by infected sheep.

Sheep, pastured on irrigated pastures or allowed to run in dry lots that become muddy when wet, have a higher incidence of the disease than typical range sheep.

Symptoms. The most common symptom is extreme lameness in one or possibly all four feet. Upon examination, a break between the claws and a swelling will likely be found. As the condition continues, a rupture will occur. The disease is characterized by a very offensive odor.

Prevention and Treatment. Prevention consists of keeping sheep away from muddy lots, isolating all infected animals, and providing a foot bath at regular intervals, especially in areas where the disease is a problem. The foot bath consists of bluestone (copper sulfate) or a formalin solution. The bluestone solution is made by dissolving one pound of fresh bluestone in one gallon of water.

If a formalin solution is used, it should consist of 2 per cent formalin. The solution should be about two inches deep and placed in a long narrow trough. The sheep should be moved through the trough single file, allowing each animal to remain from one to three minutes in the solution. Sheep should be carefully watched and prevented from lying down in the copper sulfate solution, as it will stain the wool.

Treatment of infected animals consists of several steps outlined as follows:

(1) Clean the foot thoroughly and use a pocket knife to trim back the hoof until there is some oozing of blood. This is necessary

in order to remove all of the horn that may harbor the germs. Remove all of the thin flap of the horn between the toes and scrape around the side of the hoof. All dead tissue must be uncovered and removed. Caution is necessary when trimming so as not to trim too deeply at the point of the toe, where a large blood vessel is located.

(2) The second step is to thoroughly disinfect the trimmed foot. For this purpose, several good disinfectants are available. Butter of antimony, which is cheap, may be applied with a swab, working it into the tissue all around the foot.

(3) The third step is to run sheep through the bluestone or formalin foot bath as a final disinfectant. The foot bath should be repeated once a week until complete recovery takes place. Animals that do not respond to the above treatment may be successfully treated with the sulfa drug under the direction of a veterinarian.

Mastitis (Blue Bag). Mastitis is a disease resulting from one or both of two organisms that enter the udder, probably as a result of injury or chilling, although the exact cause is not known. The disease is serious and may cause the death of the animal infected, but usually it does not cause heavy losses. Ewes that have the disease are no longer fit for breeding purposes as the udder is spoiled even though the animal recovers.

Symptoms. The first noticeable symptom is the lagging behind the flock and a spraddle-legged walk. Due to the soreness in the udder the ewe will not allow her lamb to suckle. Examination will reveal a caked or hard condition of the udder. While the entire udder may be affected usually only one half will show infection. As the disease advances, gangrene sets in, giving the udder a blue appearance.

Prevention and Treatment. Prevention consists primarily of providing a clean, dry place for the ewes to bed down and eliminating sources of udder injury such as sharp objects. Hot applications of a solution containing a tablespoonful of Epsom salts in a quart of water may help. One cc. of procaine penicillin in oil syringed into the udder is effective against one of the organisms while dihydrostreptomycin is effective against the other.

Anthrax. Anthrax is a disease that will appear with little warning and death will occur within an hour. The disease is caused by a germ which can survive for years in the soil. The disease may strike any place, but it is more prevalent in certain areas.

Symptoms. Grinding of the teeth, hard and rapid breathing, pounding of the heart, and sudden death are the common symptoms.

Prevention and Treatment. A vaccine has been perfected which gives immunity and in areas where the disease is a problem, animal vaccination is recommended. Treatment is unsatisfactory. Since humans may contract the disease, extreme caution should be used when handling infected animals. Dead animals should be burned.

Shipping Fever. This disease is caused by a group of organisms that are most likely to gain a foothold in lambs soon after birth, or in older sheep that have lowered resistance because of shipping or exposure to inclement weather.

Symptoms. Discharge from the eyes and nostrils, coughing, rapid breathing, high temperature, and loss of appetite are the most noticeable symptoms.

Prevention and Treatment. The elimination of practices that cause fatigue, such as hard driving or long hauls, without rest, regular feeding, and giving protection against inclement weather constitute the chief preventative measures. All animals that have been purchased, or otherwise obtained, should be isolated until the danger of shipping fever is past.

A bacterin is available that has given considerable protection, if administered before the disease develops. When sheep are to be shipped or moved over long distances, the bacterin should be administered one to two weeks before moving. Sick animals may best be treated with antibiotics, although serum has been beneficial in many cases. Animals that are fed regularly while being moved have much more resistance to the organisms that cause shipping fever than those that go hungry. Taking time to feed regularly is very important in preventing shipping fever.

Sore Mouth. This disease is more common in lambs than older sheep. It is caused by a virus. The disease is transmissible to humans.

Figure 27-9. Sheep with sore mouth infection. (Courtesy U.S.D.A.)

Symptoms. The first symptoms are refusal to eat and a depressed appearance. Small sores may be found on the lips, gums, and tongue. The sores break and run, but they will usually heal by themselves without treatment. However, the animal loses weight and because of the sore mouth, lambs may not suckle the ewes, resulting in caked udders.

Prevention and Treatment. Sanitation, and a vaccine applied to a scratch made under the tail, will prevent the disease. Treatment consists of isolating the infected animals and treating the sores with iodine or a 2 per cent potassium permanganate solution.

Lamb Dysentery. This disease may develop in very young lambs. The death rate is high and an outbreak may cause heavy losses.

Symptoms. Lambs two to five days old are most susceptible. The lambs scour considerably, become depressed, weak, and unable to suck. Death will usually occur in a few hours if the lambs are not treated.

Prevention and Treatment. Sanitation, preventing the lambs from chilling, and keeping them in a well-ventilated and lighted place are the best preventative measures. Antibiotics, streptomycin, aureomycin, and terramycin given in doses of 0.5 gr. once or twice daily by mouth have all been relatively effective in treating the disease. A veterinarian should be called.

Foot and Mouth Disease. This is a highly contagious disease of sheep, swine, and cattle. So far, the disease has been kept out of the United States, but every precaution will be necessary if it is to be kept outside of our boundaries.

Symptoms. The disease is characterized by blisters found on the tongue, lips, cheeks, and skin around the claws of the feet. The animals infected have a heavy flow of saliva which hangs from the lips in strings. Death losses are not generally high, but the economic value of infected animals is considerably reduced.

Prevention and Treatment. Prevention consists of the elimination of all infected animals by slaughtering and burning or burying. If the disease is suspected, the government authorities should be notified. The foot and mouth disease virus is quickly destroyed by a solution of lye. The lye solution for cleaning quarters where infected animals have been will destroy the virus, if the area is properly and thoroughly disinfected. A new vaccine has been de-

Control of Diseases and Parasites • 523

veloped which is being recommended for areas outside of the United States. Unless the disease spreads into this country to a considerable extent, American farmers and ranchers will not likely be advised to vaccinate. Vaccines have not been regarded as favorable to complete eradication of the disease.

Noncontagious Ailments of Sheep

Overeating Disease (Enterotoxemia). This disease is probably the greatest killer of feed lot lambs. It also attacks lambs that are on lush pastures and are suckling ewes that are milking heavily. The disease is caused by an organism that is usually found in the digestive tract and in the soil. When lambs are on concentrates or lush pastures, the growth rate of the organisms is increased and a very lethal poison is produced.

Symptoms. Very few symptoms are noted. The lambs go off feed, are depressed and develop a diarrhea. Some may stagger or develop convulsions.

Prevention and Treatment. A very effective vaccine has been developed and lambs going into the feed lot should be vaccinated. In ranges where there is a history of the disease, it will probably pay to vaccinate.

Stiff Lamb Disease. There are a number of diseases that cause stiffness in lambs. Complete knowledge relative to their cause and

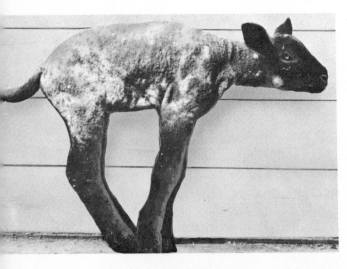

Figure 27-10. Lockjaw and joint swelling due to navel infection. (Courtesy University of Wisconsin)

prevention or treatment is lacking. A brief discussion of the more common ones will be given in this book.

White Muscle Disease. This disease is more common in farm flocks where early spring or winter lambing is practiced than in range flocks or lambs dropped on pasture.

The hind legs are especially affected and the lamb is unable to get around. Death usually results from starvation. A vitamin E deficiency is the most likely cause. Treating affected lambs with 10 cc. of cold-pressed wheat germ oil daily is recommended both as a preventative and treatment. Alpha tocopherol injected into the muscle at the rate of 5 cc. for a first treatment and 2½ cc. on alternate days is somewhat faster than the wheat germ oil.

Navel Ill and Joint Ill. These two types of diseases are caused by the entry of germs into the lamb through the navel or through wounds made when castrating and docking. Swelling of the knees and other joints are common symptoms. Lambs affected with navel ill will often be seen lying down and thrashing the legs.

Prevention consists of disinfecting the navel of newborn lambs with a tincture of iodine and castrating and docking under sanitary conditions.

The sulfa drugs, antibiotics, or injections of hemorrhagic septicemia bacterin may be used in the treatment.

Chronic Arthritis. This disease is probably caused by the entry of certain organisms into the body through wounds made during the docking and castrating operations. It affects the joints but seldom causes death, although few affected animals make a complete recovery. Prevention consists of sanitation during the castrating and docking operations.

Stiffness Due to Feed Changes. Lambs subjected to rapid, radical feed changes either by being separated from their mothers and moved to new pasture or rapidly changed to concentrate rations often develop stiffness.

Most of these lambs will recover in time. However, making gradual feed changes will reduce the incidence of this disease.

Lambing Paralysis or Pregnancy Disease. Pregnancy disease attacks ewes shortly before lambing, usually during the fourth month of gestation. Ewes carrying twins are more susceptible than those with single lambs. The disease is due to a carbohydrate deficiency, especially sugar, and lack of exercise.

Symptoms. Ewes will often develop a highly nervous condition followed by paralysis, coma, and death. In the early stages they tend to lag behind the flock and appear to be stiff. The head is held upwards; the neck is stiff; blindness may occur.

Prevention and Treatment. Ewes receiving good roughage and one-half pound of shelled corn daily (in the last six weeks of pregnancy) and getting plenty of exercise are seldom affected. Some shepherds feed one pint of molasses per head daily during the last six weeks of pregnancy. No successful treatment exists.

Bloat. This is a condition in which the rumen becomes filled with gas, which the animal is unable to expel. The condition may be caused by a growth or other obstruction in the esophagus, but is more often caused by feeds that ferment rapidly in the rumen causing large amounts of gas to form. Feeding on legume pastures is one of the most common causes of bloat. Saponins (plant materials that produce a soapy lather) are probably the principal ingredient in legumes responsible for bloat.

Symptoms. The chief symptom is a great distention of the upper left side of the abdomen. Rapid breathing and uneasiness occur. If the pressure becomes great enough to prevent lung action, death will result from suffocation.

Prevention and Treatment. Experiment stations are carrying on extensive research in an attempt to find a method of bloat prevention. Antibiotics, detergents, and other materials have been fed with some success. However, at this writing there is no drug or other material that can be recommended. Undoubtedly research will discover some reliable bloat preventative in time.

Since legume pastures are the main cause of bloat, some recommendations as to how to use them, if followed, will reduce the incidence of bloat.

Sheep going onto a legume pasture should, if possible, first be placed on a good lush grass pasture for a few days. This will condition the digestive system to lush green feed. Then, toward evening, after the sheep are full, place them on the legume pasture and let them alone.

Sheep that are moved about are more apt to die from bloat than if allowed to remain quiet. Some losses may result from bloat, but disturbing the flock to help one or two bloaters will probably result in more deaths.

If no green grass pasture is available, give the sheep a fill of high-quality hay before turning them on the legumes. Never turn sheep into a legume pasture the first time when it is wet.

Poisonous Plants

There are a number of poisonous plants that may affect sheep. Following is a list of the most common ones found in the United States: greasewood, horsebrush, death camass, sneezeweed, lupines, halogeton, rubberweed, locoweed or poison vetch, water hemlock, larkspur, copperweed, chokecherries, arrowgrass, corn cockle, dogbane, white snakeroot, nightshade, poison hemlock, jenson weed, laurels, castor bean, and sorghums.

Summary

The use of proper sprays, dips, or dust at least once a year are essential for the control of external parasites. Internal parasites may be controlled through pasture rotation and the use of a recommended vermifuge.

Disinfecting the navels of newborn lambs and clean, dry, well-lighted and ventilated lambing areas will prevent most diseases of newborn lambs. Stiff lambs due to vitamin E deficiency may be prevented by the oral administration of wheat germ oil or injecting alpha tocopherol into the muscle.

Feeding the proper amounts of sugar or other carbohydrates together with adequate exercise will prevent lambing paralysis.

Open wounds should be treated with a fly repellent to prevent fly strike and screw worm infestation. Docking and tagging will do much to prevent filth accumulations that attract blowflies.

• *Questions*

1. Give the steps in a management program that will help to prevent sheep diseases and parasite infestation.
2. Which of these steps do you apply to your flock or band?
3. Give the treatments recommended for external parasites.
4. What are the recommended control measures for internal parasites?
5. List the internal parasites common to your area.
6. Which diseases may be prevented by vaccination?

7. What are the common ailments of very young lambs?
8. How can young lamb diseases be prevented?
9. What is the most common ailment of fattening lambs and what is the prevention?
10. What is the cause and prevention of pregnancy disease?
11. How would you recognize and treat infectious foot rot?
12. What is bloat? Give some preventative measures.

• *References*

Animal Diseases, The Year Book of Agriculture, United States Department of Agriculture, Washington, D.C., 1956.

Elder, Cecil, and Donald E. Rodabaugh, *Internal Parasites of Sheep,* Agriculture Experiment Station Bulletin 527, University of Missouri, Columbia, Missouri.

Prier, J. C., *Disease Prevention in Young Livestock,* Agriculture Experiment Station Circular 47, University of Wyoming, Laramie, Wyoming.

Ryff, J. F., and Ralph F. Honess, *Internal Parasites of Sheep,* Agriculture Experiment Station Circular 42, University of Wyoming, Laramie, Wyoming.

28

Marketing Sheep and Wool

The sheep producer or lamb feeder is especially interested in the price of live sheep or lambs, and wool. We will attempt to discuss some of the factors that affect price and profit. The reader can determine when it is best for him to buy, sell, or both, depending upon his own situation.

Marketing Slaughter Lambs

Most fat lambs and sheep are sold to the packers to be slaughtered. The producer may sell directly to the packer or his buyer, through a commission firm, at a terminal market, or to a private dealer. Regardless of how he sells slaughter lambs or sheep, the price they bring at any one particular time will depend largely upon their grade and classification.

Grades and Classes of Slaughter Sheep. Slaughter sheep are those animals intended for immediate slaughter. The price per pound paid for them depends largely upon the value of the dressed animal. Young, well-finished lambs produce the best-flavored car-

PRIME

CHOICE

GOOD

UTILITY

Figure 28-1. Grades of feeder lambs. (Courtesy U.S.D.A.)

casses and generally sell higher per pound than older or poorly finished animals.

Sex. *Ewes.* Ewes are female sheep or lambs.

Wether. A wether is a male lamb that has been castrated before reaching sexual maturity.

Ram. A ram is an uncastrated male sheep of any age.

Age. *Hothouse Lambs.* Hothouse lambs are young lambs, usually born in the fall or early winter, that are milk fat, and sold during the Christmas to Easter season. They are usually sold by the time they are three months of age and weigh 60 pounds.

Spring Lambs. Spring lambs are those that reach the market in the spring as fat lambs weighing from 70 to 90 pounds. These lambs are usually born in the fall, but are older and heavier than typical hothouse lambs.

Lambs. Animals under a year old, that do not classify as spring or hothouse lambs, are considered lambs. When the term *lambs* is used by the packers, it generally designates grass-fat lambs. Those receiving grain are referred to as *fed lambs*. However, the term lamb when used in the broad sense by the packer, refers to all carcasses when the forefeet are removed at the break-joint. The break-joint is a temporary cartilage located just above the ankle. The break-joint of lambs is red and moist and has four points or ridges. In yearlings, the break-joint is more porous and does not have the red, moist appearance of the lamb joint. In older sheep, this joint will no longer break, and the foot is taken off at the ankle leaving a round or spool-joint. Carcasses with the spool-joint are sold as mutton, indicating older animals, rather than lamb.

Yearlings. Animals between one and two years of age.

Two-Year-Olds and Older. Sheep that are two years old and older are classified as mature in the slaughter market.

Weight. Slaughter sheep and lambs are classified as heavies, medium, or light. The weight divisions are determined by the age.

Grades. Grades are determined by the amount of finish and body conformation. Animals that are low-set, blocky, and well-developed in the areas of valuable cuts, such as the back, loin, and leg, and, with the proper amount of finish, are graded prime or choice. Those animals lacking in these qualities are placed in the lower grades. Thin animals with poor body conformation fall into the utility or cull grades.

Figure 28-2. (left) The two types of joints found on the forelegs of sheep. Upper: the round joint or spool joint and Lower: the break joint or lamb joint. (Courtesy Rath Packing Company)

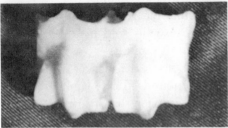

Figure 28-3. (below) Here are three grades of slaughter lambs. The lambs have been sheared to show their conformation. Left: utility. Center: good. Right: choice. (Courtesy Rath Packing Company)

Figure 28-4. Top-quality slaughter lambs. (Courtesy Rath Packing Company)   Figure 28-5. Hothouse lambs dressed with pelts left on and wrapped. (Courtesy Cornell University)

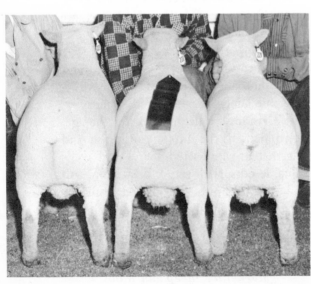

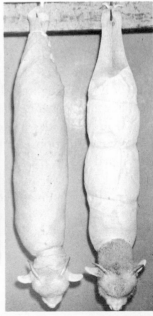

TABLE 49

MARKET CLASSES AND GRADES OF SLAUGHTER SHEEP

Sheep or Lambs	Sex	Age	Weight	Pounds	Grade
Sheep	Ewes	Yearlings	Light Medium Heavy	90 down 90 to 100 100 up	Prime, choice, good, utility, cull.
		Mature	Light Medium Heavy	120 down 120-140 140 up	Choice, good, utility, cull.
	Wethers	Yearlings	Light Medium Heavy	100 down 100-110 110 up	Prime, choice, good, utility, cull.
		Mature	Light Medium Heavy	115 down 115-130 130 up	Choice, good, utility, cull.
	Rams	Yearlings	All weights		Choice, good, utility, cull.
		Mature	All weights		Choice, good, utility, cull.
Lambs	Ewes, wethers, rams	Hothouse		60 down	Prime, choice, good, utility, cull.
	Ewes, wethers, rams	Spring lambs	Light Medium Heavy	70 down 70-90 90 up	Prime, choice, good, utility, cull.
	Ewes, wethers, rams	Lambs	Light Medium Heavy	75 down 75-95 95 up	Prime, choice, good, utility, cull.

Types of Marketing Procedure. The sheepman who is selling slaughter sheep or lambs has a choice of markets and methods of selling similar to that described for beef cattle (see Chapter 15). A good job of selling is important if he is to profit from his labor and management.

Shrinkage. Shrinkage is the loss in body weight of the animals from the time they leave the feed yards or range until they arrive at their destination. Most of the shrinkage is the result of feed and water the animal eliminates that is not being replaced by regular feeding and watering. However, there may be a tissue shrink. The amount of shrinkage depends upon the fill, the time in transit, weather conditions, the length of time the animals are allowed to rest, feed and drink before weighing, how the animals are loaded, and the age of the animals. The amount of shrinkage may be as high as 10 per cent or more, but a normal shrink will range from 3 to 5 per cent.

When to Sell Slaughter Lambs and Sheep. Western lamb producers make more money by selling weight than price per pound. This condition arises from the comparatively cheap price of grass and the fact that the grass crop will not be harvested unless eaten by sheep. However, weather conditions vary from year to year. Lambs on lush pasture will soon lose their bloom when pastures start to dry up. This makes it advisable to move the lambs earlier some years than others. Also many western range areas have grass varieties that produce sharp awns when the grass matures. Lambs will lose weight when irritated by awns that are caught in the wool. Lambs will need to be sold or shorn before the stickers develop. It is usually advisable to sell them.

Seasonal Prices. Lamb marketing is seasonal. During the periods of heavy marketing, prices usually decline. As the marketing tapers off, the price trend is upward. The heavy marketing of lambs starts in August and reaches a peak in October. The average Chicago

Figure 28-6. Feeder lambs at a central market. (Courtesy Rath Packing Company)

534

Figure 28-7. Here are examples of the various grades of wool. (Courtesy U.S.D.A.)

October price paid on slaughter lambs is 6 per cent below the 12 month average. The run of lambs begins to taper off in November and the price trend continues upward, reaching a peak in June. The June price at Chicago averages about 6 per cent above the 12 month average. This makes an average seasonal spread of 12 per cent from the October low to the June high.

When to Sell Ewes. Ewe prices fluctuate more on the slaughter market than do lambs. The mid-summer low occurs just after shearing and is about 15 per cent less than the year's average price. The March price of ewes is normally about 22 per cent above the year's average level. The months of January, February, March, April, and May average considerably higher prices for slaughter ewes than the rest of the year.

Marketing Feeder Lambs

Feeder lambs are usually marketed by the following methods; (1) private sale directly by producer to feeder; (2) through a dealer, (3) through a commission firm at a terminal market, and (4) at auction sales. (See material on feeder cattle in Chapter 15.)

When to Sell Feeder Lambs. The heavy period in shipments of feeder lambs to the Corn Belt occurs during the months of July, August, September, October, and November. Naturally the average seasonal price of feeder lambs is lower during these months.

Pricewise, it would be better to avoid selling during the summer and the fall months under average conditions. However, the

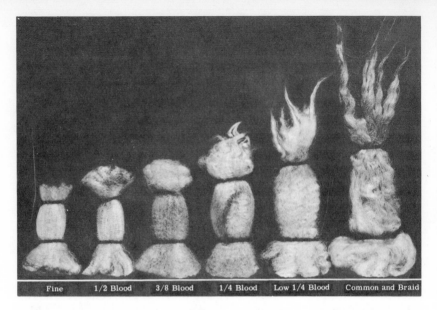

| Fine | 1/2 Blood | 3/8 Blood | 1/4 Blood | Low 1/4 Blood | Common and Braid |

Figure 28-8. Here are examples of defective and off-type fleeces. (Courtesy U.S.D.A.)

producer must consider the amount of available feed and the additional weight he can get on his lambs by utilizing this feed.

Marketing Purebred Breeding Stock

The marketing of purebred breeding stock is primarily limited to direct dealing between buyer and seller, or by auction sale. Unlike other classes of sheep, each transaction is limited to a single animal or to very small groups.

Grading and Marketing Wool

The producers of wool should have a working knowledge of the problems involved in wool marketing. They should be able to determine the value of the wool raised so as to look out for their own interests. Otherwise, they will find themselves at the mercy of the wool buyers at market time.

Wool is graded according to its *fineness;* the diameter of the individual fibers of wool within the fleece. Within limits of the grades, the finer wools are more valuable and the coarser wools less valuable. The *length* of the wool fiber determines the use that may be made of it in manufacture. Within limits of the length classifications, long wool is more valuable than short wool. A wool fleece, as it is shorn from the sheep, will contain, in addition to the wool, grease, dirt, various kinds of vegetable matter, and possibly other materials. The buyer looks at how much clean wool the grease fleece will *yield*. The difference in the amount of clean wool and the grease fleece weight is called *shrinkage*. Therefore, the value of a fleece of wool depends upon:

a. Fineness;

b. Length;

c. Shrinkage or yield.

How Wool Is Graded According to Fineness. The fineness of wool refers to the diameter of the individual fibers of wool. Standard grades have been set up by the United States Department of Agriculture, which are used in the wool trade. Prices paid are based on these standard grades.

Grades According to Fineness. The American or Blood System of grading wool refers to the amount of Merino breeding in the sheep from which the wool was shorn. The English woolen mills devised a very complicated system of grading wool, based on the number of hanks of yarn that one clean pound of wool would spin. This is known as the English or Spinning Count System of grading. In the years between 1920 and 1925, the two were combined into the present United States Department of Agriculture Standard Grades as follows:

TABLE 50

STANDARD GRADES OF WOOL IN TERMS OF GRADING BY
AMERICAN AND ENGLISH SYSTEMS

Type of Wool	American Blood System	English Spinning Count System	Approximate Diameter (inches)*
Fine	Fine	64's, 70's, 80's	.00077-.00090
Medium	½ Blood	60's	.00090-.00098
Medium	⅜ Blood	56's, 58's	.00106
Medium	¼ Blood	50's	.00120-.00130
Coarse	Low ¼ Blood	46's, 48's	.00138
Coarse	Common	44's	.00144
Coarse	Braid	36's, 40's	.00152-.00157

* These measurements are not exacting limits for each grade. They are simply given to give the reader an idea of the comparative differences in the grades.

The English Spinning Count System. When wool is graded according to the Spinning Count System, the grader actually indicates the number of hanks of yarn that can be spun from one pound of clean wool. A hank of yarn is 560 yards long. This being true, a clean pound of 64's quality wool will spin 64 x 560 yards or 35,840 yards of yarn. On the other hand, a clear pound of 50's quality wool will spin 28,000 yards of yarn. This is the reason why wool that grades fine is worth more per pound than wool grading one-half or three-eighths blood.

Fleece Grading. There is always some variation in the fineness of the wool grown on various parts of the sheep's body. The finest wool will usually be found on the head, while the coarsest wool is on the britch. For market purposes, wool is usually graded according to the fineness of the majority of the fleece.

The Relation Between Breed and Fineness. While there may be quite a lot of variation in fineness of fleece grown by individual sheep within a breed, the bulk of the individuals will grow a fleece of about the same fineness. The following table represents the fineness of fleece for the breed.

TABLE 51

GRADE OF FLEECE PRODUCED BY THE COMMON BREEDS OF SHEEP

Breed	American Blood Grade	English Spinning Count
Rambouillet	Fine	64's & better
Delaine Merino	Fine	64's & better
Southdown	½ Blood	58's & 60's
Hampshire	⅜ Blood	56's
Shropshire	⅜ Blood	56's
Suffolk	¼ Blood	48's & 50's
Corriedale	⅜ Blood	56's
Columbia	⅜ Blood	56's
Dorset Horned	¼ Blood	48's & 50's
Cheviot	¼ Blood	48's & 50's
Targhee	½ Blood	58's & 60's
Lincoln	Low ¼ Blood	46's
Leicester	Braid	36's & 40's
Cotswold	Braid	36's & 40's

How Wool Is Classified According to Length. Wool is generally classified according to the use that is made of it. Two broad

Figure 28-9. Grading wool. The fleece on the left is of poor quality and contains much foreign material. The fleece on the right is clean and high in quality. (Courtesy Iowa, Minnesota, Nebraska, South Dakota Wool Growers Assn.)

classes are *carpet* wool, used in the manufacture of floor coverings, and *apparel* wool, used in the manufacture of clothing. Carpet wool is long and coarse and comes from the long wool breeds. Apparel wool is further classified by length into *strict combing* or *staple*, *French combing*, and *clothing wools*. The first is most valuable and the latter least valuable.

Length and Uses Made of Wool. Apparel wools may be used in either the *worsted* or the *woolen* process of manufacture. In the worsted process, the wool must be combed so that the fibers lie side by side when the wool is spun into yarn. The yarn made by the worsted process is a strong, relatively smooth, twisted yarn that may be woven into a very durable, well-finished fabric. The wool usually used in the woolen process is too short to comb and is therefore spun into yarn, which is relatively large, soft, and weak because the fibers do not lie parallel.

Length as Related to Fineness. Under the worsted and woolen systems of wool manufacture, the fineness of the wool determines the length it must be before it can be combed. The coarser the wool is, the longer it must be before it can be handled by the combing process. This being true, the coarser the grade, the longer the wool must be to stay in the strict combing class.

Classes of Wool According to Length. The following chart shows length requirements for each market grade of wool.

TABLE 52

Grade	Strict Combing or Staple	French Combing	Clothing
Fine	2½" or longer	1½" to 2½"	1½" or less
½ Blood	2¾" or longer	1¾" to 2¾"	1¾" or less
⅜ Blood	3" or longer	2" to 3"	2" or less
¼ Blood	3¼" or longer	2¼" to 3¼"	2¼" or less
Low ¼ Blood	3½" or longer	None	3½" or less
Common	3¾" or longer	None	3¾" or less
Braid	4" or longer	None	4" or less

Putting the Grade and Class Together. In actual practice, wool is graded and classed at the same time. The fleece is inspected and the fineness grade is determined. Then the length of the fleece is studied and the length class determined. The fleece is then identified as to grade and class by using the name of each in describing that fleece. For example, fleeces will be called *Fine Staple, Fine French Combing, Fine Clothing, one-half-Blood Staple, one-half-Blood French Combing, one-half-Blood Clothing,* etc. Each of these descriptions has a different market value.

Shrinkage—How It Is Determined and What Causes It to Vary. One of the first processes in the manufacture is to remove the grease, dirt, and vegetable matter. This process is called scouring. The remaining wool is called *clean wool.* The weight of the grease, dirt, and vegetable matter expressed as a percentage of the grease fleece weight is called *shrinkage.* The weight of the clean wool expressed as a percentage of the grease fleece weight is called *yield.* Example—

- 100 pounds of grease wool is scoured
- 40 pounds of clean wool remains
- 60 pounds of grease, dirt, and vegetable matter is lost in the scouring process
- 40 pounds clean wool = 40 per cent *yield*
- 60 pounds lost in scouring = 60 per cent *shrinkage*

TABLE 53

SHRINKAGE BY GRADES OF THE 1946 U. S. WOOL CLIP

Grade	Range in Shrinkage
Fine	56-65%
½ Blood	51-60%
⅜ Blood	41-50%
¼ Blood	41-45%

Wool may vary in shrinkage from 35 to 80 per cent. Fine wool breeds produce more oil in their fleeces and therefore shrink more than medium and long wool breeds.

Defective and Offtype Wools. The several kinds of defective and offtype wools are less valuable to the mills because of the added expense of processing them or because of the limited uses that may be made of these wools. When these "off" wools are found at shearing time, they definitely should be packed and marketed separately from the sound wool. Some of the common defective and offtype wools are:

Burry. These wools contain large amounts of the seed of bur clover, grassbur, threeawn or needlegrass, or other seeds or vegetable matter. These can be removed from the wool by a carbonizing or acid treatment process which is not necessary in the normal processing of wool. This increases the processing cost and therefore reduces the market value. It is almost impossible to remove some of the seeds from the wool.

Cotted Fleeces. These are fleeces in which the fibers are badly tangled or matted. A special treatment not needed in processing sound wool is necessary to open these fleeces before manufacture.

Black or Gray Wool. Black fleeces or fleeces that contain a large percentage of black or brown fibers can not be dyed with all colors and are therefore less valuable.

Kempy Fleeces. These are fleeces that contain a large proportion of coarse hair called kemp. Kemp will not take a dye and is inferior to wool in quality. These fleeces can be used only in the manufacture of white fabrics of low quality.

Tags and Clippings. This wool is parts of fleeces that are taken off when the ewes are tagged before the fleece is tied, or swept off the shearing floor.

How a Grower May Sell His Wool

Sale to Independent Buyers. Independent buyers of one kind or another offer a market for wool in all localities in the areas where wool is produced. They offer to the grower an opportunity for immediate sale of his wool clip. There is no direct charge of marketing cost to the grower. He simply brings his wool to town, checks with one or more independent buyers, and sells his wool to the buyer making the best offer. His wool is weighed and he is

Figure 28-10. Stored wool which has been graded. (Courtesy Iowa, Minnesota, Nebraska, South Dakota Wool Growers Assn.)

paid immediately. The wool bought must later be sold on the going market. The buyers must, therefore, buy the wool at a price lower than its value if they are to make a profit.

Sale Direct to a Dealer or Mill Representative. Sales of this type are very unusual and are confined to growers who produce large clips of very desirable wool. These growers have established a reputation of producing and putting up a top clip of wool over a period of years. Dealer and mill representatives know who they are and where they are located, and often seek these growers out to buy their clip. A grower, in this position, may contact several buyers and develop a competitive situation between these buyers to his own advantage. To do this, usually the grower must have a large clip of wool for the buyers are not interested in buying one small clip. Often the grower will be faced with providing his own storage, carrying his own insurance, and delivering the wool to the buyers' concentration point. These costs might offset any advantage that he might otherwise gain.

Consignment to a Commission Warehouse for Later Sale. This is the most common system of marketing wool in the range states. In Texas, some 95 per cent of the wool produced is handled in this manner. The grower delivers his wool clip to the warehouse. The warehouseman weighs and marks each bag and issues the grower a receipt for his wool. The warehouse provides storage to the grower, and the wool is insured immediately. The warehouse operator inspects the wool and selects sample bags to be shown to the buyer. He will then place the grower's clip in one of several "lines" of wool that the warehouse will offer for sale. These "lines" of wool contain all the wool in the warehouse that grade the same, in so far as fineness and length are concerned.

The consignment system of marketing has some definite advantages:

1. The price received for the wool will be nearer its real value than when marketed under any other system, except in rare cases.
2. The grower is in a better position in the market, since the system of "lining up" his wool with other similar type wool offers the buyer a large volume of uniform wool.
3. If the market is slow, the grower has his clip safely stored and insured and can easily hold it until the market is stronger.
4. The warehouse operator spends his entire time studying the wool market. He is in a better position to sell the wool than is the average individual grower.
5. Wool can be offered in a sealed bid sale to several buyers under this system also.

Some of the disadvantages of this system of marketing are:

1. The grower may need the income from his wool before the warehouse gets the "line" his wool is in sold.
2. A warehouseman can be mistaken in judging the wool market occasionally. When he does, the grower loses money.

Contracting for Future Delivery. Many times a mill will be in a position to close a contract for future delivery of a certain type fabric. The mill will contact warehouses and offer a specific grease price per pound for wool to be delivered by the grower at shearing time. The warehouse will contact the growers and give them this information. Those growers who are interested will contact the warehouseman and will sign a binding contract with the Eastern mill or dealer. The grower agrees to deliver a certain number of fleeces to the warehouse at shearing time. The buyer agrees to pay the grower $1 per head advance at the time of signing the contract and the specified price per pound when the fleeces are delivered. The buyer usually reserves the right to discount the contract price if the fleeces delivered do not meet the description. In contracting, the grower stands to gain if the price of wool goes down at shearing time. On the other hand, if the price goes up, the grower will lose.

Cooperative Marketing Agencies. Throughout the wool-producing area are located cooperatives which perform the same services as the commission warehouse. Some of these operate under the cooperative marketing laws of the various states, while others operate under the general corporation laws. The cooperative or grower-owned warehouses do not buy wool from the grower direct. They only handle the grower's wool on a consignment basis.

Summary

Slaughter lambs and sheep are classified according to sex, age, weight, and grade. They may be sold directly to a packer or a packer buyer on a live weight or grade-and-yield basis. Other methods of selling are through a commission company at a central market or directly to a private buyer.

Feeder lambs and sheep may be marketed by direct selling on either contract for future delivery or immediate transfer from buyer to seller. Other methods of selling feeder sheep are through auctions, dealers, and central markets.

The shipping cost, shrinkage, and prices are important considerations in determining the methods of marketing.

Generally speaking, lambs should be sold when they are ready for market. The highest seasonal prices for slaughter lambs usually occur in June and the lowest in October.

Ewe prices average highest during March and lowest after the shearing season is over and during the late spring and summer months.

The heavy shipments of feeder lambs takes place during July, August, September, October, and November. Price declines usually follow heavy shipments of feeder lambs.

Purebred animals are usually sold for breeding purposes, and auction sales or private sales offer the principal outlet for purebreds.

A progressive wool grower will learn to do the best job possible of preparing his wool clip for market. He will be in the shearing pen while his wool clip is being harvested. He will see that the tags and clippings are kept out of the wool bag. He will see that offwools are packed separately. He will pack fleeces of different grades, lengths, and yields separately. When he has done this, he will take to the warehouse a clip of wool that his commission agent can sell for him at a price that is fair.

A progressive grower should study the marketing facilities in his locality. He should determine which system of marketing will be the most profitable for him. He might look at other systems of marketing available in other localities.

A grower can lose the profit he has made from 12 months of hard work in five minutes in the shearing pen or at the market place. This can be prevented. He should study this phase of his sheep operation very carefully.

● *Questions*

1. Give the grades and classes of slaughter sheep and lambs and describe each.
2. Explain the various methods of marketing both slaughter and feeder sheep and lambs.
3. Discuss the seasonal prices of both feeder and slaughter animals.
4. What determines when to sell?
5. What is shrinkage, and what are the principal factors that affect the amount of shrinkage?
6. Why is it important for the wool producer to understand how wool is classified and graded?
7. What determines the value of a fleece? Explain.
8. What is the blood system of grading wool? The English count system?
9. Give the blood grades and English spinning count of average fleeces from the common United States breeds of sheep.
10. How is wool classified according to length?
11. What is the required length of the various market classes of wool?
12. How is shrinkage determined?
13. Describe the defective and offtype wools.
14. How does the wool buyer determine the value of wool?
15. How can the grower improve the quality of his wool?
16. What practices should the grower follow to improve the market value of his fleeces?
17. Discuss the various methods which may be used by a grower to sell his wool.

● *References*

Ensminger, M. E., *Sheep Husbandry*, The Interstate Printers and Publishers, 1955.

Hamilton, Eugene, *Seasonal Market Variations and Their Importance to the Iowa Farmer,* Bulletin P 5, Agricultural Experiment Station and Extension Service, Iowa State College, Ames, Iowa.

Hultz, Fred S., John A. Hill, *Range Sheep and Wool,* John Wiley and Sons, Inc., 1931.

Kammlade, W. G., *Sheep Science,* J. B. Lippincott Co., 1957.

Marketing Feeder Cattle and Sheep in the North Central Region, Agricultural Experiment Bulletin 410, University of Nebraska, Lincoln, Nebraska.

Potler, E. L., *The Marketing of Oregon Livestock,* Agricultural Experiment Station, Bulletin 514, Oregon State College, Corvallis, Oregon.

Texas Agricultural Experiment Station, *Marketing Texas Wool on a Quality Basis,* Bulletin No. 823, 1955.

Texas Agricultural Experiment Station, *Marketing Wool Through Texas Warehouses,* Bulletin No. 740, 1951.

United States Department of Agriculture, *Grading Wool,* Farmer's Bulletin No. 1805, 1939.

POULTRY
PRODUCTION

The Poultry
Production Industry

Poultry and egg production was at one time a minor farm enterprise. Chickens or other fowl were kept either as a hobby or largely to produce meat and eggs for family consumption. The young couple beginning farming always had a small flock of hens and raised some young chickens to help pay the grocery bill until they had income from other enterprises.

The poultry enterprise today is big business. Flock owners consider the enterprise an economic unit which provides a source of income and a means of livelihood. Chickens are to be found on about 71 per cent of the five million farms in the United States. On January 1, 1958, there were 370 million chickens (excluding commercial broilers) on our farms.

Income from Poultry and Eggs

In 1955, poultry and eggs contributed 11.6 per cent of our national farm income. Chickens were responsible for 1.0 per cent,

Figure 29-1. A large commercial broiler enterprise. One man can care for 10,000 or more broilers when adequate facilities are provided. (Jimmie Willis photo. Courtesy Arbor Acres Farm, Inc.)

eggs for 6.6 per cent, broilers for 2.9 per cent, and turkeys for 1.1 per cent of our 1955 farm income. The income from poultry during that year compared very favorably with the income from other livestock enterprises. Hogs produced 9.9 per cent; dairy, 14.2 per cent; and beef cattle 16.7 per cent.

High States in Percentage of Income from Poultry. The states having the highest percentages of farm income obtained from poultry in 1955 were: Delaware, with 64.5 per cent; New Hampshire, with 48.1 per cent; New Jersey, with 42.8 per cent; Connecticut, with 40.1 per cent; and Maine, with 37.8 per cent. These states did not have the highest total production in terms of pounds or dollars.

Leading States in Percentage of Income from Broilers. The states having the highest percentages of farm income obtained from the sale of broilers in 1955 were Delaware, with 54.0 per cent; Maryland, with 19.8 per cent; Georgia, with 19.7 per cent; Connecticut, with 16.1 per cent; and Maine, with 15.4 per cent.

Leading States in Percentage of Income from Eggs. New Jersey led all states in 1955 in percentage of farm income from the sale of eggs, with 35.6 per cent. New Hampshire ranked second, with

29.1 per cent. Next in order were Pennsylvania, 21.0 per cent; Massachusetts, 20.7 per cent; and Connecticut, 18.5 per cent.

High States in Gross Income from Poultry. California led all other states in total income from chickens, broilers, turkeys, and eggs in 1954. Pennsylvania ranked second, Iowa third, Texas fourth, Minnesota fifth, Georgia sixth, New Jersey seventh, Indiana eighth, Ohio ninth, and New York tenth.

Trends in Poultry Production

Chickens. In 1940, nearly 95 per cent of the farms on which chickens were reported had flocks of 200 birds or less. Flocks of 1,000 or more chickens were reported on less than 1 per cent of the farms. The percentage of farms on which chickens are being raised is decreasing each year, but the size of flocks is increasing. A larger number of individuals are becoming specialized poultry farmers.

The production of chickens in the United States, excluding broilers, in 1956 amounted to 485 million birds. This was a decrease of about 250 million birds under the 1945-49 average.

California led all states in the number of chickens on farms on January 1, 1958, with 29.2 millions; Iowa ranked second, with 26.7 millions. The next states in order of numbers were: Pennsylvania, 21.8 millions; Minnesota, 21.3 millions; Illinois, 17.0 millions; and Texas with 15.0 millions.

Iowa, California, Minnesota, Pennsylvania, and Illinois led the states in number of farm chickens raised in 1956. In 14 states, more chickens were consumed on farms where produced than were sold.

Broilers. Broilers are young chickens about eight to ten weeks of age which have been raised for meat production. Broiler production is a comparatively new industry, yet more than 1.4 billion birds were produced in 1957. The production in 1950 was 616 millions. Nearly three-fourths of all chicks hatched now become broilers. Fried chicken is always popular at the dinner table.

The leading states in broiler production in 1957 were: Georgia, 261 millions; Arkansas, 110 millions; N. Carolina, 106 millions; Alabama, 104 millions; Texas, 101 millions; and Delaware, 94 millions.

Turkeys. The production of turkeys in this country has increased rapidly since 1920. During 1920 there were about 4 million turkeys on farms. By 1930 there were 17 millions, and by 1940 the

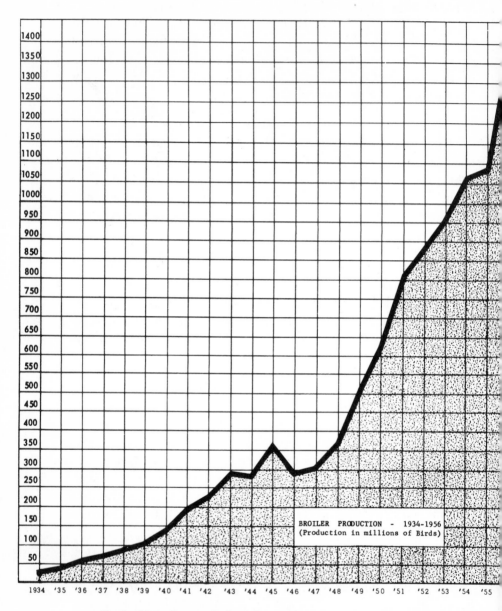

Figure 29-2. Commercial Broiler Production, 1934-1956. (Courtesy *The Broiler Growing Magazine*)

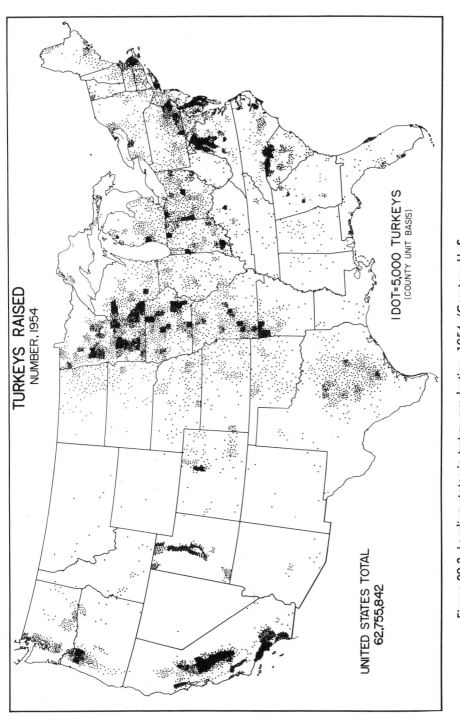

TURKEYS RAISED
NUMBER, 1954

UNITED STATES TOTAL
62,755,842

1 DOT = 5,000 TURKEYS
(COUNTY UNIT BASIS)

Figure 29-3. Leading states in turkey production, 1954. (Courtesy U. S. Department of Commerce, Bureau of Census)

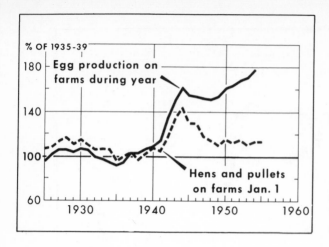

Figure 29-4. Chicken numbers and egg production. (Courtesy U.S.D.A. Agricultural Marketing Service)

number had increased to 33 millions. The number of turkeys produced in this country decreased somewhat following World War II, but increased after 1948, and by 1957 approximately 80.6 million birds were produced.

Turkey is no longer just a Thanksgiving and holiday treat. It is served the year around and competes with beef, pork, mutton, and chicken at the consumer markets.

California led all states in the production of turkeys in 1957, with 14.5 million birds produced. Minnesota ranked second, with 9.8 millions. Other states with high production were: Virginia, 6.8 millions; Iowa, 6.3 millions; Texas, 4.7 millions; Missouri, 3.0 millions; and Ohio, 3.0 million birds.

Eggs. The average hen in this nation up to 1937 produced about 120 to 130 eggs per year. Since 1937 the average production per hen has increased annually, with an average production in 1956 of 196 eggs.

The high states in value of eggs produced in 1956 were California, 148 million dollars; Pennsylvania, 137 million; and Iowa, 133 million. Next high-ranking states were Minnesota, New Jersey, Illinois, New York, and Ohio.

Consumption of Poultry Products

Poultry and eggs rate with milk as the best-balanced protein foods for the human diet. These foods have always been considered essential in our diet, but we have not always been able to provide quantities of the products in the amounts needed by the peoples of this nation and of the world. Refrigeration, improvements in methods of processing, and improved methods of distribution have increased the demand for poultry products.

Per Capita Consumption. Consumption of poultry products during the 1945 to 1958 period was at near peak levels. Production of these products has been high and per capita income has also been high. Too, we have had increases in population of about 3 million persons yearly. Each year we have more people to feed.

Chicken and Broiler Consumption. The per capita consumption of chicken and broilers in 1957 was estimated to be 25.6 pounds per person. Nearly 76 per cent of this amount was consumed as broiler meat. During the 1935-1939 period, chicken consumption averaged 16.5 pounds, while only 1.4 pounds of broilers were consumed. Broiler consumption per person in 1957 was double the 1950 figure.

Turkey Consumption. The average person in the 1930 to 1934 period consumed about 2 pounds of turkey each year. In 1957 the average person consumed 5.8 pounds. Turkey production and consumption is on the increase.

Per Capita Egg Consumption. Egg consumption in the United States averaged 369 eggs per person in 1956. The per capita consumption between 1935 and 1939 was 298 eggs. During the 1947 to 1951 period, it averaged 389 eggs per person.

Opportunities in Poultry Production

Farmers must always be alert for methods of increasing net farm income. Poultry production on the average farm may be a small, secondary industry, but changes in production and management can bring about sizable increases in farm income. An increase in flock size from 300 to 600 hens will more than double the gross income from the enterprise, providing other factors remain constant. By increasing the average egg production per hen, it is possible to increase further the income from the laying flock. The use of better methods in growing out larger numbers of broilers and roasters also presents opportunities for increasing farm income.

Specialized Poultry Farms. On some farms poultry production may be made the major enterprise. According to the 1954 *Census of the United States*, specialized poultry farms comprised 4.6 per cent of the total farms of the nation, but they had on them about 33 per cent of the nation's chickens, and produced nearly 70

Figure 29-5. The Schenk Hatchery farm located at the foot of the mountains near Harrisburg, Virginia. (Courtesy The Schenk Hatchery)

per cent of all poultry and poultry products sold, 45 per cent of the eggs sold, and 90 per cent of the broilers and turkeys raised. Young men find specialized poultry raising stimulating and profitable, but a large percentage of our poultry farms are operated by men over 50 years of age. Specialized poultry production apparently attracts men who retire from general farming, or from other employment.

Opportunities in Poultry for Youth on the Home Farm. The poultry enterprise on the average farm provides excellent farming program opportunities for 4-H Club and Future Farmers of America chapter members. In most cases it is a small enterprise and rather poorly managed. Dad and Mother may be very happy to turn the flock or enterprise over to son or daughter on a partnership basis. Some very excellent poultry enterprises have been developed in this way, and several of our best commercial poultrymen and poultrywomen got their starts in this manner.

Advantages of Poultry Farming. Poultry production as a minor enterprise, and as a specialized business, has many advantages for the farmer who likes poultry and is industrious. For success a poultryman must be familiar with the best practices of production and marketing, and must use good judgment in managing the enterprise. The following are desirable features of poultry production.

Poultry and Eggs Are Essential Foods. The demand for poultry and eggs is quite permanent. Poultry is appetizing and popular as a meat. Eggs are highly digestible and nutritious. Future demand for high-quality poultry and eggs appears bright.

Quick Returns. Three-pound broilers can be produced in eight or ten weeks. Pullets begin laying in four months.

Efficient Production. A three-pound broiler can be produced on seven and one-half to eight pounds of feed. No other meat product can be produced as efficiently on the farm. A dozen eggs can be produced on five to seven pounds of feed.

Poultry Income Is Distributed Throughout the Year. Income from a laying flock and from broiler production is distributed throughout the year. All of the income does not come once or twice during the year.

Poultry Production Is Adapted to Acreages and Small Farms. The average size of specialized poultry farms is less than 70 acres. Chickens, turkeys, and broilers may be produced in the backyards in cities and small towns, on acreages, or on farms.

Quick Turnover of Capital. Capital invested in broiler production is returned in less than three months, and capital invested in a laying flock starts coming back in about four months. Income from turkeys is somewhat slower, depending upon the weight of turkeys produced.

Poultry Markets Are Standardized and Well-established. Eggs and poultry are sold according to grade, and many avenues are available for marketing of poultry products.

Poultry Nets High Returns per $100 Worth of Feed Fed. According to Illinois Farm Bureau Farm Management records, poultry enterprises on the Illinois farms studied returned $162 for each $100 invested in feed over a 23 year period, 1933 to 1955. Only dairy cattle returned more income per $100 worth of feed fed. Dairy cattle returned $171.00.

Poultry Production May Be a Full-time or Part-time Occupation. On most farms and acreages, poultry production is a part-time activity. On specialized farms, it may require all of the time of one or more persons. A sizable income may be obtained from poultry production, even though the individual producer also has other employment.

Poultry Production Is a Science which Involves Knowledge and Proven Practices. Much experimentation has taken place in poultry breeding, feeding, management, and marketing. An individual has information available to plan profitable production and management programs.

Women, Children, and Elderly Men Can be Successful in Poultry Production. Few farm enterprises can compete with poultry as sources of income for women, children, and elderly men. The work is not strenuous, and does not require high skill. Women and children may be very successful in poultry production.

Problems in Poultry Production. The production of broilers, chickens, turkeys, and eggs involve many problems. Certain limiting factors are apparent.

Disease and Parasite Problems. While chickens and turkeys are normally healthy, they are subject to many diseases and parasites. Losses may be heavy if proper methods of prevention and treatment have not been followed.

Problems in Feeding and Management. Feed costs may become excessive and the enterprise unprofitable, if the birds are not fed balanced rations in proper amounts. Housing, ventilation, and labor problems may also affect the profit from the enterprise.

Selection of Chicks, Poults, and Mature Birds. It takes good seed stock to have profitable production. Chicks and poults must be selected according to the use to be made of them, and they must be bought right. The laying flock must be carefully culled, and birds used in breeding pens must be carefully selected.

Problems in Marketing. The profit from the poultry enterprise is influenced by the market. Eggs, broilers, roasters, and turkeys bring more money during some seasons than others.

Size of Enterprise. The fact that a chick, hen, or turkey is short lived and requires only a small investment may cause the producer to become careless. The larger the unit, the easier it is to give the enterprise the care and management which it should receive.

Finance. Specialized poultry production requires a large volume for efficient production; hence capital is an important item.

Surplus Production. Improvement in production efficiency may bring about surpluses. Producers must control production to maintain a satisfactory market.

Quality of Products. Poultry products must compete with other products for the consumer food dollar. Products which are of poor quality cause a loss of market.

Summary

Nearly 12 per cent of our national farm income is derived from the sale of poultry products. This percentage almost equals the percentage of income from dairy, and exceeds the income from hogs. In some New England states, poultry brings in as much as 40 to 60 per cent of farm income. California, Pennsylvania, Iowa, and Texas led all states in total income from chickens, eggs, broilers, and turkeys in 1954.

In 1956 nearly 1.3 billion broilers and 485 million chickens were produced in this country. California and Iowa led all states in the number of chickens on farms on January 1, 1958. Broiler production has increased rapidly during the past few years especially in Delaware, Georgia, Maryland, and Arkansas.

Turkey production has increased from a production of 4 millions in 1920 to 80.6 millions in 1957. California, Minnesota, Virginia, and Iowa were the high production states in 1957.

Egg production per hen has increased from about 120 eggs per hen in 1937 to 196 eggs per hen in 1956. California, Pennsylvania, Iowa, and Minnesota led the states in value of eggs produced in 1956.

Nearly 26 pounds of chickens and broilers, 5.8 pounds of turkey, and about 369 eggs were consumed by each person in the United States in 1957.

Poultry production is big business. Chickens are raised on about 71 per cent of our farms. Poultry production offers excellent opportunities for youth, women, and elderly men.

Poultry production has many advantages. Chickens and eggs are staple foods. Chickens are efficient converters of feeds into meat. The returns from the enterprise are rapid, as is the capital turnover. The income is distributed throughout the year, and the enterprise is adapted to large or small farms. Poultry production may be a full or part-time occupation.

Raising chickens and turkeys involves management problems related to selection of stock, feeding, housing, disease control, brooding, management, and marketing. Knowledge is available, however, regarding proven practices. Poultry production can be a very profitable enterprise.

● Questions

1. What percentage of your home farm income is derived from the sale of: a. chickens? b. broilers? c. turkeys? d. eggs?
2. What states lead in the production of: a. chickens? b. broilers? c. turkeys? d. eggs?
3. How much feed does it take to produce a pound of broiler?
4. How much feed does it take to produce a dozen eggs?
5. What changes have come about in the production of poultry products during the past twenty years?
6. Is poultry production increasing or decreasing in your home community? Why?
7. What are the advantages of poultry production over swine, sheep, dairy, and beef production?
8. What problems have you encountered in producing poultry products on your farm?
9. What should be the place of poultry production on your farm? Explain.

● References

Botsford, Harold E., *The Economics of Poultry Management,* John Wiley and Sons, Inc., New York, 1952.

Card, Leslie E., *Poultry Production,* Lea and Febiger, Philadelphia, 1952.

U. S. Department of Agriculture, *Dairy and Poultry Market Statistics, 1956,* Agricultural Marketing Service, Washington, D. C., 1957.

U. S. Department of Agriculture, *Livestock and Poultry Inventory,* Agricultural Marketing Service, January 1, 1958.

Winters, A. R. and E. M. Funk, *Poultry Science and Practice,* J. B. Lippincott Company, Philadelphia, 1956.

Selecting Chicks and Birds for Production

The successful poultryman is very careful in buying chicks, and in selecting birds for his breeding or laying flock. The poultry enterprise is something like a twenty-story building in the city. The building is no better than its foundation. If it is built on a poor foundation, the building is weak, requires considerable upkeep, and is a poor investment. The chicks or pullets that you buy are the foundation for your poultry enterprise. Good feeding, housing, management, and marketing practices can overcome in part poor foundation stock, but for maximum profits you must begin with good stock.

Selecting a Breed

We have breeds of cattle which are kept primarily for milk production, and breeds which are kept for the production of meat. We have much the same situation in chickens. We have numerous

Figure 30-1. White Plymouth Rocks. (Courtesy *Poultry Tribune*)

Figure 30-2. White Wyandottes. Note the rose combs. (Courtesy *Poultry Tribune*)

Figure 30-3. Single-comb Rhode Island Reds. (Courtesy *Poultry Tribune*)

Figure 30-4. New Hampshires. (Courtesy *Poultry Tribune*)

560

Figure 30-5. Single-comb white Leghorns. (Courtesy *Poultry Tribune*)

Figure 30-6. Single-comb white Minorcas. (Courtesy *Poultry Tribune*)

Figure 30-7. Buff Orpingtons. (Courtesy *Poultry Tribune*)

Figure 30-8 White Cornish. (Courtesy *Poultry Tribune*)

561

breeds, varieties, and crosses. Some of them are kept primarily for egg production, while others have as their major function the production of meat.

When we buy a tractor, we select one which is best adapted to the needs of our farm, one which is efficient in operation, and one which is available at a reasonable price. We select chicks or foundation poultry in the same manner. There is no one best make or size of tractor, and there is no one best breed or variety of chicken. We select a breed, or cross, to suit our individual farm, community, and market needs.

Classes of Chickens. There are many classes of chickens, but most of the chickens produced in this country are produced from breeding stock of the following four classes: (1) American, (2) Mediterranean, (3) English, and (4) Asiatic.

American Class. The Plymouth Rock, Wyandotte, Rhode Island Red, New Hampshire, and Jersey Black Giant are the most popular of the American Class. Other breeds in this class are the Rhode Island White, the Java, the Dominique, and the Holland.

No birds in this class have feathered shanks. They all have yellow shanks and skin, and have red ear lobes. The breeds of the American class have been bred for both meat and egg production.

Mediterranean Class. The Leghorn, Minorca, and Ancona breeds are the most popular Mediterranean breeds in this country. The other breeds of this class grown in this country are the Blue Andalusian, Buttercup, and Spanish. The Mediterranean breeds are kept primarily for egg production. They are smaller than the American, English, and Asiatic breeds, and have white ear lobes. They all lay white eggs.

English Class. The most popular breeds of this class are the Cornish, Australorp, and the Orpington. Three other breeds are grown, the Dorking, Sussex, and Red Cap. The English breeds have good meat quality. They are large, and with the exception of the Cornish, have white skin.

Asiatic Class. The three breeds of this class, the Brahma, Cochin, and Langshan, are not grown in large numbers in this country, but have been used in producing the American breeds. All three breeds have feathered shanks, are large and heavy boned, and have red ear lobes. With the exception of the Black Langshan, they have yellow skin. The Asiatic breeds are produced largely for meat production.

Figure 30-9. Australorps. (Courtesy *Poultry Tribune*)

Figure 30-10. Light Brahmas. (Courtesy *Poultry Tribune*)

Figure 30-11. Buff Cochins. (Courtesy *Poultry Tribune*)

Figure 30-12. White Langshans. (Courtesy *Poultry Tribune*)

563

Breeds and Varieties of Chickens. The characteristics of the most common breeds of chickens are shown in Table 54. Some breeds are subdivided into varieties according to color of feathers and type of comb. There are seven varieties of Plymouth Rocks, the barred, white, buff, silver penciled, partridge, Columbian, and blue. Wyandottes have eight varieties classified according to color of feather. There are four varieties of Orpingtons, the buff, black, white, and blue. The Leghorn and Minorca breeds are subdivided into varieties according to both color and type of comb. White and buff are the most popular colors.

TABLE 54

CHARACTERISTICS OF COMMON BREEDS OF CHICKENS

Breed	Weight (lbs.)	Color of Skin	Color of Shank	Shanks Feathered	Type of Comb	Color of Earlobe	Color of Egg
AMERICAN BREEDS:							
Jersey White Giant	10 -13	Yellow	Yellow	No	Single	Red	Brown
New Hampshire	6½-8½	Yellow	Yellow	No	Single	Red	Brown
Plymouth Rock	7½-9½	Yellow	Yellow	No	Single and rose	Red	Brown
Rhode Island Red	6½-8½	Yellow	Yellow	No	Single and rose	Red	Brown
Wyandotte	6½-8½	Yellow	Yellow	No	Rose	Red	Brown
MEDITERRANEAN BREEDS:							
Ancona	4½-6	Yellow	Yellow	No	Single and rose	White	White
Leghorn	4½-6	Yellow	Yellow	No	Single and rose	White	White
Minorca (white)	6½-8	White	White	No	Single	White	White
ENGLISH BREEDS:							
Australorp	6½-8½	White	Dark slate	No	Single	Red	Brown
Cornish (white)	8 -10	Yellow	Yellow	No	Pea	Red	Brown
Orpington (buff and white)	8 -10	White	White	No	Single	Red	Brown
ASIATIC BREEDS:							
Brahma (light)	9 -11	Yellow	Yellow	Yes	Pea	Red	Brown
Cochin	8½-11	Yellow	Yellow	Yes	Single	Red	Brown
Langshan (black)	7 -10	White	Bluish-black	Yes	Single	Red	Brown

Nearly 200 varieties of chickens are listed in the *American Standard of Perfection*, but only five were of commercial importance in 1943. The White Leghorn, the New Hampshire, the White

Plymouth Rock, the Barred Plymouth Rock, and the Rhode Island Red accounted for about three-fourths of all chickens raised.

Hybrid and Crossbred Chickens. Considerable work has been done recently in the production of crossbred or hybrid chickens. Agricultural experiment stations and commercial poultry breeders have developed inbred lines, and have made line crosses similar to those in the production of hybrid corn. The use of hybrid and crossbred chickens has been on the increase, both in the production of eggs and in broiler production.

Figure 30-13. Austra-Whites (An Australorp male—white Leghorn female cross). (Courtesy *Poultry Tribune*)

Most farmers rely upon the commercial hatcheryman to maintain the breeding flocks and make the crosses necessary to produce hybrid or crossbred chicks. The lines and crosses available vary with the community and with the section of the country.

White Rocks crossed with the New Hampshires and with Wyandottes are popular crosses. The crossing of white Cornish chickens with White Rocks, with White Wyandottes, and with New Hampshires produces excellent broilers. Most broilers produced in this nation are from parent stock of these breeds.

It has been found that increased egg production may be obtained by crossing inbred lines of high-producing strains of our standard breeds of chickens. Many of the commercial laying flocks in some areas are composed of crossbred or hybrid chickens. Crosses of the Black Minorca, White Leghorn, New Hampshire, and Rhode Island Red breeds are widely used in egg production.

TABLE 55

OFFICIAL EGG LAYING TESTS FOR 1955-1956

Breed	No. of Birds Entered	Points per Bird	Eggs per Bird	Per cent Mortality	Ave. Egg Size Oz./Doz.
Incrossbred	247	254	244	7.7	25.6
White Leghorn	3,276	247	237	11.4	25.4
Rhode Island Red	1,014	247	235	9.6	25.7
Crossbred	975	245	232	11.3	25.6
White Wyandotte	13	243	232	0.0	24.7
Barred Plymouth Rock	195	238	227	9.2	25.5
New Hampshires	156	216	211	10.2	25.3
White Plymouth Rock	286	209	202	11.2	25.5
Black Australorp	130	207	207	11.5	24.6
Brown Leghorn	26	203	194	11.5	25.5
Black Minorca	13	179	171	0.0	25.4
Anconas	26	169	156	7.7	25.9
Columbian Plymouth Rock	13	164	165	15.4	24.1
All Breeds	6,370	242	232	10.8	25.1

Report 18, Council of American Official Poultry Tests, 1955-56

TABLE 56

DISTRIBUTION OF BIRDS IN NATIONAL POULTRY
IMPROVEMENT PLAN HATCHERY FLOCKS, 1950-1954

Breed	Year				
	1950	1951	1952	1953	1954
	Per cent	Per cent	Per cent	Per cent	Per cent
New Hampshire	38.9	41.4	36.2	25.4	16.0
S. C. White Leghorn	21.6	18.9	20.1	18.9	19.2
White Plymouth Rock	10.1	11.9	14.8	23.1	29.5
Barred Plymouth Rock	5.8	4.0	3.5	2.2	1.3
Rhode Island Red	4.1	3.3	3.2	2.7	2.7
Cross-mated	16.4	14.3	16.0	19.7	21.2
Incross-mated	—	3.4	4.0	5.1	7.0
Other	3.1	2.8	2.2	2.9	3.1
Total	100.0	100.0	100.0	100.0	100.0

Agricultural Statistics, 1955, U.S.D.A.

Popularity of the Breeds. Some breeds and varieties of chickens are more popular in certain areas than in others. An indication of the popularity of the breeds is shown in the summaries of entries in the official poultry production tests conducted in this nation, and in the list of breeds represented in the National Poultry Improvement plan.

Buying Baby Chicks

Most poultrymen buy their chicks. According to U.S.D.A. data, less than 8 per cent of the chicks produced in this nation in 1949 were hatched on farms. The number hatched on farms in the Corn Belt is very small. Farmers rely upon the commercial hatcheries for their chicks, for they are able to maintain better breeding flocks and can produce healthier chicks at a lower cost than can be done on farms.

The hatchery business has become a large industry. More than 6,000 hatcheries are in operation in the nation, and nearly one-fourth of them are located in the North Central region or the Corn Belt states.

Georgia, California, Texas, Indiana, North Carolina, Missouri, and Arkansas led the states in number of chicks hatched in 1955. Of the 1,853 million chicks hatched in the nation in 1955, 545 million were hatched in the South Atlantic states and 518 million were hatched in the East and West North Central States.

Chicks are raised each year to replace the laying flock, and for broiler or roaster production. While the use to be made of chickens may vary, much the same factors are involved in selecting and buying chicks. They are: (1) source, (2) time to order, (3) breeding and quality, (4) sex, (5) age, and (6) price.

Source. *Buy Near Home.* It is best to buy chicks from hatcheries close to home where you can pick them up, if other factors are equal. Chicks can be transported long distances, but losses are usually lighter when chicks are moved only short distances. It is easier to get an adjustment in case of loss when you buy close to home, and you are better able to determine the reputation of the hatchery.

Reputation and Reliability of Hatchery. The reputation of a hatchery spreads rapidly from one person to another. Before ordering chicks, check with other poultrymen concerning the reliability of the various hatcheries. Hatcheries which are operating under the supervision of the National Poultry Improvement Plan, through the official state agency, are usually good sources.

Shipping Chicks. Chicks should be placed in the brooder and fed within 24 to 48 hours after the hatching time. Government regulations limit the time chicks can be in transit to 72 hours. Choose a hatchery which can transport the chicks to you in as short a time as possible. Chicks should be shipped in ventilated boxes, with no more than 25 chicks in a section.

Time to Order. The time to order chicks will vary with the hatchery, but it is usually best to place your order several weeks or months before you wish delivery. The best hatcheries have orders booked several weeks in advance.

Early Hatched Chicks Make the Most Money. Broilers and roasters hatched in February and March will reach the market before prices drop in the early summer. Early hatched pullets can be brought into production before egg prices reach their peak in the fall. February and March chicks are best as laying flock replacements. Allow a few more weeks for heavy breeds to mature than for lighter breeds.

Figure 30-14. Breed selection should be given careful consideration in both broiler and egg production. These birds are foundation stock in broiler production. (Courtesy DeKalb Agricultural Assn., Inc.)

Breeding and Quality. The most important factor in buying chicks is to get healthy chicks of desirable breeding.

Cheap Chicks Are Usually Expensive. The few cents difference between the price of a good chick and that of an inferior one may result in as much as a dollar or more increase in egg production per bird, or the difference between profit and loss in raising broilers.

Buy Chicks from Pullorum-Free Flocks. Check with the hatcheryman concerning the health of the flocks. Pullorum may be communicated from the hen to the chick through the egg. Flocks supervised by the state agency of the National Poultry Improvement Plan are preferred.

Check the Production Records of the Parent Stock. Certain strains of the various breeds of chickens have been proven as egg producers, and as good broiler producers. Find out everything possible about the birds used in the hatchery flocks. Visit the flocks if possible. Check broiler production and egg laying test records. Buy chicks that are bred to produce.

Sex. The use to be made of the chicks and the price determine the sex to buy.

Straight-Run Chicks. Chicks as they come from the incubator are straight-run chicks. The number of males is about equal to the number of females. Some farmers like to buy straight-run chicks. They feed out the cockerels as broilers and keep the pullets for the home flock. In raising straight-run chicks, about three chicks should be purchased for every pullet that is to be placed in the laying house.

Sexed Chicks. It is sometimes advantageous to buy sexed chicks. Leghorn cockerels are not usually profitable as broilers. Poultrymen desiring pullet replacements often prefer to pay nearly twice as much per chick for sexed pullets than they would have to pay for straight-run chicks. The price spread between straight-run and sexed heavy breeds is not as wide as with Leghorns.

Methods of Sexing. Efficient chick sexers can determine the sex of chicks without injuring them. Three methods are in use. Some crosses may be sexed by the color of down on the newly hatched chicks, while the sex of others may be determined by the length of primary wing feathers, or by the number of secondary wing feathers. The third method involves an examination of the rudimentary sex organs of the chick.

Selecting Chicks and Birds for Production • 569

Age. Some purchasers like to buy started chicks which are from two to four weeks old. Chick losses usually occur during the first week or two. By buying started chicks these losses may be avoided. The price of started chicks is usually high. There are times when it is more practical, convenient, and profitable to buy started chicks.

Price. When all other factors are equal, price may be the determining factor in buying chicks. Usually, however, other factors are not equal. Consider price in buying chicks, but remember that money invested in high-quality chicks brings in a better income than capital invested in poor-quality chicks.

Culling the Flock

Feed cost in poultry production is an important item. According to a three-year study based upon Missouri poultry records, hens that laid an average of 225 eggs each paid their owner a labor income of $2.86 each. Hens that laid an average of 124 eggs produced a labor income of only 22 cents each. When feed costs are high, the importance of culling is magnified. Every nonproductive and inefficient bird in a flock lowers the profit from the enterprise. Each hen in the average flock must lay 150 or more eggs to come out even. During some seasons, the production must be higher to keep out of the red. One of the best means of increasing egg production per hen is to cull out the nonlaying boarders.

Chicks and broilers need culling as well. There is no need to waste feed by feeding inferior birds.

Culling Chicks. Crippled, weak, and runty chicks should be disposed of when chicks are placed in the brooder house. It does not pay to keep cull chicks. They seldom make a profit and they may become carriers of disease.

Culling Pullets. Pullets should be culled carefully as they are placed in the laying house in the fall. Only well-grown, healthy, mature birds should be kept. Birds which are undersized, deformed, or diseased should be culled out. Keep only pullets which have attractive heads, bright eyes, good beaks, and bright feathers.

Culling the Laying Flock. Most poultrymen try to maintain flocks with 60 to 70 per cent egg production. They want 60 or 70 eggs from each 100 hens each day. To do this, they must watch the flock closely and remove the nonlayers. Culling is not a practice

Figure 30-15. Birds to be used in hatchery flocks are carefully selected. (Courtesy Automatic Poultry Feeder Company)

to be done once a year when the pullets are placed in the laying house. It is a continuous process. Some culling should be done each week or month. The longer you leave the nonlayer in the flock, the greater the loss in feed.

Some poultrymen do their culling at night with the aid of a flashlight. The culled birds are placed in a coop where they can be examined more carefully the following morning.

Culling Formula. Dr. N. R. Mehrhof of the University of Florida has developed a formula which gives the percentage of laying below which we should cull. The formula is as follows:

$$\frac{\text{Price of 100 pounds of feed}}{\text{Price of 1 dozen eggs}} \times 3 = \begin{array}{l}\text{Per cent production necessary to} \\ \text{pay feed bill.}\end{array}$$

Using the formula, if feed is $4.50 per 100 pounds and eggs are 35 cents per dozen, a poultryman would need a 38½ per cent rate of lay to pay the feed bill.

How to Select Good Layers. It is not difficult to select the layers from the nonlayers. Anyone familiar with chickens can become quite skilled in culling practices in a rather short time. Selection and culling are usually based upon the following: (1) condition of comb and wattles, (2) brightness of the eye, (3) body capacity, (4) handling quality, (5) condition of the vent, (6) amount of pigment, (7) stage of molt, (8) health and vigor.

Selecting Chicks and Birds for Production • 571

Figure 30-16. (A) The head of a good layer. (B) An undesirable head. (Courtesy *Poultry Tribune*)

Condition of Comb and Wattles. The comb of a layer is large, red, and glossy. It is warm because of blood circulation. The comb of a nonlayer is small, pale, dry, stiff, and scaly. The head of a non-layer may be puffed or swollen. The wattles of layers are large, bright red, and warm. The wattles shrink and become pale when the hen goes out of production.

Brightness of Eye. A good layer has a large, prominent, and bright eye. Poor layers have small, sunken, or dull eyes. The eye is a good indication of health. Birds with gray eyes or irregular-shaped pupils should be culled. They may be infected with leucosis.

Body Capacity. To be a good layer, a bird must have a big body. Layers consume large quantities of feed and need space in the body cavity for the production of eggs. The abdomen of a layer is expanded. There should be room for two to four fingers between the pubic bones. These bones are on either side of the vent. The pubic bones in nonlayers are close together. There may be room for only one finger between them.

The width of the abdomen is determined by the width between the pubic bones. The depth is measured in terms of the number of fingers which can be placed between the pin, or pubic bones, and the breast bone, or the keel bone. There is room for three or four fingers between these bones on a good layer, while there is space for only one or two fingers on the nonlayer.

Handling Quality. The body of a layer is soft and pliable, while that of a nonlayer is hard and contracted. The layer has little fat on its abdomen, while that of the nonlayer may be fatty. Quite often the pubic bones of nonlayers are thickened because of fat.

Condition of the Vent. The best way to tell if a hen is now laying is to examine the vent and the distance between the pubic bones. The vent of a layer is large, moist, and oblong. The vent of a nonlayer is small, dry, and round.

Amount of Pigment. Many of the common breeds of chickens have yellow skin due to yellow pigment. The color is also evident around the eyes, on the beak, around the vent, and on the shanks. As pullets go into production, this pigment and the pigment in feeds

Figure 30-17. (Upper arrows) Measuring the space between the pubic bones. There is room for three fingers between the pubic bones of the good layer at the left, whereas only two fingers can be placed between the pubic bones of the poor layer on the right. (Lower arrows) Measuring the depth of abdomen. Four fingers can be placed between the pubic bones and the breast bone of the good layer at the left. There is room for only two fingers between these bones on the poor layer at the right. (Courtesy *Poultry Tribune*)

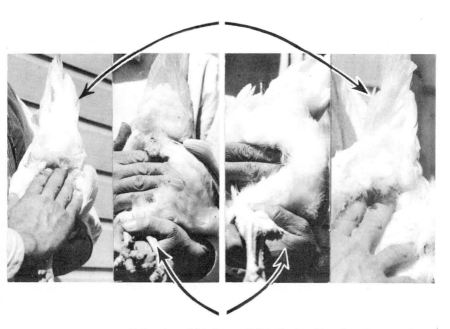

Selecting Chicks and Birds for Production • 573

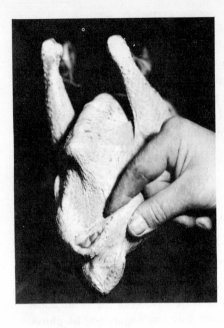

Figure 30-18. The abdomen of a layer is loose and pliable. The vent is large, moist, and oblong. (Courtesy *Poultry Tribune*)

goes to produce the yolks of the eggs. The heavier the production, the more pigment that is removed from the bird. An examination of the pigment is an excellent method of telling how long a hen has been laying, or how long she has been out of production.

When a hen begins to lay, the pigment leaves the vent rapidly. No pigment will remain after five or six eggs have been laid. A yellow vent is a sign of a nonlayer. A white vent in a yellow skinned breed indicates that the hen is a layer.

The pigment begins to leave the eye-ring shortly after it leaves the vent. After the second week of production, there usually is no pigment remaining in the eye-ring. The pigment in the ear lobes of the Mediterranean breeds leaves just a little later.

It takes a longer period of time for the pigment to leave the beak and shanks. The beak begins to fade at the face, and is fully bleached after five to seven weeks of production. The shanks lose their color more slowly than the beak, and are not completely bleached until the hen has been in production from four to six months.

Hens which continue to show yellow pigment should be examined carefully. Sometimes they can be culled on the basis of pigment alone, but it is usually best to consider other factors before marketing the bird.

Figure 30-19. (A) The wing of a hen previous to the start of the molting period. (B) The wing of a hen in process of molting. (Courtesy Poultry Science Department, Oklahoma State University)

Stage of Molt. Chickens grow new crops of feathers each year. Poor layers shed their feathers, or molt, slowly. Good layers molt rapidly. Poor layers usually begin to molt early in the year, while good layers delay molting until late in the fall. Poultrymen who keep over their pullet flocks for a second year of production can use molt as a means of selecting the good layers.

An examination of the feathers on a hen will indicate the stage of molt. Feathers are shed in the following order: (1) head, (2) neck, (3) breast, (4) body, and (5) wings and tail.

Pullets put into the laying house in the fall should not molt until late the following fall. Pullets which begin molting in May or June should be sold since they go out of production during the molting period, and it takes about three or four months to molt.

The length of time a hen has been out of production can be estimated by counting the number of new primary feathers in the wing. There are ten of these feathers in each wing. The feathers are shed from the axial feather, which separates the primary from the secondary wing feathers, at two week intervals. Slow molters shed one feather at a time. Rapid molters may shed two or three feathers at a time. It takes about six weeks to grow a new feather.

Selecting Chicks and Birds for Production • 575

By adding to the six weeks required to produce the first new feather, and two weeks for each additional new feather, it is possible to calculate the length of time the bird has been out of production. A hen with three new feathers has been out of production for ten weeks.

Farmers who maintain pullet flocks can make very little use of molt in culling the flock. It is an important factor in selecting hens to hold over for a second year of production.

Health and Vigor. A good layer is well developed and has size and body capacity, as well as a bright eye and clean-cut face. She is active, carries herself well, and appears vigorous. Small, weak hens, with little body capacity or with poor heads, should be culled.

Table 57 is a guide for selection and culling of layers.

TABLE 57

GUIDE FOR SELECTION AND CULLING OF LAYERS

Select	Characters	Cull
Vigorous, active, good capacity.	Health and vitality	Weak, sluggish, undersized, lacking capacity.
Full, smooth, a glossy bright red.	Comb and wattles	Shrunken, dry, dull, pale, scaly.
Prominent, keen, sparkling.	Eye	Sunken, listless.
Large, smooth, moist, elliptical in shape.	Vent	Small, puckered, dry, round.
Thin, flexible, well spread.	Pubic bones	Thick, hard, close together.
Soft, pliable, expanded, covered with thin velvety skin.	Abdomen	Contracted, firm, covered with thick, coarse skin.
Bleached vent, eye-ring, ear lobe, beak, shanks.	Pigmentation	Yellow pigment in vent, eye-ring, ear-robe, beak, shanks.
Late, rapid.	Molt	Early, slow.

Florida Bulletin 149

Summary

Most chickens produced in the United States are of the American, English, or Mediterranean breeds. The Asiatic breeds are grown largely for meat production. The Orpington, Australorp, and Cornish are English breeds produced in this country. Only five breeds of chickens are of commercial importance here. They are the White Leghorn, the New Hampshire, the White Plymouth Rock, the Barred Plymouth Rock, and the Rhode Island Red. The other breeds are grown in limited numbers and are used in making crosses.

The production of hybrid and crossbred chicks is increasing. Hybrid chicks are produced by crossing inbred lines of one breed with inbred lines of one or more breeds. Crossbred chicks are produced by crossing noninbred birds of two or more breeds. Crosses of New Hampshire, White Plymouth Rock, Wyandotte, and Cornish breeds are popular in broiler production. New Hampshire, White Leghorn, Rhode Island Red, and Minorca breeds are popular in producing laying stock.

Chicks should be ordered early and from a reliable hatcheryman. Only chicks from pullorum-free and production-tested flocks should be purchased. It is best to buy chicks locally.

Culling is important in poultry production. Baby chicks should be culled when they are placed in the brooder house. Pullets should be carefully culled when they are placed in the laying house. Layers should be culled periodically throughout the year.

Keep only large, well-developed, healthy hens with large, bright red combs, prominent and bright eyes, and good body capacity. There should be room for two to three fingers between the pubic bones, and three or four fingers between the pubic bones and the breastbone.

Layers of the yellow skin breeds should have no pigment around the vent, eye-ring, beak, or the shanks. Early and slow molters should be sold. They go out of production during the molting period which may last three or four months.

Buy only high-quality chicks. Keep only the best pullets for laying flock, and cull them periodically. Don't waste feed, labor, and housing on inferior birds.

- ## Questions

1. What are the major classes of chickens produced in this country?
2. How do these classes differ in conformation and use?
3. Which breeds of chickens are best for egg production?
4. Which breeds, or crosses, are best for broiler production?

Selecting Chicks and Birds for Production • 577

5. What is the place of hybrid and crossbred chickens on our farms?
6. What factors must be considered in deciding where to obtain chicks?
7. Does it pay to buy started chicks?
8. Which is better to buy, straight-run or sexed chicks?
9. What factors should be considered in culling laying hens?
10. What type of head, comb, and wattles are desired in a laying hen?
11. How can pigment be used in culling a flock of chickens?
12. How can you measure the body capacity of a hen?
13. How can molt be used in culling hens?
14. Explain the formula used to determine the rate of culling based upon rate of lay, price of feed, and price of eggs.

● *References*

American Poultry Association, Inc., *American Standard of Perfection*, Oklahoma City, Oklahoma, 1953.

Council of American Official Poultry Tests, *Report No. 18, Production Records For the Period 1955-1956.* Cornell University, Ithaca, New York.

Hall, G. O. and D. R. Marble, *Culling for Egg Production*, Extension Bulletin 887, Cornell University, Ithaca, New York, 1954.

U. S. Department of Agriculture, *Breeds of Chickens for Meat and Egg Production*, Farmer's Bulletin 2065, Washington, D.C., 1954.

Feeding and Management
of the Laying Flock

The spread between the price of eggs and the cost of production has gradually become smaller since about 1929. Poultrymen now must use better laying stock and methods of production in order to have profitable enterprises. A few years ago, the U. S. Department of Agriculture indicated that hens must produce at least 150 eggs per year to break even. The average hen in a Nebraska study in 1951-1952 laid 184 eggs at a loss of about 65 cents per hen. Hens in New York which produced an average of 152 eggs lost their owners an average of 25 cents each. Production costs vary from farm to farm, but it appears that hens must produce an average of 200 to 215 eggs per year to be profitable.

Methods of Increasing Profits

There are four ways of increasing the profit from our laying flocks: (1) by increasing production, (2) by decreasing production costs, (3) by better marketing, or (4) by using a combination of the three methods just named.

Feed and labor costs make up 75 to 85 per cent of the cost of producing eggs. Feed costs per dozen eggs go down with increased production per hen. Labor costs go down with increases in flock size. In a Pennsylvania study, flocks averaging 241 hens lost their owners 28 cents per hen per year. Flocks averaging 645 birds netted their owners an average of $1.28 per hen, while flocks averaging 1,531 hens showed a profit of $1.67 per hen.

A profitable flock should average 50 to 70 per cent production during the entire year. It takes good feeding and management to get this kind of production. We must start out with good pullets, and they have to be properly housed. Adequate rations must be provided in proper amounts. Desirable roosting, feeding, watering, and laying equipment must be provided. Adequate lighting and ventilation are essential, and we have to guard against health problems. Careful consideration of these factors may be the key to profitable production on your farm.

Moving Pullets to the Laying House

Pullets of the light breeds will have their hen feathers and red combs, and are ready to start laying when they are about five months of age. Heavy pullets begin laying a few weeks later. February-hatched pullets should be moved to the laying house in August or early September.

Have the Laying House Clean. Clean the laying house thoroughly a week or two before time to move the pullets. Spray the floor, walls, and equipment with disinfectant. Clean and disinfect the dropping pit if used, and place new litter on the floor. Clean feeders and waterers, and have them in working condition. Clean and disinfect the nests, and provide new nesting materials, if they are to be used. If you keep over any old hens, have them in a separate place.

Care of Pullets at Moving Time. Each pullet should be carefully examined at the time it is moved to the laying house. All culls should be removed, and those which are to be kept should be treated for lice with powdered sulphur or sodium fluoride. Try not to excite the birds at moving time. Watch the pullets the first night or two to see that they roost on the perches, rather than on the feeders or nests.

Figure 31-1. (above) Rhode Island Red pullets on range in Washington. (Courtesy Linn's Hatchery)

Figure 31-2. (below) An Illinois laying house, 26 feet by 46 feet. (Courtesy *Poultry Tribune*)

Housing the Laying Flock

The laying house is an important part of the poultry enterprise. Hens are very responsive to their environment. They need a clean, dry, well-ventilated, quiet, and comfortable house. On many farms the laying house is inadequate, and the hens are permitted to have the run of the farmstead. It pays to keep the laying flock confined to the laying house at all times.

Space Required. It does not pay to crowd the hens in the laying house. Two and one-half to three square feet of floor space should usually be provided for each bird for light breeds, and three and one-half square feet for the heavy breeds. Hens do not produce well under crowded conditions, and the house becomes

Feeding and Management of the Laying Flock • 581

difficult to ventilate properly and to keep clean. Crowding may encourage disease outbreaks. A house 20 feet by 40 feet will accommodate about 265 hens of the light breeds or 200 heavies.

Poultrymen can reduce the floor space area to 1½ or two square feet per bird when the feeders and waterers are placed in the roost area, the hens are debeaked to control cannibalism, and the birds are provided adequate feeder space and rations.

Roosts. From seven to eight inches of roost space should be provided for each bird. A flock of 200 hens will require from 120 to 130 feet of roost space. Roosts usually are located at the back of the house away from drafts. The roosts should be made of 2-x-2- or 2-x-3-inch material and should be placed 13 to 16 inches apart. Low roosts are preferred.

Dropping Pits. Dropping pits should be constructed below the roosts. They are much more satisfactory than dropping boards. The pits may be made in sections for ease in cleaning. A pit 16 to 18 inches deep will allow for use of deep litter on the floor. The pit should be closed on all sides with boards or wire, and 1-x-2-inch welded wire should be placed under the roosts to keep the birds out of the pit. The pit will need to be cleaned during hot weather to avoid ammonia injury to the eyes of the hens.

Deep Litter Is Recommended. Deep, or built-up, litter is the name applied to a system of litter management which involves the placing of four to six inches of fresh material on the floor of the house in August or September, and allowing it to build up with droppings and added litter until it is eight to 12 inches deep. The layer of litter is easier to keep dry than a thin layer, and has an insulating effect. The floor is warmer and drier. The addition of one

Figure 31-3. A good arrangement of roosts, dropping pit, and waterers. (Courtesy Wallaces' Farmer and Iowa Homestead)

Figure 31-4. Ground corn cobs make excellent litter. Note the arrangement of dropping pit. (Courtesy *Poultry Tribune*)

pound of hydrated lime to ten square feet of floor space aids the micro-organism action in the litter, thus reducing dampness.

Litter Materials. Chopped straw, shavings, ground corn cobs, or whole corn cobs properly used make good litters. Some poultry-men make a litter of 2/3 ground cobs and 1/3 whole cobs. Cane pulp, peanut hulls, and peat moss may also be used when free from injurious materials.

Care of Litter. The surface of the deep litter should be stirred frequently to prevent matting. The finely pulverized bottom layer should not be disturbed. The litter should be spread evenly on the floor, and wet material around the waterer should be removed and replaced with new dry material. The new litter should be mixed with the old and kept level.

Figure 31-5. (A) Community roll-away nest. Eggs roll to the front. (B) Individual nests placed on the wall of the laying house. (Courtesy of *Wallaces' Farmer and Iowa Homestead*)

A

B

Nests. There should be one square foot of nesting space for every four or five hens, and the nests should be alike to keep the hens from crowding into certain ones. The number, location, and type of nests affects egg breakage, shell cleanliness, and the labor required in gathering eggs.

Community nests are becoming popular. They are two feet wide and from four to 12 feet long. Eight-inch openings are made each four or five feet. Eggs are gathered from the front when the openings are in the back. Some nests have hail screen bottoms which slope so that the eggs roll into a trough.

Regardless of the type of nest used, they should have the following features:

1. The inside of the nests is dark.
2. They are easy to keep clean.
3. They provide an easy way to gather the eggs.
4. They are sturdy and easy for the hens to get into.
5. They can be closed at night.

Watering Equipment. A flock of 100 hens will drink from five to seven tons of water in a year. Eggs are about 65 per cent water, so the hens should have ample supply at all times. Automatic waterers will provide a ready supply of water and will eliminate much of the labor required to carry water and fill fountains.

The waterer may be placed on a stand above the litter. A wire platform aids in keeping the water clean. A pendulum guard may be placed over the opening to keep chickens out of it. If water is not piped into the chicken house, air pressure fountains may be used. Two five-gallon fountains or a four-foot automatic watering trough should be available for each 100 birds. Additional drinking space may be needed during hot weather.

Housing space and litter may be conserved by locating the waterers in the roost section of the house over the dropping pit. Some place containers below the waterers to catch splashed water.

Feeders. There should be about five inches of feeder space per hen, and the feeders should not be more than ten inches above the litter level. It is usually best to have one end of the feeder toward a window so that the feed will not be shaded. All feeders should be at the same height and have reels or grills to keep the feed clean and to prevent waste.

Figure 31-6. (left) A commercial feeder and automatic waterer in use in a laying house. (Courtesy *Wallaces' Farmer and Iowa Homestead*) Figure 31-7. (right) A beautiful flock of layers being fed a pelleted ration. (Grant Heilman photo. Courtesy Beacon Milling Co.)

A rack of lath or of two-inch poultry netting can be made to feed hay and greens. Each 100 hens should have about a half-foot space for grit and a foot space for oyster shell in small feeders along the wall.

Ventilation. Adequate insulation and ventilation make it possible for poultrymen to control the temperature in the laying house during all seasons of the year. Ventilation is needed to provide fresh air for the hens and to remove the moisture given off in breathing and droppings. Three to four gallons of moisture will be given off by 100 hens in one day.

Slot-Type Ventilation. An eight- to ten-inch slot ventilator located on the south wall just below the ceiling or eave and extending the length of the building is one of the best systems of ventilating the average farm laying house. An adjustable board can be used to regulate the amount of air admitted. The amount of opening will vary with the extent the house is insulated, the outside

TABLE 58

SCHEDULE FOR OPERATING SLOT VENTILATORS

Outside Temperature	House Temperature	Size of Opening
Below 0° F	25°-35° F	¼ to 1 inch opening
0°-30° F	35°-50° F	1 to 2 inch opening
30°-65° F	40°-65° F	2 inches to full opening
65° F and up	50° F and up	Full opening with windows out

Bulletin P108, Iowa State College

Feeding and Management of the Laying Flock • 585

temperature, and the number of birds in the house. Slot ventilators and windows are usually adequate, if properly managed, in ventilating houses from 20 to 25 feet wide.

Straw-Loft. The straw loft may be used effectively in many houses. It requires some labor and may be neglected, but it is an inexpensive method of providing desirable ventilation.

A layer of straw 1½ to three feet deep in the loft of a gable house with open or partially opened windows at either end is recommended.

Roof Ventilators. One 12-inch roof ventilator for each 125 birds is recommended in houses greater than 20 to 25 feet in width where forced ventilation is not used. The flue of the ventilator should extend to about 18 inches from the floor.

Forced Ventilation. Forced air ventilation systems are usually recommended for commercial laying houses that are 25 feet or wider. Most systems involve the use of exhaust fans, and air intakes. Poultry and electric power specialists should be consulted in planning the installation of a fan system of ventilation. A 600 bird capacity laying house will require two exhaust fans, each with a capacity of 750 cubic feet per minute. Eight intakes should be provided.

Insulation. Insulation conserves the heat generated by the birds in winter and keeps out the heat of the summer. In northern sections it is impossible to maintain desirable temperatures in the winter without the use of insulation. Accordion-type aluminum foil, blanket-type insulation, and ground corn cobs make excellent insulations.

Lighting. Artificial lights may stimulate egg production during the winter months from October until March. A hen should have a day of at least 13 hours. When there are ten hours of daylight, artificial light will be needed for three hours.

Figure 31-8. A forced-air ventilation system. Intake fan takes air in through divided overhead shaft. Foul air is drawn out at opposite end of house. A thermostat keeps temperature variation to four degrees or less. (Courtesy *Wallaces' Farmer and Iowa Homestead*)

586

Figure 31-9. This 30- x 50-foot laying house is fully insulated and has gravity ventilation. Note the slot ventilators under the eave. (Courtesy *Poultry Tribune*)

Figure 31-10. Using an inclining false ceiling as well as large glass windows and open areas with sliding doors on its south side, this house makes use of self-ventilation and solar heating. (Courtesy Honegger Farms and *Poultry Tribune*)

Morning Light Preferred. Providing artificial light in the morning avoids the problem of a dimming device to get the birds on the roosts at night. Time switches are available which turn the lights on and off automatically. One 60-watt bulb should be used for each 200 square feet of floor space, and each light should have a 16-inch reflector four inches deep. The lights should be placed in a row six or seven feet above the floor and directly over the feeders.

Types of Laying Houses. Plans for many types of laying houses are available. Those pictured are examples of satisfactory types.

Materials. Laying houses may be constructed of lumber, tile, concrete blocks, or metal.

Foundation and Floor. A six-inch concrete foundation is needed, extending 18 to 24 inches in the ground. The floor should slope about one inch in four feet.

Roof. A shed or low gable roof is satisfactory.

Windows. One square foot of window space for each 20 to 25 square feet of floor space is ample. Windows may be placed on only one side of houses 25 feet wide or less.

Insulation. Rigid board insulation made of wood or fiber is recommended because of its excellent insulation quality, ease in construction, and comparative low cost.

Feeding Laying Hens

Feed is the most important item of cost in producing eggs. Carefully culled pullets from high-production strains will usually produce profitably, if they are fed good rations, and are properly housed. Good rations alone, or good laying stock alone, will not insure good production. Most flocks are capable of producing more eggs than they are now producing. They have been fed inadequate rations. Hens use much the same nutrients as other farm animals, but they use them in different proportions and amounts. Hens consume very little roughage and bulky feeds. They need a large amount of protein of high quality, and they require certain vitamins and minerals.

Amounts of Feeds Needed

The amount of feed needed by a hen depends upon the breed, her body size, her production of eggs, and her environment. A pullet producing an egg every other day uses nearly three-fourths of her feed in maintaining her body, in providing muscular activity, and in maintaining a body temperature of about 107.5 degrees F. About one-fourth of the feed consumed is for egg production.

Heavy Producers Need More Feed. Heavy-producing hens need some additional feed for body maintenance and activity, but need considerable increases in feeds for egg production. After meeting the maintenance needs, it takes about one pound of dry feed to produce each seven eggs.

The high ten flocks of the Iowa Poultry Production Demonstration Flocks in 1951-1952, however, consumed 110 pounds of feed to produce an average of 241 eggs per hen, while the low ten flocks ate 108 pounds, but produced only 160 eggs per hen.

Small Hens Need Less Feed. It takes about 24 pounds more of feed to maintain an eight-pound hen a year than is required to maintain a five-pound hen. The lighter breeds such as the Leghorns and Minorcas are efficient converters of feed into eggs, so are popular in commercial egg production.

Four-pound hens at 70 per cent lay use about 4.4 pounds of feed to produce a dozen of eggs. Hens of the same weight at 40 per cent lay use about 6.4 pounds of feed.

Essential Nutrients

Hens in heavy production must receive adequate amounts of the following nutrients: (1) carbohydrates and fats, (2) proteins, (3) fiber, (4) minerals, (5) vitamins, and (6) water.

Carbohydrates and Fats. Chickens are active and have high body temperatures, so they require large amounts of heat- and energy-producing feeds. Corn, oats, barley, wheat, grain sorghums, and mill by-products are our chief heat- and energy-producing feeds. They usually make up 75 to 80 per cent of the ration.

Availability, price, and quality usually determine the grains to be fed. Yellow corn and oats are popular in much of the Corn Belt, but sorghums, barley, and wheat are fed in many areas. Hens like variety. The feeding of two or more grains is recommended.

Proteins. Eggs are rich in protein of high quality. If our hens are to produce a large number of eggs, they must receive rations which are high in the amino acids essential in egg production. Since feeds vary in their amino acid content, it is usually desirable to include three or four different protein supplements in the ration. Protein should make up about 15 per cent of the total ration.

Animal Proteins. Approximately 25 per cent of the protein in the ration should be of animal origin. Dried, condensed, or liquid skim milk and buttermilk are high in riboflavin, and provide protein of high quality. Meat scraps and fish meal of good quality are also excellent sources of animal protein.

Plant Proteins. Soybean meal is an excellent source of protein. It is available in most areas, and is palatable and reasonable in price. Corn-gluten, peanut, and cottonseed meals are used in some areas. Cottonseed meal, when fed in large amounts, may produce an objectionable yolk color.

The addition of vitamin B_{12} to a ration will permit a reduction in the percentage of animal proteins.

Fiber. Fiber is not usually considered to be a nutrient, but it has been found that it is essential in the ration for maximum production. The feeding of whole grains and legume hays will provide adequate amounts of fiber.

Minerals. A hen has only about two ounces of mineral in her body when she begins to lay, but in producing 200 eggs in a year she puts into them nearly 40 ounces of mineral, which is quite largely calcium.

Calcium. The shell of an egg is made up of calcium, which must be fed to the hen in the form of oystershell, ground limestone, or steamed bonemeal. Most poultrymen self-feed oystershell, or include mineral feeds in the mash ration.

Phosphorus. Chickens need only small amounts of phosphorus, which is available in steamed bonemeal, meat scraps, fishmeal, and milk, and in small amounts in farm grains.

Salt. Salt should make up ½ to 1 per cent of the total ration.

Grit. Hens which are fed all-mash rations do not need grit. Those which are fed whole or cracked grains should have hard grit available free choice.

Vitamins. Vitamins in small quantities are essential in feeding hens for egg production.

Vitamin A. About 2,000 International Units of vitamin A should be included in each pound of ration. Yellow corn, fresh green forage, alfalfa meal, fortified fish oils, and vitamin A concentrates are the best sources.

Vitamin D. This vitamin is needed by the hens in order to utilize the minerals in the feeds. It should be provided at the rate of 225 International Units per pound of ration. Hens which have access to sunlight can manufacture their own vitamin D. Hens confined to the laying house should be fed fortified vitamin A and D oils, or commercially mixed mashes which contain an adequate amount of vitamin D.

Riboflavin. Laying hens should have about 1.0 milligram of riboflavin per pound of ration, while breeding hens need about 1.3 milligrams. This vitamin is available in milk, yeast, liver, and in alfalfa meal. Commercial premixed concentrates containing this vitamin are available. Riboflavin is very essential in the production of hatching eggs.

Vitamin B_{12}. This vitamin, when fed with plant proteins, permits a reduction in per cent of animal proteins. It is available in vitamin premixes and in commercially mixed feeds. From 1.5 to 2 micrograms of B_{12} should be provided in each pound of ration.

Water. Water is essential in poultry feeding. It permits normal body processes. A pint of water is contained in each dozen eggs. Keeping plenty of clean, fresh water before the hens at all times is a must.

Antibiotics. The feeding of antibiotics to healthy, laying hens has not proven profitable. Egg production and feed efficiency, however, may be increased by feeding of antibiotics to hens that are in poor health or housed under poor conditions.

Systems of Feeding

No combination of farm grains alone will provide the nutrients needed by laying hens in proper amounts. Grains must be supplemented with proteins, and mineral and vitamin feeds. This means that both grain and mash feeds must be fed. Several systems are used in feeding laying hens.

Grain and Mash Feeding. With this method whole grains may be fed in hoppers each evening and mash fed in the morning, or both types of feeds may be self-fed. The mash should contain approximately 20 per cent protein. In feeding whole grain, it should not be spread in litter. Regular feed hoppers should be used.

Grain and Protein Concentrate. This system is much like the grain-mash system, but in this system a 26 per cent protein concentrate is self-fed instead of the 20 per cent mash.

All Mash Ration. The grain is ground and mixed with the mash feed or with the protein concentrate to make up a complete ration. This system involves more expense in grinding, but a uniform ration results. All hens get the same feeds, providing they have been well mixed.

TABLE 59

SCRATCH GRAIN MIXTURES

Grain	Formula number					
	1	2	3	4	5	6
Corn	75	50	50	50	40	30
Wheat	25	50	25	25	40	30
Barley	—	—	25	—	—	20
Oats	—	—	—	25	20	20

University of Maryland

Tables 59 and 60 may be guides in planning rations for your home flock. In formulating rations, figure the content of the ration in relationship to the nutritional needs of the hens. Calculate the cost of a pound of protein, and of a pound of the total ration.

Shown in Table 60 are three mash rations recommended by Iowa State College. Very little scratch grain is fed with the 16 per cent protein mash. The 20 and 26 per cent protein mashes are fed with scratch grains.

TABLE 60

MASH RATIONS FOR LAYER AND BREEDER HENS

Ingredient	Per cent protein		
	16	20	26
	pounds	pounds	pounds
Ground yellow corn	1,120	620	130
Ground heavy oats	200	200	200
Wheat middlings	200	400	400
Dehyd. alfalfa meal (17%)	100	150	250
Soybean oil meal (44%)	200	400	600
Meat and bone scraps (50%)	100	100	200
Fish solubles	50	75	100
St. bone meal (or equiv.)	40	60	100
Gr. oyster shell or limestone	20	30	60
Iodized salt ·	9.5	19	28
Manganese sulfate	0.5	1	2
2250-A, 300-D concentrate	3	5	8
Vitamin D concentrate (1500 ICU per gr.)	1	2	3
Riboflavin concentrate (227 mg./lb.)	6	10	20
Vitamin B_{12} (mg.)	(2 mg.)	(3 mg.)	(4 mg.)
Antibiotics	—	—	—
Total pounds	2,000	2,000	2,000
Calculated analysis (%):			
Protein (Min.)	16.0	20.5	26.2
Fat	4.0	3.8	3.6
Fiber	4.8	6.1	7.6
Calcium	1.6	2.1	3.6
Phosphorus	0.86	1.0	1.5

Iowa State College

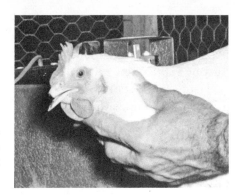

Figure 31-11. A hen de-beaked to prevent cannibalism. (Courtesy DeKalb Agricultural Assn., Inc.)

Cannibalism

The picking of each other by hens is referred to as *cannibalism*. Occasionally hens, in attempting to lay too large an egg, will rupture the oviduct, or a part of the cloaca will protrude from the vent. Hens see this soft, red membrane and pick at it. The intestines may be pulled out before it is noticed by the caretaker. Cannibalism can also be caused by inheritance, by deficiencies in the ration, and by close confinement. Once hens get in the habit of picking at each other, it is difficult to stop and heavy losses may result.

Prevention. The following are some of the best methods of preventing cannibalism:

1. Cut off ½ to ⅔ of the upper beak.
2. Purchase and attach metal appliances to the beaks as the pullets are placed in the laying house.
3. Allow plenty of feeder and floor space.
4. Provide good ventilation.
5. Feed fresh, green feeds or dry, green alfalfa hay.
6. Feed whole oats to growing pullets and to laying hens.
7. Darken windows and nests.
8. Delouse birds and disinfect quarters.

Records

The merchant on Main Street discontinues the handling of any item which does not show a profit, unless he has to carry the item to get other business. He keeps records of his business and they are carefully analyzed. Poultrymen need to do the same thing. There is no way of telling how much profit is obtained from the laying flock if no records are kept. Neither is it possible to determine methods of cutting down production costs. Good business methods must be applied to egg production as in any other enterprise.

Kinds of Records. The following records will be valuable in analyzing the enterprise:

1. Inventories of birds, equipment, and feeds at the beginning and at the close of the laying period. A monthly check of hen numbers is necessary.
2. Egg production records by days and by months.
3. A record of death loss by months.
4. A record of income from sales and products used at home.
5. Feed records by months.
6. Records of cash expenditures.

Figure 31-12. Caged layers. Note dropping boards and egg record charts. (Courtesy Northco Ventilating Co.)

Use of Records. A carefully kept set of records is of no value unless it is used. The following summary, included in the Iowa Poultry Demonstration Flocks in 1956-1957, indicates the type of analysis which should be made of the records.

TABLE 61

FINANCIAL STATEMENT FOR LAYING FLOCKS

Item	Average of All	High Profit	Low Profit
Average size of flock	486	305	271
Average eggs per hen per day	210	234	196
Per cent mortality	17.3	10.9	21.1
Investment per hen	$4.62	$4.12	$4.41
Gross income per hen	4.26	5.02	3.49
Expense per hen	3.23	2.90	3.35
Pounds of feed per hen	94.4	91.4	99.0
Pounds of feed per dozen eggs	5.4	4.7	6.1
Average sale price per dozen eggs	$0.32	$0.32	$0.30
Cost to produce a dozen eggs	$0.28	$0.22	$0.31
Feed cost per hen	$2.93	$2.84	$2.94
Flock profit and interest earned	$500.18	$645.02	$36.87
Interest charge at 6 per cent	$135.78	$75.51	$71.80
Net income except hired labor	$364.40	$569.51	−$34.93
Labor income per hen	$0.75	$1.86	−$0.13
Net income per hour of labor	$0.75	$1.61	−$0.14
Hours labor per hen	1.0	1.1	.9
Market eggs sold per hen	$5.34	$5.89	$4.64
Market poultry sold per hen	$0.53	$0.56	$0.86
Hatching eggs or breeding stock sold per hen	$0.12	—	—
Cost of total ration per 100 lbs.	$3.10	$3.10	$2.97
Return per 100 lbs. of feed	$1.45	$1.76	$1.18
Replacement cost (pullets at 5 mo.) per dozen eggs	$0.044	$0.035	$0.065

Report Iowa Poultry Demonstration Flocks 1956-1957, Iowa State College

Cage Layers

Nearly 90 per cent of the layers in California are housed on wire. Most of them are in individual cages. Cages are also being used in the Southern and Central states.

Cage laying usually results in increased egg production, decreased mortality, control of cannibalism, ease in culling and in record keeping, and decreased feed costs per dozen eggs produced. The initial cost of equipment is high, and the cage laying system of management requires more skill than does floor management. Flies may be a problem and overhead costs may be excessive if equipment is not used to full capacity.

Summary

We can increase egg profits by increasing production per hen, by reducing production costs, by use of better marketing methods, or by use of a combination of these methods. Feed and labor costs make up 75 to 85 per cent of production costs. Feed costs per dozen eggs go down with increased production per hen. Labor costs go down with increased size of flock. A flock should average about 210 eggs per hen per year to make a profit.

Pullets should be carefully culled and deloused before putting them in the laying house. The laying house should be thoroughly cleaned and disinfected. New litter should be placed on the floor and equipment prepared for use. House pullets when about five months of age.

Allow 2½ to three square feet of floor space, seven to eight inches of roost space, and four to five inches of feeder space per bird. Provide a deep litter and dropping pits. A five-gallon waterer should be provided for each 50 hens. Use community nests with one square foot of nesting space per bird.

Insulate the house and provide straw-loft, slot, or forced air ventilation. Provide one square foot of window space for each 20 to 25 square feet of floor space. Provide artificial lights to lengthen the day to about 13 hours.

Feed hens a ration containing 15 per cent protein. The self feeding of grain and mash is recommended. Feed two or three kinds of grain. Hens will consume about equal parts of 22 per cent protein mash and grain. A hen will consume about 110 pounds of feed in a year. Grains should make up about 75 per cent of the ration.

Include in the mash at least three protein feeds with one of them of animal origin. Soybean meal, meat scraps, and dried milk is a good combination. Hens need vitamin A and D which may best be supplied in a premix supplement. Vitamin B_{12} is especially needed when the ration is lacking in animal protein.

Provide hens with oyster shell, ground limestone, and salt. Riboflavin is especially needed in producing hatching eggs. The feeding of antibiotics to healthy hens has not proven profitable; however it may be profitable to feed them to unhealthy hens.

• Questions

1. How many eggs does the average hen on your farm have to lay to produce a profit?
2. How many square feet of floor space should a Leghorn hen have in the laying house?
3. What rules do you need to follow in providing feeders, roosts, nests, and waterers?
4. What are the advantages and disadvantages of a dropping pit?
5. What are the advantages of deep litter?
6. What part of the total ration should be made up of protein?
7. Which of the farm grains make the best feed for laying hens? Why?
8. Is an all-mash ration better than a grain-mash ration? Why?
9. Should laying hens be self-fed or hand-fed?
10. Plan a ration and feeding program for your flock.
11. What are the advantages of the use of cages in the management of layers?
12. Outline a program for improving the housing of your home flock.

• References

Card, L. E., *Practical Poultry Feeding*, Cir. 606, University of Illinois, Urbana, Illinois, 1956.

Combs, G. F. and M. A. Jull, *Feeding Chickens*, Ext. Bul. 126, University of Maryland, College Park, Maryland, 1953.

Eggleton, L. Z., *et al.*, *Poultry Feeding*, P-A1-A, Iowa State College, Ames, Iowa, 1956.

Titus, H. W., *The Scientific Feeding of Chickens,* The Interstate Printers and Publishers, Danville, Illinois, 1955.

Feeding and Management
of Young Chickens

The methods used in feeding and managing young chickens vary somewhat according to the number being raised and the use to be made of them, but the principles involved are much the same. Chicken raising is profitable only under certain conditions. The chicks must be healthy and bred for production. They must be housed properly with adequate space, heat, and sanitation. The ration must provide the nutrients necessary for rapid and economical growth. Mortality must be kept to a minimum, and the health of the chicks must be protected from diseases and parasites.

Brooder Houses

The average farm poultryman usually uses small, movable colony brooder houses, since he normally grows out fewer than 500 to 1000 chicks each year. Specialized poultrymen and broiler growers may, however, grow out thousands of chicks. They use large permanent houses.

A satisfactory brooder house must be capable of maintaining the desired temperature under the hover regardless of weather conditions. It must provide space for the brooder and areas away from the brooder which will be cool. It should be tightly constructed, yet provide for ventilation. Windows should usually be provided, but an excess of sunlight should be avoided. It is difficult to maintain even temperatures in houses with large window areas on the south.

The floor and walls of the house should be such that they can be cleaned and disinfected easily. A portable house set on skids is desirable, since it can be moved to clean range.

Size of House. In most cases it is not desirable to brood more than 350 chicks in one lot. A house 12 x 14 feet will accommodate a 56-inch hover and provide the recommended seven square inches of hover space per chick. There should be one square foot of floor space for each two chicks during the first month. Each chick should have a square foot of floor space the second and third months.

Many brooder houses for broiler production are 30 to 50 feet wide and 50 to 200 feet long. One square foot of floor area is provided for each chick, and the house is divided into pens if chicks of varying ages are being housed.

Ventilation. There should be sufficient ventilation to keep the litter dry. Slot ventilators or windows may be adequate in small houses. Electric fans provide the best movement of air through large brooder houses.

Getting the House Ready for Chicks. The brooder house should be thoroughly cleaned several weeks before the chicks arrive.

Figure 32-1. (left) Baby chicks nicely started in a colony-type brooder house. (Courtesy DeKalb Agricultural Assn., Inc.)
Figure 32-2. (right) The chicks are being started in a brooder house with a wire floor. More heat is necessary when no litter is used on the floor. (Courtesy *Wallaces' Farmer and Iowa Homestead*)

The walls, ceiling, and floor should be swept or scraped. The lower walls and floor should be scrubbed with hot water, and disinfected with lye water (one 13-ounce can to 15 gallons of water), or with a 5 per cent chlorine solution. The house should be given plenty of time to dry out before using it. The feeders and fountains should be cleaned and disinfected at the same time. The house and equipment must be free of diseases and parasites.

Litter

A good litter on the floor serves as an insulator in maintaining uniform temperature, and as a blotter in absorbing moisture. Litter should be fairly course to permit the droppings to sift through to the floor. Shavings, ground corncobs, peanut shells, and sugar cane fiber make excellent litters. Hay chaff is satisfactory if it is not moldy or dusty.

A layer of three to four inches of litter should be placed on the floor a day or two before the chicks arrive, and it should be piled up in the corners so the chicks will not pile up. Litter should be stirred up two or three times each week to permit drying and to avoid matting. When new litter is needed, it should be placed on top of the old. It may be built up to a depth of six to eight inches.

Wire or Slat Floors. Wire or slat floors may be used. They keep the chicks from walking over manure or damp litter. More heat must be provided to houses with this type of floor and they are somewhat unhandy in management of the chicks.

Brooder and Management

The brooder should be set up and put into operation a few days before the chicks arrive. It must be properly regulated. The temperature, two inches above the litter near the edge of the hover, should be from 90 to 95 degrees during the first week.

Kinds of Brooders. Coal or oil brooders heat the houses as well as the areas under the hovers. The temperature under the hover can be maintained a little lower with these brooders than with gas or electric brooders.

Gas or electric brooders heat the hover area but not the room. The temperature under the hover should be maintained at 95 to 100 degrees at the start. Many poultrymen like these brooders because of their ease of operation.

Brooder Management. Ideal brooding conditions provide ample heat for the chicks under the brooder, but the rest of the house is comparatively cool.

Hover Guard. During the first few days a guard made of cardboard, wood or sheet metal 15 to 18 inches high should be placed around the hover at a distance of about two or three feet to keep the chicks from getting away from the brooder and becoming chilled. The guard also helps to keep out drafts and cold air.

Decrease Temperature. The temperature can be reduced gradually about five degrees each week until it is down to about 75 or 80 degrees.

Starting the Chicks

Feed and water should be available for the chicks when they are placed in the brooder house. The first feed for pullorum-free chicks may be placed on paper, on new egg case flats, or in small chick feeders. Chicks must learn to eat and drink. Ordinarily chicks are ready to eat 18 to 24 hours after hatching. It is important that they receive feed within 36 hours after being hatched.

Feeders and Waterers. Small lath troughs may be used as feeders during the first week or ten days. The troughs should be kept about ⅔ filled. One inch of trough space should be provided for each baby chick for the first five weeks. Several small water fountains should be used during the first few days. Four half-gallon fountains will provide adequate water for 100 chicks.

After a week or ten days the lath troughs should be replaced with 3- x 6-inch troughs. Two inches of feeder space per chick is recommended after the fifth or sixth week.

Figure 32-3. Interior of a large commercial house. Note the automatic feeders that are adjusted low enough for these 4- or 5- day-old chicks. (Courtesy Automatic Poultry Feeder Company)

Large feeders, or automatic feeders which are elevated, should be provided when the chicks are eight to ten weeks of age. Three gallon waterers or automatic waterers should be used and they should be placed on wire-covered platforms six inches high. Most breeding chicks will be out on range by the time they are eight to ten weeks of age, and can be fed with the use of protected outdoor feeders. At least one feeder should be left indoors for use during rainy weather.

Nutritional Needs of Chicks

Chicks require rations containing about 20 per cent protein during the first few weeks, and the protein must be of high quality. Baby chicks have little capacity and cannot consume coarse or bulky feeds. Most poultrymen feed a commercial starter feed. Large commercial producers may need a sufficient volume of starter feeds to justify mixing their own rations. Starter and growing mashes are formulated which meet the nutritional needs of the chicks. Proteins, carbohydrates and fats, mineral, vitamins, and antibiotics are essential for rapid and economical chick growth. Growing mashes usually contain about 16 per cent protein if no scratch grain is fed.

Proteins. The muscular tissue produced in chick and broiler production is quite largely made up of protein. The body of a five-pound Leghorn cockerel is about 25 per cent protein. Starter and growing mashes must be high in proteins containing at least 13 of the amino acids. Arginine, lysine, methionine, tryptophane, and cystine may be critical in some rations. To guard against protein deficiency, three or four different protein supplements should be included in the ration. About 25 per cent of the protein should be animal origin. Milk products, meat scraps, fishmeal, soybean meal, and corn gluten meal are good feeds to include in the chick mash.

Carbohydrates and Fats. The cereal grains, corn, wheat, oats, barley, and grain sorghums are usually used to provide carbohydrates. The use of two or three grains in the mash is recommended. They should be ground.

After the chicks are from five to six weeks old, they may be fed cracked corn, pellet feeds, or whole small grains in feeders in addition to the mash. Eight-week-old chicks should receive about 90 per cent mash feeds and 10 per cent scratch grains or pellet feeds.

By the time breeding chickens are three months old, the grain ration should make up 30 per cent of the total ration. Four-month-old birds should get about equal amounts of scratch and mash feeds.

Mineral. Common farm feeds contain most of the minerals needed by chicks with the exception of calcium, phosphorus, sodium, chlorine, and manganese. Calcium is easily supplied in ground limestone or marine shells. Phosphorus may be supplied in the form of steamed bone meal, defluorinàted rock phosphate, or as meat and bone meal. Salt provides sodium and chlorine. Manganese must be purchased in a drug store as technical anhydrous manganous sulfate. It is usually supplied in the form of a mineral premix as the mash is manufactured.

Starter mashes should contain about 1 per cent calcium, .6 per cent phosphorus, .5 per cent salt, .2 per cent potassium, 25 milligrams per pound of manganese and .5 milligrams per pound of iodine.

Vitamins. Vitamins are very essential for rapid and economical chick growth. Vitamins A, D, riboflavin, niacin, pantothenic acid, and choline may be most critical in the ration.

Vitamin A. Chicks should receive rations containing 1,200 I.C.U.'s of vitamin A per pound. This vitamin promotes growth and infection-resistance in chicks. Green feeds, yellow corn, and fish oils are our best sources.

Vitamin D. This vitamin promotes efficient use of calcium and phosphorus and prevents rickets in chicks. About 90 I.C.U.'s per pound of ration is recommended. Late-hatched chicks grown in the sunlight can produce their own vitamin D.

Riboflavin. Riboflavin is needed for chick growth and should be provided at the rate of 1.3 milligrams per pound of ration. Liver, yeast, milk products, and fermentation by-products resulting from the manufacture of lentyl alcohol are best sources.

Niacin. Chicks need niacin for normal growth and development. Chicks lose their appetites and become nervous when this vitamin is lacking. Niacin may be supplied in liver, yeast, and fermentation by-products. Wheat bran and middlings contain niacin, and it can be purchased in crystalline form. For chicks, 12 milligrams of niacin are recommended per pound of ration.

Pantothenic Acid. There should be 4.2 milligrams of pantothenic acid in each pound of chick ration. This vitamin prevents dermatosis, aids feathering, promotes normal pigmentation, and is essential for healthy nerves. Succulent green feed, alfalfa meal, milk products, yeast, and liver meal are good sources.

Choline. Chicks should receive about 600 milligrams of choline per pound of ration. It prevents perosis or slipped tendon conditions. Fish and animal products, soybean meal, and distillers' solubles are main sources of this vitamin.

Other Vitamins. Several other vitamins are essential, but they are usually available in the feeds included in the ration. Vitamin K (anti-hemorrhagic), biotin (prevents dermatosis), and pyridoxin (stimulates appetite and growth) are examples.

Antibiotics. Most poultrymen prefer starter mash that contains about five grams of antibiotics per ton of feed. The maximum growth stimulation due to the feeding of antibiotics occurs during the first four or five weeks. Rate of gain may be increased 10 to 15 per cent and feed efficiency 5 per cent by the feeding of antibiotics. Aureomycin and procaine penicillin are the two most widely used antibiotics in chick rations. Antibiotics, like vitamins and minerals, are usually provided in the form of premixes and used in ration formulation.

Arsenicals. Tests indicate that the feeding of 3-Nitro and other arsenicals to chicks in starter feeds, alone and with an antibiotic, increased the rate of gain and feed conversion, and reduced mortality. The value of arsenicals is dependent upon the quality of the ration, the health of the chicks, and the feeding methods being followed.

Arsenicals are used by most broiler producers. The directions of the manufacturer should be followed closely.

Surfactants. The feeding of surface active agents, or wetting agents, to chicks is in process of experimentation. Illinois tests showed no increases due to surfactants when fed to chicks on a good ration containing aureomycin. Cornell University tests showed growth increases, when surfactants were fed both during the first and second four-week periods. They found, however, that penicillin was a better growth stimulator than any of the surfactants studied.

Rations for Chicks

Most poultrymen rely upon commercial feed concerns for their chick rations. The materials needed can be purchased in large quantities by mixing firms, and they can put out a high-quality product at a reasonable price if they care to do so. Studies must be made of the contents of the various starter and grower mashes, and selection should be based upon the extent to which the feeds meet the nutritional needs of chicks, and upon cost.

Starting Mash Formulas

Farmers usually have home-grown grains available and may wish to have their chick feeds mixed at the local elevator using home-grown grains, vitamin-mineral-antibiotic premixes, and other commercial feeds. Following are suggested starting mashes for chicks:

TABLE 62

STARTING MASH FORMULAS

University of Maryland		University of Illinois	
Pounds per Ton		*Pounds per Ton*	
Ground yellow corn	1,224.4	Gound yellow corn	669
Fish meal, 60%	125	Pulverized oats	400
Meat scrap, 55%	50	Ground wheat	200
Soybean meal, 44%	400	Alfalfa meal	100
Corn gluten meal	75	Soybean meal (41%)	360
Dehy. alfalfa meal, 17%	40	Meat and bone scraps	
Dr. dist. sol. (grain)	25	(50%)	200
Dr. molasses dist. sol.	20	Dried whey	60
DL-methionine	0.4	Dry vitamin D	
Ground limestone	20	(1500 units per gm.)	.4
Dicalcium phosphate		Iodized salt	10
(18% P, 26% Ca)	10	Manganese sulfate	.6
Salt, iodized	6	(feed grade)	
Vitamin A supplement		Approximate total	2,000 lbs.
(4000 I. U./gm.)	2		
Vitamin D$_3$ supplement		Calculated analysis:	
(1500 I.C.U./gm.)	1.2	Protein, per cent	20
Trace mineral mix	1	Calcium, per cent	1.20
Coccidiostad	*	Phosphorus, per cent	.86
Grams per Ton			
Antibiotic	*		
Arsenical	*		
Riboflavin	4		
Niacin	30		
Calcium pantothenate	6		
Choline chloride	227		
Vitamin B$_{12}$	.003		
Total	2,000 pounds		

* Added according to manufacturer's recommendations.

TABLE 63

BROILER AND GROWING CHICKEN RATIONS

Broiler Ration 20% Protein (To be fed as all-mash ration) University of Maryland		Growing Mash Ration 20.5% Protein (To be fed with scratch grain) Iowa State College	
Pounds per Ton			Pounds
Gr. yellow corn	1,278.8	Gr. yellow corn	580
Stabilized animal fat	40	Gr. heavy oats	200
Fish meal, 60%	100	Wheat middlings	400
Poultry by-prod. meal,		Dhy. alfalfa meal (17%)	200
56%	50	Soybean oil meal (44%)	400
Soybean meal, 50%	360	Meat and bone scrap	
Dhy. alfalfa meal, 17%	40	(50%)	100
Dr. dist. col. (grain)	40	St. bone meal (or equiv.)	50
Dried whey	30	Gr. oyster shell or limestone	30
Dl-methionine	1.0	Iodized salt	19
Ground limestone	20	Manganese sulfate	1
Bone meal, steamed	30	2250-A, 300-D concentrate	5
Iodized salt	6	Vitamin D concentrate	
Vitamin A supplement,		(1500 I.C.U./gm.)	1
(4,000 I.U./gm.)	2	Riboflavin conc. (227	
Vitamin D₃ supplement,		mg./lb.)	20
(1500 I.C.U. gm.)	1.2	Choline chloride (25%)	3
Trace mineral mix[1]	1	Niacin (grams)	20 gm.
Coccidiostad[2]	*	Pantothenic acid (grams)	5 gm.
Grams per Ton		Vitamin B₁₂ (mg.)	4 mg.
Antibiotics[3]		Antibiotics*	—
Arsenicals[4]		Total pounds	2,000
Riboflavin	3.2		
Niacin	30		
Calcium pantothenate	6		
Choline chloride	200		
DPPD[5]	100		
Vitamin B₁₂	.003		

* Feed according to manufacturer's directions.
[1] Should contain at least 12% manganese or equivalent.
[2] Add preferred coccidiostad at level recommended by manufacturer.
[3] Add 4 gms. of procaine penicillin or 10 gms. of bacitracin per ton.
[4] Add either 90 gms. of arsenalic acid or 45 mgs. of 3-nitro per ton.
[5] DPPD may be added to increase vitamin A utilization and pigment of skin.

Range Shelters

The brooder house usually will not accommodate the chicks as they acquire a little size. Portable range shelters should be provided. Shelters enclosed with wire netting will permit the confining of chickens at night to avoid losses due to predators.

Figure 32-4. Poultry range feeder built of plywood and fastened with casein glue. Midwest Plan Service Plan No. 87410. (Courtesy V. J. Morford)

The range shelter may also be used as a sun porch in caring for the baby chicks. Some poultrymen grow their chicks for the first eight weeks in the brooder house using the range shelter as a sun porch.

Roosts

Chicks will begin to roost at about six weeks of age. Roosts should be placed along the back of the brooder house. Perches should be placed low at the beginning and raised after the chicks have learned to roost. Placing a frame covered with wire netting under the roosts aids in getting the birds on the roosts. Placing roosts level with the floor avoids the tendency for chickens to get to the top roosts.

Wide, flat roosts are recommended. They prevent chicks from developing crooked breast bones. At least four inches of perch space should be provided for each bird.

Figure 32-5. Pullets on range should be provided nests. (Courtesy Nichols, Incorporated)

Cannibalism

Cannibalism in chicks may cause serious losses and the pullets may continue picking each other after being placed in the laying house. The same factors are involved in preventing cannibalism in chicks as were discussed in connection with the laying flock. Avoid crowding, overheating, and insufficient feeder and water space. Use a sun porch to increase floor area. Debeaking is recommended.

Feeding finely ground oats to young chicks, or coarse-ground or whole oats to older chickens may help. Adding salt up to about 4 per cent of the mash for a few days, may give good results. Injured and crippled chicks should be removed as soon as they are discovered.

Separate Cockerels from Pullets

Many poultrymen separate the cockerels from the pullets when six to eight weeks of age. The pullets are put on range while the cockerels are fed broiler ration and sold. Leghorn cockerels will use as much feed, putting on a pound of weight after 2½ pounds, as was required to put on the first 2½ pounds. It pays to separate the cockerels of the light breeds and dispose of them at 2½ pounds as broilers.

Range for Chickens

Chicks should be moved to range at eight weeks of age. Be certain to provide clean ground on which no chickens have been grown for at least two years.

Figure 32-6. Chickens being reared on range with adequate equipment. (Courtesy *Poultry Tribune*)

Figure 32-7. Automatic feeders and waterers in use in a southern broiler house. Note the open-slat side walls which can be used in the South. (Terry Wood photo. Courtesy Automatic Poultry Feeder Co.)

Ladino clover, lespedeza, alfalfa, and red clover make excellent pasture crops for young chickens. From 10 to 30 per cent of the feed can be saved by providing good range. Provide movable equipment and move it from time to time to maintain sanitary quarters. Provide plenty of fresh water and keep the feeders filled.

Broiler Production

The feeding and management of broilers is quite similar to the methods used in starting and growing out chicks, with the exception that the latter are kept in confinement until they are sold.

During the winter months three-fourths to four-fifths of a square foot of floor space per bird is recommended. One square foot per bird is desired in the summer. Roosts are not used in broiler production.

The feeders, waterers, and deep litter recommendations for chick production apply also in the production of broilers.

Broiler Rations. Most broiler producers feed starting mashes for the first eight weeks, and continue feeding an all-mash ration until the birds are sold. Others start feeding pellet feeds or cracked corn with mash at about seven weeks and continue until the broilers are ready for market. Grain feeding slows up rate of gain but permits the feeding of home-grown grains. Most broilers are marketed when about ten weeks old weighing about three pounds.

Antibiotics for Broilers. One to four milligrams of antibiotics should be fed with each pound of feed. Antibiotics induce a 10 per cent increase in growth rate to ten weeks of age and save about 10 per cent of feed. One milligram of procaine penicillin or four milligrams of other antibiotics per pound is the recommended feeding level.

Figure 32-8. Capons on a Washington County, Iowa, farm. (Courtesy *Wallaces' Farmer and Iowa Homestead*)

Caponettes and Capons

The implanting of synthetic female hormones in young cockerels produces caponettes. The removal of the male organs produces capons.

Caponettes. Stilbesterol pellets implanted under the skin of the neck at the back of the head causes the cockerels to become quiet, lose their male characteristics, and take on the appearance of a pullet. Cockerels are usually treated when eight to ten weeks old and sold when 12 to 16 weeks old. The treatment lasts only four to six weeks. If not sold they take on male characteristics again.

The U.S. Food and Drug Administration in 1959 prohibited further use of stilbestrol or diethylstilbestrol implants in poultry because of a possible relationship of these hormones to cancer in humans.

Capons. A capon must be kept six to nine months before it is ready for market, and six or seven pounds of feed are required to produce a pound of meat. On the market capons compete with turkey. The capon business has not been promising in most areas.

Cockerels are caponized when they weigh 1½ to two pounds. The caponizing is usually done by a specialist. While many farmers have done some caponizing, the job is for a person who does the work sufficiently often to become skilled.

The removal of the testicles in a cockerel produces a bird with the appearance of a pullet. They grow larger and meatier, but it requires many months to produce a good capon. Two pounds of broiler meat can be produced on the amount of feed needed to produce a pound of capon. The price of capon usually is not twice the price of a broiler.

A careful record of chicken and broiler production, income, expense, mortality, feed consumption, egg production, and rate of gain will assist in developing a profitable enterprise. Following is a summary of broiler production by an integrated firm in 1956-1957.

TABLE 64

TOTAL COST OF BROILER PRODUCTION BY AN
INTEGRATED FIRM—FOUR FLOCKS—1956-57

Cash Costs	Cost per 1,000 Broilers Sold	Cost per Pound Live Weight Sold
	Dollars	Cents
Chicks	143.16	4.3382
Feed	420.32	12.7370
Fuel	27.34	.8285
Litter	5.22	.1582
Misc. Supplies	5.80	.1758
Sub Total	601.84	18.2377
Overhead Costs		
Interest on borrowed money, property taxes, etc.*	24.77	.7506
Supervisory labor	7.20	.2182
Production labor	59.66	1.8079
Maintenance and repair of buildings—labor	8.39	.2542
Maintenance and repair of equipment—labor	.30	.0091
Maintenance and repair of buildings—materials	2.07	.0627
Maintenance and repair of equipment—materials	1.13	.0342
Depreciation of buildings	14.09	.4270
Depreciation of equipment	.35	.0106
Fire insurance	3.44	.1042
Taxes—Workmen's Compensation	1.26	.0382
Taxes—Payroll	1.45	.0439
Electricity	5.38	.1603
Misc. expenses	6.33	.1918
Sub total	135.82	4.1111
Grand total	737.66	22.3488

Courtesy *Broiler Growing*, Mt. Morris, Ill.
* This item includes real estate taxes, interest on borrowed money, water supply, road upkeep, and other minor plant overhead expenses.

Chick costs amounted to 4.3 cents, feed 12.7 cents, fuel and litter 3 cents, labor 2 cents, and other overhead costs amounted to 2.1 cents per pound of live broiler sold. The total cost of production was 22.3 cents per pound. The selling price of the broilers was not shown. The difference between selling price and cost of production represents the profit, or the loss, in producing a pound of broiler.

Summary

Chicks may be brooded in a colony-type or in a permanent brooder house. Each chick should be provided seven square inches of hover space and one-half square foot of floor space. For broiler production each chick should have .8 to one square foot of floor area. The glass area in brooder houses should be kept to a minimum. There should be sufficient ventilation to keep the litter dry.

The brooder house and equipment should be cleaned and disinfected several days before the chicks arrive. The heating unit should be operated and three to four inches of peanut hulls, ground corncobs, or other good litter should be on the floor for a day or two before chicks arrive.

Feed and water should be available when chicks arrive. A hover guard should be used the first few days. The temperature under the hover should be about 95 degrees the first week. The best room temperature is 65 degrees. The temperature may be reduced five degrees each week.

A 20 per cent protein starter feed should be fed in adequate feeders. The starter mash should meet National Poultry Council recommendations. Usually it pays to feed antibiotics, arsenicals, and a coccidiostad. Most broiler growers feed a 20 per cent protein ration during the entire growing period. Breeding chickens are usually fed mash and scratch grain rations after the seventh week. Grower rations contain about 16 per cent protein.

Nearly three-fourths of the chickens reared in this country are reared in confinement as broilers. Most farm chickens, breeders, and capons are reared on range. Alfalfa and ladino clover provide excellent range. Adequate shelters, feeders, and waterers are necessary in range feeding.

Cannibalism is best controlled by debeaking. It usually does not pay to caponize chickens.

Questions

1. How much of the following should be provided per baby chick: (a) floor space, (b) feeder space, (c) waterer space, and (d) hover space?
2. What temperature is desired under the hover during the first week?
3. Outline the essentials of a good starter feed.
4. What kind of litter is recommended for chicks and broilers?
5. What vitamins are most critical in formulating chick rations?
6. Does it pay to feed chicks surfactants and arsenicals?
7. How can you best provide antibiotics to your chicks?
8. Outline a program for feeding and managing chickens on range.
9. In what respects are the methods of feeding and managing broilers different than those used in growing out breeding chickens or laying pullets?
10. What methods can you use to prevent cannibalism in young chickens?
11. Which will be most profitable on your farm, raising broilers, roasters, or capons?

References

Card, L. E., *Practical Poultry Feeding,* Cir. 606, University of Illinois, Urbana, Illinois, 1956.

Combs, G. F. and M. A. Jull, *Feeding Chickens,* Ext. Bul. No. 126, University of Maryland, College Park, Maryland, 1953.

National Research Council, *Nutrient Requirements for Poultry,* Revised 1954, Washington, D. C.

Rice, J. E. and H. E. Botford, *Practical Poultry Management,* John Wiley and Sons, New York, 1956.

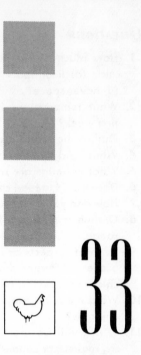

33

Turkey Production and Management

Turkey production has become a highly specialized industry. More than one-half of the turkeys produced in the nation in 1957 were produced in five states, California, Minnesota, Virginia, Iowa, and Texas. Four counties in California produced one-third of that state's 1954 production. Rockingham County in Virginia produced, in 1954, more turkeys than were produced in the 14 low-producing states combined. Nearly 75 per cent of our turkeys are grown on farms which have more than 1,600 birds.

Few turkey raisers maintain breeding flocks. Turkey poults are usually purchased from specialized producers who maintain high-quality breeding flocks and hatchery facilities. The problems encountered by the average turkey grower have to do with the obtaining of high-quality poults, the management of the poults during the brooding and range feeding periods, the control of diseases and parasites, and with the marketing of birds which have been produced. We will deal, in this chapter, with the problems in production and management. Disease problems are considered in Chapter 34 and the marketing of turkeys is covered in Chapter 35.

Buy Good Poults

The same factors need to be considered in buying poults that were considered in buying chicks, but their importance is magnified because of the higher prices paid for poults and received from the sale of market turkey.

Selection of Variety. The most popular varieties of turkeys are the Broad Breasted Bronze, the Broad Breasted White, the White Holland, and the Beltsville (U.S.D.A.) Small White. Other varieties

Figure 33-1. (upper left) Bronze Turkeys. (Courtesy *Turkey World*)
Figure 33-2. (upper right) Beltsville Small White Turkey. (Courtesy *Wallaces' Farmer and Iowa Homestead*)
Figure 33-3. (below) Broad White Toms ready for the fall market. (Courtesy *Turkey World*)

grown in small numbers are the Bourbon Red, Narragansett, Black Slate, and Jersey Buff.

In setting up a turkey business, the grower should choose the variety that is best suited to his market, is available in the desired quality and quantity, and can be purchased at the best price.

Production Bred. Poults should be purchased from flocks where pullorum-control programs have been followed, and where meat production has been stressed. Thrifty, disease-free poults are essential to success. When possible, poults nearby should be bought in order to avoid over-heating and chilling in transporting them. Data from official random sample meat production tests are helpful in selecting source of poults.

Time to Start Poults. It takes from 24 to 28 weeks to grow out a prime turkey. Poults should be started about six months before you plan to sell them, unless you are producing turkey broilers. Broilers may be marketed in 12 to 15 weeks.

Brooding Young Poults

Brooder House. The brooder house should be thoroughly cleaned and disinfected several weeks before it is to be used. All litter should be removed and the interior of the house scrubbed with lye water. All equipment should be cleaned and disinfected.

Figure 33-4. Young poults on good litter. The gas brooder is economical and provides constant temperature. (Courtesy *Turkey Tribune*)

Movable houses 10 x 12 or 10 x 16 feet, or centralized, stationary, brooder houses divided into pen units may be used. Large houses may be 24 feet wide with a south exposure, or about 40 feet wide with a six-foot alley in the middle and a row of pens on each side facing east and west.

Floor. Movable houses usually are built on skids and have wooden floors. Permanent houses usually have concrete floors underlaid with gravel.

Litter. Litter is very important in turkey production. A deep litter of six to eight inches aids in keeping the quarters dry and sanitary. Poults will eat litter, however, the first week or ten days. Many growers use clean, silt-free sand, or litter paper, the first week. If litter is used the first week, it should be coarse, with particles ¼ inch or more in diameter. Permanent litter of crushed corncobs, peanut hulls, cane pulp, or peat moss may be used after the first week or ten days.

Wire or Slat Floors. Some growers use a fine mesh wire on the floor. Welded 14 gauge wire with ½- x 2-inch mesh is recommended. Slat floors, made in sections with the slats placed on edge about three fourths of an inch apart, are also used.

Brooder. The brooder should be set up and in operation a couple of days before getting the poults. Brood only 150 to 200 poults per hover.

Brooding Temperatures

First Week	90-95 degrees
Second Week	85-90 degrees
Third Week	80-85 degrees
Fourth Week	75-80 degrees
Fifth Week	70-75 degrees
After Fifth Week	Maintain 70 degrees until heat is no longer needed.

Brooder Guard. A guard of wood, cardboard, metal, or wire should be placed completely around the hover to keep the poults from getting lost or chilled. Guard should be three to four feet from the hover. Corners should be closed off.

Starting Poults. Poults should be placed under the hover as soon as possible after they leave the hatchery.

Feeding. The beak of every third poult should be dipped in water and feed to get them to start to eat. Putting in a few poults five or six days old will help to teach young birds to eat. Spreading oatmeal or finely ground, yellow corn on mash will help to get poults eating. A bright light should be kept over the feeders and waterers during the first week.

Each five poults need one foot of feeder space for the first three weeks. The feeder space should be increased gradually. At four weeks, a four-foot feeder should be provided for each 25 poults.

Starter Rations. During the first eight weeks, poults need rations containing 28 per cent protein, 2 per cent calcium, 1 per cent phosphorus, .5 per cent salt, and the following amounts of vitamins and minerals per pound of feed: 2,400 U.S.P. units of vitamin A, 400 I.C.U.'s of vitamin D, 1.7 milligrams of riboflavin, 5 milligrams of pantothenic acid, 750 milligrams of choline, .4 milligrams of folacin, and 25 milligrams of manganese.

Farmers who grow turkeys in small numbers usually buy commercial mixed feeds. Large producers may mix their own, but the trend is to feed commercial mixed rations.

Presented in Table 65 are rations recommended by the University of Connecticut for turkey poults during various stages of production and for breeding birds.

Figure 33-5. Notice the guard which keeps the poults from crowding in the corner. (Courtesy James Mfg. Co.)

TABLE 65

Mash Ingredients	Starter	Grower	Grower	Breeder
	lbs.	lbs.	lbs.	lbs.
Soybean oil meal (44%)	650	580	680	200
Ground yellow corn	800	950	800	1000
Standard wheat middlings	100	200	200	300
Ground Oats	—	—	—	150
Fish meal (60%)	200	50	50	100
Meat scrap (50%)	100	—	50	50
Alfalfa meal (17%) (100,000 A/lb.)	60	60	60	60
Butyl fermentation product	40	40	50	40
Dicalcium phosphate or equivalent	8	52	40	32
Ground limestone (feeding grade)	30	40	55	55
Iodized salt	5	10	10	10
Antibiotic supplement	*	—	—	—
Vitamin B_{12} supplement (6 mg/lb. or equivalent)	1	*	*	2
Niacin	45 gm.	45 gm.	45 gm.	45 gm.
Choline chloride (dry, 25%)	4.0	2.0	2.0	2.0
Dry vitamin D (1500 D/gm.)	1.0	1.0	1.0	1.0
Dry vitamin A (5000 A/gm.)	1.8	1.8	1.8	1.8
Manganese sulphate or equivalent	0.25	0.25	0.25	0.25
Vitamin E concentrate (20,000 I.U./lb.)	0.4	0.2	0.2	0.4
Pantothenic acid	—	—	—	5 gm.
Totals	2001.45	1987.25	2000.25	2004.45

CALCULATED ANALYSIS OF TURKEY RATIONS

		Starter	Grower	Grower	Breeder
Productive energy	Cal./lb.	830	830	790	850
Protein	%	28.7	21.5	24.5	17.3
Fat	%	3.2	2.8	2.7	3.7
Fiber	%	4.1	4.1	4.2	4.4
Calcium	%	1.94	1.82	2.20	2.17
Total phosphorus	%	0.98	0.95	0.97	0.93
Readily available phosphorus	%	0.77	0.71	0.73	0.69
Manganese	Mg/lb.	25.5	26.5	27.4	28.7
Vitamin A	I.U./lb.	5957	6134	5974	6223
Vitamin D	I.U./lb.	340	342	340	340
Riboflavin	Mg/lb.	3.7	3.5	4.1	3.4
Pantothenic acid	Mg/lb.	6.1	6.1	6.7	8.3
Choline	Mg/lb.	960	706	777	577
Niacin	Mg/lb.	39.7	39.0	39.6	42.1

University of Connecticut

Feeder Space. The following amounts of feeder space should be provided for each 100 poults.

First two weeks—16 linear feet
Third and fourth weeks—24 linear feet
Fifth and sixth weeks—32 linear feet
Seventh and eighth weeks—40 linear feet

Sun Porch. A sun porch about the same size as the house is needed to provide sunlight, exercise, and floor space as poults become older. The floor may be of 1- x 1-inch welded wire or of wood slats placed about an inch apart. Start using the sun porch the third week if weather permits.

Roosts. Poults will begin roosting at three to four weeks. Roosts three to four inches wide should be provided at the back of the brooder house about 12 inches from the floor. Four to six inches of roost space should be provided for each bird.

Waterers. Small quart-jar waterers should be used for the first few days; then larger ones should be provided. A three-gallon waterer will accommodate 75 poults. Healthy poults need plenty of fresh water.

Lights. The small lights over the feeders and waterers will assist in keeping the poults from piling up as well as encouraging them to eat and drink.

Range Management

The grower should plan to move the poults to range when they are eight to 12 weeks of age. By that time the ration should have been gradually changed from a starter feed to a grower mash and grain.

Pastures for Turkeys. Turkeys on alfalfa in Kansas consumed 17 per cent less feed than turkeys raised in confinement. Green pasture furnishes vitamins, protein, and minerals which supplement the grower mash and grain.

Pasture Crops. Alfalfa, lespedeza, ladino, and red clover make excellent pastures for poults. Sudan grass and fall seeded rye may also be used.

Rotate Pasture. Clean ground is a must in turkey production. Land should not be used for turkey range which has been used in growing either chickens or turkeys during the preceding three

Figure 33-6. A flock of 3,600 turkeys on rape and oats range. (Courtesy *Wallaces' Farmer and Iowa Homestead*)

or four years. Blackhead disease may be spread by cecal worms which may live in the ground following chicken production.

Most poultrymen move their turkeys each week or ten days. The lower areas of the range should be used first so the new range will not be contaminated later in the season. Temporary fences may be used. In wet weather, the poults should be moved more often. One acre of good range for each season for each 65 birds is recommended.

Range Shelters. Portable range shelters with roosts both over and under the roof may be used. Shelters made on skids are easily moved. Birds need protection from both the sun and from the weather.

A 10- x 16-foot shelter will accommodate 200 to 250 poults. From nine to 12 inches of roost space should be provided per bird. Roosts may be made of 2 x 4's or of poles and should be placed about three feet off the ground.

Feeders. One foot of feeder space should be provided for each three birds. Many types of feeders may be made or purchased. The feeder should provide for continuous feeding, without waste, and provide protection of the feed in case of rain. Half of the feeders should be filled with grain and the other half-filled with mash.

Growing Rations. *Grains.* Cracked corn or a mixture of corn, oats, wheat, and sorghums are good feeds for young turkeys on range. After birds can eat whole grain, it need not be ground. Oats help to feather the birds and may prevent feather picking.

Turkey Production and Management • 621

Figure 33-7. Young turkeys are heavy eaters but grow rapidly. (Courtesy *Turkey World*)

Mineral and Grit. Turkeys consume much fibrous material, so need grit at all times. Granite grit should be provided. Minerals are usually fed as a part of the mash.

Mash Feeds. Most mash supplements for growing turkeys contain from 26 to 35 per cent protein. These concentrates permit the grower to feed large quantities of farm grains. The contents of any purchased supplement should be checked carefully, and the cost per pound of protein calculated. The best way to keep turkeys healthy is to keep them eating.

Growing turkeys eight to 16 weeks old need rations containing 20 per cent protein, 2 per cent calcium, 1 per cent phosphorus, .5 per cent salt and the following amounts of vitamins per pound of feed: 2,400 U.S.P. units of vitamin A and 400 I.C.U.'s of vitamin D. The exact amounts of riboflavin, pantothenic acid, choline, folacin, and manganese needed by growing turkeys is not known.

Most poultrymen feed grains and mash concentrates. The amounts of grains fed vary with the protein content and amounts of mash feed consumed by the birds. The rations in Table 65 may be helpful in formulating feeding programs and in evaluating commercial feeds.

Feeds Required per Pound of Gain. Some turkey growers estimate that it will take from 90 to 100 pounds of feed to grow out a turkey to market weight. Feed required per pound of gain runs from three to five pounds. A turkey broiler can put on a pound of gain on 2 ½ to 2 ¾ pounds of feed.

Antibiotics. Antibiotics will stimulate turkey growth as in chicken production. The greatest increases occur during the brooding stage, but 5 per cent increases in growth at 24 weeks of age has resulted from antibiotic feeding.

Aureomycin, bacitracin, penicillin, and terramycin have been

Figure 33-8. The effect of feeding aureomycin to turkey poults. (Courtesy *Turkey World*)

fed with excellent results. The rate of feeding penicillin is from two to four grams per ton. The other antibiotics should be fed at the rate of six to ten grams per ton.

Arsenicals. Arsanilic acid and 3-nitro-4-hydroxyphenyl arsonic acid produce increased growth when fed to turkeys in about the same amounts as antibiotics. Since they are toxic, they should be fed with care and according to the manufacturers' recommendations.

Water. Turkeys need plenty of clean, fresh water while on range. Provide waterers which will maintain a supply of water, but will not permit the birds to contaminate it. It is better to place the waterer in the sun than in the shade.

Hormones. Feeding hormones to growing turkeys speeds rates of gains and fattening. Hormones should be fed according to manufacturers' recommendations. Implanting hormones is prohibited.

Cannibalism. Feather-pecking and cannibalism can be controlled in turkeys in the same manner as with chickens. Feeding oats in the ration, providing adequate range, and debeaking are the best methods.

Confinement Rearing in Pole Sheds

A recent development is the use of pole sheds in confinement rearing of turkeys. Sheds may be 40 to 60 feet wide and several

Figure 33-9. Turkeys being reared in confinement in a large pole shed. (Courtesy *Wallaces' Farmer and Iowa Homestead*)

623

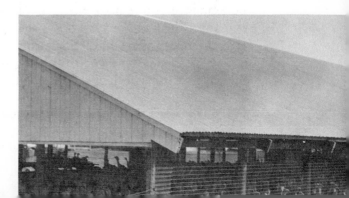

Figure 33-10. A long, low pole building and feeding equipment used in a large scale turkey enterprise. (Courtesy Aluminum Company of America)

hundred feet long. The poles are set in the ground three and one-half to four feet. The sheds usually are gable roofed with five- to seven-foot side walls, and have two- to three-foot roof overhang. The walls and ends may be enclosed with strong wire or a combination of siding and wire. In Northern states, provision is made to enclose the sheds during bad weather with wood or steel panels, or with canvas.

Dirt floors and deep litters are used. The turkeys are kept in the shed at all times. New litter is added as necessary. Four to five square feet of floor space is provided for each bird.

Wire partitions are used to separate the turkeys into groups of 300 to 400 birds. Most growers find it necessary to debeak the birds. Feeders and waterers are placed along the sides. No roosts are used. The birds roost on the litter.

Finishing Turkeys for Market

As long as a turkey is growing, it is impossible to get it to put on a thick covering of flesh. Turkeys must be mature to be properly finished. Operations must be planned so that the poults are started in time to be finished for the desired market. The larger varieties will finish out weighing from 24 to 28 pounds. The smaller varieties will finish out weighing from 14 to 18 pounds.

Turkeys can be finished on grass and mash, but should receive a large amount of whole yellow corn in the ration. The birds should be examined before marketing them to see that the breast is broad and full. The back and hip bones should be well covered, and the skin should appear white because of the layer of fat underneath. The bird should have good feather growth. Pin feathers indicate immaturity and a general lack of condition.

Turkey Broiler Production

The production of turkey broilers has increased rapidly with the development of the Beltsville Small White turkey. Turkey broilers are fed and managed in much the same manner as chicken broilers. They dress out with more breast meat and less leg meat than the chicken broiler, and there is less loss in the dressing process. Turkey broilers dress out at five to seven pounds.

Day-old turkeys sell for 60 to 80 cents while chicks sell for 10 to 18 cents. The selling price of turkey broilers must be high to show a profit. Turkey broilers are very efficient consumers of feed, but the original cost of the poults limits the profit from the enterprise.

There are three limiting factors in turkey broiler production; (1) the high price of the day-old poults, (2) the difficulty of getting a high finish on the young turkey, and (3) finding a sufficiently high market for the birds to yield a profit.

Summary

Turkey growers should buy poults from pullorum-free flocks which have been bred for broad breasts and meat production. Broad Breasted Bronze, Broad Breasted White, White Holland, and Beltsville Small White are the most popular varieties.

It takes about 12 to 15 weeks to produce a turkey broiler and six to seven months to finish out a mature bird.

Turkeys are brooded in much the same manner as chicks, but not more than 150 to 200 poults should be brooded under one hover. Turkeys are more difficult to get to eat than chickens. A starter ration containing 24 to 28 per cent protein and fortified with penicillin or other antibiotics should be fed.

Deep coarse litter should be provided for the poults. The brooder house should be kept dry. A sun porch should be used to increase floor space. A foot of feeder space for each five poults should be provided during the first three weeks. The feeder space should be doubled after four weeks. Three one-gallon waterers should be provided for each 75 poults. Small lights will assist the poults to keep from piling up while feeding.

The poults should be moved to a good legume range at eight to ten weeks. Clean ground should be used. Feeders and shelters should be moved to new range each week or ten days. Good pasture may save 15 to 20 per cent of the feed. One foot of feeder space should be provided for each three birds. Birds on range should be fed a 26 to 35 per cent protein mash and grains, or a complete mash ration. Provide self-feeders. It pays to feed antibiotics even to market time at the rate of two to ten grams per ton.

It takes about 90 pounds of feed to grow out a turkey, or five to six pounds of feed per pound of turkey. Turkey broilers will put on a pound of gain on less than three pounds of feed.

Sanitation, good rations, and careful management are essential in turkey production.

• Questions

1. What is the place of turkey production on your farm?
2. Outline a plan for successful brooding of turkey poults.
3. Formulate a starting mash for turkeys.
4. What are the essentials of a good growing mash for turkeys on range?
5. Outline a program of management of turkeys while on range.
6. Of what value is range to turkeys?
7. How can you tell when a turkey is ready for market?
8. What place do antibiotics and arsenicals have in turkey production?
9. What is the future of turkey broiler production?
10. What factors should be considered in buying poults?
11. Under what conditions can turkeys be grown in confinement?

• References

Council of American Official Poultry Tests, *Production Records for the Period 1955-56,* Ithaca, New York, 1957.

Hamilton, S. W., *Profitable Poultry Management,* The Beacon Milling Company, Cayuga, New York, 1954.

Smith, E. Y., *Growing Turkeys for Market,* Cornell Ext. Bul. 884, Cornell University, Ithaca, New York, 1953.

Weeks, John P., *The Poultry Profit Guide,* Vulcan Press, Birmingham, Alabama, 1953.

Winter, A. R. and E. M. Funk, *Poultry Science and Practice,* J. B. Lippincott Company, Philadelphia, 1956.

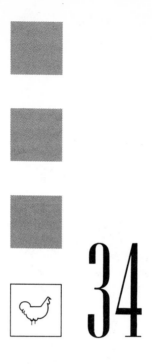

34

Control of Diseases and Parasites

It has been estimated that of the 15 to 25 per cent of the chickens and turkeys produced in this country which die each year, 60 to 75 per cent die because of disease. Poultrymen need to be familiar with the causes and symptoms of the diseases and parasites most likely to cause trouble in order to plan programs of prevention and cure. Careful selection of chicks and laying stock, providing adequate housing, feeding satisfactory rations, and practicing sanitation in management will aid in avoiding disease and parasite losses, but disease outbreaks occur even when these practices are carried out.

Diseases

The most serious diseases of chicks are pullorum and coccidiosis. Infectious synovitis and coccidiosis cause heavy losses in broiler

627

A

Figure 34-1. (A) A baby chick with pullorum disease. (Courtesy Dr. Salsbury's Laboratories) (B) A hatchery blood-testing crew at work in a flock owner's house. (Courtesy Automatic Poultry Feeder Company)

B

production. Newcastle disease, CRD (chronic respiratory, or air sac disease), lymphomatosis, bronchitis, fowl pox, and blue comb cause heavy losses in laying flocks. Many of these diseases and blackhead cause heavy losses in turkeys.

Pullorum. This is an acute, highly infectious, bacterial disease which occurs between the second and third day after hatching and the time the chicks or poults are about three weeks old.

Symptoms. Infected baby chicks or poults become weak and unthrifty, and show a white diarrhea or "pasted-up behind." Chicks which have been shipped or chilled are most susceptible to the disease. Losses may exceed 30 to 40 per cent.

The disease occurs in the egg organ of infected hens and passes into the eggs. The chicks which are hatched from these eggs are infected. Most states have control programs under the National Poultry Improvement Program which encourage hatcheries to use only pullorum-free flocks as sources of hatching eggs.

Prevention. The best preventative is to buy chicks from hatcheries cooperating in the State pullorum control programs. These programs require the blood testing of all birds used in hatchery flocks.

Treatment. Infected chicks should be given sulfamethazine or other sulfa drugs in water. Follow the instructions of the manufacturer. Keep chicks warm and dry, and keep the quarters sanitary.

Coccidiosis. Coccidiosis is a protozoan disease which affects the intestinal tract of chicks, usually when they are from three to five weeks of age. Outbreaks occur most often during warm, humid weather in early summer. Cecal coccidiosis is considered the most serious chick disease in this country. It is estimated that from 15 to 20 per cent of all chicks hatched in this nation die from this disease before they are a month old.

Symptoms. Chicks infected with the cecal type show bloody diarrhea, become listless, and have ruffled feathers. The birds eat little feed, and the comb and wattles become pale. Chicks with intestinal coccidiosis show the same symptoms as those with the cecal form with the exception of having less blood in the droppings.

Prevention. The litter must be kept loose and dry. Adequate rations containing aureomycin or other antibiotics have been proven

Figure 34-2. A young chicken with coccidiosis. (Courtesy Dr. Salsbury's Laboratories)

to be helpful in preventing and treating coccidiosis outbreaks. Chicks develop an immunity from the disease, if it is present at low levels.

Treatment. When coccidiosis strikes, it moves rapidly. Diseased birds or the flock should be treated immediately with sulfa drugs according to the directions of the manufacturer or the veterinarian. Sulfaquinoxaline may be fed in mash at the rate of four ounces per ton as a control, or at the rate of one pound per ton of chick feed as a treatment. About 3½ ounces of aureomycin and 2½ pounds of sulfamethazine mixed in each ton of feed is a very effective treatment.

Infectious Synovitis. This is a comparatively new disease which may affect 75 per cent of the birds. It is widespread in broiler producing areas. It may also affect layers and turkeys.

Symptoms. Infected birds lose their appetites and flesh, become listless, and have pale combs. They walk with a stiff, halting gait, and sit on their haunches much of the time. The hock joints of the legs are swollen and hot to touch.

Prevention. Good management consisting of sanitation, plenty of floor space, good ventilation, humidity control, adequate rations, and careful culling of suspicious birds appear to be the best preventative measures. Medication may be used but is costly if used for long periods of time at high levels.

Treatment. In Delaware tests, the feeding of 200 grams of NF-180 (a nitrofuran derived from oat hulls and corncobs) or 100 grams of aureomycin or terramycin per ton of feed gave the best results.

Newcastle Disease. Newcastle disease has spread rapidly since about 1942 when it was discovered in California. It is a filterable virus which enters the birds through the respiratory tract. It affects chickens, turkeys, and sometimes other species. It is highly infectious and causes death losses amounting to 25 to 80 per cent in both young chickens and in pullet flocks.

Symptoms. The usual symptoms are similar to those of bronchitis, tracheitis, and colds. Chicks sneeze, gasp, and have difficulty in breathing. They are weak and have ruffled feathers. Within a few days, nervous symptoms begin. They may twitch their heads and necks, and the head may become twisted and be drawn between the legs, or back over the shoulders. Birds may walk in circles or backwards.

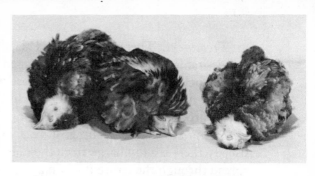

A

Figure 34-3. (A) Birds showing symptoms of Newcastle disease. (Courtesy of Dr. Salsbury's Laboratories) (B) Vaccinating birds for Newcastle by use of the spray method. (Courtesy American Scientific Laboratories, Inc.)

B

Laying hens have breathing trouble, and they gasp, wheeze, and rattle. Although they do not have serious nervous symptoms, egg production drops to zero in a few days, and soft-shelled floor eggs are found.

Prevention. If Newcastle disease has not been present on the farm or in the community, practice sanitation in production and management. Isolate all new birds. Keep visitors out of the poultry houses and yards.

On farms where Newcastle is known to exist, all chicks should be vaccinated with Newcastle disease vaccine.

Newcastle vaccines may be used alone, or with bronchitis vaccine in dust form, or in drinking water. Commercial vaccines are available and should be used according to manufacturers' directions.

Control of Diseases and Parasites • 631

Treatment. There is no cure. Palatable rations should be fed, and desirable housing quarters maintained.

Bronchitis. This respiratory disease may affect chickens at any age, but death loss is highest among chicks. Infected layers may be out of production for several weeks, but few birds die.

Symptoms. Infected birds have a raspy cough and gasp, and usually there is a discharge from the nose and eyes. The disease may spread through the entire flock in a day's time. Bronchitis resembles Newcastle disease, laryngotracheitis, and coryza.

Prevention. Chicks, poults, or mature birds may be immunized by use of a live-virus vaccine. It can be administered as a dust, in drinking water, or by the nose-drop method. Day-old birds can be vaccinated by the nose-drop method.

Treatment. There is no cure. Affected birds can be made comfortable and fed good rations when they begin to eat.

Chronic Respiratory Disease. This disease, which is commonly called CRD or air-sac infection, was discovered in 1943. It is now considered the number one disease of the broiler industry.

The infection is caused by a pleuropneumonia-like organism, which can be transmitted by direct contact or through the eggs of infected hens.

Symptoms. CRD causes young chickens to sneeze and lose weight. They continue to eat. The sinuses become swollen and breathing is accompanied by respiratory rales. Adult birds appear to have colds and production decreases. Inflammation of the sinuses and trachea and thickening of the air-sacs is common in chicks.

Prevention. Adequate rations, proper sanitation, good ventilation, and careful timing of vaccination to avoid stresses (periods when birds are weak physically) are musts. Chicks should be obtained from hatcheries which produce lines resistant to the disease, or from lines which by test have been proven free from the disease. The feeding of antibiotics is desirable as a preventative. It retards the growth of the organism.

Treatment. There is no vaccine or treatment other than the feeding of antibiotics and use of good management practices.

Laryngotracheitis. Fowl laryngotracheitis is a highly communicable and fatal virus disease. It attacks the larynx and windpipe and is most serious in pullets from five to ten months old. Birds that recover may be carriers and spread the infection to others.

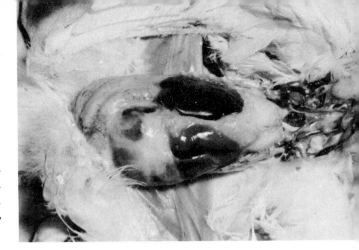

Figure 34-4. The slimy, grayish material covering the viscera due to CRD (chronic respiratory disease). (Courtesy Dr. Salsbury's Laboratories)

Symptoms. The infection strikes rapidly. Dead birds may be found before symptoms are discovered. The chief symptoms are labored, gasping, and rattling breathing, with the bird's head extended and the beak open. Watery discharge from the eyes and nostrils may also be present. Birds may cough violently and expel bloody mucus, and they often die due to suffocation.

Prevention. Birds should be vaccinated when six weeks of age or shortly thereafter. The vaccine is applied in the vent with a brush. Immunity develops in six to nine days. All vaccinated birds should be checked after four or five days to see if the vaccination took effect. A reddening of the vent or a cheesy mucus indicates a "take."

Treatment. Vaccinate all birds. Rely upon a veterinarian, feed a good ration, and practice sanitation. Burn all dead birds immediately.

Infectious Sinusitis. This is a serious respiratory disease of turkeys and is caused by the same micro-organism that causes CRD in chickens. Air-sac infection, a form of infectious sinusitis, may affect birds of all ages and cause high mortality in poults. The more common form of infectious sinusitis does not result in high mortality, but heavy losses due to retarded growth and poor condition.

Symptoms. One or both sides of the face become swollen. The eyes may become closed, and the birds have difficulty in breathing.

Prevention. There is no vaccine. Poults should be purchased from reliable hatcheries, and good management practices should·be followed.

Figure 34-5. A severe case of turkey sinusitis. (Courtesy Dr. Salsbury's Laboratories)

Treatment. Two treatments are used: 1. A mixture of streptomycin and penicillin may be injected into the muscle of infected birds, and the birds permanently removed from the flock. 2. Remove the fluid from the swollen sinuses by the use of a sterile syringe and a 1½-inch, 18- or 19-gauge needle. Inject four cubic centimeters of 1 per cent silver nitrate solution into the sinus. Do not put the bird with the flock.

Lymphomatosis or Leukosis. Poultrymen may know the disease as fowl paralysis, big-liver disease, gray-eye, or thick-leg disease. All are forms of leukosis. The group of diseases is one of the greatest causes of mortality in half-grown and adult chickens.

Symptoms. The symptoms vary with the form of the disease. Range paralysis affects young birds from six to twelve weeks old. Infected birds show partial paralysis of one or both legs or wings. With the gray-eye form, the iris loses its normal color and becomes gray and distorted. Birds affected with visceral lymphomatosis develop pale combs and lose appetites and flesh. The liver and other organs become enlarged. Birds with the big-bone or thick-leg type develop abnormally thick legs.

Prevention. The causal organism is a virus which can be transmitted from hen to chick in the egg, or from bird to bird. Chicks or poults should be purchased from reliable hatcheries and reared in sanitary quarters, in isolation from all other mature birds. Isolated clean ground is most important. All questionable birds should be removed from the flock as soon as identified.

Figure 34-6. Leukosis. The ocular form causes the bird to have gray eyes, with irregular pupils. (Courtesy Dr. Salsbury's Laboratories)

Treatment. The disease is cancerous in nature. There is no treatment. Isolation of infected birds and proper feeding and management of the flock should be practiced.

Fowl Pox. Chicken pox or sore-head is caused by a virus. It is quite infectious and shows up in two different forms. One form affects the skin and comb, the other affects the throat.

Symptoms. Small blister-like spots appear on the face, comb, and wattles. Light infection results in a few scattered spots. Heavy infection may cover the face, comb, and wattles. The diphtheritic form affects the mouth and throat, and yellow pus-like patches appear. The eyes may water, the birds will lose their appetites, and production will diminish.

Prevention. Almost complete protection will result from the vaccination of chickens while they are from six to 16 weeks of

Figure 34-7. Fowl pox. (Courtesy Dr. Salsbury's Laboratories)

age. Veterinarians may use the stick method. If the disease has been present on the farm, vaccination each year is recommended.

Treatment. There is no satisfactory treatment.

Roup. This infection is also known as coryza or cold. It is an infectious inflammation of the sinuses and upper respiratory tract and is caused by a bacteria. Death losses are low, but financial losses result from decreased growth and production of diseased birds.

Symptoms. A thin, watery discharge from the nostrils during the early stages of infection changes to a thick, sticky discharge which has an offensive aroma. Roup is usually detected by this aroma. Yellow masses of mucus form around the nostrils and eyes, and the birds may cough and sneeze.

Prevention. The isolation of birds brought onto the farm, and the use of sanitation in feeding and management are the best preventative methods.

Treatment. Sulfa drugs are effective in controlling roup. One-half pound of sulfathiazine to each 100 pounds of mash is recommended, or sulfamethazine may be fed in water. The directions of the manufacturer must be followed.

Typhoid. Fowl typhoid is a bacterial disease which affects both chickens and turkeys. Losses average about 25 per cent, but 80 per cent losses have been reported. The disease occurs mostly in mature birds.

Symptoms. Birds with typhoid are droopy, have little appetite, and crave water. The livers are infected, and birds show a profuse, watery, green diarrhea. Chickens may suffer from a few days to about two weeks. Turkeys die within two or three days.

Prevention. All birds in the laying or breeding flock should be blood-tested and carriers eliminated. Birds may be vaccinated for typhoid with avisepticus-gallinarum bacterin. It is a job for a veterinarian, or a poultry specialist.

Treatment. Sulfa-drug treatments, with or without repeated injections of bacterins, will aid in controlling the disease. Sodium sulfamerazine fed in the drinking water is recommended. The directions of the manufacturer or veterinarian must be followed.

Fowl Cholera. This disease affects all species of poultry and causes heavy losses. It is very contagious and spreads rapidly, and at times, birds begin to die before the disease has been discovered. It is caused by a bacterium.

Symptoms. Birds which appear healthy die suddenly. Other infected birds are weak, droopy, and inactive. They have ruffled feathers, a loss of appetite, and a fever. The heads, combs, and wattles become dark-colored, and a greenish or yellowish diarrhea is evidenced. Birds rarely recover.

Prevention. All healthy birds should be vaccinated if the disease is prevalent in the community or on the farm. The vaccine is a dual-purpose bacterin which controls both typhoid and cholera.

Treatment. Sulfamethazine in the drinking water will aid in checking death loss. Sanitation is an absolute necessity in controlling cholera.

Tuberculosis. Tuberculosis is caused by mycobacterin tuberculosis avium. It is infectious and occurs in many types of poultry.

Symptoms. The disease rarely affects young birds because it takes many months for the disease to take effect. Birds over 18 months of age are more likely to be affected than young birds. Infected birds lose weight, are inactive, and quit laying. The combs and wattles shrink and become dry and pale in color. The birds finally die.

Prevention. There is no treatment for tuberculosis, and the best control method is to sell off all hens at the end of the first laying season. Pullets which have been raised under sanitary conditions, and are housed in a well-disinfected house, rarely show signs of the disease during the first laying season.

Since the infection can spread from chickens to hogs, it is necessary that all diseased or dead birds be kept away from the hogs.

Blackhead. This is one of the very infectious protozoan diseases. It affects chickens, turkeys, and other fowl. It is highly fatal in turkeys.

Symptoms. The common symptoms of the disease in turkeys are lowered head, drooping wings, ruffled feathers, drowsiness, and a yellowish diarrhea. Young turkeys may die without showing signs of the infection.

The disease is mild in chickens but spreads from chickens to turkeys. It lives over in the cecal worms, or worm eggs, of the chickens.

Prevention. Grow poults and chicks on clean ground and in separate quarters. Worm flocks with phenothiazine at the rate of one pound per 100 pounds of mash for each 1000 birds.

Figure 34-8. Blackhead. A typically affected turkey. (Courtesy Dr. Salsbury's Laboratories)

Treatment. When an outbreak occurs, healthy turkeys should be removed to a clean range, and the birds treated with phenothiazine mash to remove cecal worms. Enheptin, and other materials which are helpful in treating infected birds, are available from veterinarians.

Many turkey producers use 4-nitro phenylarsonic acid in blackhead control. The drug may be given in feed or water throughout the growing period to prevent the establishment of the disease.

Blue Comb. This disease in chickens is similar to blue comb or mud fever in turkeys. They are not caused by the same organism. The causal organism has not been found for either disease. Losses, however, may be heavy, especially in turkeys.

Symptoms. In chickens, the disease usually shows up in young pullets just coming into production. Birds lose their appetites, become listless, and develop diarrhea. The comb and face become dark or bluish in color. Egg production drops and birds lose weight. Dehydration takes place. The disease appears to be infectious. The entire flock may be affected. The disease runs its course in ten to 14 days.

Prevention. Good sanitation, housing, feeding, and management are recommended. Vaccination and housing of pullets should be timed to avoid stresses which may influence the possibility of blue comb infection.

Treatment. The use of aureomycin and other antibiotics in drinking water is recommended. Potassium chloride may be fed in drinking water at the rate of one tablespoonful per gallon. The feeding of 3-nitro or 4-nitro phenylarsonic acid is also recommended. The directions of the manufacturers must be followed.

Erysipelas in Turkeys. This disease is caused by the same organism that causes swine erysipelas. Outbreaks usually occur in September and October. Young poults are not usually affected. Turkey toms are more susceptible to the disease than hens. Most outbreaks occur in flocks three to six months of age.

Symptoms. Birds may be listless and weak with wings and tails drooped. There may be some diarrhea. The snood of the toms appears reddish-purple. There may be mottling of the face color. Some birds die without showing outward signs of the disease.

Prevention. Birds should be vaccinated when eight to 12 weeks old with erysipelas bacterin if erysipelas has been prevalent.

Treatment. Penicillin and streptomycin may be used in treating infected birds.

Parasites

Large roundworms and cecal worms are the most serious internal parasites of poultry. Lice and mites are the serious external parasites.

Large Roundworms. These worms live in the small intestines, and the eggs are passed with the droppings. These eggs, which mature in about two months, are picked up by other chickens.

Symptoms. When heavily infested, young chickens become unthrifty and stunted. Some may die. Mature birds are droopy, have pale combs and wattles, and ruffled feathers. Their appetites are poor, and they stop laying. The large worms live on food which has already been digested, thus using food needed by the bird in growth and egg production.

Figure 34-9. (A) Large roundworms in intestine. (B) Tapeworms in intestine. (Courtesy Dr. Salsbury's Laboratories)

B

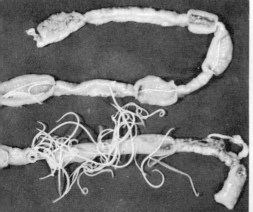

Prevention. Sanitation and rotated ranges are the best preventatives. Thorough cleaning and disinfecting of the houses and equipment is a must. Good litter, well managed, and the use of dropping pits are good aids. Young pullets ought to be grown on a clean range.

Treatment. One ounce of phenothiazine in one feeding for 60 medium weight mature birds, or one ounce per 100 three-pound young chickens is recommended.

Piperazine compounds which can be fed in water, are now available. They can be fed to young birds and layers without harmful results.

Cecal Worms. These worms are usually about half an inch long and grayish-white in color. They live in the ceca or blind pouches. The eggs are expelled with droppings, and the life cycle of the parasite is similar to that of the roundworm. To get rid of the worm is important because it serves as a host for blackhead disease.

Symptoms. The worms cause inflammation of the ceca but there are usually no outward symptoms.

Prevention. These worms are prevented in the same manner as roundworms. Sanitation practices and rotated ranges are necessary. Chickens and turkeys should be kept on separate, clean ranges.

Treatment. Phenothiazine may be fed in the mash at the rate of one pound to 100 pounds of mash for 1000 birds. A compound containing 15 grams of 40 per cent nicotine sulfate, 151 grams of phenothiazine, 287 grams of bentonite, and 44 pounds of chicken mash has produced excellent results.

Lice. Head, body, and shaft lice infest poultry and cause loss in egg production and growth, feeding on feathers and skin.

Symptoms. Birds are unthrifty, feathers may be ruffled, and production decreases.

Treatment. Dust birds with sodium fluoride, and spread two pounds of agricultural sulphur on the litter on each 100 square feet of floor space in the house. Apply lindane in nests and on litter and roosts. One part of 50 per cent malathion concentrate to 49 parts water, or one part of 20 per cent lindane concentrate in 19 parts water, or two tablespoonfuls of 15 per cent wettable aramite powder in one gallon of water may be used in spraying inside of house and equipment.

Mites. Chicken mites live on the roosts or on other parts of the house during the day and attack the birds at night. They are blood-sucking insects.

Symptoms. Birds may appear droopy or listless. Masses of mites may be found during the day on roosts and in cracks.

Treatment. Roosts, nests, boards, and the lower part of the hen house should be sprayed with an insecticide, creosote oil, or carbolineum mixed with kerosene. Scaly leg mite can be controlled by dipping the shanks in kerosene. The chemicals recommended for control of lice will also control chicken mites.

Summary

Pullorum in chicks and poults can be controlled by buying chicks from hatcheries cooperating in the National Poultry Improvement Program. Coccidiosis is our most serious chick disease. It can be prevented by buying early chicks, keeping litter dry, and by feeding antibiotics. Sulfaquinoxaline and sulfamethazine are the best treatments. NF-180 or other nitrofurans provide the best treatments for infectious synovitis.

A veterinarian should be called when an outbreak of the respiratory diseases takes place. There is no cure for typhoid. Birds may be vaccinated for laryngotracheitis when they are six weeks of age or older. On farms where Newcastle has not been present, sanitary methods should be used, and new birds must be isolated. Where Newcastle is known to exist, all birds should be vaccinated.

Buy chicks from strains known to be free from range paralysis, because there is no cure. You can tell roup by the aroma. Use sulfa drugs and good management as controls.

For typhoid, give the birds blood-tests. Vaccinate birds for typhoid and cholera, and burn dead birds. Practice sanitation, and feed sulfa drugs as controls.

Tuberculosis affects older birds. Pullets should be grown on clean ground, and all old hens should be sold off after one year's production. Any old birds held over should be given blood-tests. Clean and disinfect the house and premises.

Blackhead is best controlled by using clean range and by getting rid of cecal worms. Enheptin and other medicines are available, and should be fed according to directions. Infected birds should be kept moving to new range.

Vaccination can be used for infectious bronchitis, Newcastle disease, infectious laryngotracheitis, fowl pox, fowl cholera, and typhoid.

Worm chickens with piperizine compound, phenothiazine, or nicotine-bentonite compounds. Follow directions. Lice and mites can be controlled by spraying facilities and equipment with lindane, malathion, or aramite solutions.

• Questions

1. What practical method do you have for control of pullorum on your farm?
2. What methods would you use to control an outbreak of coccidiosis on your farm?
3. How can you tell the difference between Newcastle disease, bronchitis, roup, and laryngotracheitis? How would you treat these diseases?
4. Which of the diseases of poultry are transmitted through the egg from the hen to the chick?
5. How can you control range paralysis?
6. What are the means of controlling cholera and typhoid?
7. What are the best methods of controlling CRD?
8. Describe the various forms of leukosis and indicate how this disease may be controlled on your farm.
9. Which is preferred in vaccinating broilers for fowl pox, pigeon pox, or fowl pox vaccine? Why?
10. List treatments which will control both chicken lice and mites.
11. How can you control round and cecal worms in chickens?
12. Outline a program for maintaining a healthy poultry enterprise on your home farm.

• References

Bankowski, R. A., and A. S. Rosenwald, *Poultry Vaccination . . . Why and How*, Circular 455, University of California, Davis, California, 1956.

Brandly, C. A., *et al.*, *Respiratory Diseases of Poultry*, Circular 517, University of Illinois, Urbana, Illinois, 1954.

Gooding, P. H., *Poultry Sanitation and Health*, Circular 147, Clemson Agricultural College, Clemson, South Carolina, 1954.

North Carolina State College, *Common Poultry Diseases*, Ext. Cir. 344, Raleigh, North Carolina, 1956.

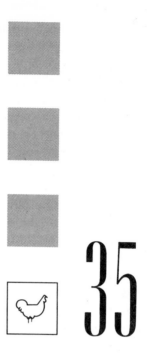

Marketing Poultry Products

Poultrymen are confronted with three major problems in marketing their products: (1) how to plan production to be able to market the products at the peak seasonal price; (2) how to produce the quality of products desired by the processor and consumer; and (3) how to locate the best market.

The large-scale producer analyzes his marketing program very carefully, for his livelihood depends upon the profit from the enterprise. The small producers are quite often careless in marketing their products, and many of our poultrymen are small producers. The poultry enterprise is a minor one in most states. Less than 8 per cent of the total cash livestock income in 37 states results from the sale of chickens, and in 34 states less than 8 per cent of the livestock income is received from the sale of eggs. In most states, considerable increases in poultry income would result from the use of improved marketing methods.

It has been estimated that egg income per hen can be increased from 50 cents to $1.00 per year by having maximum production during the periods of high prices, by producing high quality eggs, and by careful selection of markets.

Seasonal Price Trends. Egg prices fluctuate during the year in much the same manner as hog prices.

Egg Production Trends. Production has been high during March, April, May, and June. The price of eggs during those months is low. Egg production during September, October, November, and December is comparatively low, and prices are high. With improved methods of production, flock owners are now producing a higher percentage of the eggs during the months when prices are high than was done 15 or 20 years ago. Presented in Figure 35-1 are the average monthly egg production and the average price received by farmers for eggs each month during the seven-year period 1950 to 1956.

Note that fewer than 12 million cases of eggs were produced during the months of August and September. Peak production of 15 to 16 million cases of eggs were produced each month during March, April, and May.

Price Trends. As shown in Figure 35-1, egg prices during the months of peak production, March, April, and May, averaged 37.8 cents per dozen. The average price during August, September,

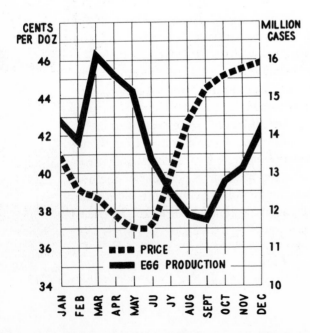

Figure 35-1. U. S. egg production and average monthly prices (seven-year period, 1950-1956).(Courtesy U.S.D.A. Agricultural Marketing Service)

October, and November, when production was low, was 44.4 cents per dozen. One of the keys to egg profits is to get high production during the months when prices are high.

Classes and Grades of Eggs. Care in the production and handling of eggs may net from two to six cents more per dozen if they are sold by grade. If a flock of hens average 180 eggs a year,

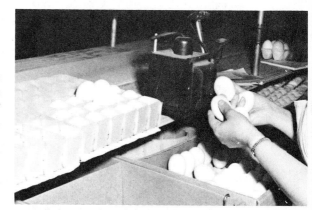

Figure 35-2. (right) Candling is necessary to determine egg grade. (Courtesy *Wallaces' Farmer and Iowa Homestead*)

Figure 35-3. (below) U. S. standards for quality of eggs. (Courtesy U.S.D.A. Agricultural Marketing Service)

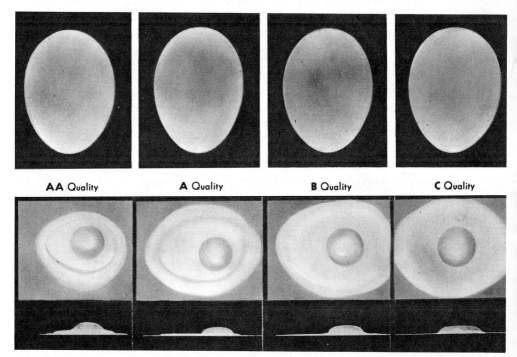

AA Quality   **A** Quality   **B** Quality   **C** Quality

from 30 to 90 cents a hen can be cleared by properly caring for the eggs and selling them by grade.

Eggs are classed in grading according to color, weight, and quality.

Consumer Grades of Shell Eggs. The main factors in determining the quality of an egg are the albumen quality, the freedom from defects, and shell quality. Commercially, egg quality is determined by candling. The four United States consumer grades of eggs are shown in Figure 35-3. The characteristics of these grades are as follows:

AA Quality. Clean, unbroken, practically normal shell. Practically regular air-cell one-eighth inch or less in depth. Clear, firm, white. Yolk well centered; outline defined; free from defects.

A Quality. Clean, unbroken, practically normal shell. Practically regular air-cell one-fourth inch or less in depth. Clean, reasonably firm, white. Yolk fairly well-centered; outline fairly well defined; practically no defects.

B Quality. Clean, unbroken shell but may be slightly abnormal. Air-cell three-eighth inch or less in depth. May show movement not over three-eighth inch if not over one-fourth inch; may be free. Clear, slightly weak, white. Yolk may be off-center. Outline well-defined; may be slightly enlarged or flattened; may show definite but not serious defects.

C Quality. Clean, unbroken shell, may be abnormal. Air-cell may be over three-eighth of an inch in depth; may be free or bubbly. Clear, white; may be weak and watery; small blood clots or spots may be present. Yolk may be enlarged, off-center, and flattened; may show visible germ development but no blood; may show other serious defects; outline plainly visible.

Weight Classes of Eggs. The United States consumer weight classes of eggs are shown in Figure 35-4. Wholesale eggs are graded according to weight as follows:

Extra large ....Minimum weight, 26 ounces per dozen
Large ....Minimum weight, 23 ounces per dozen
Medium ....Minimum weight, 20 ounces per dozen
Small ....Minimum weight, none

Commercial Grades of Eggs. Less than 20 per cent of the eggs produced and available for market in the United States in 1955 were graded under Federal or Federal-state grading programs.

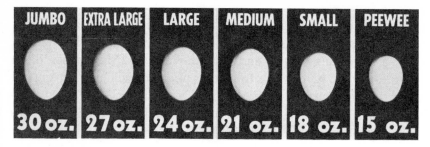

JUMBO	EXTRA LARGE	LARGE	MEDIUM	SMALL	PEEWEE
30 oz.	27 oz.	24 oz.	21 oz.	18 oz.	15 oz.

Figure 35-4. U. S. weight classes of eggs (minimum weight per dozen). (Courtesy U.S.D.A. Agricultural Marketing Service)

Graded eggs almost always sell for a few cents more per dozen than do ungraded eggs.

State Egg Laws. As of January 1956, 47 states had some type of egg law. Sixteen states passed new or revamped egg laws in 1955. Most of the egg laws were enacted (1) to improve the quality of eggs on the consumer market, and (2) to insure the producer of high-quality eggs a higher price than that received for ungraded or eggs of inferior quality.

Egg laws should improve the market for eggs. Improvement in egg quality is desirable. In some states, egg laws have tended to reduce the number of small-flock owners and increase the number of large, specialized egg producers.

Figure 35-5. Modern egg merchandising in an Iowa food market. (Courtesy Wallaces' Farmer and Iowa Homestead)

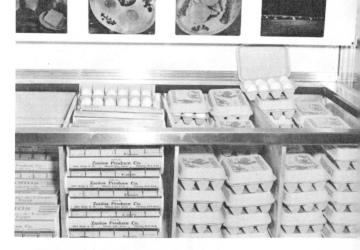

Marketing Poultry Products • 647

Practices in Maintaining Egg Quality. The marketing of eggs begins as soon as they are laid. Fresh eggs have high quality, but a few hours of heat and dry air will lower the quality of an egg to second grade. The following practices will aid in maintaining the high quality of fresh eggs. No practice should be disregarded. It takes all of them to maintain high quality in the eggs produced.

1. Gather eggs twice a day in winter and three times a day in summer.
2. Use wire baskets for gathering and cooling eggs.
3. Cool the eggs overnight. Take them to a cool place immediately when gathered.
4. Case eggs after cooling in precooled cases.
5. Pack eggs with the small end down.
6. Store eggs in cave, basement, or in a mechanical cooler where temperature is 50° to 60° F. and the air is moist.
7. Sort out the small, irregular, and dirty eggs.
8. Keep male birds away from the laying flock. Produce infertile eggs.
9. Feed complete rations in adequate amounts.
10. Confine layers in morning during wet weather.
11. Provide at least one nest for each five hens.
12. Keep clean shavings, excelsior, or Chick Bed in the nests.

Figure 35-6. A mechanical egg cooler. (Courtesy Buckeye Incubator Co.)

13. Do not permit birds to roost in nests at night.
14. Keep dropping boards or pits covered with wire.
15. Provide ample floor space and keep the litter dry.
16. Keep broody hens out of the nests.

Marketing Poultry

The rapid increase in turkey and broiler production has changed the poultry marketing picture. At one time, practically all the poultry marketed in this country came from farm flocks, and in the main, was a by-product of egg production.

In 1956, more than four times as many pounds of commercial broilers and turkeys as of farm-raised chickens were marketed in this country. According to U.S.D.A. data, 4,275 million pounds of commercial broilers, 1,249 million pounds of turkeys, and 1,203 million pounds of farm-raised chickens were marketed in this country in 1956.

The production of chicken and turkey broilers, and improved methods of refrigeration and storage, have helped to distribute marketing throughout the year and minimize seasonal price variations.

Market Classes of Poultry

Market classes are provided for chickens, turkeys, ducks, geese, guineas, and pigeons. Three classes are provided—live poultry, dressed poultry, and ready-to-cook poultry. Most poultry sold by farmers is sold as live poultry, although the marketing of dressed and ready-to-cook birds is done on a small scale by some farmers. Commercial producers may process the birds or sell them as live poultry.

Chickens. The following classes of chickens are specified by the Poultry Branch, Production and Marketing Administration of the United States Department of Agriculture.

Broiler or Fryer. A broiler or fryer is a young chicken (usually under sixteen weeks of age) of either sex that is tender-meated with soft, pliable, smooth-textured skin and flexible breastbone cartilage.

Roaster. A roaster is a young chicken (usually under eight months of age) of either sex that is tender-meated with soft, pliable, smooth-textured skin and breastbone cartilage that is somewhat less flexible than that of a broiler or fryer.

Capon. A capon is an unsexed male chicken (usually under ten months of age) that is tender-meated with soft, pliable, smooth-textured skin.

Stag. A stag is a male chicken (usually under ten months of age) with coarse skin, somewhat toughened and darkened flesh, and considerable hardening of the breastbone cartilage. Stags show a condition of fleshing and a degree of maturity intermediate between that of a roaster and a cock, or old rooster.

Hen or Stewing Chicken or Fowl. These birds are mature female chickens (usually more than ten months old) with meat less tender than that of a roaster, and nonflexible breastbones.

Cock or Old Rooster. A cock or old rooster is a mature male chicken with coarse skin, toughened and darkened meat, and hardened breastbone.

Turkeys. The five official classes of turkeys follow.

Fryer or Roaster. A fryer or roaster is a young, immature turkey (usually under sixteen weeks of age) of either sex that is tender-meated with soft, pliable, smooth-textured skin, and flexible breastbone cartilage.

Young Hen Turkey. A young hen turkey is a young female turkey (usually under eight months of age) that is tender-meated with soft, pliable, smooth-textured skin, and breastbone cartilage that is somewhat less flexible than in a turkey fryer or roaster.

Young Tom Turkey. A young tom turkey is a young male turkey (usually under eight months of age) that is tender-meated with soft, pliable, smooth-textured skin, and breastbone cartilage that is somewhat less flexible than in a turkey fryer or roaster.

Hen Turkey. These birds are fully matured female turkeys (usually over ten months of age) that are less tender-meated than a young hen turkey, have hardened breastbones, and may have coarse-textured skin and patchy areas of surface fat.

Tom Turkey. A tom turkey is a mature male turkey (usually over ten months of age) with coarse skin, toughened flesh, and hardened breastbone.

Ducks. Three classes of ducks are specified: (1) broiler duckling or fryer duckling, (2) roaster duckling, and (3) mature or older duck.

Geese. There are but two classes of geese: (1) young goose and (2) mature or old goose.

Guineas. Classes are provided for (1) young guineas and for (2) mature or old guineas.

Pigeons. Two classes of pigeons are specified: (1) squab and (2) pigeon.

Marketing Live Poultry

Much of the live poultry sold by producers goes directly, or through dealers, to commercial dressing plants. A common practice, up to about 1930, was to ship live poultry in cars by rail to processing plants in our large cities. The practice was expensive because of transportation costs and shrinkage. Processing and dressing plants are now located within trucking distance of practically all producers. Most live poultry is now transported by truck.

Finishing Poultry for Market. Most poultry dressing plants follow the practice of putting fowl purchased from farmers and commercial producers in batteries and feeding the birds heavily on soft feeds from two to four days before slaughtering them. The added finish improves the meat quality and the market grade of the carcass. Usually the weight increases are very profitable.

It is a good idea to confine for a few days the birds that are going to be marketed, if satisfactory facilities are available, and to feed them heavily on a wet mash ration. If adequate and sanitary quarters cannot be provided, the birds can be hand-fed the wet mash rations while on range. This short feeding period will increase the market grade of the bird, and the added gain in weight will further increase the returns when the birds are sold.

Standards of Quality for Live Poultry. Official United States Standards for quality of individual live birds have been set up for the classes described earlier in this chapter. The following factors are considered in determining the quality of an individual bird: (1) health and vigor; (2) feathering; (3) conformation; (4) fleshing and fat covering; and (5) the degree of freedom from defects.

Three standards of quality are specified: (1) A or No. 1 Quality; (2) B or No. 2 Quality; and (3) C or No. 3 Quality. A description of the minimum requirements and maximum defects permitted in each of the quality standards is shown in Table 66.

TABLE 66

SUMMARY OF STANDARDS OF QUALITY FOR LIVE POULTRY ON AN INDIVIDUAL BIRD BASIS

(Minimum Requirements and Maximum Defects Permitted)

Factor	A or No. 1 Quality	B or No. 2 Quality	C or No. 3 Quality
Health and Vigor:	Alert, bright eyes, healthy, vigorous	Good health and vigor	Lacking in vigor
Feathering:	Well covered with feathers showing luster or sheen. Slight scattering of pin feathers.	Fairly well covered with feathers. Moderate number of pin feathers.	Complete lack of plumage feathers on back. Large number of pin feathers.
Conformation:			
Breast bone	Normal	Practically normal	Abnormal
	Slight curve, 1/8" dent (chickens), 1/4" dent (turkeys)	Slightly crooked	Crooked
Back	Normal (except slight curve)	Moderately crooked	Crooked or hunched back
Legs and Wings	Normal	Slightly misshapen	Misshapen
Fleshing:	Well-fleshed, moderately broad and long breast	Fairly well finished	Poorly developed, narrow breast, thin covering of flesh.

652

Factor	A or No. 1 Quality	B or No. 2 Quality	C or No. 3 Quality
Fat Covering:	Well-covered, some fat under skin over entire carcass.	Enough fat on breast and legs to prevent a distinct appearance of flesh thru skin.	Lacking in fat covering on back and thighs, small amount in feather tracks.
	Chicken fryers, turkey fryers, and young toms only moderate covering. No excess abdominal fat.	Hens or fowl may have excessive abdominal fat.	
Defects:			
Tears and broken bones	Slight	Moderate	Serious
	Free	Free	Free
Bruises, scratches, and calluses	Slight skin bruises, scratches, and calluses	Moderate (except only slight flesh bruises)	Unlimited to extent no part unfit for food.
Shanks	Slightly scaly	Moderately scaly	Seriously scaly

Standards effective March 1, 1955, U.S.D.A.

653

Marketing Dressed and Ready-to-Cook Poultry

Consumers buy very little live poultry. Most of the poultry sold to consumers is sold as dressed or ready-to-cook fowl.

Dressed Fowl. The term "dressed fowl" refers to birds which have been slaughtered, bled, and have had the feathers removed. Dressed birds are usually sold as fresh-killed poultry. The dressed carcass weighs from 9 to 12 per cent less than the live weight of the bird.

Ready-to-Cook Poultry. Much of the poultry on the consumer market is ready-to-cook poultry. The birds have been slaughtered and bled, and the feathers, entrails, head, feet, and shanks have been removed. The gizzard, liver, heart, and neck are usually wrapped in waxed paper and placed inside the bird. The carcass may or may not be cut up for frying.

A three-pound broiler will produce a dressed carcass weighing from about 2.6 to 2.7 pounds, and an eviscerated or ready-to-cook carcass (with giblets) weighing about 2.1 pounds. A six-pound roaster will yield a 5.3- to 5.4-pound dressed carcass, and a 4.2- to 4.4-pound ready-to-cook carcass. The loss in dressing and drawing usually amounts to 25 to 35 per cent.

Standards of Quality for Dressed and Ready-to-Cook Poultry. Official standards for quality of individual dressed and

Figure 35-7. (A) Young Chicken Carcass—A Quality; (B) Young Chicken Carcass—B Quality; (C) Young Chicken Carcass—C Quality (U.S.D.A. Agricultural Marketing Service).

A   B   C

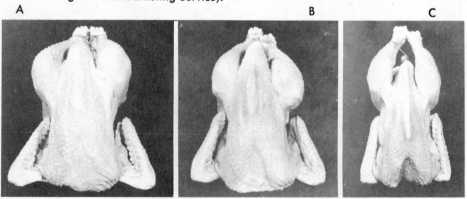

ready-to-cook poultry have been outlined by the Poultry Branch of the Production and Marketing Administration. The factors considered in determining the quality of an individual carcass are as follows: (1) conformation; (2) fleshing; (3) fat covering; (4) freedom from pinfeathers; (5) freedom from cuts, tears, disjointed and broken bones; (6) freedom from discolorations of skin, flesh blemishes, and bruises, and (7) freedom from freezer burn.

The minimum requirements and maximum defects permitted in each of the quality or grade standards for dressed and ready-to-cook chickens are shown in Table 67. The minimum requirements and allowable defects in the quality standards for dressed and ready-to-cook turkey are presented in Table 68.

A   B   C

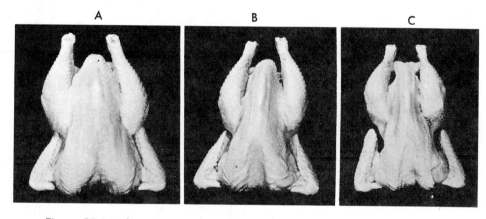

Figure 35-8. (above) (A) Hen, Stewing Chicken—A Quality; (B) Hen, Stewing Chicken—B Quality; (C) Hen, Stewing Chicken—C Quality (U.S.D.A Agricultural Marketing Service).

Figure 35-9. (below) (A) Young Tom Turkey—A Quality; (B) Young Tom Turkey—B Quality; (C) Young Tom Turkey—C Quality (U.S.D.A. Agricultural Marketing Service).

A   B   C

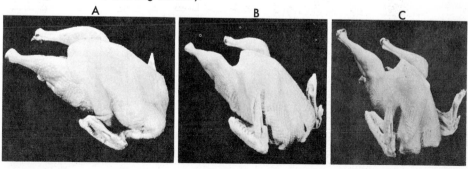

TABLE 67

SUMMARY OF STANDARDS FOR QUALITY OF DRESSED AND READY-TO-COOK CHICKENS

(*Minimum Requirements and Maximum Defects Permitted*)

Factor	A Quality	B Quality	C Quality
Conformation:			
Breastbone	Normal Slight curve, ⅛" dent	Practically Normal Dented, curved, slightly crooked	Abnormal Seriously crooked ⎱ If fairly well
Back	Normal (except slight curve)	Moderately crooked	Seriously crooked ⎰ fleshed
Legs and Wings		Moderately misshapen	Misshapen
Fleshing:	Normal Well-fleshed, moderately long, with broad breast	Fairly well fleshed on breast and legs	Poorly fleshed
Breastbone	Not prominent	Not prominent	May be prominent
Fat Covering:	Well covered—some fat under skin over entire carcass Broilers or fryers only moderate covering	Sufficient fat on breast and legs to prevent distinct appearance of flesh through skin	Lacking in fat covering over all parts of carcass

Factor	A Quality — Breast and Legs	A Quality — Elsewhere	B Quality — Breast and Legs	B Quality — Elsewhere	C Quality
Pinfeathers:					
Dressed:					
Pins and hair	Pract. free	Pract. free	Relatively few	Slight scattering	Numerous
Ready-to-cook:					
Nonprotruding pins	Pract. free	Pract. free	Few scattered	Few scattered	Scattering
Hair	Pract. free	Pract. free	Few scattered	Few scattered	Few scattered
Protruding pins	Free	Free	Free		Free

656

The quality designations specified herein are not applicable to birds possessing any of the following conditions: dirty or bloody head or carcass, dirty feet or vent; fan feathers, garter feathers, or feed in the crop.

Cuts and Tears:[1]	Free	1½"	1½"	3"	No limit
Missing skin:[2]	None		Three areas totaling not more than ¾ inch	Tail to hip bones width of feather tract	No limit
Disjointed bones	1		2		No limit
Broken bones	None (except 1 nonprotruding wing bone if fryer)		1 Nonprotruding		No limit
Missing parts	Wing tips		Wing tips and if R-to-C 2nd wing joint and tail		Wing tips and if R-to-C wings and tail
Discolorations:[3]	*Breast and Legs*	*Elsewhere*	*Breast and Legs*	*Elsewhere*	
Flesh bruises	0"	½"	½"	1½"	No limit[4]
Skin bruises	½"	¾"	¾"	1½"	No limit[4]
All discolorations	1"	1½"	1½"	3"	No limit[4]
Freezer Burn:	Few small (⅛" diameter) pockmarks		Moderate-dried areas not in excess of ½" in diameter		Numerous pockmarks and large dried areas

[1] Total aggregate length of all cuts and tears including incision for removal of the crop or its contents.

[2] Total to be included in total permitted cuts and tears.

[3] Maximum diameter of aggregate areas of all flesh bruises, skin bruises, and discolorations.

[4] No limit on size and number of areas of discoloration and flesh bruises, if such areas do not render any part of the carcass unfit for food.

TABLE 68

SUMMARY OF SPECIFICATIONS FOR STANDARDS OF QUALITY FOR
INDIVIDUAL CARCASSES OF DRESSED AND READY-TO-COOK TURKEYS

(Minimum Requirements and Maximum Defects Permitted)

Factor	A Quality		B Quality		C Quality	
Conformation:						
Breastbone	Normal		Practically Normal		Abnormal	
	Slight curve, ¼″ dent		Dented, curved, slightly crooked		Seriously crooked	if fairly well fleshed
Back	Normal (except slight curve)		Moderately crooked		Seriously crooked	
Legs and wings	Normal		Moderately misshapen		Misshapen	
Fleshing:	Well-fleshed, moderately long and broad breast		Fairly well-fleshed on breast and legs		Poorly fleshed	
Breastbone	Not prominent		Not prominent		May be prominent	
Pouchiness	Slight		Definite		Extended	
Fat Covering:	Well covered—some fat under skin over entire carcass.		Sufficient fat on breast and legs to prevent a distinct appearance of flesh through skin.		Lacking in fat covering over all parts of carcass	
	Fryers and young toms only moderate covering					
Pinfeathers:	*Breast and Legs*	*Elsewhere*	*Breast and Legs*	*Elsewhere*		
Dressed:						
Pins and hair	Pract. free	Pract. free	Relatively few	Slight scattering	Numerous	

658

Ready-to-cook:

Ready-to-cook:	Pract. free	Few scattered	Scattering
Non-protruding pins and hair	Pract. free	Few scattered	Scattering
Protruding pins	Free	Free	Free
Cuts and Tears:[1]	3"	6"	No limit
Missing skin[2]	None	Three areas none of which exceed 1", total aggregate 1½".	Width of feather tract tail to hips
Disjointed bones	1	2	No limit
Broken bones	None	1 Nonprotruding	No limit
Missing parts	Wing tips	Wing tips and if R-to-C 2nd wing joint and tail	Wing tips and if R-to-C wings and tail
Discolorations:[3] — Flesh bruises	Breast and Legs 0"; Elsewhere 1"	Breast and Legs 1"; Elsewhere 3"	No limit[4]
Skin bruises	Breast and Legs 3/4"; Elsewhere 1½"	Breast and Legs 1½"; Elsewhere 3"	No limit[4]
All discolorations	Breast and Legs 2"; Elsewhere 3"	Breast and Legs 3"; Elsewhere 6"	No limit[4]
Freezer Burn:	Few small (¼" diameter) pockmarks	Moderate-dried areas not in excess of ½" in diameter	Numerous pockmarks and large dried areas

The quality designations specified herein are not applicable to birds possessing any of the following conditions: dirty or bloody head or carcass, dirty feet or vent; fan feathers, neck feathers, garter feathers, or feed in the crop.

[1] Total aggregate length of all cuts and tears including incision for removal of the crop or its contents.

[2] Total included in permitted tears and cuts.

[3] Maximum diameter of aggregate areas of all flesh bruises, skin bruises, and discolorations.

[4] No limit on size and number of areas of discoloration and flesh bruises if such areas do not render any part of the carcass unfit for food.

U.S.D.A.

Weight Specifications. Dressed and ready-to-cook poultry is also sold according to weight specifications. The carcasses are weighed and grouped. Broilers, roasters, and hen classifications are at half-pound intervals, while capon, stag, and cock classifications are based upon one-pound differences in weights. The classifications of turkeys and geese are based upon two-pound differences in weights.

Turkey hens and light-weight birds bring higher prices than toms and heavy birds. The discount for heavy birds is greatest in the spring. The average weight of all turkeys marketed in 1956 was 16.6 pounds. Small-type turkeys made up 18 per cent of the 1956 turkey crop.

Seasonal Price Trends. Nearly 50 per cent of the poultry produced in this country is marketed in the months of October, November, December, and January. The increase in broiler production is helping to spread production throughout the year and decrease seasonal price differences. The freezing of poultry has also helped to minimize seasonal price differences.

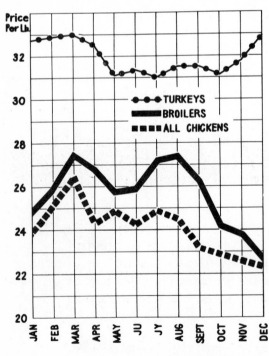

Figure 35-10. Average monthly prices of turkeys, broilers, and chickens (seven-year period 1950-1956). (U.S. D.A. Agricultural Marketing Service)

As shown in Figure 35-10 the average price of chickens during the months of October, November, and December for the 1950-1956 period was 22.1 cents per pound. The average price during the February, March, and April period was 25.3 cents. Chickens sold in July, August, and September sold for an average of 24.2 cents.

Turkey prices were lowest during the May to November period and highest in December, January, February, and March. The spread in price between the low in July and high in March was only two cents per pound. Broilers sold best in March, July, and August. November and December were the poorest broiler marketing months. There was a spread of 4.8 cents per pound between the low market in December and the high market in March. It will pay to plan production and marketing so that the birds will be sold during the periods of high prices.

Improved Meat-Type Poultry. National Chicken-of-Tomorrow contests have been conducted since 1946 to encourage the development of a chicken with a higher percentage of the carcass in the breast, thighs, and legs. Considerable progress has been made.

Figure 35-11. Cross sections of *Chicken of Tomorrow* wax models. The center carcass is the average market-type bird at twelve weeks. Left shows progress made to date. The carcass on the right is the ideal. (Courtesy *Broiler Growing*)

The Broad Breast Bronze turkey has done much to improve the carcasses of heavy turkeys. Nearly 80 per cent of the turkeys produced in this country carry Broad Breast Bronze breeding.

The Small White Beltsville turkey has become popular because of its early maturity and good quality carcass. Our best lightweight turkeys are of this breed.

Summary

Increased returns from the poultry enterprise may be obtained by (1) marketing poultry and eggs during the periods of high prices, (2) by improving the quality of the poultry products, and (3) by a careful selection of the method of marketing. Eggs sold in August, September, October, and November sell for several cents more per dozen than eggs sold in February, March, and April.

The four United States consumer grades of eggs are AA Quality, A Quality, B Quality, and C Quality. The quality is determined by candling the egg. Albumen quality, freedom for defects, shell quality, and age are important in determining egg quality.

Eggs are classed according to size as extra large, large, medium, and small. Most commercial eggs are now sold as graded eggs. Most states have egg grading laws.

To improve egg quality, gather eggs several times a day; cool them in a wire basket in a cool, moist room or in a mechanical cooler; case them the following morning, placing the large end up. Sort out small, irregular, and dirty eggs. Produce infertile eggs. Provide good nesting facilities. Market eggs twice a week, and sell them by grade.

Chickens are sold as broilers, roasters, capons, stags, hens, or cocks. Turkeys are sold as fryers or roasters, young hen turkeys, young tom turkeys, hen turkeys, and tom turkeys. Live birds are graded according to health and vigor, feathering, conformation, fleshing, fat covering, and degree of freedom from defects. There are three standards of quality: A or No. 1 Quality, B or No. 2 Quality, and C or No. 3 Quality.

Dressed and ready-to-cook poultry is graded on: conformation; fleshing; fat covering; freedom from pinfeathers; freedom from cuts, tears, and disjointed or broken bones; freedom from bruises, flesh blemishes, discolorations of skin, and freezer burn. Three quality grades are used: A, B, and C.

Heavy and tom turkeys sell for less than hens and lightweight finished turkeys.

Turkey prices are best in December, January, and February. March, July, and August are the best months to sell broilers. Farm chickens sell best in March, May, and July. Have the desired quantity and quality of birds ready when the market is best.

• Questions

1. Egg prices are highest during which months of the year?
2. What are the characteristics of each of the U.S.D.A. consumer grades of eggs?
3. What are the advantages and disadvantages of selling eggs by grade?
4. What are the weight classes of eggs?
5. Does it pay to clean dirty eggs? Why?
6. Outline a program for improving the quality and the marketing of eggs on your farm.
7. What are the market classes of chickens and turkeys?
8. Describe the standards of quality and the grades for live poultry.
9. What are the standards of quality and the grades of dressed and ready-to-cook poultry?
10. What is the difference between dressed and ready-to-cook fowl?
11. During which months will farm chickens sell for the highest prices? Broilers? Turkeys?
12. Plan a feeding program for finishing broilers, farm chickens, and turkeys.
13. Outline a program for improving the quality and methods of marketing poultry on your farm.

• References

Agricultural Marketing Service, *Grading and Inspection of Eggs and Egg Products,* U. S. Department of Agriculture, Washington, D. C., 1956.

Agricultural Marketing Service, *Poultry Grading Manual,* Agriculture Handbook No. 31, U. S. Department of Agriculture, Washington, D. C., 1956.

Funk, E. M., and James Forwerd, *Producing Quality Eggs,* Bul. 654, University of Missouri, Columbia, Missouri, 1955.

Hamann, J. A., et al., *Marketing Farm Poultry,* Farmers' Bulletin 2030, U. S. Department of Agriculture, Washington, D. C., 1955.

Pond, T. H., et al., *Marketing Eggs,* Farmer's Bulletin 1378, U. S. Department of Agriculture, Washington, D. C., 1955.

REPRODUCTION, INHERITANCE, AND PEDIGREES

36

Reproduction, Inheritance, and Pedigrees in Animal Breeding

Much of the improvement in the conformation and type of livestock has come about through the use of carefully planned breeding programs. An understanding of the basic principles in reproduction and inheritance is essential in planning livestock breeding programs. These principles are much the same, regardless of the type of animal, but there may be variations in application. We present in this chapter a brief explanation of (1) reproduction; (2) the reproductive organs of male and female animals; (3) the laws of inheritance which affects reproduction; and (4) the value of pedigree information in animal breeding.

Reproduction

Reproduction is the process by which new individuals are produced in plant and animal life and begins when the female germ cell is fertilized by the male germ cell. The female cell is called the *ovum*, or egg, and the male cell is called the *sperm*. This fertilization process follows closely the breeding of the female by the male.

The egg or ovum contains the hereditary materials of the mother, while the sperm contains the materials of inheritance contributed by the father or sire. The contributions of the sire and dam, so far as inheritance is concerned, are equal. The fertilization of the egg, however, takes place within the body of the mother, and the offspring is nourished and protected by the mother until birth.

Female Reproductive Organs. As shown in Figure 36-1, the reproductive system of the female consists of the ovaries, the oviducts, the uterus, the vagina, and the vulva.

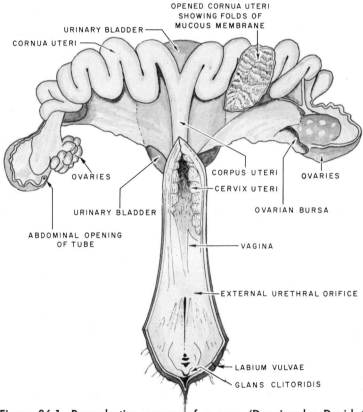

OPENED CORNUA UTERI
SHOWING FOLDS OF
MUCOUS MEMBRANE

URINARY BLADDER

CORNUA UTERI

OVARIES

URINARY BLADDER

ABDOMINAL OPENING
OF TUBE

CORPUS UTERI

CERVIX UTERI

OVARIES

OVARIAN BURSA

VAGINA

EXTERNAL URETHRAL ORIFICE

LABIUM VULVAE

GLANS CLITORIDIS

Figure 36-1. Reproductive organs of a sow. (Drawing by David C. Opheim)

Reproduction, Inheritance, and Pedigrees in Breeding • 665

Ovaries. These two glandular organs are located in the sub-lumbar region and produce eggs. Each ovary contains many follicles, in which the eggs are produced. As the eggs mature, they are dropped into the oviduct. The process is called ovulation and takes place during or shortly after the heat period.

Oviducts. These tubes lead from the ovaries to the horns of the uterus. The fertilization of the egg usually takes place near the upper end of the oviduct.

Uterus. This is a hollow organ containing two horns, which are connected to the oviducts. The fertilized egg moves from the oviduct into the uterus, becomes attached to the wall, and develops.

Cervix. This is the neck of the uterus and separates it from the vagina.

Vagina. This tube connects the vulva and the cervix.

Vulva. Both the urinary and reproductive organs of the female terminate in the vulva.

Male Reproductive Organs. The reproductive system of the male consists of the testicles, the sperm ducts, the seminal vesicles, the prostate, Cowper's glands, the urethra, and the penis.

Testicles. Sperm cells are produced in the two testicles, which are suspended in the scrotum.

Sperm Ducts. These tubes connect the testicles with the urethra. Sperms pass through and may be stored at the upper end of these tubes.

Seminal Vesicles. These glands open to the urethra and secrete a fluid.

Prostate. The prostate gland is located near the bladder and the urethra. It also produces a secretion that becomes a part of the seminal fluid.

Cowper's Glands. These glands secrete a fluid that precedes the passage of the sperm cells down the urethra.

Urethra. This long tube extends from the bladder to the penis and carries both urine and semen.

Penis. This organ deposits the sperm cells within the female reproductive system.

Conception. Reproduction begins with the heat period in the female or the time when she will be receptive to the male. The heat period varies with type of animal, but in cows usually occurs on an average of every 21 days. From six to 20 hours after the heat period, the female germ cell or egg is released from the ovaries. If the female is bred and a sperm (male germ cell) comes in contact with the egg, fertilization takes place and the female becomes pregnant. It takes from four to nine hours for the sperms to travel from the vagina to the oviducts, where fertilization normally takes place. Therefore, a female bred near the end of her heat period is more apt to conceive than if she were bred early in the heat period.

Growth of Fetus. *Fetal Membranes.* These consist of three separate structures which surround the fetus or unborn progeny. One contains many blood vessels which lead into the placenta and unite the mother and her unborn offspring. Another membrane contains a fluid which protects the fetus from injury. The third membrane serves as a holding place for the urine from the fetal bladder.

Placenta. This vascular structure is the portion of the fetal membrane that unites the mother and the fetus. The blood vessels of each lie close together, which permits the interchange of food materials through their extremely thin walls.

Navel Cord. This cord connects the fetus and the placenta and serves as a passageway for blood to and from the fetus.

Laws of Inheritance

Chromosomes and Genes. Each germ cell (sperm and egg) contains chromosomes, which in turn carry genes. The genes determine the characteristics to be found in the individual. The color of hair, the conformation of the body, the type, and other characteristics are determined by the genes in the germ cells.

The number of chromosomes in the nucleus of a cell is constant. They occur in pairs. In swine there are 19 pairs, whereas in sheep, cattle, and horses there are 30 pairs. The members of each pair carry genes that affect the same characteristics of the animal's physical condition, but they may not affect them in the same way. For example, in breeding sheep, factor A on chromosome 1 may affect color of wool by producing black color, whereas factor A on the other chromosome of the pair may produce white color. If neither color is dominant, the progeny will possess both colors.

Dominant and Recessive Characters. When a pure polled ram is mated to a horned ewe, the offspring is polled. Certain characteristics are dominant, whereas others are recessive. When dominant and recessive characters are brought together, the progeny will possess the dominant characteristics, but will produce in the next generation some animals that will show the dominant characteristics, whereas others will possess the appearance of the recessive. The best example of dominant and recessive factors and how the ratio works out is that of the color and polled characteristics in cattle.

Black color in cattle is dominant to red. When an Angus cow is mated to a Hereford bull, the calf produced will be black with a white face. Darker colors are usually dominant to lighter colors.

When a polled beef animal such as the Angus is mated to a horned animal such as the Hereford, the first generation or first cross will be polled. However, the crossbred offspring will carry the recessive factor for horns and if a crossbred from this parentage is mated to a similar crossbred, an average of one animal in four will be horned.

White hair color in hogs is dominant to black and to red. Many of the factors which affect vigor, rate of gain, feed efficiency, and carcass quality in hogs are thought to be dominant, while those which affect these factors in a negative manner are thought to be recessives. Navel hernias appear when two recessive genes are brought together.

Chromosome Segregation. The normal reproductive cell in sheep and cattle contains 30 pairs of chromosomes, yet when two cells are brought together there still are only 30 pairs of chromosomes. This is because of a reduction process of germ cell production, reducing the number of chromosomes by one-half. Only one chromosome of each pair is included in the germ cell. The bringing together of the two germ cells through fertilization restores the normal number of chromosomes.

Hybrid. An animal is considered a hybrid for any one character when it possesses one dominant and one recessive gene. When a hybrid is crossed with another hybrid, about 75 per cent of the progeny show dominance, but only about one-third of the group are pure dominant for the one character. The other two-thirds have the appearance of the dominant but are hybrid. Those that show recessive characteristics are pure recessives.

Hybrid Vigor. The crossing of two superior animals of different breeds usually results in increased growth rate, increased

Figure 36-2. Market hogs resulting from the use of a hybrid boar on crossbred gilts. (A. M. Wettach photo. Courtesy Farmers Hybrid Hogs)

efficiency of fertilization, improvement of body conformation, and increased production. Crossbreeding in hogs, cattle, sheep, and chickens has been done for years, but not until rather recently has it been done on a truly scientific basis.

Heterosis, or *Hybrid Vigor*, is the term applied to the increase in vigor and performance resulting when two animals of unrelated breeds are crossed. The increase in vigor may be explained in the terms of the genetic principles discussed in previous paragraphs. The genes producing vigor are dominant to those producing a lack of vigor. By crossing breeds, a larger number of dominant genes are brought together in the progeny than are involved in breeding animals of the same breed.

Grading and Purebreeding. These two systems of breeding involve the mating of animals of the same breed. Upgrading involves the mating of purebred sires and grade females of the same breed.

Purebreeding involves the mating of purebred sires and purebred females of the same breed. In both cases, animals to be mated are selected according to their body conformation, vigor, growth rate, and production record. Purebred animals are quite *homozygous*—the genes are usually alike. The hybrid condition referred to previously does not exist. The animals tend to reproduce progeny like themselves—like begets like.

Inbreeding and Linebreeding. Inbreeding is the mating of closely related animals, such as (1) brother to sister, (2) son to dam, and (3) sire to daughter. It is done primarily to intensify the degree of homozygosity, or the similarity of the genes in the reproductive cells of the animals. The crossing of inbred lines of two or more breeds results in hybrid vigor greater than that produced when two or more noninbred lines are crossed.

Linebreeding is similar to inbreeding but involves the breeding of animals less closely related. The mating of cousins and of grandsire with granddaughters are examples of linebreeding. It is done to conserve and perpetuate the good traits of certain outstanding breeding animals. It tends to produce an homozygous genetic condition.

Value of Pedigrees in Animal Breeding

Pedigree information is very valuable in livestock breeding. Most breeding programs involve the use of purebred sires for which pedigree information is available, and some breeding programs involve females which are purebred. A careful analysis of the pedigree may indicate the prolificacy, productiveness, and conformation of the animal and of its progeny.

Pedigrees of dairy animals not only provide a list of the ancestors but may also provide the production records of the animals. Shown on pages 672 and 673 is an extended pedigree of a Holstein bull. Note that ancestry and production information are provided for the sire and dam, for the grandsires and granddams, and for the great grandsires and great granddams. This pedigree is more complete than most, but shows the type of information which may be available concerning breeding animals. This information, supplemented by an inspection of the animal, and of the herd from which it came, provides the breeder with sufficient information to decide upon the desirability of using the animal or his progeny in his breeding program.

Summary

The reproductive cell of the female is called an ovum. The male cell is called a sperm. Each parent contributes equally in the reproduction process.

The ovum is produced in a follicle of the ovary and is dropped into the oviduct. It is fertilized by a sperm in the upper end of the oviduct. From there it moves to the uterus, where it becomes attached to the wall and develops.

The sperm is produced in the testicle and moves through the sperm ducts to the urethra and the penis. The seminal vesicles, prostate, and Cowper's glands add secretions to the seminal fluid.

The heat period in cows occurs about every 21 days and ovulation takes place from six to 20 hours after the cow has gone out of heat. Breeding should be timed so that the sperm is in the oviduct when the ovulation occurs. It normally takes the sperm from four to nine hours to reach the ovum after being introduced.

The chromosomes in the reproductive cells carry genes which determine the characteristics to be transmitted to the progeny. Chromosomes occur in pairs, with one of each pair in the male cell uniting with one of each pair in the female cell to produce the new individual. The reproductive cell in swine has 19 pairs of chromosomes while the germ cell of cattle, sheep, and horses has 30 pairs. The two members of a pair of chromosomes carry genes which affect the same physical conditions of the animal, but they may not affect them in the same way.

Some factors of inheritance are dominant, while others are recessive. A hybrid condition exists when the germ cell has one dominant and one recessive gene.

The most common systems of breeding are upgrading, purebreeding, inbreeding, linebreeding, and crossbreeding. Upgrading involves the successive use of purebred sires on grade females of the same breed. Purebreeding involves the mating of purebred males and females of the same breed. Inbreeding is the mating of closely related animals. Linebreeding is similar but involves animals less closely related. Crossbreeding involves the crossing of two breeds.

Hybrid vigor is produced by crossing two unrelated breeds. The crossing of inbred lines of two or more breeds increases the heterosis, or hybrid vigor.

Pedigree of

CARNATION MADCAP
BUTTER BOY

Born: May 21, 1951
Classified: "Excellent"
Silver Medal Type Sire

Herd sire owned by
Carnation Milk Farms
Carnation, Washington

CARNATION IMPERIAL
   MADCAP LAD   837650
"Very Good"
"Gold Medal Proven Sire"
Sire, 1st "Get," Pacific International
   and W. Wash., 1952
36 A R daughters
1 with 1050 lbs.
27 from 510 to 686 lbs.
Carn. Violet Inka Bracelet "VG"
Fat 365d   7y   1050
Milk (3x-3.9%)   27623
   44 H T daughters
   3 from 800 to 913 lbs.
   28 from 501 to 774 lbs.

Sire of—
   Carnation Violet Cameo
   All-American Sr. Yrlg., 1954

FRASEA BUTTER GIRL
   WAYNE   3097125
"Excellent"

365d	13y 3x 26325	3.8 %	1008.0
365d	8y 3x 22612		805.8
365d	8y 3x 20849		732.0
365d	9y 3x 22040		763.5
365d	5y 2x 17242	3.69	637.0
348d	4y 2x 13483	3.86	520.0
365d	3y 2x 11595	4.07	472.0

Res. All-Can. Aged Cow, 1948
Hon. Men. A-A. Aged Cow, 1949 and 1950
Grand Champion, Pacific International,
   1949 and 1950
Grand Champion, Texas Pan-American
   & Texas State Fair, 1953

CARNATION GOVERNOR IMPERIAL 698462

All-American Aged Bull, 1939
All-American Aged Bull, 1938
All-American Sr. Calf, 1934
102 A R daughters
32 from 808 to 1194 lbs.
55 from 480 to 799 lbs.
Carn. Heilo Josephine Madcap
  365d 8y 3x 29153 1194.60 4.1%

CARNATION HOMESTEAD VIOLET 1909689

365d 7y 4x 29010 3.8% 1115.7
365d 2½y 3x 19514 • 711.1
Mem., All-American "Get," 1939
  and 1940
Dam of two "Gold Medal" sons
Dam of Silver Medal Prod. sire
  2 A R daughters
Carnation Heilo Violet "VG"
  365d 5½y 3x 24026 4.2% 1000.7
Carnation Bracelet Violet
  5y 4x 25723 3.7% 959.1
2 "Excellent" and 2 "VG" sons

COLONY COLANTHUS PERFECTION 94137C

"Extra Sire"
All-Canadian "Get," 1943, 1944, 1948
113 tested daughters
7 "E," 44 "VG," 46 "GP," 4 "G,"
  daus.
4 from 805 to 1040 lbs.
84 from 480 to 789 lbs.

FRASEA BUTTER GIRL POSCH 244893C

"Very Good"
4y 305d 3x 15052 482 3.20
2y 305d 3x 11478 396 3.45
Dam of
  1 daughter with 1000 lbs.
  1 "Excellent" daughter

GOVERNOR OF CARNATION 629472

Leading Honor List Sire, 1944-1951
All-Amer. "Get," 1939, 1940
163 A R daughters
68 from 807 to 1511 lbs.
38 with over 1000 lbs.

CARNATION HEILO ORMSBY MATADOR 1524728

Fat 365d 7½y 1006.70
Milk (4x-4.04%) 24946.00
Jr. Champ., Pac. Int., 1932-33.

GOVERNOR OF CARNATION 629472

Leading Honor List Sire, 1944
  and 1951
All-Amer. "Get," 1939, 1940
163 A R daughters
68 from 807 to 1511 lbs.
38 with over 1000 lbs.

CARNATION HAZELWOOD VIOLET 1742023

Fat 365d 2y 436.00
Milk (3x-3.7%) 11766.00
1 A R daughter with 1115 lbs.

COLONY KOBA McKINLEY 78639C

"XX" 64th
Sire, 1st prize Sr. "Get," Vancouver, 1935
21 tested daughters
3 from 830 to 888 lbs.

COLONY FLOOD COLANTHA 194433C

"Excellent"
365d 8y 3x 23680 744.0
365d 3½y 4x 21117 741.0
365d 9y 3x 22823 739.0
All-Time All-Amer. 3-yr.-old

COLONY POSCH HENGERVELD 87502 (CHB)

18 tested daughters
Frasea White Posch (Ex)
1st Aged Cow Victoria, 1940
3y 3x 18976 640 3.37 365d

FRASEA WAYNE BUTTER GIRL 196907 (CHB)

4y 305d 3x 16931 660 3.90
2y 305d 3x 12536 492 3.92

Pedigrees provide the ancestry of an animal and, in some cases, the prolificacy and productiveness. The pedigree supplemented by an inspection of the animal, and of the herd from which it came, provides the breeder with information necessary in selecting animals for a breeding program.

• Questions

1. Name the reproductive organs of the male, and indicate the function of each.
2. What are the reproductive organs of the female, and what are their functions?
3. What is meant by ovulation, and when does it take place in relationship to the heat period?
4. What is the difference between a gene and a chromosome?
5. Explain the process of making and fertilizing of germ cells.
6. Which contributes most to inheritance, the ovum or the sperm? Explain.
7. Explain hybrid vigor in terms of the gene composition of the chromosomes.
8. What differences exist in the gene composition of the chromosomes in purebred and crossbred animals?
9. Explain the following systems of breeding: upgrading; purebreeding; inbreeding; linebreeding; and crossbreeding.
10. Of what value are pedigrees in livestock breeding?

• References

Lush, J. H., *Animal Breeding Plans*, Collegiate Press Incorporated, Ames, Iowa, 1937.

Winters, L. M., *An Introduction to Breeding Farm Animals*, John Wiley and Sons, New York, 1942.

INDEX

A

ACTH, for ketosis, 412
APF (animal protein factor), 136
Aberdeen-Angus cattle, 189-190
Abomasum, 34
Active Acres Bessie, 310
Additives, feed *see* Feed additives
Age and Size to Breed Dairy Heifers (table), 369
Ailments, cattle, 396-415
  ACTH, 412
  anthrax, 405
  blackleg, 404-405
  bloat, 413-414
  Brome-Thymol-Blue test for mastitis, 407-408
  brucellosis, 403-404
  calf scours, 408-410
  chlorinated naphthalene, 413
  coccidiosis, 402
  Co-Ral spray, 400
  cortisone, 412
  deer flies, 400-401
  external parasites, 397-401
  foot-and-mouth disease, 408
  foot rot, 406
  grubs (heel flies), 398-399
  horn flies, 400
  horse flies, 400-401
  infectious diseases, 403-411
  internal parasites, 402
  ketosis, 412
  leptospirosis, 410-411
  lice, 399
  lindane spray, 401
  mastitis, 406-408
  milk fever, 411-412
  mites, 401
  mosquitoes, 400-401
  noninfectious ailments, 411-414
  pink eye, 406
  pneumonia, 411
  poisonous plants, 414
  prevention program, 396-397
  prussic acid in plants, 414
  ringworm, 410
  screw worms, 397-398
  shipping fever, 405-406
  Smear EQ 335, for screw worms, 398
  stable flies, 400

Ailments, cattle (*Cont.*)
  stomach worms, 402
  ticks, 401
  Trolene, for grubs, 398-399
  tuberculosis, 404
  warts, 408
  X disease, 413
Ailments, hogs, 47-48, 100-101, 106, 120-121, 143, 147-163
  atrophic rhinitis, 153
  black scours, 151-153
  brucellosis, 154
  cholera, 148-150
  erysipelas, 150-151
  flu, 155
  leptospirosis, 157
  lice, 161-162
  lungworms, 160
  mange, 160-161
  necro (necrotic enteritis), 151
  parakeratosis, 157-158
  parasites, 49, 158-162
  prevention vs. cure, 147-148
  roundworms, 120-121, 158-160
  transmissible gastroenteritis, 155-157
  trichinosis, 143
  vesicular exanthema, 143, 154-155
Ailments, poultry, 627-642
  blackhead, 637-638
  blue comb, 638-639
  bronchitis, 632
  CRD (chronic respiratory disease), 632, 633
  cecal worms, 640
  coccidiosis, 629-630
  erysipelas in turkeys, 639
  fowl cholera, 636-637
  fowl pox, 635-636
  infectious sinusitis, 633-634
  infectious synovitis, 630
  large roundworms, 639-640
  laryngotracheitis, 632-633
  lice, 640
  lymphomatosis or leukosis, 634-635
  mites, 641
  Newcastle disease, 630-632
  parasites, 639-641
  pullorum, 628-629
  roup, 636

Ailments, poultry (*Cont.*)
  tuberculosis, 637
  typhoid, 636
Ailments, sheep, 508-528
  anthrax, 521-522
  bloat, 526-527
  blowflies, 509-510
  broad tapeworm, 516-517
  chronic arthritis, 525
  coccidiosis, 518-519
  contagious diseases, 520-524
  detergents, 512
  E.Q. 335 smear, 510, 511
  external parasites, 509-514
  feed changes, stiffness due to, 525
  foot rot, 520-521
  gid tapeworms, 517-518
  grub in head (sheep bots), 518
  internal parasites, 514-519
  joint ill, 525
  lambing paralysis, 525-526
  lice, 511-512
  lindane powder, 512
  navel ill, 525
  noncontagious ailments, 524-527
  overeating disease (enterotoxemia),
    524
  poisonous plants, 527
  pregnancy disease, 525-526
  program of prevention, 509
  scab, 513-514
  screw worms, 510-511
  shipping fever, 522
  sore mouth, 522-523
  sprays, 514
  stiffness, 525
  stomach worms, 514-516
  teniatol, 517-518
  ticks (keds), 512-513
  white muscle disease, 525
Alfalfa, 23, 88, 121, 253
American Class chickens, 562 *see also*
    Chickens, selection of
American Landrace swine, 61, 69
American Standard of Perfection, 564
Amino acids, 3-4, 14, 15, 20, 32, 35, 128
Anemia, in pigs, 116-117
Animal breeding, 665-672
  chromosome segregation, 668
  chromosomes and genes, 667
  conception, 666-667
  dominant and recessive characters,
    667-668
  female reproductive organs, 665-666
  fetus, growth of, 667
  grading and purebreeding, 669-670

Animal breeding (*Cont.*)
  hybrid vigor, 668-669
  hybrids, 668
  inbreeding and linebreeding, 670
  inheritance, laws of, 667-670
  male reproductive organs, 666
  pedigrees, value of, 670
  reproduction, 664-667
Animal fats and oils, 17, 252
Animal products, vitamins in, 21, 22
Animal proteins, 14, 18, 24, 589
Anthrax, in cattle, 405
Anthrax, in sheep, 521-522
Antibiotic vitamin premixes, 23, 136
Antibiotics, 6, 10, 24
  for broilers, 609
  for cattle, 259
  for chickens, 591
  for chicks, 604
  for dairy calves, 357
  for growing heifers, 236
  for lambs, 499
  for pigs, 118, 132-134
  for suckling calves, 235
  for turkeys, 623-624
Arsenicals, 7, 10, 28
  for chicks, 604
  for pigs, 138
  for turkeys, 623
Arthritis, chronic, in sheep, 525
Artificial breeding, of dairy cattle, 341-
    343
Asiatic Class chickens, 562 *see also*
    Chickens, selection of
Atrophic rhinitis, in hogs, 153
Auction sales, of cattle, 275
Average Production of Cows in Dairy
    Herd Improvement Associations
    (table), 291
Average Retail Prices of Pork Cuts and
    Lard (table), 166
Ayrshire cattle, 307-308

B

BDI butterfat test, 314
Babcock butterfat test, 313-314
Baby Pig Feeding Program (table), 112
Bang's disease *see* Brucellosis
Barley, 16, 251, 325
Barnum, P. T., 310
Barrow, Richard, 195
Beef cattle, breeding cattle, 187-204
  Aberdeen-Angus breed, 189-190
  availability of stock, 188
  Beefmaster breed, 197
  body conformation, 198

Beef cattle (*Cont.*)
  Braford breed, 197
  Brahman breed, 195-196
  Brangus breed, 197
  breeds developed in U.S., 196-197
  breeds from Europe, 189-195
  breeds from India, 195-196
  Charbray breed, 197
  Charolais breed, 194
  crossbred cattle, 197
  dwarfism, 203-204
  environment, as selection factor, 188
  feeding and management *see* Feeding
    and management, breeding cattle
  final judgment in selection, 202
  foundation stock, selection of, 198-203
  Galloway breed, 190
  Hereford breed, 190, 192
  importation of breeds, 187
  outlet for surplus animals, 188
  personal likes, in selecting, 188
  points to consider in selection, 199-
    202
  Polled Hereford breed, 192
  Polled Shorthorn breed, 192
  production records, selection by, 202-
    203
  progeny testing, 202-203
  Red Angus breed, 190
  Santa Gertrudis breed, 196-197
  Scotch Highland breed, 194-195
  Shorthorn breed, 192
Beef cattle, feeder cattle, 204-212
  age, 205
  bulls, 208, 209
  choice cattle, 206
  classes and grades of, 205-209
  Classes and Grades of Feeder Cattle
    (table), 208
  common cattle, 207-208
  cows, 208-209
  fancy cattle, 206
  feed, 209-210
  feed prices, 210
  feeding period, length of, 211
  good cattle grade, 206-207
  inferior cattle, 208
  market outlook, 211
  medium cattle, 207
  prices, feeder-and-slaughter-cattle re-
    lationship, 210
  selection of class and grade, 209-211
  sex of feeder cattle, 205-206
  stags, 208, 209
  weight classes of feeder cattle, 206
Beef production industry, 181-186

Beef production industry (*Cont.*)
  classes of producers, 182-185
  combined enterprises, 185
  fat or slaughter cattle, 183-184
  feeder cattle, 182-183
  opportunities in, 181
  purebred beef cattle, 184-185
Beefmaster cattle, 197
Beet pulp, for dairy cattle, 324
Beet tops, 248
Beltsville Small White turkeys, 625
Berkshire swine, 63
Biotin, 604
Birdsfoot trefoil, 121-122
Black-Faced Highland sheep, 434-435
Blackhead, in poultry, 637-638
Black scours, in hogs, 151-153
Blackleg, in cattle, 404-405
Bloat, in cattle, 413-414
Bloat, in sheep, 526-527
Blood meal, as protein source, 18
Blowflies, 509-510
Blue comb, in poultry, 638-639
Bone meal, 24, 38
Braford cattle, 197
Brahman cattle, 195-196
Brangus cattle, 197
Breeding and Calving Record, (table),
    369
Breeding and management, dual-purpose
    cattle *see* Dual-purpose cattle
Breeding systems, hogs, 55-60
Brewers' yeast, vitamin B-complex in, 21
Broad Breast Bronze turkeys, 661
Broad tapeworms, in sheep, 516-517
Broadtail sheep pelts, 423
Broiler and Growing Chicken Rations
    (table), 606
Broilers, 549 *see also* Poultry production
    industry
Broilers (fryers), term, 649
Brome-Thymol-Blue test, for cattle
    mastitis, 407-408
Bronchitis, in poultry, 632
Brown Swiss cattle, 308-310
Brucellosis (Bang's disease), 106, 154,
    157, 319, 403-404
Bull, term, 205
Butter *see* Dairy industry
Buttermilk, as protein source, 18
Buying and selling, of beef cattle, 273-
    286
  auction sales, 275
  classes and grades of slaughter cattle,
    277-281

Buying and selling (*Cont.*)
Classification and Grades of Slaughter Cattle (table), 278
contract sales, 274
cooperative marketing, 283
damaged carcasses, 283
direct buying and selling, 273-275
direct selling with immediate delivery, 274
market information sources, 277
marketing feeder cattle, 273-277
marketing slaughter cattle, 277-283
order buyers, 275
seasonal price trends, 283
selection of marketing method, 276-277
selling on grade and yield, 282
selling through commission firms, 282-283
selling through dealers, 275
selling to packers, 281-282
selling to private buyers, 283
terminal markets, 276
types of market procedure, 281-283

C

CRD (chronic respiratory disease), in poultry, 632, 633
Calcium, 24, 38, 137, 590
Calf scours, 408-410
Cannibalism in poultry, 593, 608, 623
Capon, term, 650
Carbohydrates, 2, 8-9, 15-17, 37-38, 602-603
Carcass Results, 1957 National Barrow Show (table), 62
Carnation Homestead Daisy Madcap (pedigree form), 311
Carpet-wool sheep, 434-435
Castration
cattle, 232
pigs, 117
sheep, 467-470
Catron, Dr. Damon, 129
Cattle yards and lots, 241
Cecal worms, in poultry, 640
Cervix, 666
Charbray cattle, 197
Charolaise cattle, 194
Cheese, 292
Chester White swine, 63
Cheviot sheep, 425-427
Chickens (*See also* Poultry)
American Class, 562
American Standard of Perfection, 564
Asiatic Class, 562

Chickens (*Cont.*)
baby chicks *see* Chicks, baby
body capacity, 572
breeds, 559, 562-567
Characteristics of Common Breeds (table), 564
classes of chickens, 562
combs and wattles, 572
culling, 570-571
culling formula (Mehrhof), 571
Distribution of Birds in National Poultry Improvement Plan Hatchery Flocks, 1950-1954 (table), 566
English Class, 562
eyes, brightness of, 572
feeding and management of laying stocks *see* Feeding and management, laying chickens
good layers, selection of, 571-577
Guide for Selection and Culling of Layers (table), 576
handling quality, 573
health and vigor, 576
hybrid and crossbred, 565
market classes, 649-650
Mediterranean Class, 562
molt stage, 575-576
pigmentation, 573-574
popularity of breeds, 567
production of, 549 *see also* Poultry production industry
Production Summary of Egg Laying Tests, 1955-1956 (table), 566
selection of, 559-578
vents, condition of, 573
Chicks, baby, 567-570
age, 570
breeding and quality, 569
culling, 570
early hatched, 568
hatcheries, 567-568
price, 570
production records, 569
pullorum, 569
sex, 569
source, 567
when to order, 568
Chlorinated naphthalene, 413
Choice cattle, term, 206
Cholera, of hogs, 148-150
Choline, for chicks, 604
Chromosome segregation, 668
Chromosomes and genes, 667
Chronic arthritis, in sheep, 525
Citrus, for heifers, 366
Citrus pulp, as dairy cattle feed, 324

Classes and Common Breeds of Sheep
(table), 423
Classes and Grades of Feeder Cattle
(table), 208
Classes and Grades of Feeder Sheep
(table), 443
Classification and Grades of Slaughter
Cattle (table), 278
Closed formula feeds, 40-41
Coccidiosis, 629-630
in cattle, 402
in lambs, 504
in sheep, 518-519
Cocks (old roosters), term, 650
Cod liver oil, 9, 21, 22
Colley, Howard H., 306
Collins, D. C., 425
Colostrum, 357-358
Columbia sheep, 432-433
Common cattle, term, 207-208
Complete Rations Including Salt and
Mineral, for lambs (table), 502
Concentrate Mixture for Dairy Cows
(table), 332-333
Concentrates, 14-15
for calves, 363
for dairy cattle, 325-326, 331-334
Conception, in animal breeding, 666-667
Co-Ral spray, for cattle, 400
Corn, 15, 71, 128, 250-251, 325
Corn, hybrid, 71
Corn Belt, hog production in, 44-45, 127
Corn gluten meal, as protein source, 20
Corn stalks, for cattle, 249
Corncobs, for cattle, 249
Corning, Erastus, 190
Corriedale sheep, 433
Cortisone, for ketosis, 412
Cost of Gains in Cattle Feeding (table),
268
Cottonseed meal and cake, 19, 36-37,
253, 326
Cow, term, 205
Cowper's glands, 666
Cows, dairy see Dairy industry
Criss-crossing, in hog breeding, 58
Crop, of poultry, 34
Crossbred cattle, 197
Crossbred and Purebred Pigs (table),
57
Crossbred-Wool sheep, 432-434
Crossbreeding, of hogs, 56, 58

D

Daily Feeding Rate of Milk Replacement, calves (table), 359

Daily Maintenance Requirements of
Dairy Cows (table), 328
Dairy calves see Feeding and manage-
ment, dairy calves
Dairy cows, 299-372
artificial insemination, 318-319
Ayrshire breed, 307-308
Babcock test, 313-314
Bang's disease, 319
BDI butterfat test, 314
breeds, 300-311
Brown Swiss breed, 308-310
Dairy Herd Improvement Association, 299, 300
dairy industry see Dairy industry
Dutch Belted breed, 310-311
factors in selection of, 300
feeding and management of producing herd see Feeding and management, dairy cows
Guernsey breed, 303, 306
health of herd, 319
Holstein-Friesian breed, 302-303
Jersey breed, 306-307
owner-sampler testing, 312-313
parts of cow, 300, 301
pedigrees, 311
physical appearance, 315-318
production records, 312-314
proven sires, 312
Red Danish breed, 310
Schain detergent test, 314
score cards, 315-318
selection of bulls, 318-319
selection of breeding stock, 299-321
testing home herds, 312-314
Dairy industry, 287-298
advantages and disadvantages, 293-295
average milk production per cow,
291-292
Average Production of Cows in Dairy
Herd Improvement Associations
(table), 291
butter vs. margarine, 289
cheese, 292
condensed milk, 289
consumption of products, 287-288
creamery butter production, 292
dry milk solids, 289
evaporated milk, 289
factors in profitable production, 295-
296
fluid milk and cream, 289
herd improvement associations, 291-
292
High Producing Cows (table), 296

Dairy industry (*Cont.*)
  ice cream, 292
  leading cow states, 290
  methods of increasing profits, 296-297
  number of cows, 290
  production of products, 290-293
  quantity, effect on cost, 295-296
  Returns Per $100 Worth of Feed Fed
    to Different Livestock (table), 295
  skim milk, 294
  U.S. Per Capita Consumption (table),
    288
  Use of Milk Sold by Farmers (table),
    289
  utilization of milk, 290
Dairy products, marketing of, 373-389
  Average Milk-Feed Price Ratios
    (table), 376
  butterfat prices, 375
  cream, 387
  form in which to sell milk, 376-377
  improving quality of products, 378-
    379
  markets, 378
  milk, Grade A *see* Milk, Grade A
  milk-feed price ratios, 375-376
  milk prices, 374-375
  Milk Processing Plants (table), 378
  seasonal price trends, 374-376
Dairy products, as protein sources, 18
Deer flies, 400-401
Dehorning, of calves, 368
Dehorning, of cattle, 228-231
Dehydrated hays, 248
Detergents (surfactants), 8, 10, 28, 521,
  604
Devon (Ruby Reds) cattle, 393-394
Digestible nutrients, 10-11, 37, 329
Digestible Nutrients Required for Pro-
  ducing One Pound of Milk
  (table), 329
Digestive systems, 31-35
  poultry, 34-35
  ruminants, 31-34
  simple-stomach animals, 34
Dimensions for Cow Stalls (table), 345
Diseases *see* Ailments
Distillers' solubles, vitamin B-complex
  in, 21
Distribution of Birds in National Poul-
  try Improvement Plan Hatchery
  Flocks, 1950-1954 (table), 566
Dominant and recessive characters, 667-
  668
Dorset sheep, 427
Dressed fowl, term, 654

Dry-lot pigs, 140-142
Dry Roughages, Composition of
  (table), 26
Dual-purpose cattle, 390-395
  adaptability, 390-391
  breeds, 391-394
  Devon (Ruby Reds) breed, 393-394
  Milking Shorthorn breed, 391-393
  production records, 394
  Red Poll breed, 393
  selection of breed, 391
  selection of breeding stock, 394
Ducks, market classes, 650
Duroc swine, 66
Dutch Belted cattle, 310-311
Dwarfism, in cattle, 203-204
Dynafac, 6, 8, 28, 260
Dysentery, in lambs, 523

E

E. Q. 335 smear, for sheep, 510, 511
Ear-notching, of hogs, 107-109
Eggs, 552, 644-649 *see also* Poultry
  industry
  classes and grades, 645-647
  commercial grades, 646-647
  consumer grades of shell eggs, 646
  price trends, 644-645
  production trends, 644
  quality maintenance, 648-649
  seasonal price trends, 644-645
  state laws, 647
  weight classes, 646
English Class chickens, 562 *see also*
  Chickens, selection of
Enterotoxemia, in sheep, 524
Erysipelas, in hogs, 150-151
Erysipelas, in turkeys, 639

F

Fancy cattle, term, 206
Fats, 2, 9, 17, 37-38
Feed, for feeder cattle, 209-210
Feed additives
  antibiotics, 6, 10 *see also* Antibiotics
  arsenicals, 7, 10 *see also* Arsenicals
  detergents, 8, 10 *see also* Detergents
  Dynafac, 6, 8, 28, 260
  functions of, 8-10
  hormones, 7, 10 *see also* Cortisone;
    Hormones; Stilbestrol
  iodinated casein, 7, 28, 111
  rumen organisms, 8, 10

Feed additives (*Cont.*)
  sources of, 24, 28
  tranquilizers, 8, 10, 28
Feed prices, cattle, 210
Feed Value, Comparative, of Grains
    and Substitutes (table), 252
Feeding floors, for pigs, 142
Feeding and management of breeding
    cattle, 214-245
  age to breed heifers, 226
  age of bull, 226
  antibiotics for growing heifers, 236
  antibiotics for suckling calves, 235
  castration, 232
  cattle yards and lots, 241
  chemical method of dehorning, 228-
    229
  clippers and saws for dehorning, 231
  creep-feeding calves, 234
  cutting and hauling of pasture, 220,
    222-223
  dehorning, 228-231
  feeding in dry lot, 223
  feeding equipment, 238-240
  feeding on pasture, 214-223
  feeding replacement heifers, 236
  feeding suckling calves, 234-235
  feeding young bulls, 236-237
  fences, 241
  grain, 216
  Grass and Legume Mixtures (table),
    221
  grasses, 219-220
  hay mangers, 239
  hot iron dehorning, 229
  housing for beef cattle, 237-238
  housing and handling equipment, 237-
    242
  legumes, 219
  loading chutes, 240
  marking, 232-233
  mating, 226-227
  mechanized feeding systems, 242
  mineral feeders, 239-240
  mineral mixtures, 216-217
  nutrient values of pasture, 220
  nutritional deficiencies, 223-224
  pastures compared, 219-220
  proteins, 217-218
  Purdue University studies, 220
  Rations for Suckling Calves (table),
    235
  Rations for Wintering (table), 225
  restraint equipment, 241
  salt, 216, 217-218
  self-feeders, 239

Feeding and management of breeding
    cattle (*Cont.*)
  shelters for calves, 227
  silage, 215-216
  spoons and tubes for dehorning, 229-
    231
  supplements to pasture grass, 215-218
  time for calving, 227
  vitamins, 217
  water, 218
Feeding and management of breeding
    hogs, 84-97 *see also* Hogs
  age to breed, 85-86
  amount of feed for sows, 93
  boars, 88-89
  breeding records, 90
  during breeding season, 85-90
  during gestation, 91-92
  exercise, 95
  flushing, 87-88
  gain in sows, 93
  gestation period, 86
  hand-feeding vs. self-feeding, 93-94
  heat period, 86
  multiple farrowing, 90-91
  non-breeders, 89
  nutritional allowances for sows, 93
  pasture, 95
  pen- vs. lot-breeding, 89
  profits and losses, 84-85
  ranty and inactive boars, 89-90
  rations for boars, 88
  rations for bred sows and gilts, 92-95
  shelter, 95-96
  silage, 95
  "squealers," 92
  Swine Breeding and Farrowing Dates
    (table), 87
  three litters program, 91
  time to breed, 86-87
  two litters program, 91
  water, 95
Feeding and management of dairy
    calves, 356-372
  age to breed, 369
  Age and Size to Breed Dairy Heifers
    (table), 369
  antibiotics, 357
  birth to six months, 356-363
  breeding and calving records, 369
  calf pens, 367-368
  care of newborn, 366-367
  citrus, 366
  colostrum, 357-358
  concentrates, 363

Feeding and management of dairy
     calves (*Cont.*)
Daily Feeding Rate of Milk Replace-
     ment (table), 359
dehorning, 368
extra teats, 369
feedboxes, 368
feeding first three days, 357-358
feeding heifers in dry lot, 365-366
feeding heifers on pasture, 365
grain feeding, 361-363
Guide for Feeding Concentrates
     (table), 363
heifers, 363-366
legumes, 362
limited milk feeding, 360-361
management of calves, 366-369
marking, 368
milk feeding, 358
milk replacers, 358-360
minerals, 363
nurse cow method, 361
pasture, 363
roughage, 362-363
six months to freshening, 363-366
Standards for Growing Dairy Heifers
     (table), 364
starter mixtures, 360-361
systems of feeding, 358-363
vitamins, 358, 361
water, 363
Feeding and management of dairy
     ·cows, 323-372
artificial breeding, 341-343
barley, 325
beet pulp, 324
breeding, 340-343
bulls, 348-350
care at calving time, 340
citrus pulp, 324
cleaning and grooming, 337
computing rations, 329-337
Concentrate Mixture Amounts (table),
     332-333
concentrates, 325-326, 331-334, 335
corn or sorghum silage, 324, 325
cottonseed meal, 326
Daily Maintenance Requirements of
     Dairy Cows (table). 328
Digestible Nutrients Required for
     Producing One Pound of Milk
     (table), 329
Dimensions for Cow Stalls (table),
     345
drying off, 339-340
elevated stall system for milking, 348

Feeding and management of dairy cows
     (*Cont.*)
estrus cycle, 340
exercise, 337, 349-350
feeding bulls, 349
feeding before calving, 336-337
feeding after calving, 337
feeding dry cows, 335-336
feeding non-pasture cows, 331-334
feeding on pasture, 334-335
feeding requirements, 328-329
feeding and storage areas, 347
feeds, 322-328
feeds for dry cows, 336
floor level system for milking, 348
fodder, corncobs, cornstalks, straw,
     324
gestation periods, 343
grain sorghums, 325
ground ear corn, 325
heat periods, 340
herd sires, 348-350
hormones, 338-339
housing for bulls, 350
housing and equipment, 344-347
insulation and ventilation of barns,
     345, 347
legume and grass silage, 324
legumes, 322-323
limitations of pasture, 334-335
linseed oil meal, 326
loafing areas, 347-348
loose housing system, 347-348
managing bulls, 349-350
managing herds, 337-343
milking, 337-339
milking parlors, 348
minerals, 327-328
molasses, 326
natural breeding, 341
nonlegume hays, 323
nutrient value of pasture, 334-335
oats, 325
pastures, 324-325, 334-335
paved areas, 348
preparation of feeds, 334
producing herd, 322-355
protein and T. D. N. requirements,
     328, 329-330
rations, 329-337
Rations for Conditioning Dry Cows
     (table), 336
ringing bulls, 349
roughages, 322-324, 330-331
rye, 326
service age, bulls, 350

Feeding and management of dairy cows
(*Cont.*)
soybean oil meal, 326
soybeans, 326
stanchion barns, 344-347
T. D. N. (total digestible nutrients),
328, 329-330
temperature in barns, 347
time to breed, 343
urea, 326-327, 334
vitamins, 327, 334, 335
wheat, 325
wheat bran, 326
young dairy stock, 356-372
Feeding and management of laying
chickens, 579-597
cage layers, 595-596
feeders, 584-585
feeding and feeds, 588-592
all mash ration, 591
amounts needed, 588-589
antibiotics, 591
cannibalism, 593
carbohydrates and fats, 589
fiber, 589-590
grain and mash, 591
grain and protein concentrate, 591
Mash Rations for Layer and
Breeder Hens (table), 592
minerals, 590
nutrients, essential, 589-591
proteins, 589
rations, suggestions for, 592
Scratch Grain Mixtures (table), 591
systems of feeding, 591
vitamins, 590
water, 591
Financial Statement for Laying
Flocks (table), 595
laying flock, housing of, 581-588
laying houses, 580-588
care of litter, 583
deep litter, 582-583
dropping pits, 582
foundation and floor, 587
insulation, 586, 588
lighting, 586-587
litter, 582-583
materials, 587
morning light, 587
nests, 584
roofs, 587
roosts, 582
Schedule for Operating Slot Ventilators (table), 585

Feeding and management of laying
chickens (*Cont.*)
space required, 581-582
types of, 587-588
ventilation, 585-586
windows, 588
profits, methods of increasing, 579-
580
pullets, moving to laying house, 580
records, 593-596
Feeding and management of market
hogs, 98-146
anemia control, 116-117
antibiotics, 118, 132-134
arsenicals, 138
assistance at farrowing time, 105-106
baby pig feeding program, 112-115
bedding, 101
castration, 117
complete ration for growing and fattening, 138, 139
creep-feeding, 111-115
dry-lot feeding, advantages of, 123-
124
dry-lot production, 140-142
dry-lot protein supplements, 129
ear-notching, 107-109
farrowing stalls, 104-105
farrowing time, 98-108
feeding floors, 142
feeding pigs on pasture, 126-140
feeding of sow, 109-110
garbage feeding, 143
grower rations, 115
guard rails, 102
heat lamps or brooders, 102-104
hog wallows, 140
hogging down corn, 143
housing, 99-100
iodized casein, 111
lactation rations, 110
ladino clover, 123
"Least-Time" Growing-Finishing Rations (table), 139
location of feeders and waterers, 125
methods of feeding, 126
minerals, 137
navel cords, 106
needle teeth, 106
"originals," 117
pasture, 118-119, 123-126
pasture crops, 121-123
pasture vs. dry-lot feeding, 121
pasture protein supplements, 129
pepsin in rations, 113
Pig Grower Rations (table), 115

Feeding and management of market hogs (*Cont.*)
Pig Pre-Starter Rations (table), 113
pigs per acre of pasture, 125
Pig Starter Rations (table), 114
pre-starter and creep rations, 112-115
pre-weaning, 116-119
production registry, 119
proteins, 128
protein supplements, value of, 128-129
protein supplement tables, 130-133
rations, 127
rations at farrowing time, 105
rations for sows, 109-110
ridglings, 117
ringing of pigs, 125-126
rotated pastures, 124
saccharin in rations, 113-114
salt, 137
sanitation, 100-101
self-feeders, 126-127
shade, 140
starter rations, 114-115
suckling period, 109-111
summer and fall pigs, 140
time of farrowing, 98-99
vaccinations, 117-118
Value of Various Pasture Crops for Swine (table), 122
vitamins, 128-129, 135-137
water, 138-139
weaning, 119
from weaning to market, 120-143
weights of litters, 119
worming, 120-121
Feeding and management of sheep, 448-490
Australian shearing table, 476
breeding age of ewes, 459
breeding of ewe lambs, 459
breeding season, 455
brooders, 462
care of feet, 457
castrating, 467-470
catching, 478
chilled lambs, 465
cutting chutes, 483-484
delivering the lamb, 462-464
dividing flock before lambing, 460
docking, 470-472
ear notches, 474
elastrator, 470
emasculator, 469

Feeding and management of sheep (*Cont.*)
ewe-ram ratio and age of ram, 458-459
ewe-lamb relationship, 465
eyeing, 456
feeding breeding rams, 454-455
feeding equipment, 481-483
feeding ewes, 449-450, 453-454
feeds for pregnant ewes, 450
fleece, packing, 477
fleece, sacking for market, 476
fleece, storage, 478
fleece, tying, 477
flushing, 448-449
gestation periods, 455
grafting, 466
handling of ewes about to lamb, 461
heat periods, 455
lambing jails, 461-462
lambing pens, 461-462
lambing, preparation for, 462
loading chutes, 483
management of breeding flock, 455
management during lambing season, 460-462
management of growing lambs, 467-478
management of newborn lambs, 464-467
managing during gestation, 460
marking, 472-474
marking ewes, 461
marking the ram for breeding, 457-458
metal tags, 473
overfat ewes, 449
paint brands, 473
panels for jails, 483
pinning passages, 467
preparing for breeding, 456
production records, 441
productive life of ewes, 459
productive life of rams, 460
raising orphans, 466-467
rations for flushing, 449
rations for gestation period, 451-453
rations for suckling lambs, 454
record card of ewe, 480
record card on ewe's progeny, 479
records, 478
ringing, 456-457
shearing, 474-478
shearing for breeding, 456
shelters and equipment, 478-481
stiff lamb disease, 524-525

Feeding and management of sheep
     (*Cont.*)
  tagging, 456
  weak lambs, 465
  white muscle disease, 525
Feeding and management of stockers
     and fattening cattle, 246-272
  age and weight factors, 263-264
  animal fats, 252
  antibiotics, 259
  barley, 251
  beet tops, 248
  concentrate rations, 264-265
  condition, physical, and grass, 264
  corn, 250-251
  corncobs, 249
  Cost of Gains in Cattle Feeding
     (table), 268
  cottonseed meal, 253
  dehydrated alfalfa meal or pellets,
     253
  dehydrated hays, 248
  dry roughages, 247-250
  Dynafac, 260
  economy of gains, 267-268
  fattening on grass, 265-266
  Feed Value, Comparative, of Grains
     and Substitutes (table), 252
  feeding efficiency, 267-268
  fishmeal, 253
  gains on grass, 263-264
  grain sorghums, 251
  grains and substitutes, 250-252
  grass, 248, 263-266
  green lot feeding, 265
  hauling pasture, 265
  hormones, 257-259
  legume hays, 248
  linseed oil meal, 253
  minerals and vitamins, 257
  mixed feeding supplements, 255-257
  mixed hays, 248
  molasses, 251-252
  oats, 251
  pasture fattening, 265-266
  pastures, 263
  peanut oil meal, 253
  pelleting dry feeds, 263
  preparation of feed, 263
  profits from manure value, 247
  profits from margin and gain, 247
  proteins and substitutes, 252-257
  rate of gain, 267-268
  rations, 260-263
  Rations for Cattle (tables), 260-263

Feeding and management of stockers
     (*Cont.*)
  Roughages, Comparable Value of
     (table), 250
  rye, 251
  self-feeding, 268
  silage, 249-250
  sources of profit, 247
  soybean oil meal, 253
  soybeans, 253
  starting on feed, 266-267
  stilbestrol, 256n, 257-259
  stilbestrol premix, 258
  tankage, 253
  tapazole, 260
  urea, 253-255
  vitamin D, 248
  wheat, 251
  wintering feeders, rations for, 262-
     263
  Wintering Rations for Feeder Cattle
     (table), 262-263
Feeding and management of young
     chickens, 598-613
  antibiotics, 604, 609
  arsenicals, 604
  Broiler and Growing Chicken Rations
     (table), 606
  broiler production, 609
  broiler rations, 609
  brooder houses, 598
  brooder and management, 600-601
  cannibalism, in chicks, 608
  caponettes and capons, 610
  carbohydrates and fats, 602-603
  cockerels and pullets, separation of,
     608
  feeders and waterers, 601-602
  floors for young chickens, 600
  hover guards, 601
  litter, 600
  minerals, 603
  nutritional needs, of chicks, 602-604
  proteins, 602
  range for chickens, 608-609
  range shelters, 606-607
  rations for chicks, 604-605
  records, 611-612
  roosts for chicks, 607
  starting chicks, 601-602
  starting mash formulas, 605-606
  Starting Mash Formulas (table), 605
  surfactants, 604
  temperature of chick houses, 601
  Total Cost of Broiler Production
     (table), 611

Feeding and management of young
    chickens (*Cont.*)
  vitamins, 603-604
Feeds, 13-29 *see also* Nutrients
  animal by-products, 18
  animal fats and oils, 17
  animal proteins, 14, 18, 24
  balanced rations, 40
  barley, 16
  blood meal, 18
  carbohydrates, 15-17
  closed formula feeds, 40-41
  concentrates, 14-15
  corn, 15
  corn gluten meal, 20
  cottonseed meal and cake, 19, 36-37
  dairy products, 18
  digestibility, 40
  digestion *see* Digestive systems
  fats, 17
  fish meal, 18
  grains, 15
  grain sorghums, 16
  legume roughages, 13-14, 20
  limestone, 38
  linseed meal, 19
  meat and bone scraps, 18
  minerals, 23-24
  mixed feeds, 40-41, 134
  molasses, 16
  nonlegume roughages, 14
  nutrient values, 28
  oats, 15
  open formula feeds, 41
  peanuts, 17, 20
  phosphorus, 38
  protein concentrates, 14, 17, 24
  quality of, 39-40
  roughages, 13-14, 17, 36
  rye, 16
  salt, 24
  seed by-products, 19
  soils, effect of, 39
  sources of fats, 17
  soybeans, 19
  tankage, 18
  trace mineral mixture, 24
  urea, 20
  values, 36-42
    carbohydrates and fats, 37-38
    and classes of animals, 36-37
    cost method, 37
    and digestible nutrients, 37
    mineral content, 38
    proteins, 38
  vegetable proteins, 15, 19-20

Feeds (*Cont.*)
  vitamins *see* Vitamins
  weather, effect of, 40
  wheat, 16
Female reproductive organs, 665-666
Fences, cattle, 241
Fertility, and vitamin E, 22
Fetal membranes, 667
Fetus, growth of, 667
Fiber, 2, 10-11, 589-590
Financial Statement for Laying Flocks
    (table), 595
Fish meal, 18, 24, 253
Flu, in hogs, 155
Fluorine, 137
Food nutrients, *see* Nutrients
Foot-and-mouth disease, cattle, 408
Foot-and-mouth disease, sheep, 523-
    524
Foot rot, cattle, 406
Foot rot, sheep, 520-521
Forages, vitamins in, 20-21, 22
Fowl, term, 650
Fowl cholera, 636-637
Fowl pox, 635-636
Fryers (roasters), turkey, 650
Fur sheep, 435

G

Galloway cattle, 190
Gammon, Warren, 192
Garbage feeding, of pigs, 143
Geese, market classes, 651
Genes, 667
Gid tapeworm, in sheep, 517-518
Gizzard, 34
Good cattle, term, 206-207
Grade A Milk, Major Costs to Convert
    to (table), 386 *see also* Milk,
    Grade A
Grade of Fleece Produced by the
    Common Breeds of Sheep
    (table), 538
Grading and purebreeding, 669-670
Grain sorghums, 16, 251, 325
Grains
  as carbohydrate source, 15-16
  fat content, 17
  vitamin A in, 21
  vitamin B-complex in, 21
Grant, George, 189
Grass hays, as roughage, 248
Grass and Legume Mixtures (table),221
Grasses, for cattle, 219-220, 263-266
Green, Merle H., 302
Green lot feeding, 265

Green Meadow Lily Pabst, 302
Grit, for chickens, 590
Ground ear corn, 325
Grub in head (sheep bots), 518
Grubs, cattle, 398-399
Guernsey cattle, 303, 306
Guide for Feeding Concentrates to Dairy Calves (table), 363
Guide for Selection and Culling of Layers (table), 576
Guineas, market classes, 651

H

Haddon's M. Ida, 306
Hampshire sheep, 427-428
Hampshire swine, 66-67
Haven Hill Crescent Gewina Count, 302
Hay mangers, 239
Heat periods, animals, 666-667
Heel flies (cattle grubs), 398-399
Heifer, term, 205
Hen, term, 650
Hen turkey, term, 650
Hereford cattle, 190, 192
Heterosis (hybrid vigor), 667-668
High Energy and Fat Concentrates (table), 25
High Producing Cows (table), 296
Hog-corn ratio, 46-47
Hogging down corn, for pigs, 143
Hogs, 45-180 see also Feeding and management of breeding hogs; Feeding and management of market hogs; Pork production
  age as selection factor, 78
  American Landraces, 61, 69
  back fat probe, 77
  bacon type, 60, 68
  Berkshires, 63
  boars, 75-76
  breeding systems, 55-60
    criss-crossing, 58
    crossbreeding, 56, 58
    crossline breeding, 59-60
    crosslines, 58
    hybrid vigor, 59-60
    inbreeding, 59
    Iowa State College, 56, 58
    line breeding, 59
    Ohio tests, 57, 58
    purebred, 56
    rotation breeding, 58-59
    upgrading, 56

Hogs (Cont.)
  Carcass Results, 1957 National Barrow Show (table), 62
  carcasses, breed differences in, 62
  Chester Whites, 63
  classification of breeds, 60-62
  Crossbred and Purebred Pigs (table), 57
  diseases see Ailments, hogs
  disposition as selection factor, 79-80
  dressing percentages, 73-74
  Durocs, 66
  economics of meat-type, 55
  factors in selection of breeds, 60
  feeder pigs, 80-81
  "hamless wonders," 55
  Hampshire swine, 66-67
  health as selection factor, 79
  hybrid defined, 71
  hybrid production, 71
  ideal type for breeding, 74-75
  ideal type for market, 72-74
  inbred lines, new breeds from, 69-70
  lard-type, 52, 54, 60
  market hogs see Feeding and management of market hogs
  marketing of see Marketing of hogs
  meat-type, 52-55, 60
  new breeds, 68-70
  New Breeds from Inbred Lines (table), 70
  OICs, 67
  old-established breeds, 62-68
  parasites see Ailments, hogs
  parts of a hog, 72, 73
  pedigree as selection factor, 78
  performance records, 78-79
  Physical Characteristics of Breeds (table), 61
  Poland Chinas, 67
  price of feeder pigs, 81
  pork production see Pork production
  Purdue electric lean-fat meter, 78
  selection of, 51-83
  sows, 75
  Spotted Poland Chinas, 67-68
  Tamworths, 68
  teats, 76, 77
  terms of description, 72, 73
  tests for lean and fat, 76-78
  underlines, 76
  wallows, 140
  "Wiltshire Sides," 52
  Yorkshires, 68
Holstein-Friesian cattle, 302-303

Hormones, 7, 10, 24, 26, 111, 256n, 257-259, 268, 338-339, 412, 499, 623
Horn flies, 400
Horse flies, 400-401
Hybrid animals, 668-669
Hybrid corn, 71
Hybrid hogs, 71
Hybrid vigor, in hog breeding, 59-60

I

Ice cream production, 292
Inbreeding, of hogs, 59
Inbreeding and linebreeding, 670
Infectious sinusitis, poultry, 633-634
Infectious synovitis, poultry, 630
Inferior cattle, term, 208
Inheritance, laws of, 667-670
Iodinated casein, 7, 28, 111
Iowa Economy Supplement (table), 256
Iowa Supplement (table), 256

J

Jersey cattle, 306-307
Joint ill, in sheep, 525
June Volunteer Fantasy, 307

K

Karakul sheep, 423, 424, 435
Keds, on sheep, 512-513
Ketosis, in cattle, 412

L

Ladino clover, 123
Laidlaw and Brockie, 434
Lambs
 antibiotics, 499
 coccidiosis, 504
 Complete Rations Including Salt and Mineral (table), 502
 corn field feeding, 503
 creep feeding, 491-493
 creep rations, mixed, 493
 daily gains, 503
 dry-lot feeding, 495
 fat lambs from milk and grass, 491-493
 fattening of lambs, 494-503
 feed lot troubles, 503-504
 feed requirements per hundred weight gain, 503
 feeding of, 491-507
 feeding replacement ewes, 494
 grains and grain substitutes, 496-497

Lambs (Cont.)
 ground feed, 499
 hand-feeding, 500-501
 hormones, 499
 hothouse lambs, production of, 493-494
 methods of fattening, 495, 500-503
 minerals, 499
 Mixed Supplements (list), 498-499
 overeating disease, 504
 pasture fattening, 495
 pelleted rations, 500
 preparation of feed, 499
 Protein Concentrates (table), 498
 proteins and substitutes, 497-498
 Rations for Fattening Lambs Hand-Fed in Dry Lot (table), 501
 roughages, 496
 Self-Fed Rations for Fattening Lambs on Full Feed (table), 502
 self-feeding, 501-502
 shipping fever, 504
 starting on feed, 500
 urea, 498
Langmeadow Minnie, 306
Lard, 45, 46, 52, 54, 165-167
Large roundworms, in poultry, 639-640
Laryngotracheitis, in poultry, 632-633
"Least-Time" Growing-Finishing Rations (table), 139
Legumes, 13-14, 20, 22, 23, 219, 248, 322-323, 362
Legumes and Grasses (table), 27
Leicester sheep, 431
Length Requirements for the Market Classes of Wool (chart), 540
Leptospirosis, in cattle, 410-411
Leptospirosis, in hogs, 157
Lice
 cattle, 399
 hogs, 161-162
 poultry, 640
 sheep, 511-512
Limestone, 24, 38, 137
Lincoln sheep, 432
Lindane, 401, 512
Line breeding, 59, 670
Linseed meal, 19, 253, 326
Litsey, R. F., 310
Livestock feeds, nutrient values of, 28
 see also Feeds
Loading chutes, for cattle, 240
Loraine No. 3020 (Dutch Belted cow), 311
Lungworms, in hogs, 160

Lymphomatosis (leukosis), in poultry, 634-635
Lysine, 128

M

McLean County clean-ground system, 121
Male reproductive organs, 666
Mange, in hogs, 160-161
Manure value, cattle, 247
Margarine *see* Dairy industry
Market Classes and Grades of Hogs and Pigs (table), 170
Market Classes and Grades of Slaughter Sheep (table), 533
Marketing, feeder lambs, 535-536
Marketing, of hogs, 164-180
  Average Retail Prices of Pork Cuts and Lard (table), 166
  bruises, location of, 177
  changes in market, 165-167
  cripples and dead, 177
  cull grade, 172
  efficiency in, 164-165
  factors in choosing market, 176-177
  heavy hogs, 169
  lard *see* Lard
  light hogs, 169
  market classes and grades, 169-172
  Market Classes and Grades of Hogs and Pigs (table), 170
  markets available, 176
  meat-type hog, 167
  medium grade, 172
  prevention of losses, 177-178
  season price variations, 167-168
  selling on weight and grade, 172-176
  time to sell, 167-168
  U.S. Hog Carcass Grades (table), 171
  U. S. D. A. hog grades, 171-172
  weight to sell, 168-169
Marketing, poultry and poultry products, 643-663
  dressed and ready-to-cook poultry, 654-661
  dressed fowl, 654
  improved meat-types, 661
  ready-to-cook poultry, 654
  seasonal price trends, 660-661
  standards for, 654-659
  Standards for Quality of Chickens (table), 656-657
  Standards of Quality for Turkeys (table), 658-659
  weight specifications, 660

Marketing (*Cont.*)
  eggs *see* Eggs
  finishing poultry for market, 651
  live poultry, 651-653
  market classes, 649-651
    chickens, 649-650
    ducks, 650
    geese, 651
    guineas, 651
    pigeons, 651
    turkeys, 650
  marketing poultry, 649
  standards for live poultry, 651-653
  Standards of Quality for Live Poultry (table), 652-653
Marketing, purebred sheep breeding stock, 536
Marketing, slaughter lambs, 529-535
  age, 531
  grades, 531
  Market Classes and Grades of Slaughter Sheep (table), 533
  ewes, term, 531
  fed lambs, term, 531
  grades and classes, 529-533
  hothouse lambs, term, 531
  rams, term, 531
  seasonal prices, 534-535
  sex, 531
  shrinkage, 534
  spring lambs, term, 531
  two-year-olds and older, 531
  types of marketing procedure, 534
  weight, 531
  wethers, term, 531
  when to sell ewes, 535
  when to sell lambs and sheep, 534
  yearlings, term, 531
Marking, of calves, 368
Marking, of cattle, 232-233
Marlu Milady, 307
Mash Rations for Layer and Breeder Hens (table), 592
Mastitis, in cattle, 406-408
Mastitis (blue bag), in sheep, 521
Mattingly, E. H., 428
Meat and bone scraps, 18, 24
Meat-type hogs, 52-55; 60, 167 *see also* Hogs
Mediterranean Class chickens, 562 *see also* Chickens, selection of
Medium cattle, term, 207
Mehrhof, Dr. N. R., culling formula for poultry, 571
Menadione, 23
Merino sheep, 424-425

Microorganisms, of rumen, 32-33
Milk, Grade A, 379-387 *see also* Dairy products, marketing of
  bulk tanks, 383
  cleaning of cows, 384, 386
  cleansing of bulk tanks, 384
  cleansing of utensils and milking machines, 383-384
  cooling facilities, 382
  cost in changing to Grade A production, 386, 387
  definition, 379
  health of herds, 380
  housing facilities, 380-381
  Major Costs to Convert to Grade A (table), 386
  milk houses, 382
  milking, 386
  production of, 380-386
  requirements, 379
  utensils, 383
Milk fever, 411-412
Milk Processing Plants (table), 378
Milking Shorthorn cattle, 391-393
Miller and Gough, 192
Minerals, 4, 9
  for calves, 363
  for cattle, 239-240, 257, 327-328
  for chickens, 590
  for chicks, 603
  and feed value, 38
  for hogs, 137
  for lambs, 499
  mixtures, 24, 137
  sources of, 23-24
  supplements, 24
Mites, cattle, 401
Mites, poultry, 641
Mixed feeds, 40-41
Mixed hays, 248
Moffat, Grace and Robert, 306
Molasses, 16, 250, 251-252, 326, 452, 497, 502, 526
Montadale sheep, 428
Mosquitoes, 400-401

N

N. F. E. (nitrogen-free extract), 2
Navel cord, 667
Navel ill, in sheep, 525
Necro (necrotic enteritis), in hogs, 151
Neshaminy Miss Phett, 308
Newcastle disease, poultry, 630-632
Niacin, for chicks, 603
Nonlegume roughages, 14, 323

Nutrients *see also* Feeds
  amino acids, 3-4, 14, 15
  balanced rations, 11
  carbohydrates, 2, 8-9, 15-17
  classes of, 2-6
  cod liver oil, 9
  digestible nutrients, 10-11
  fats, 2, 9, 17
  feed additives *see* Feed additives
  feeds *see* Feeds
  fiber, 2, 10-11, 589-590
  functions of, 8-10
  minerals *see* Minerals
  proteins, 2-4, 9, 14-15
  term, 1
  values of feeds, 28
  vitamins *see* Vitamins
  water, 6

O

OIC swine, 67
Oats, 15, 251, 325
Oil seed crops, 17
Oils and animal fats, 17
Oleomargarine *see* Dairy industry
Omasum, 33-34
Open formula feeds, 41
Ova, 665
Ovaries, 666
Oviducts, 666
Oxford sheep, 428

P

Panama sheep, 433-434
Pantothenic acid, 603-604
Parakeratosis, in hogs, 157-158
Pasture
  for calves, 363
  crops, 121-123
  for dairy cattle, 324-325
  for feeders and fattening cattle, 263
  legumes, 219
  for pigs, 118
  for sows, 95
  for turkeys, 620
Pasture Crops for Swine (table), 122
Peanuts, 17, 20, 253
Pedigrees, value of, 670
Penis, 666
Pepsin, in pig diets, 113
Persian Lamb pelts, 423-424
Phosphorus, 24, 38, 137, 590
Physical Characteristics of Breeds (table of hog breeds), 61
Pig Grower Rations (table), 115
Pig Pre-Starter Rations (table), 113
Pig Starter Rations (table), 114

Pigeons, market classes, 651
Pink eye, in cattle, 406
Placenta, 667
Plant proteins, for chickens, 589
Pneumonia, in cattle, 411
Poisonous plants, and cattle, 414
Poland China swine, 67
Polled Hereford cattle, 192
Polled Shorthorn cattle, 192
Pork production, 44-50 *see also* Hogs
  advantages and disadvantages, 47-48
  consumer demand, 45
  in Corn Belt, 44-45
  efficiency in, 48-49
  hog ailments *see* Ailments, hogs
  hog-corn ratios, 46-47
  hybrid hogs, 71
  lard *see* Lard
  leading states, 44-45
  selection of hogs *see* Hogs
Poultry (*See also* Chickens; Chicks,
    baby; Turkeys)
  ailments *see* Ailments, poultry
  amino acids for, 3
  digestion in, 34-35
  marketing *see* Marketing, poultry
    and poultry products
  rations for, 35
  vitamins, 4-6, 35
Poultry production industry, 547-558
  advantages of poultry farming, 554-
    556
  broilers, 549
  chickens, 549
  chicken and broiler consumption, 553
  chicken numbers and egg produc-
    tion, 552
  commercial broiler production, 550
  consumption of products, 552-553
  eggs, 552
  income from poultry and eggs, 547-
    548
  leading states, 548-549, 551
  opportunities, 553-557
  per capita consumption of products,
    553
  per capita egg consumption, 553
  problems in poultry production, 556-
    557
  specialized poultry farms, 553-554
  trends in poultry production, 549-
    552
  turkeys, 549, 551-552
  turkey consumption, 553
  youth on home farms, 554

Production Summary of All Entries in
    the Official Egg Laying Tests for
    1955-1956 (table), 566
Progeny testing, in cattle, 202-203
Prostate, 666
Protein concentrates, 14, 17, 24
Protein Concentrates, Composition of
    (table), 25
Protein Concentrates for Lambs (table),
    498
Protein Supplements (tables), 130-133
Proteins, 2-4, 9, 33, 128-129, 356
  cattle, 217-218, 252-257
  chickens, 589
  chicks, 602
  feed value, 38
  lambs, 497-499
Proventriculus, 34
Pullorum, 569, 628,-629
Purdue Cattle Supplement with Urea
    (table), 255
Purdue Cow Supplement, 224
Purdue Electric Lean-Fat Meter, for
    hogs, 78
Purdue Supplement G (table), 256
Purebred beef cattle industry, 184-185
Purebred breeding, of hogs, 56
Pyridoxin, 604

R

Roughages, 13-14, 36, 330-331
  for calves, 362-363
  for cattle, 247-250
  for dairy cows, 322-324
  for lambs, 496
  as source of carbohydrates, 17
Roughages, Comparable Value of
    (table), 250
Roughages, Dry (table), 26
Roundworms, in hogs, 120-121, 158-160
Roup, in poultry, 636
Royal's Rapture, 310
Rumen, 32-33, 356
Rumen organisms, 8, 10, 28
Ruminants, 3, 6, 31-34
Rye, 16, 251, 326

S

Saccharin, in pig rations, 113-114
Salt, 24, 216, 217-218, 590
Santa Gertrudis cattle, 196-197
Scab, on sheep, 513-514
Schain Detergent Test, for butterfat,
    314
Schedule for Operating Slot Ventila-
    tors (table), 585

Schluter, Fred, 310
Scotch Highland cattle, 194-195
Scratch Grain Mixtures (table), 591
Screw worms, in cattle, 397-398
Screw worms, in sheep, 510-511
Seed by-products, as protein source, 19
Self-Fed Rations for Fattening Lambs
    on Full Feed (table), 502
Self-feeders, for cattle, 239
Seminal vesicles, 666
Shade, for pigs, 140
Sheep, selection of breeding and feed-
    ing stock, 421-447
  age, as selection factor, 441
  ailments see Ailments, sheep
  Black-Faced Highland breed, 434-435
  body conformation, 439-441
  breeds, 424-435
  Broadtail pelts, 423
  carpet-wool breeds, 434
  Cheviot breed, 425-427
  Classes and Common Breeds of Sheep
    (table), 423
  Classes and Grades of Feeder Sheep
    (table), 443
  classes of sheep, 421-424
  Columbia breed, 432-433
  Corriedale breed, 433
  cost and availability of breeding
    stock, 437
  Cotswold breed, 431
  crossbred-wool breeds, 432-434
  crossbred-wool type, 422-423
  Dorset breed, 427
  environment, effect of, 436-437
  feeder lambs, 441-443
  feeder sheep, 443-444
  feeding and management see Feed-
    ing and management of sheep
  fine-wool breeds, 421-422, 424-425
  fur purposes, 423-424
  fur sheep breeds, 435
  grade of feeder lambs, 444-445
  Hampshire breed, 427-428
  health, as selection factor, 438
  Karakul breed, 423, 424, 435
  lambs see Lambs
  Leicester breed, 431
  Lincoln breed, 432
  long-wool breeds, 422, 431-432
  market price and demand, 437
  marketing slaughter lambs see Mar-
    keting, slaughter lambs
  medium-wool breeds, 422, 425-432
  Merinos, 424-425
  Montadale breed, 428

Sheep (Cont.)
  Oxford breed, 428
  Panama breed, 433-434
  Persian Lamb, 423-424
  personal likes in selection, 437
  Rambouillets, 425
  Romeldale, 434
  Romney breed, 432
  selection of breeding stock, 436-437
  selection of feeder lambs, 441-445
  selection of foundation stock, 437-
    441
  shearer lambs, 444
  Shropshire breed, 428
  slaughter lambs see Marketing, slaugh-
    ter lambs
  soundness, as selection factor, 438-
    439
  Southdown breed, 428, 429
  Suffolk breed, 430
  Targhee breed, 434
  Tunis breed, 431
  uniformity, 439
  weight and grade of feeder lambs,
    444-445
  wethers, 443
  wool see Wool, grading and market-
    ing of
  wool classification, 421-424
Sheep production industry, 416-420
  advantages of sheep, 416-417
  classes of producers, 417-419
  combination enterprises, 419
  farm flocks, 418
  lamb feeders, 418
  purebred breeders, 419
  ranches, 418
Shipping fever, in cattle, 405-406
Shipping fever, in lambs, 504
Shipping fever, in sheep, 522
Shorthorn cattle, 192
Shropshire sheep, 428
Silage, Composition of (table), 27
Silage, for cattle, 249-250
Silage, for sows, 95
Silver, L. B., 67
Skim milk, as protein source, 18, 294,
    360
Small White Beltsville turkeys, 661
Smear EQ 335, for screw worms, 398
Soils, effect on feeds, 39
Sore mouth disease, in sheep, 522-523
Sotham, William H., 190
Southdown sheep, 428, 429
Soybeans and soybean oil, 17, 19, 37,
    38, 128, 253, 326

Spencer, A. T., 434
Sperm, 665
Sperm ducts, 666
Spotted Poland China swine, 67-68
Squabs, term, 651
Stable flies, 400
Standard Grades of Wool in Terms of
    Grading by American and Eng-
    lish Systems (table), 537
Standards for Growing Dairy Heifers
    (table), 364
Standards for Quality of Dressed and
    Ready-to-Cook Chickens (table),
    656-657
Standards of Quality for Dressed and
    Ready-to-Cook Turkeys (table),
    658-659
Standards of Quality for Live Poultry
    (table), 652-653
Starting Mash Formulas (table), 605
Steer, term, 205
Stewing chicken, term, 650
Stiff lamb disease, 524-525
Stilbestrol, 7, 24, 26, 256n, 257-259,
    268, 499
Stilbosol, 256
Stomach worms, cattle, 402
Stomach worms, sheep, 514-516
Sudan grass, 325
Suffolk sheep, 430
Surfactants see Detergents
Swine see Hogs
Swine Breeding and Farrowing Dates
    (table), 87

T

Tamworth swine, 68
Tankage, 18, 24, 253
Tapazole, 260
Targhee sheep, 434
Teniatol, 517-518
Terminal markets, for cattle, 276
Terramycin, 357
Testicles, 666
Thyroxine, 111
Ticks, cattle, 401
Ticks (keds), on sheep, 512-513
Tom turkey, term, 650
Total Cost of Broiler Production
    (table), 611
Trace mineral mixture, 24
"Trace minerals," 137
Tranquilizers, 8, 10, 28
Transmissible gastroenteritis, in hogs,
    155-157

Trichinosis, 143
Trolene, 398-399
Tryptophan, 128
Tuberculosis, in cattle, 404
Tuberculosis, in poultry, 637
Tunis sheep, 431
Turkey Rations (table), 619
Turkeys, 549, 551-552 see also Poultry
    production industry
  ailments see Ailments, poultry
  antibiotics, 623-624
  arsenicals, 623
  Beltsville Small Whites, 625
  Broad Breast Bronze, 661
  broiler production, 625
  brooder guards, 617
  brooder houses, 616-617
  brooders, 617
  brooding temperatures, 617
  brooding young poults, 616-617
  Calculated Analysis of Turkey Ra-
      tions (table), 619
  cannibalism, 623
  confinement rearing in pole sheds,
      623-624
  feeder space, 620
  feeders, 621
  feeding poults, 617-618
  feeds per pound of gain, 622
  finishing for market, 624
  floors for brooder houses, 617
  grains, 621
  growing rations, 621-622
  hormones, 623
  lights, 620
  litter, 617
  market classes, 650
  mash feeds, 622
  mineral and grit, 622
  pastures, 620-621
  poults, buying of, 615-616
  production bred, 616
  production and management, 614-626
  range management, 620-623
  range shelters, 621
  roosts, 620
  rotation of pastures, 620-621
  selection of variety, 615-616
  Small White Beltsvilles, 661
  sources for poults, 616
  starter rations, 618-619
  starting poults, 617-618
  sun porches, 620
  Turkey Rations (table), 619
  water, 623
  waterers, 620

U

U.S. Hog Carcass Grades (table), 171
U.S. Per Capita Consumption of Dairy Products (table), 288
Undulant fever, 106, 154, 403 *see also* Brucellosis
Upgrading, in hog breeding, 56
Urea, 20, 253-255, 326-327, 334, 498
Use of Milk Sold by Farmers (table), 289

V

Vaccination, of pigs, 117-118
Vagina, 666
Vegetable proteins, 15, 19-20, 24
Vesicular exanthema, 143, 154-155
Vitamin premixes, 23, 136
Vitamin A, 4, 5, 9, 39, 135, 257, 317, 327, 335, 356, 358, 361, 450, 497, 498, 590, 603, 618, 622
Vitamin B-complex, 4-5, 9, 21, 33, 327, 356
Vitamin B_1, 135
Vitamin B_{12}, 5, 6, 10, 22, 128-129, 135, 136, 590
Vitamin C, 5
Vitamin D, 4, 5, 6, 10, 22, 135, 217, 248, 257, 327, 335, 356, 358, 361, 412, 497, 590, 603, 618, 622
Vitamin E, 6, 10, 22-23, 135, 525
Vitamin K, 5, 10, 23, 604
Vitamins, 4-6, 9-10, 39, 257
  for cattle, 217
  for chickens, 590
  for chicks, 603
  for dairy cattle, 327
  and feed value, 39
  for pigs, 135-137
  for poultry, 35
  riboflavin, 590
  sources of, 20-23

W

Wallows, for hogs, 140
Water and watering, 6
  calves, 363
  cattle, 218
  pigs, 138-139
  poultry, 591
  sows, 95
  turkeys, 620, 623
Watering equipment, for chickens, 584
Weaning, of pigs, 119
Weather, effect on feeds, 39
Wethers, 443

Wheat, 16, 251, 325, 326
Wheat germ oil, as vitamin E source, 23
"Wiltshire Sides," 52
Wintering Rations for Feeder Cattle (table), 262-263
Wisconsin Swine Selection Program, ear-notching system, 109
Wool
  American or Blood System of Grading, 537
  apparel, 539
  black or gray, 541
  breed and fineness, relation, 538
  burry, 541
  carpet, 539
  classes according to length, 539-540
  classification according to length, 538-541
  classification of sheep, 421-424
  clean wool, 540
  consignment to commission warehouses, 542-543
  consignment marketing, 542-543
  cooperative marketing agencies, 544
  cotted fleeces, 541
  defective and offtype, 541
  English Spinning Count System of Grading, 537, 538
  fleece grading, 538
  future delivery contracts, 543
  grade and class combination, 540
  Grade of Fleece Produced by the Common Breeds of Sheep (table), 538
  grades according to fineness, 537
  grading and marketing of, 536-544
  kempy fleeces, 541
  length as related to fineness, 539
  Length Requirements for the Market Classes of Wool (chart), 540
  length and uses of apparel wools, 539
  sale to dealers, 542
  sale to independent buyers, 541-542
  sale to mill representatives, 542
  scouring, 540
  selling of, 541-544
  shrinkage, 540-541
  Shrinkage by Grades of 1946 U.S. Wool Clip (table), 540
  Standard Grades in Terms of Grading by American and English Systems (table), 537
  tags and clippings, 541
  yield, term, 540
Worming, of pigs, 120-121